INDUSTRIAL VENTILATION

A Manual of Recommended Practice

24th Edition

2001

American Conference of Governmental Industrial Hygienists
1330 Kemper Meadow Drive
Cincinnati, Ohio 45240-1634
(513) 742-2020
www.acgih.org

CONTENTS

50th Anniversary Edition
Dedication

Ventilation systems in the 1940's had to be designed with information taken in tidbits from dozens of books. While good publications were available, none provided a single source for design information. In an effort to resolve this problem, a team of engineers from the Bureau of Industrial Health, Michigan Department of Health, undertook the task of creating a single manual which gathered all of the information necessary to design a ventilation system. This manual was completed in 1948. In 1951 the first edition of *Industrial Ventilation: A Manual of Recommended Practice* was published under the sponsorship of the American Conference of Governmental Industrial Hygienists (ACGIH).

The focus of the Ventilation Manual from its first to this 24th edition has been to present practical information in a user friendly format; one that could be used by plant engineers and designers to solve ventilation problems and also be revised and updated frequently. The 55 figures and 41 VS plates showing ventilation recommendations for specific operations in the first edition has grown to 193 figures and 151 specific operations in this 24th edition. The Ventilation Manual has also been printed in a Spanish version (20th edition, out of print) and a metric version (23rd edition).

Closely allied with the design function of the Ventilation Manual is its use as a teaching tool. It was first used in 1952 as a text in a ventilation conference at Michigan State University. Shortly thereafter it was used at ventilation conferences held in North Carolina, Alabama, Connecticut, and Washington. The Michigan, North Carolina, and Alabama conferences have been held annually since their inception. It has also been used as a text for university ventilation courses and various other short courses.

The 50 year success of this manual can be attributed to the its widespread acceptance as a practical design guide and teaching tool and to the dedication of the Ventilation Committee members, past and present. A major contributor to this success has been Mrs. Norma Donovan, Ventilation Committee Editorial Consultant. Mrs. Donovan was a major contributor to the publication of the first edition and as the official secretary of the Ventilation Committee has had primary responsibility for the typing and assembly of all editions since. She also was responsible for the printing, publishing, storage, and distribution of the Ventilation Manual until ACGIH assumed this effort in 1986. Her loyalty, dedication, and knowledge of Committee activities have provided and continue to provide immeasurable assistance to the Committee effort.

It is with the sincere appreciation of ACGIH and the Ventilation Committee that this 50th anniversary edition of *Industrial Ventilation: A Manual of Recommended Practice* is dedicated to Norma Donovan.

FOREWORD

INDUSTRIAL VENTILATION: A Manual of Recommended Practice is the outgrowth of years of experience by Committee members and a compilation of research data and information on design, maintenance, and evaluation of industrial exhaust ventilation systems. The Manual attempts to present a logical method of designing and testing these systems. It has found wide acceptance as a guide for official agencies, as a standard for industrial ventilation designers, and as a textbook for industrial hygiene courses.

The Manual is not intended to be used as law, but rather as a guide. Because of new information on industrial ventilation becoming available through research projects, reports from engineers, and articles in various periodicals and journals, review and revision of each section of the Manual is an ongoing Committee project. The Manual is available in a hardbound edition only. In a constant effort to present the latest techniques and data, the Committee desires, welcomes, and actively seeks comments and suggestions on the accuracy and adequacy of the information presented herein.

In this 24th edition, the Committee has made a number of revisions. The duct and hood loss coefficients have been revised to be consistent with the system component nomenclature. Alternate hood centerline equations are referenced in Appendix 3. The "3-eye" duct friction charts have been returned to Chapter 5. Chapter 5 has been revised to include methodology for including the effects of non-standard conditions in duct

calculations. Chapter 7 has been rewritten to provide more detailed information on replacement air. Chapter 9 has been rewritten to provide added information on instruments and to include detailed procedures for duct system measurements and troubleshooting.

This publication is designed to present accurate an authoritative information with regard to the subject matter covered. It is distributed with the understanding that neither the Committee nor its members collectively or individually assume any responsibility for any inadvertent misinformation, for omissions, nor for the results in the use of this publication.

COMMITTEE ON INDUSTRIAL VENTILATION

R. T. Hughes, Retired, Ohio, Chair
A. G. Apol, Retired, Washington
G. Carlton, USAF, Texas
W. M. Cleary, Retired, Michigan
Mrs. Norma Donovan, Editorial Consultant
M. Franklin, ADC Communications, Minnesota
S. E. Guffey, West Virginia University, West Virginia
G. S. Knutson, Knutson Ventilation Consultants, Minnesota
G. Lanham, KBD/Technic, Ohio
K. Mead, NIOSH, Ohio
K. M. Paulson, NFESC, California
A. L. Twombly, Pfeiffer Engineering Co. Inc., Kentucky
A. W. Woody, Albert Kahn Associates, Inc., Michigan

ACKNOWLEDGMENTS

Industrial Ventilation is a true Committee effort. It brings into focus in one source useful, practical ventilation data from all parts of the country. The Committee membership of industrial ventilation and industrial hygiene engineers represents a diversity of experience and interest that ensures a well-rounded, cooperative effort.

From the First Edition in 1951, this effort has been successful as witnessed by the acceptance of the "Ventilation Manual" throughout industry, by governmental agencies, and as a worldwide reference and text.

The present Committee is grateful for the faith and firm foundation provided by past Committees and members listed below. Special acknowledgment is made to the Division of Occupational Health, Michigan Department of Health, for contributing their original field manual which was the basis of the First Edition, and to Mr. Knowlton J. Caplan who supervised the preparation of the manual.

The Committee is grateful also to those consultants who have contributed so greatly to the preparation of this and previous editions of *Industrial Ventilation* and to Mrs. Norma Donovan, Secretary to the Committee, for her untiring zeal in our efforts.

To many other individuals and agencies who have made specific contributions and have provided support, suggestions, and constructive criticism, our special thanks.

COMMITTEE ON INDUSTRIAL VENTILATION

Previous Members

A.G. Apol, 1984–present
H. Ayer, 1962-1966
R. E. Bales, 1954-1960
J. Baliff, 1950-1956; Chair, 1954-1956
J. C. Barrett, 1956-1976; Chair, 1960-1968
J. L. Beltran, 1964-1966
D. Bonn, Consultant, 1958-1968
D. J. Burton, 1988-1970
K. J. Caplan, 1974-1978; Consultant, 1980-1986
W. M. Cleary, 1978-present; Chair, 1978-1984
L. Dickie, 1984-1994; Consultant 1968-1984
T. N. Do, 1998–2000
B. Feiner, 1956-1968
M. Franklin, 1991-1994; 1998-present
S. E. Guffey, 1984-present
G. M. Hama, 1950-1984; Chair, 1956-1960
R. P. Hibbard, 1968-1994
R. T. Hughes, 1976-present; Chair, 1989-present
H. S. Jordan, 1960-1962
J. Kane, Consultant, 1950-1952
J. Kayse, Consultant, 1956-1958
J. F. Keppler, 1950-1954; 1958-1960

G. W. Knutson, Consultant, 1986-present
G. Lanham, Consultant, 1996–present
J. J. Loeffler, 1980-1995; Chair, 1984-1989
J. Lumsden, 1962-1968
J. R. Lynch, 1966-1976
K. R. Mead, 1995 to date
G. Michaelson, 1958-1960
K. M. Morse, 1950-1951; Chair, 1950-1951
R. T. Page, 1954-1956
K. M. Paulson, 1991-present
O. P. Petrey, Consultant, 1978-1999
G. S. Rajhans, 1978-1995
K. E. Robinson, 1950-1954; Chair, 1952-1954
A. Salazar, 1952-1954
E. L. Schall, 1956-1958
M. M. Schuman, 1962-1964; Chair, 1968-1978
J. C. Soet, 1950-1960
A. L. Twombly, Consultant, 1986-present
J. Willis, Consultant, 1952-1956
R. Wolle, 1966-1974
A. W. Woody, Consultant, 1998-present
J. A. Wunderle, 1960-1964

DEFINITIONS

Aerosol: An assemblage of small particles, solid or liquid, suspended in air. The diameter of the particles may vary from 100 microns down to 0.01 micron or less, e.g., dust, fog, smoke.

Air Cleaner: A device designed for the purpose of removing atmospheric airborne impurities such as dusts, gases, vapors, fumes, and smoke. (Air cleaners include air washers, air filters, electrostatic precipitators, and charcoal filters.)

Air Filter: An air cleaning device to remove light particulate loadings from normal atmospheric air before introduction into the building. Usual range: loadings up to 3 grains per thousand cubic feet (0.003 grains per cubic foot). Note: Atmospheric air in heavy industrial areas and in-plant air in many industries have higher loadings than this, and dust collectors are then indicated for proper air cleaning.

Air Horsepower: The theoretical horsepower required to drive a fan if there were no loses in the fan, that is, if its efficiency were 100 percent.

Air, Standard: Dry air at 70 F and 29.92 in (Hg) barometer. This is substantially equivalent to 0.075 lb/ft^3. Specific heat of dry air = 0.24 btu/lb/F.

Aspect Ratio: The ratio of the width to the length; AR W/L.

Aspect Ratio of an Elbow: The width (W) along the axis of the bend divided by depth (D) in plane of bend; AR = W/D.

Blast Gate: Sliding damper.

Blow (throw): In air distribution, the distance an air stream travels from an outlet to a position at which air motion along the axis reduces to a velocity of 50 fpm. For unit heaters, the distance an air stream travels from a heater without a perceptible rise due to temperature difference and loss of velocity.

Brake Horsepower: The horsepower actually required to drive a fan. This includes the energy losses in the fan and can be determined only by actual test of the fan. (This does not include the drive losses between motor and fan.)

Capture Velocity: The air velocity at any point in front of the hood or at the hood opening necessary to overcome opposing air currents and to capture the contaminated air at that point by causing it to flow into the hood.

Coefficient of Entry: The actual rate of flow caused by a given hood static pressure compared to the theoretical flow which would result if the static pressure could be converted to velocity pressure with 100 percent efficiency. It is the ratio of actual to theoretical flow.

Comfort Zone (Average): The range of effective temperatures over which the majority (50% or more) of adults feel comfortable. Convection: The motion resulting in a fluid from the differences in density and the action of gravity. In heat-transmission, this meaning has been extended to include both forced and natural motion or circulation.

Density: The ratio of the mass of a specimen of a substance to the volume of the specimen. The mass of a unit volume of a substance. When weight can be used with out confusion, as synonymous with mass, density is the weight of a unit volume of a substance.

Density Factor: The ratio of actual air density to density of standard air. The product of the density factor and the density of standard air (0.075 lb/ft^3) will give the actual air density in pounds per cubic foot; d × 0.075 actual density of air, lb/ft^3.

Dust: Small solid particles created by the breaking up of larger particles by processes crushing, grinding, drilling, explosions, etc. Dust particles already in existence in a mixture of materials may escape into the air through such operations as shoveling, conveying, screening, sweeping, etc.

Dust Collector: An air cleaning device to remove heavy particulate loadings from exhaust systems before discharge to outdoors. Usual range: loadings 0.003 grains per cubic foot and higher.

Entry Loss: Loss in pressure caused by air flowing into a duct or hood (inches H_2O).

Fumes: Small, solid particles formed by the condensation of vapors of solid materials.

Gases: Formless fluids which tend to occupy an entire space uniformly at ordinary temperatures and pressures.

Gravity, Specific: The ratio of the mass of a unit volume of a substance to the mass of the same volume of a standard substance at a standard temperature. Water at 39.2 F is the standard substance usually referred to. For gases, dry air, at the same temperature and pressure as the gas, is often taken as the standard substance.

Hood: A shaped inlet designed to capture contaminated air and conduct it into the exhaust duct system.

Humidity, Absolute: The weight of water vapor per unit volume, pounds per cubic foot or grams per cubic centimeter.

Humidity, Relative: The ratio of the actual partial pressure of the water vapor in a space to the saturation pressure of pure water at the same temperature.

Inch of Water: A unit of pressure equal to the pressure exerted by a column of liquid water one inch high at a standard temperature.

Lower Explosive Limit: The lower limit of flammability or explosibility of a gas or vapor at ordinary ambient temperatures expressed in percent of the gas or vapor in air by volume. This limit is assumed constant for temperatures up to 250 F. Above these temperatures, it should be decreased by a factor of 0.7 since explosibility increases with higher temperatures.

Manometer: An instrument for measuring pressure; essentially a U-tube partially filled with a liquid, usually water, mercury or a light oil, so constructed that the amount of displacement of the liquid indicates the pressure being exerted on the instrument.

Micron: A unit of length, the thousandth part of I mm or the millionth of a meter (approximately 1/25,000 of an inch).

Minimum Design Duct Velocity: Minimum air velocity required to move the particulates in the air stream, fpm.

Mists: Small droplets of materials that are ordinarily liquid at normal temperature and pressure.

Plenum: Pressure equalizing chamber.

Pressure, Static: The potential pressure exerted in all directions by a fluid at rest. For a fluid in motion, it is measured in a direction normal to the direction of flow. Usually expressed in inches water gauge when dealing with air. (The tendency to either burst or collapse the pipe.)

Pressure, Total: The algebraic sum of the velocity pressure and the static press-Lire (with due regard to sign).

Pressure, Vapor: The pressure exerted by a vapor. If a vapor is kept in confinement over its liquid so that the vapor can accumulate above the liquid, the temperature being held constant, the vapor pressure approaches a fixed limit called the maximum or saturated vapor pressure, dependent only on the temperature and the liquid. The term vapor pressure is sometimes used as synonymous with saturated vapor pressure.

Pressure, Velocity: The kinetic pressure in the direction of flow necessary to cause a fluid at rest to flow at a given velocity. Usually expressed in inches water gauge.

Radiation, Thermal (Heat) Radiation: The transmission of energy by means of electromagnetic waves of very long wave length. Radiant energy of any wave length may, when absorbed, become thermal energy and result in an increase in the temperature of the absorbing body.

Replacement Air: A ventilation term used to indicate the volume of controlled outdoor air supplied to a building to replace air being exhausted.

Slot Velocity: Linear flow rate of contaminated air through Slot, fpm.

Smoke: An air suspension (aerosol) of particles, usually but not necessarily solid, often originating in a solid nucleus, formed from combustion or sublimation.

Temperature, Effective: An arbitrary index which combines into a single value the effect of temperature, humidity, and air movement on the sensation of warmth or cold felt by the human body. The numerical value is that of the temperature of still, saturated air which would induce an identical sensation.

Temperature, Wet-Bulb: Thermodynamic wet-bulb temperature is the temperature at which liquid or solid water, by evaporating into air, can bring the air to saturation adiabatically at the same temperature. Wet bulb temperature (without qualification) is the temperature indicated by a wet-bulb psychrometer constructed and used according to specifications.

Threshold Limit Values (TLVs): The values for airborne toxic materials which are to be used as guides in the control of health hazards and represent time-weighted concentrations to which nearly all workers may be exposed 8 hours per day over extended periods of time without adverse effects (see Appendix).

Transport (Conveying) Velocity: See Minimum Design Duct Velocity.

Turn-Down Ratio: The degree to which the operating performance of a system can be reduced to satisfy part-load conditions. Usually expressed as a ratio; for example, 30:1 means the minimum operation point is 1/30th of full load.

Vapor: The gaseous form of substances which are normally in the solid or liquid state and which can be changed to these states either by increasing the pressure or decreasing the temperature.

ABBREVIATIONS

A . . . . .area
acfm .flow rate at actual condition
AH . . . . .air horsepower
AR . . . . .aspect ratio
A_s . . . . .slot area
B . . . . .barometric pressure
bhp . . . . .brake horsepower
bhp_a . . . . .brake horsepower, actual
bhp_s . . . . .brake horsepower, standard air
btu . . . . .British Thermal Unit
btuh . . . . .btu/hr
Ce . . . . .coefficient of entry
cfm . . . . .cubic feet per minute
CLR . . . . .centerline radius
D . . . . .diameter
df . . . . .overall density factor
df_e . . . . .elevation density factor
df_p . . . . .pressure density factor
df_T . . . . .temperature density factor
df_m . . . . .moisture density factor
ET . . . . .effective temperature
F . . . . .degree, Fahrenheit
F_h . . . . .hood entry loss coefficient
F_{el} . . . . .elbow loss coefficient
F_{en} . . . . .entry loss coefficient
fpm . . . . .feet per minute
fps . . . . .feet per second
F_s . . . . .slot loss coefficient
ft^2 . . . . .square foot
ft^3 . . . . .cubic foot
g . . . . .gravitational force, ft/sec/sec
gpm . . . . .gallons per minute
gr . . . . .grains
h_h . . . . .hood entry loss
h_e . . . . .overall hood entry loss
h_{el} . . . . .elbow loss
h_{en} . . . . .entry loss
h_f . . . . .loss in straight duct run
HEPA . . . . .high-efficiency particulate air filters
H_f . . . . .duct loss coefficient
hp . . . . .horsepower

hr . . . . .hour
h_s . . . . .slot or opening entry loss
in . . . . .inch
in^2 . . . . .square inch
"wg . . . . .inches water gauge
lb . . . . .pound
lbm . . . . .pound mass
LEL . . . . .lower explosive limit
ME . . . . .mechanical efficiency
mg . . . . .milligram
min . . . . .minute
mm . . . . .millimeter
MRT . . . . .mean radiant temperature
MW . . . . .molecular weight
p . . . . .density of air in lb/ft^2
ppm . . . . .parts per million
psi . . . . .pounds per square inch
PWR . . . . .power
Q . . . . .flow rate in cfm
Q_{corr} . . . . .corrected flow rate at a junction
R . . . . .degree, Rankin
RH . . . . .relative humidity
rpm . . . . .revolutions per minute
scfm . . . . .flow rate at standard conditions
sfpm .surface feet per minute
sp gr . . . . .specific gravity
SP . . . . .static pressure
SP_{gov} . . . . .higher static pressure at junction of 2 ducts
SP_h . . . . .hood static pressure
SP_s . . . . .SP, system handling standard air
STP . . . . .standard temperature and pressure
TLV . . . . .Threshold Limit Value
TP . . . . .total pressure
V . . . . .velocity, fpm
V_d . . . . .duct velocity
VP . . . . .velocity pressure
VP_d . . . . .duct velocity pressure
VP_r . . . . .resultant velocity pressure
VP_s . . . . .slot velocity pressure
V_s . . . . .slot velocity
V_t . . . . .duct transport velocity
W . . . . .watt

xv

Chapter 1
GENERAL PRINCIPLES OF VENTILATION

1.1 INTRODUCTION

The importance of clean uncontaminated air in the industrial work environment is well known. Modern industry with its complexity of operations and processes uses an increasing number of chemical compounds and substances, many of which are highly toxic. The use of such materials may result in particulates, gases, vapors, and/or mists in the workroom air in concentrations which exceed safe levels. Heat stress can also result in unsafe or uncomfortable work environments. Effective, well designed ventilation offers a solution to these problems where worker protection is needed. Ventilation can also serve to control odor, moisture, and other undesirable environmental conditions.

The health hazard potential of an airborne substance is characterized by the *Threshold Limit Value (TLV®)*. The TLV is defined as that airborne concentration of a substance which it is believed that nearly all workers may be exposed to day after day without developing adverse health effects. The *time-weighted average (TWA)*, defined as the time-weighted average concentration for a normal 8-hour workday and a 40-hour workweek which will produce no adverse health effects for nearly all workers, is usually used to determine a safe exposure level. TLV values are published by the American Conference of Governmental Industrial Hygienists (ACGIH), with annual revisions as more evidence accrues on the toxicity of the substance. Appendix A of this Manual provides the current TLV list for chemical substances as of the date of publication.

Ventilation systems used in industrial plants are of two generic types. The SUPPLY system is used to supply air, usually tempered, to a work space. The EXHAUST system is used to remove the contaminants generated by an operation in order to maintain a healthful work environment.

A complete ventilation program must consider both the supply and the exhaust systems. If the overall quantity of air exhausted from a work space is greater than the quantity of outdoor air supplied to the space, the plant interior will experience a lower pressure than the local atmospheric pressure. This may be desirable when using a dilution ventilation system to control or isolate contaminants in a specific area of the overall plant. Often, this condition occurs simply because local exhaust systems are installed and consideration is not given to the corresponding replacement air systems. Air will then enter the plant in an uncontrolled manner through cracks, walls, windows, and doorways. This typically results in (1) employee discomfort in winter months for those working near the plant perimeter, (2) exhaust system performance degradation, possibly leading to loss of contaminant control and a potential health hazard, and (3) higher heating and cooling costs. Chapter 7 of this Manual discusses these points in more detail.

1.2 SUPPLY SYSTEMS

Supply systems are used for two purposes: (1) to create a comfortable environment in the plant (the HVAC system); and (2) to replace air exhausted from the plant (the REPLACEMENT system). Many times, supply and exhaust systems are coupled, as in dilution control systems (see Section 1.3 and Chapter 2.)

A well-designed supply system will consist of an air inlet section, filters, heating and/or cooling equipment, a fan, ducts, and register/grilles for distributing the air within the work space. The filters, heating and/or cooling equipment, and fan are often combined into a complete unit called an airhouse or air supply unit. If part of the air supplied by a system is recirculated, a RETURN system is used to bring the air back to the airhouse.

1.3 EXHAUST SYSTEMS

Exhaust ventilation systems are classified in two generic groups: (1) the GENERAL exhaust system and (2) the LOCAL exhaust system.

The general exhaust system can be used for heat control and/or removal of contaminants generated in a space by flushing out a given space with large quantities of air. When used for heat control, the air may be tempered and recycled. When used for contaminant control (the dilution system), enough outdoor air must be mixed with the contaminant so that the average concentration is reduced to a safe level. The contaminated air is then typically discharged to the atmosphere. A supply system is usually used in conjunction with a general exhaust system to replace the air exhausted.

Dilution ventilation systems are normally used for contaminant control only when local exhaust is impractical, as the large quantities of tempered replacement air required to offset the air exhausted can lead to high operating costs. Chapter 2 describes the basic features of general ventilation systems and their application to contaminant and fire hazard control.

Local exhaust ventilation systems operate on the principle of capturing a contaminant at or near its source. It is the preferred method of control because it is more effective and the smaller exhaust flow rate results in lower heating costs compared to high flow rate general exhaust requirements. The present emphasis on air pollution control stresses the need for efficient air cleaning devices on industrial ventilation systems, and the smaller flow rates of the local exhaust system result in lower costs for air cleaning devices.

Local exhaust systems are comprised of up to four basic elements: the hood(s), the duct system (including the exhaust stack and/or recirculation duct), the air cleaning device, and the fan. The purpose of the hood is to collect the contaminant generated in an air stream directed toward the hood. A duct system must then transport the contaminated air to the air cleaning device, if present, or to the fan. In the air cleaner, the contaminant is removed from the air stream. The fan must overcome all the losses due to friction, hood entry, and fittings in the system while producing the intended flow rate. The duct on the fan outlet usually discharges the air to the atmosphere in such a way that it will not be re-entrained by the replacement and/or HVAC systems. In some situations, the cleaned air is returned to the plant. Chapter 7 discusses whether this is possible and how it may be accomplished.

This Manual deals with the design aspects of exhaust ventilation systems, but the principles described also apply to supply systems.

1.4 BASIC DEFINITIONS

The following basic definitions are used to describe airflow and will be used extensively in the remainder of the Manual.

The density (p) of the air is defined as its mass per unit volume and is normally expressed in pounds mass per cubic foot (lbm/ft^3). At standard atmospheric pressure (14.7 psia), room temperature (70 F) and 0 water content, its value is normally taken to be 0.075 lbm/ft^3, as calculated from the perfect gas equation of state relating pressure, density and temperature:

$$p = \rho RT \qquad [1.1]$$

where: p = the absolute pressure in pounds per square foot absolute (psfa)

ρ = the density, 1bm/ft^3

R = the gas constant for air and equals 53.35 ft-lb/lbm-degrees Rankine

T = the absolute temperature of the air in degrees Rankine

Note that degrees Rankine = degrees Fahrenheit + 459.7.

From the above equation, density varies inversely with temperature when pressure is held constant. Therefore, for any dry air situation at constant pressure,

$$\rho T = (\rho T)_{STD}$$

or

$$\rho = \rho_{STD} \frac{T_{STD}}{T} = 0.075 \frac{530}{T} \qquad [1.2]$$

For example, the density of dry air at 250 F would be

$$\rho = 0.075 \frac{530}{460 + 250} = 0.056 \text{ lbm/ft}^3$$

The combined effects of non-standard conditions can be expressed as a density factor, df.

$$df = (df_e)(df_P)(df_T)(df_m)$$

where: df_e = elevation density factor = $[1-(6.73 * 10^{-6})(z)]^{5.258}$ where z = elevation, ft

df_P = duct pressure density factor = (407 + SP)/(407) where SP = "wg

df_T = temperature density factor = (530)/(T + 460) where T = Fahrenheit

df_m = moisture density factor = (1 + ω)/(1 + 1.607 ω) where ω = pounds H$_2$O/pound dry air

The volumetric flow rate, many times referred to as "volume," is defined as the volume or quantity of air that passes a given location per unit of time. It is related to the average velocity and the flow cross-sectional area by the equation

$$Q = VA \qquad [1.3]$$

where: Q = volumetric flow rate, fpm

V = average velocity, fpm

A = cross-sectional area, ft^2

Given any two of these three quantities, the third can readily be determined.

Air or any other fluid will always flow from a region of higher total pressure to a region of lower total pressure in the absence of work addition (a fan). There are three different but mathematically related pressures associated with a moving air stream.

Static pressure (SP) is defined as the pressure in the duct that tends to burst or collapse the duct and is expressed in inches of water gauge ("wg). It is usually measured with a water manometer, hence the units. SP can be positive or negative with respect to the local atmospheric pressure, but must be measured perpendicular to the airflow. The holes in the side of a pitot tube (see Figure 9-8) or a small hole carefully drilled to avoid internal burrs that disturb the airflow (never punched) into the side of a duct will yield SP.

Velocity pressure (VP) is defined as that pressure required to accelerate air from zero velocity to some velocity (V) and is proportional to the kinetic energy of the air stream. The relationship between V and VP is given by

$$V = 4005 \sqrt{\frac{VP}{df}}$$

or

$$VP = df \left(\frac{V}{4005}\right)^2 \qquad [1.4]$$

where: V = velocity, fpm

VP = velocity pressure, "wg

df = density factor

If standard air is assumed to exist in the duct with a density of 0.075 1bm/ft^3, this equation reduces to

$$V = 4005 \sqrt{VP}$$

or

$$VP = \left(\frac{V}{4005}\right)^2 \qquad [1.5]$$

VP will only be exerted in the direction of airflow and is always positive. Figure 1-1 shows graphically the difference between SP and VP.

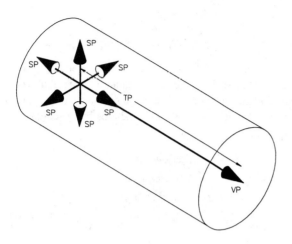

FIGURE 1–1. SP, VP, and TP at a point

Total pressure (TP) is defined as the algebraic sum of the static and velocity pressures or

$$TP = SP + VP \qquad [1.6]$$

Total pressure can be positive or negative with respect to atmospheric pressure and is a measure of the energy content of the air stream, always dropping as the flow proceeds downstream through a duct. The only place it will rise is across the fan.

Total pressure can be measured with an impact tube pointing directly upstream and connected to a manometer. It will vary across a duct due to the change of velocity across a duct and therefore single readings of TP will not be representative of the energy content. Chapter 9 illustrates procedures for measurement of all pressures in a duct system.

The significance of these pressures can be illustrated as follows. Assume a duct segment with both ends sealed was pressurized to a static pressure of 0.1 psi above the atmospheric pressure as shown in Figure 1-2. If a small hole (typically 1/16" to 3/32") were drilled into the duct wall and connected to one side of a U-tube manometer, the reading would be approximately 2.77 "wg. Note the way the left-hand manometer is deflected. If the water in the side of the manometer exposed to

the atmosphere is higher than the water level in the side connected to the duct, then the pressure read by the gauge is positive (greater than atmospheric). Because there is no velocity, the velocity pressure is 0 and SP = TP. A probe which faces the flow is called an impact tube and will measure TP. In this example, a manometer connected to an impact tube (the one on the right) will also read 2.77 "wg. Finally, if one side of a manometer were connected to the impact tube and the other side were connected to the static pressure opening (the center one), the manometer would read the difference between the two pressures. As VP = TP − SP, a manometer so connected would read VP directly. In this example, there is no flow and hence VP = 0 as indicated by the lack of manometer deflection.

If the duct ends were removed and a fan placed midway in the duct, the situation might change to the one shown on Figure 1-3. Upstream of the fan, SP and TP are negative (less than atmospheric). This is called the *suction side*. Downstream of the fan, both SP and TP are positive. This is called the *pressure side*. Regardless of which side of the fan is considered, VP is always positive. Note that the direction in which the manometers are deflected shows whether SP and TP are positive or negative with respect to the local atmospheric pressure.

1.5 PRINCIPLES OF AIRFLOW

Two basic principles of fluid mechanics govern the flow of air in industrial ventilation systems: conservation of mass and conservation of energy. These are essentially bookkeeping laws which state that all mass and all energy must be completely accounted for. A coverage of fluid mechanics is not in the purview of this manual; reference to any standard fluid mechanics textbook will show the derivation of these principles. However, it is important to know what simplifying assumptions are included in the principles discussed below. They include:

1. Heat transfer effects are neglected. If the temperature inside the duct is significantly different from the air temperature surrounding the duct, heat transfer will occur. This will lead to changes in the duct air temperature and hence in the volumetric flow rate.

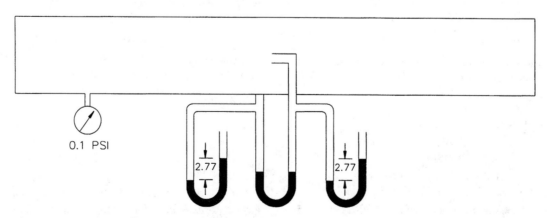

FIGURE 1–2. Measurement of SP, VP, and TP in a pressurized duct

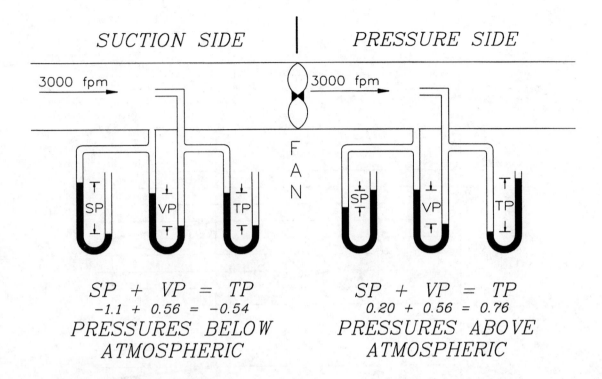

SUCTION SIDE | *PRESSURE SIDE*

3000 fpm   3000 fpm

$SP + VP = TP$
$-1.1 + 0.56 = -0.54$
PRESSURES BELOW
ATMOSPHERIC

$SP + VP = TP$
$0.20 + 0.56 = 0.76$
PRESSURES ABOVE
ATMOSPHERIC

FIGURE 1–3. SP, VP, and TP at points in a ventilation system

2. Compressibility effects are neglected. If the overall pressure drop from the start of the system to the fan is greater than about 20 "wg, then the density will change by about 5% and the volumetric flow rate will also change (see Chapter 5).

3. The air is assumed to be dry. Water vapor in the airstream will lower the air density and correction for this effect, if present, should be made. Chapter 5 describes the necessary psychrometric analysis.

4. The weight and volume of the contaminant in the air stream is ignored. This is permissible for the contaminant concentrations in typical exhaust ventilation systems. For high concentrations of solids or significant amounts of gases other than air, corrections for this effect should be included.

Conservation of mass requires that the net change of mass flow rate must be zero. If the effects discussed above are negligible, then the density will be constant and the net change of volumetric flow rate (Q) must be zero. Therefore, the flow rate that enters a hood must be the same as the flow rate that passes through the duct leading from the hood. At a branch entry (converging wye) fitting, the sum of the two flow rates that enter the fitting must leave it. At a diverging wye, the flow rate entering the wye must equal the sum of the flow rates that leave it. Figure 1-4 illustrates these concepts.

Conservation of energy means that all energy changes must be accounted for as airflows from one point to another. In terms of the pressures previously defined, this principle can be expressed as:

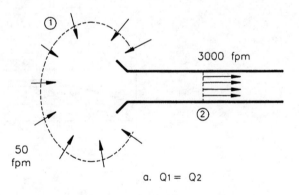

3000 fpm

50 fpm

a. $Q_1 = Q_2$

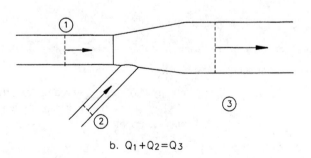

b. $Q_1 + Q_2 = Q_3$

FIGURE 1–4. Volumetric flow rates in various situations. a. Flow through a hood; b. Flow through a branch entry

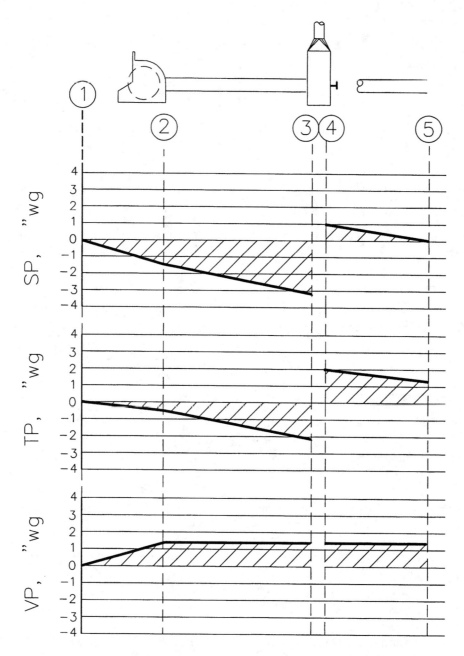

FIGURE 1–5. Variation of SP, VP, and TP through a ventilation system

$$TP_1 = TP_2 + h_l$$

$$SP_1 + VP_1 = SP_2 + VP_2 + h_l$$

where: subscript 1 = some upstream point

subscript 2 = some downstream point

h_l = all energy losses encountered by the air as it flows from the upstream to the downstream point.

Note that, according to this principle, *the total pressure must fall in the direction of flow.*

The application of these principles will be demonstrated by an analysis of the simple system shown in Figure 1-5.

The normally vertical exhaust stack is shown laying horizontally to facilitate graphing the variation of static, total, and velocity pressures. The grinder wheel hood requires 300 cfm and the duct diameter is constant at 3.5 inches (0.0668 ft^2 area).

1.6 ACCELERATION OF AIR AND HOOD ENTRY LOSSES

Air flows from the room (point 1 of Figure 1-5) through the hood to the duct (point 2 of Figure 1-5) where the velocity can be calculated by the basic equation:

$$V = \frac{Q}{A} = \frac{300}{0.0668} = 4490 \text{ fpm}$$

This velocity corresponds to a velocity pressure of 1.26 "wg, assuming standard air.

If there are no losses associated with entry into a hood, then applying the energy conservation principle (Equation 1.7) to the hood yields

$$SP_1 + VP_1 = SP_2 + VP_2$$

This is the well known Bernoulli principle of fluid mechanics. Subscript 1 refers to the room conditions where the static pressure is atmospheric ($SP_1 = 0$) and the air velocity is assumed to be very close to zero ($VP_1 = 0$). Therefore, the energy principle yields

$$SP_2 = -VP_2 = -1.26 \text{ "wg}$$

Even if there were no losses, *the static pressure must decrease due to the acceleration of air to the duct velocity.*

In reality, there are losses as the air enters the hood. These hood entry losses (h_h) are normally expressed as a loss coefficient (F_h) multiplied by the duct velocity pressure, so $h_h = F_h VP_d$ (where $VP_d = VP_2$). The energy conservation principle then becomes

$$SP_2 = -(VP_2 + h_h) \qquad \text{[1.8]}$$

The absolute value of SP_2 is known as the hood static suction (SP_h). Then

$$SP_h = -SP_2 = VP_2 + h_h \qquad \text{[1.9]}$$

(See 3.5.1, 3.5.2 and Figure 5.1 for a discussion of h_h and h_e.)

For the example in Figure 1-5, assuming an entry loss coefficient of 0.40,

$$SP_h = VP_2 + F_h VP_2$$

$$= 1.26 + (0.40)(1.26)$$

$$= 1.26 + 0.50 = 1.76 \text{ "wg}\}$$

In summary, the static pressure downstream of the hood is negative (less than atmospheric) due to two effects:

1. Acceleration of air to the duct velocity; and

2. Hood entry losses.

From the graph, note that $TP_2 = -h_e$, which confirms the premise that total pressure decreases in the flow direction.

An alternate method of describing hood entry losses is by the hood entry coefficient (C_e). This coefficient is defined as the square root of the ratio of duct velocity pressure to hood static suction, or

$$C_e = \sqrt{\frac{VP}{SP_h}} \qquad \text{[1.10]}$$

If there were no losses, then $SP_h = VP$ and $C_e = 1.00$. However, as hoods always have some losses, C_e is always less than 1.00. In Figure 1-5,

$$C_e = \sqrt{\frac{VP}{SP_h}} = \sqrt{\frac{1.26}{1.76}} = 0.845 \qquad \text{[1.10]}$$

An important feature of C_e is that it is a constant for any given hood. It can, therefore, be used to determine the flow rate if the hood static suction is known. This is because

$$Q = VA = 4005 \, A = \sqrt{\frac{VP}{df}} = 4005 \, A \, C_e \sqrt{\frac{SP_h}{df}} \qquad \text{[1.11]}$$

For standard air, this equation becomes

$$Q = 4005 \, A \, C_e \sqrt{SP_h} \qquad \text{[1.12]}$$

For the example in Figure 1-5,

$$Q = 4005 \, (0.0668) \, (0.845) \sqrt{1.76} = 300 \text{ cfm}$$

By use of C_e and a measurement of SP_h, the flow rate of a hood can be quickly determined and corrective action can be taken if the calculated flow rate does not agree with the design flow rate.

1.7 DUCT LOSSES

There are two components to the overall total pressure losses in a duct run: (1) friction losses and (2) fitting losses.

1.7.1 Friction Losses. Losses due to friction in ducts are a complicated function of duct velocity, duct diameter, air density, air viscosity, and duct surface roughness. The effects of velocity, diameter, density, and viscosity are combined into the *Reynolds number (R_e)*, as given by

$$R_e = \frac{\rho dv}{\mu} \qquad \text{[1.13]}$$

where: ρ = density, lbm/ft^3

   d = diameter, ft

   v = velocity, ft/sec

   μ = the air viscosity, lbm/s-ft

The effect of surface roughness is typically given by the *relative roughness,* which is the ratio of the absolute surface roughness height (k), defined as the average height of the roughness elements on a particular type of material, to the duct diameter. Some standard values of absolute surface roughness used in ventilation systems are given in Table 1-1.

L. F. Moody[1.1] combined these effects into a single chart commonly called the *Moody diagram* (see Figure 1-6). With a knowledge of both the Reynolds number and the relative roughness, the *friction coefficient (f),* can be found.

TABLE 1–1. Absolute Surface Roughness

Duct Material	Surface Roughness (k), feet
Galvanized metal	0.00055
Black iron	0.00015
Aluminum	0.00015
Stainless steel	0.00015
Flexible duct (wires exposed)	0.01005
Flexible duct (wires covered)	0.00301

The above roughness heights are design values. It should be noted that significant variations from these values may occur, depending on the manufacturing process.

Once determined, the friction coefficient is used in the *Darcy-Weisbach friction coefficient equation* to determine the overall duct friction losses:

$$h_f = f \frac{L}{d} VP \qquad [1.14]$$

where: h_f = friction losses in a duct, "wg

f = Moody diagram friction coefficient (dimensionless)

L = duct length, ft

d = duct diameter, ft

VP = duct velocity pressure, "wg

There are many equations available for computer solutions to the Moody diagram. One of these is that of Churchill,[1.2] which gives accurate (to within a few percent) results over the entire range of laminar, critical, and turbulent flow, all in a single equation. This equation is:

$$f = 8 \left[\left(\frac{8}{Re} \right)^{12} + (A + B)^{-3/2} \right]^{1/12} \qquad [1.15]$$

where:

$$A = \left\{ -2.457 \ln\left[\left(\frac{7}{Re} \right)^{0.9} + \left(\frac{k}{3.7D} \right) \right] \right\}^{16}$$

$$B = \left(\frac{37,530}{Re} \right)^{16}$$

While useful, this equation is quite difficult to use without a computer. Several attempts have been made to simplify the determination of friction losses for specialized situations. For many years, charts based on the Wright[1.3] equation have been used in ventilation system design:

$$h_f = 2.74 \frac{(V/1000)^{1.9}}{D^{1.22}} \qquad [1.16]$$

where: V = duct velocity, fpm

D = duct diameter, inches

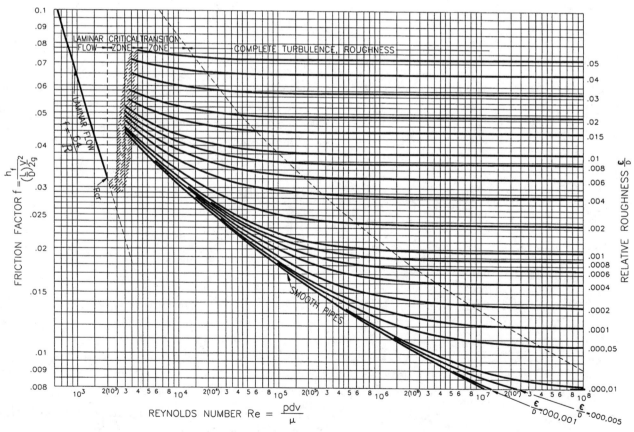

FIGURE 1–6. MOODY DIAGRAM (adapted from reference 1.1)

FIGURE 1–6. Moody diagram (adapted from reference 1.1)

This equation gives the friction losses, expressed as "wg per 100 feet of pipe, for standard air of 0.075 lbm/ft^3 density flowing through average, clean, round galvanized pipe having approximately 40 slip joints per 100 feet (k = 0.0005 ft).

The later work by Loeffler[1.4] presented equations for use in the "*velocity pressure*" calculation method. Using the standard values of surface roughness, equations were obtained that could be used with the Darcy-Weisbach equation in the form:

$$h_f = (12 \frac{f}{D})L\ VP = F_f L\ VP \qquad [1.17]$$

where the "12" is used to convert the diameter D in inches to feet.

Simplified equations were determined for the flow of standard air through various types of duct material with good accuracy (less than 5% error.) The equations thus resulting were:

$$F_f = 12 \frac{f}{D} = \frac{aV^b}{Q_c} \qquad [1.18]$$

where the constant "a" and the exponents "b" and "c" vary as a function of the duct material as shown in Table 1-2. Note that no correlation with the extremely rough flexible duct with wires exposed was made. This equation, using the constants from Table 1-2 for galvanized sheet duct, were used to develop the friction tables 5-5 and 5-6. *Note that the value obtained from the chart or from equation 1.18 must be multiplied by both the length of duct and the velocity pressure.*

1.7.2 Fitting Losses. The fittings (elbows, entries, etc.) in a duct run will also produce a loss in total pressure. These losses are given in Chapter 5.

The fitting losses are given by a loss coefficient (F_{en}) multiplied by the duct velocity pressure. Thus,

$$h_{en} = F_{en}\ VP \qquad [1.19]$$

In contractions, entries, or expansions, there are several different velocity pressures. The proper one to use with the loss coefficient will be identified where the coefficients are listed.

TABLE 1–2. Correlation Equation Constants

Duct Material	k, Ft	a	b	c
Aluminum, black iron, stainless steel	0.00015	0.0425	0.465	0.602
Galvanized sheet duct	0.00051	0.0307	0.533	0.612
Flexible duct, fabric wires covered	0.0035	0.0311	0.604	0.639

In Figure 1-5, 15 feet of straight, constant diameter galvanized duct connects the hood to a fan inlet. Because the duct area is constant, the velocity, and therefore the velocity pressure, is also constant for any given flow rate. The energy principle is:

$$SP_2 + VP_2 = SP_3 + VP_3 + h_d$$

where subscript 3 refers to the fan inlet location. Because $VP_2 = VP_3$, the losses will appear as a reduction in static pressure (there will, of course, be a corresponding reduction in total pressure). The friction loss can be found from Equation 1.17 with the aid of Equation 1.18:

$$F_d = 0.0307 \frac{V^{0.533}}{Q^{0.612}}$$

$$= 0.0307 \frac{4490^{0.533}}{300^{0.612}} = 0.0828$$

From Equation 1.17, $h_d = (0.0828)(15)(1.26) = 1.56$ "wg. Using this in the energy principle,

$$SP_3 = SP_2 - h_d = -1.76 \text{ "wg} -1.56 \text{ "wg} = -3.32 \text{ "wg}$$

Another 10 feet of straight duct is connected to the discharge side of the fan. The losses from the fan to the end of the system would be about 1.04 "wg. Because the static pressure at the end of the duct must be atmospheric ($SP_5 = 0$), the energy principle results in

$$SP_4 = SP_5 + h_d = 0 \text{ "wg} + 1.04 \text{ "wg} = 1.04 \text{ "wg}$$

Therefore, the static pressure at the fan outlet must be higher than atmospheric by an amount equal to the losses in the discharge duct.

1.8 MULTIPLE-HOOD EXHAUST SYSTEMS

Most exhaust systems are more complicated than the preceding example. It is usually more economical to purchase a single fan and air cleaner to service a series of similar operations than to create a complete system for each operation. For example, the exhaust from 10 continuously used grinders can be combined into a single flow which leads to a common air cleaner and fan. This situation is handled similarly to a simple system, but with some provision to ensure that the airflow from each hood is as desired (see Chapter 5).

1.9 AIRFLOW CHARACTERISTICS OF BLOWING AND EXHAUSTING

Air blown from a small opening retains its directional effect for a considerable distance beyond the plane of the opening. However, if the flow of air *through the same opening* were reversed so that it operated as an exhaust opening handling the same volumetric flow rate, the flow would become almost

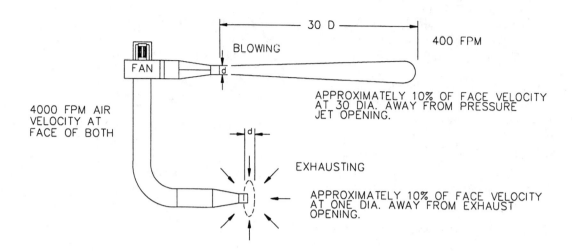

FIGURE 1–7. Blowing vs. exhausting

non-directional and its range of influence would be greatly reduced. For this reason, local exhaust must not be contemplated for any process which cannot be conducted in the *immediate* vicinity of the hood. Also, because of this effect, every effort should be made to enclose the operation as much as possible. Figure 1-7 illustrates the fundamental difference between blowing and exhausting.

This effect also shows how the supply or replacement air discharge grilles can influence an exhaust system. If care is not taken, the discharge pattern from a supply grille could seriously affect the flow pattern in front of an exhaust hood.

REFERENCES

1.1.   Moody, L.F.: "Friction Factors for Pipe Flow." ASME Trans. 66:672 (1944).

1.2.   Churchill, S.W.: "Friction Factor Equation Spans All Fluid Flow Regimes." Chemical Engineering, Vol. 84 (1977).

1.3.   Wright, Jr., D.K.: "A New Friction Chart for Round Ducts." ASHVE Trans., Vol. 51, Appendix I, p. 312 (1945).

1.4.   Loeffler, J.J.: "Simplified Equations for HVAC Duct Friction Factors." ASHRAE J., p. 76 (January 1980).

Chapter 2
GENERAL INDUSTRIAL VENTILATION

2.1 INTRODUCTION

"General industrial ventilation" is a broad term which refers to the supply and exhaust of air with respect to an area, room, or building. It can be divided further into specific functions as follows:

1. *Dilution Ventilation*—is the dilution of contaminated air with uncontaminated air for the purpose of controlling potential airborne health hazards, fire and explosive conditions, odors, and nuisance type contaminants. Dilution ventilation also can include the control of airborne contaminants (vapors, gases, and particulates) generated within tight buildings.

   Dilution ventilation is not as satisfactory for health hazard control as is local exhaust ventilation. Circumstances may be found in which dilution ventilation provides an adequate amount of control more economically than a local exhaust system. One should be careful, however, not to base the economical considerations entirely upon the first cost of the system since dilution ventilation frequently exhausts large amounts of heat from a building which may greatly increase the energy cost of the operation.

2. *Heat Control Ventilation*—is the control of indoor atmospheric conditions associated with hot industrial environments such as are found in foundries, laundries, bakeries, etc., for the purpose of preventing acute discomfort or injury.

2.2 DILUTION VENTILATION PRINCIPLES

The principles of dilution ventilation system design are as follows:

1. Select from available data the amount of air required for satisfactory dilution of the contaminant. The values tabulated on Table 2-1 assume perfect distribution and dilution of the air and solvent vapors. These values must be multiplied by the selected K value (see Section 2.3.1).

2. Locate the exhaust openings near the sources of contamination, if possible, in order to obtain the benefit of "spot ventilation."

3. Locate the air supply and exhaust outlets such that the air passes through the zone of contamination. The operator should remain between the air supply and the source of the contaminant.

4. Replace exhausted air by use of a replacement air system. This replacement air should be heated during cold weather. Dilution ventilation systems usually handle large quantities of air by means of low pressure fans. Replacement air must be provided if the system is to operate satisfactorily.

5. Avoid re-entry of the exhausted air by discharging the exhaust high above the roof line or by assuring that no window, outdoor air intakes, or other such openings are located near the exhaust discharge.

2.3 DILUTION VENTILATION FOR HEALTH

The use of dilution ventilation for health has four limiting factors: (1) the quantity of contaminant generated must not be too great or the airflow rate necessary for dilution will be impractical; (2) workers must be far enough away from the contaminant source or the evolution of contaminant must be in sufficiently low concentrations so that workers will not have an exposure in excess of the established TLV; (3) the toxicity of the contaminant must be low; and (4) the evolution of contaminants must be reasonably uniform.

Dilution ventilation is used most often to control the vapors from organic liquids with a TLV of 100 ppm or higher. In order to successfully apply the principles of dilution to such a problem, factual data are needed on the rate of vapor generation or on the rate of liquid evaporation. Usually such data can be obtained from the plant if any type of adequate records on material consumption are kept.

2.3.1 General Dilution Ventilation Equation:
The ventilation rate needed to maintain a constant concentration at a uniform generation rate is derived by starting with a fundamental material balance and assuming no contaminant in the air supply,

Rate of Accumulation = Rate of Generation − Rate of Removal

or

$$VdC = Gdt - Q'Cdt \qquad [2.1]$$

where: V = volume of room
   G = rate of generation
   Q' = effective volumetric flow rate
   C = concentration of gas or vapor
   t = time

At a steady state, $dC = 0$

$$Gdt = Q'Cdt$$

$$\int_{t_1}^{t_2} Gdt = \int_{t_1}^{t_2} Q'Cdt$$

At a constant concentration, C, and uniform generation rate, G,

$$G(t_2 - t_1) = Q'C (t_2 - t_1)$$

$$Q' = \frac{G}{C} \qquad [2.2]$$

Due to incomplete mixing, a K value is introduced to the rate of ventilation; thus:

TABLE 2-1. Dilution Air Volumes for Vapors

The following values are tabulated using the TLV values shown in parentheses, parts per million. TLV values are subject to revision if further research or experience indicates the need. If the TLV value has changed, the dilution air requirements must be recalculated. The values on the table must be multiplied by the evaporation rate (pts/min) to yield the effective ventilation rate (Q.) (see Equation 2.5).

Liquid (TLV in ppm)*	Ft^3 of Air (STP) Required for Dilution to TLV** Per Pint Evaporation
Acetone (500)	11,025
n-Amyl acetate (50)	54,400
Benzene (0.5)	NOT RECOMMENDED
n-Butanol (butyl alcohol) (C 50)	88,000
n-Butyl acetate (150)	20,400
Butyl Cellosolve(2-butoxyethanol) (20)	NOT RECOMMENDED
Carbon disulfide (10)	NOT RECOMMENDED
Carbon tetrachloride (5)	NOT RECOMMENDED
Cellosolve (2-ethoxyethanol) (5)	NOT RECOMMENDED
Cellosolve acetate (2-ethoxyethyl acetate) (5)	NOT RECOMMENDED
Chloroform (10)	NOT RECOMMENDED
1-2 Dichloroethane (ethylene dichloride) (10)	NOT RECOMMENDED
1-2 Dichloroethylene (200)	26,900
1,4 Dioxane (20)	NOT RECOMMENDED
Ethyl acetate (400)	10,300
Ethyl alcohol (1000)	6,900
Ethyl ether (400)	9,630
Gasoline (300)	REQUIRES SPECIAL CONSIDERATION
Isoamyl alcohol (100)	37,200
Isopropyl alcohol (400)	13,200
Isopropyl ether (250)	11,400
Methyl acetate (200)	25,000
Methyl alcohol (200)	49,100
Methyl n-butyl ketone (5)	NOT RECOMMENDED
Methyl Cellosolve (2-methoxyethanol) (5)	NOT RECOMMENDED
Methyl Cellosolve acetate (2-methoxyethyl acetate) (5)	NOT RECOMMENDED
Methyl chloroform (350)	11,390
Methyl ethyl ketone (200)	22,500
Methyl isobutyl ketone (50)	64,600
Methyl propyl ketone (200)	19,900
Naphtha (coal tar)	REQUIRES SPECIAL CONSIDERATION
Naphtha VM & P (300)	REQUIRES SPECIAL CONSIDERATION
Nitrobenzene (1)	NOT RECOMMENDED
n-Propyl acetate (200)	17,500
Stoddard solvent (100)	30,000-35,000
1,1,2,2-Tetrachloroethane (1)	NOT RECOMMENDED
Tetrachloroethylene (perchlorethylene) (25)	159,400
Toluene (50)	75,700
Trichloroethylene (50)	90,000
Xylene (100)	33,000

*See Threshold Limit Values 2000 in Appendix A.

**The tabulated dilution air quantities must be multiplied by the selected K value.

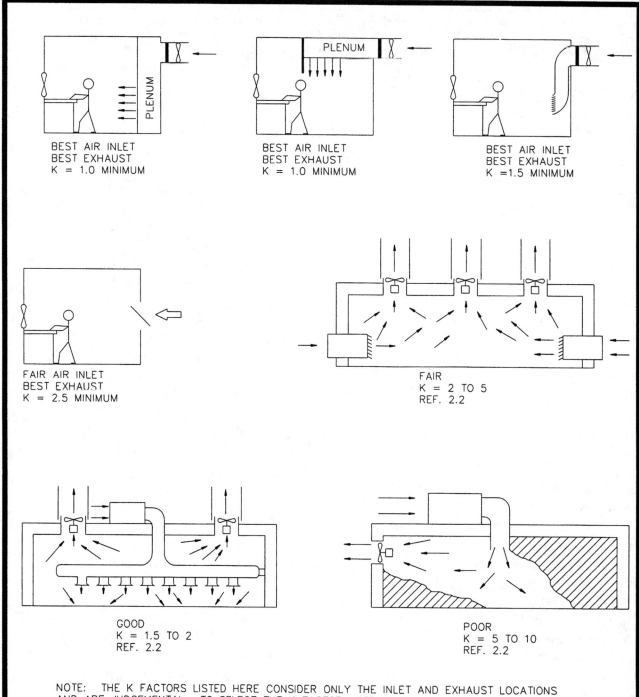

BEST AIR INLET
BEST EXHAUST
K = 1.0 MINIMUM

BEST AIR INLET
BEST EXHAUST
K = 1.0 MINIMUM

BEST AIR INLET
BEST EXHAUST
K = 1.5 MINIMUM

FAIR AIR INLET
BEST EXHAUST
K = 2.5 MINIMUM

FAIR
K = 2 TO 5
REF. 2.2

GOOD
K = 1.5 TO 2
REF. 2.2

POOR
K = 5 TO 10
REF. 2.2

NOTE: THE K FACTORS LISTED HERE CONSIDER ONLY THE INLET AND EXHAUST LOCATIONS
AND ARE JUDGEMENTAL. TO SELECT THE K FACTOR USED IN THE EQUATION, THE
NUMBER AND LOCATION OF THE EMPLOYEES, THE SOURCE OF THE CONTAMINANT,
AND THE TOXICITY OF THE CONTAMINANT MUST ALSO BE CONSIDERED.

AMERICAN CONFERENCE
OF GOVERNMENTAL
INDUSTRIAL HYGIENISTS

"K" FACTORS
SUGGESTED FOR INLET
AND EXHAUST LOCATIONS

DATE   1-88

FIGURE   2-1

$$Q' = \frac{Q}{K} \qquad [2.3]$$

where: Q = actual ventilation rate, cfm

Q' = effective ventilation rate, cfm

K = a factor to allow for incomplete mixing

Equation 2.2 then becomes:

$$Q = \left(\frac{G}{C}\right)K \qquad [2.4]$$

This K factor is based on several considerations:

1. The efficiency of mixing and distribution of replacement air introduced into the room or space being ventilated (see Figure 2-1).

2. The toxicity of the solvent. Although TLV and toxicity are not synonymous, the following guidelines have been suggested for choosing the appropriate K value:

   Slightly toxic material: TLV > 500 ppm

   Moderately toxic material: TLV ≤ 100–500 ppm

   Highly toxic material: TLV < 100 ppm

3. A judgement of any other circumstances which the industrial hygienist determined to be of importance based on experience and the individual problem. Included in these criteria are such considerations as:

   a. Duration of the process, operational cycle and normal locations of workers relative to sources of contamination.

   b. Location and number of points of generation of the contaminant in the workroom or area.

   c. Seasonal changes in the amount of natural ventilation.

   d. Reduction in operational effectiveness of mechanical air moving devices.

   e. Other circumstances which may affect the concentration of hazardous material in the breathing zone of the workers.

The K value selected, depending on the above considerations, ranges from 1 to 10.

2.3.2 Calculating Dilution Ventilation for Steady State Concentration: The concentration of a gas or vapor at a steady state can be expressed by the material balance equation

$$Q' = \frac{G}{C}$$

Therefore, the rate of flow of uncontaminated air required to maintain the atmospheric concentration of a hazardous material at an acceptable level can be easily calculated if the generation rate can be determined. Usually, the acceptable concentration (C) expressed in parts per million (ppm) is considered to be the Threshold Limit Value (TLV). For liquid solvents, the rate of generation is

$$G = \frac{CONSTANT \times SG \times ER}{MW}$$

where: G = generation rate, cfm

CONSTANT = 403 (the volume in ft^3 that 1 pt of liquid, when vaporized, will occupy at STP, ft^3/pt)

SG = Specific gravity of volatile liquid

ER = evaporation rate of liquid, pts/min

MW = molecular weight of liquid

Thus, $Q' = G/C$ can be expressed as

$$Q' = \frac{403 \times 10^6 \times SG \times ER}{MW \times C} \qquad [2.5]$$

EXAMPLE PROBLEM

Methyl chloroform is lost by evaporation from a tank at a rate of 1.5 pints per 60 minutes. What is the effective ventilation rate (Q') and the actual ventilation rate (Q) required to maintain the vapor concentration at the TLV?

TLV = 350 ppm, SG = 132, MW = 133.4, Assume K = 5

Assuming perfect dilution, the effective ventilation rate (Q') is

$$Q' = \frac{(403)(10^6)(1.32)(1.5/60)}{(133.4)(350)}$$

Due to incomplete mixing the actual ventilation rate (Q) is

$$Q = \frac{(403)(10^6)(1.32)(1.5/60)(5)}{(133.4)(350)}$$

2.3.3 Contaminant Concentration Buildup (see Figure 2-2): The concentration of a contaminant can be calculated after any change of time. Rearranging the differential material balance results in

$$\frac{dC}{G - Q'C} = \frac{dt}{V}$$

which can be integrated to yield

$$\ln\left(\frac{G - Q'C_2}{G - Q'C_1}\right) = -\frac{Q'(t_2 - t_1)}{V} \qquad [2.6]$$

where subscript 1 refers to the initial condition and subscript 2 refers to the final condition. If it is desired to calculate the time required to reach a given concentration, then rearranging $t_2 - t_1$, or Δt, gives

$$\Delta t = -\frac{V}{Q'}\left[\ln\left(\frac{G - Q'C_2}{G - Q'C_1}\right)\right] \qquad [2.7]$$

If $C_1 = 0$, then the equation becomes

$$\Delta t = -\frac{V}{Q'}\left[\ln\left(\frac{G - Q'C_2}{G}\right)\right] \qquad [2.8]$$

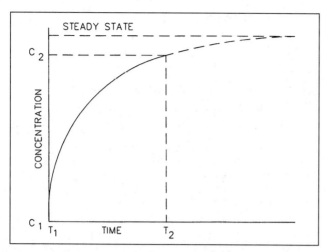

FIGURE 2–2. Contaminant concentration buildup

Note: the concentration C_2 is ppm or parts/10^6 (e.g., if C_2 = 200 ppm, enter C_2 as 200/10^6).

If it is desired to determine the concentration level (C_2) after a certain time interval, t_2 - t_1 or Δt, and if $C_1 = 0$, then the equation becomes

$$C_2 = \frac{G\left[1 - e^{\left(-V \frac{Q'\Delta t}{V}\right)}\right]}{Q'} \qquad [2.9]$$

Note: to convert C_2 to ppm, multiply the answer by 10^6.

EXAMPLE

Methyl chloroform vapor is being generated under the following conditions: G = 1.2 cfm; Q′ = 2,000 cfm; V = 100,000 cu ft; C_1 = 0; K = 3. How long before the concentration (C_2) reaches 200 ppm or 200 ÷ 10^6?

$$\Delta t = -\frac{V}{Q'}\left[\ln\left(\frac{G - Q'C_2}{G}\right)\right] = 20.3 \text{ min.}$$

Using the same values as in the preceding example, what will be the concentration after 60 minutes?

$$C_2 = \frac{G\left[1 - e^{\left(-\frac{Q'\Delta t}{V}\right)}\right]}{Q'} \times 10^6 = 419 \text{ ppm}$$

2.3.4 Rate of Purging (see Figure 2-3): Where a quantity of air is contaminated but where further contamination or generation has ceased, the rate of decrease of concentration over a period of time is as follows:

$$VdC = -Q'Cdt$$

$$\int_{c_1}^{c_2} \frac{dC}{C} = -\frac{Q'}{C}\int_{t_1}^{t_2} dt$$

$$\ln\left(\frac{C_2}{C_1}\right) = -\frac{Q'}{V}(t_2 - t_1) \qquad [2.10]$$

or,

$$C_2 = C_{1e}\left[-\frac{Q'(t_2-t_1)}{V}\right]$$

EXAMPLE

In the room of the example in Section 2.3.3, assume that ventilation continues at the same rate (Q′ = 2000 cfm), but that the contaminating process is interrupted. How much time is required to reduce the concentration from 100 (C_1) to 25 (C_2) ppm?

$$t_1 - t_2 = -\frac{V}{Q'} \ln\left(\frac{C_2}{C_1}\right) = 69.3 \text{ min}$$

In the problem above, if the concentration (C_1) at t_1 is 100 ppm, what will concentration (C_1) be after 60 minutes (Δt)?

$$C_2 = C_1 e^{\left(-\frac{Q'\Delta t}{V}\right)} = 30.1 \text{ ppm}$$

2.4 MIXTURES—DILUTION VENTILATION FOR HEALTH

In many cases the parent liquid for which dilution ventilation rates are being designed will consist of a mixture of solvents. The common procedure used in such instances is as follows.

When two or more hazardous substances are present, their combined effect, rather than that of either individually, should be given primary consideration. *In the absence of information to the contrary, the effects of the different hazards should be considered as additive.* That is, if the sum of the following fractions,

$$\frac{C_1}{TLV_1} + \frac{C_2}{TLV_2} + \cdots + \frac{C_n}{TLV_n} \qquad [2.11]$$

exceeds unity, then the threshold limit of the mixture should be considered as being exceeded. "C" indicates the observed atmospheric concentration and TLV the corresponding threshold limit. In the absence of information to the contrary, the dilution ventilation therefore should be calculated on the basis that the effect of the different hazards is additive. The air quantity required to dilute each component of the mixture to the required safe concentration is calculated and the *sum* of the air quantities is used as the required dilution ventilation for the mixture.

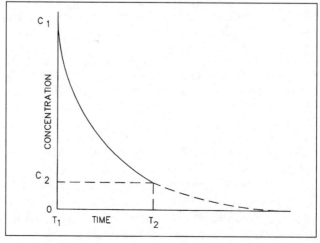

FIGURE 2–3. Rate of purging

Exceptions to the above rule may be made when there is good reason to believe that the chief effects of the different harmful substances are not additive but independent, as when purely local effects on different organs of the body are produced by the various components of the mixture. In such cases, the threshold limit ordinarily is exceeded only when at least one member of the series itself has a value exceeding unity, e.g.,

$$\frac{C_1}{TLV_1} \text{ or } \frac{C_2}{TLV_2}$$

Therefore, where two or more hazardous substances are present and it is known that the effects of the different substances are not additive but act independently on the different organs of the body, the required dilution ventilation for each component of the mixture should be calculated and the highest cfm thus obtained used as the dilution ventilation rate.

EXAMPLE PROBLEM

A cleaning and gluing operation is being performed; methyl ethyl ketone (MEK) and toluene are both being released. Both have narcotic properties and the effects are considered additive. Air samples disclose concentrations of 150 ppm MEK and 50 ppm toluene. Using the equation given, the sum of the fractions [(150/200) + (50/50) = 1.75] is greater than unity and the TLV of the mixture is exceeded. The volumetric flow rate at standard conditions required for dilution of the mixture to the TLV would be as follows:

Assume 2 pints of each is being released each 60 min. Select a K value of 4 for MEK and a K value of 5 for toluene; sp gr for MEK = 0.805, for toluene = 0.866; MW for MEK = 72.1, for toluene = 92.13.

$$Q \text{ for MEK} = \frac{(403)(0.0805)(10^6)(4)(2/60)}{72.1 \times 200} = 3000 \text{ cfm}$$

$$Q \text{ for toluene} = \frac{(403)(0.866)(10^6)(5)(2/60)}{92.13 \times 50} = 12{,}627 \text{ cfm}$$

Q for mixture = 3000 + 12,627 = 15,627 cfm

2.5 DILUTION VENTILATION FOR FIRE AND EXPLOSION

Another function of dilution ventilation is to reduce the concentration of vapors within an enclosure to below the lower explosive limit. It should be stressed that this concept is never applied in cases where workers are exposed to the vapor. In such instances, dilution rates for health hazard control are always applied. The reason for this will be apparent when comparing TLVs and lower explosive limits (LELs).

The TLV of xylene is 100 ppm. The LEL of xylene is 1% or 10,000 ppm. An atmosphere of xylene safe-guarded against fire and explosion usually will be kept below 25% of the LEL or 2500 ppm. Exposure to such an atmosphere may cause severe illness or death. However, in baking and drying ovens,

in enclosed air drying spaces, within ventilation duct, etc., dilution ventilation for fire and explosion is used to keep the vapor concentration to below the LEL.

Equation 2.5 can be modified to yield air quantities to dilute below the LEL. By substituting LEL for TLV:

$$Q = \frac{(403)(\text{sp gr liquid})(100)(ER)(S_f)}{(MW \text{ liquid})(LEL)(B)} \text{ (for Standard Air)} \quad \text{[2.12]}$$

Note: 1. Since LEL is expressed in percent (parts per 100) rather than ppm (parts per million as for the TLV), the coefficient of 1,000,000 becomes 100.

2. S_f is a safety coefficient which depends on the percentage of the LEL necessary for safe conditions. In most ovens and drying enclosures, it has been found desirable to maintain vapor concentrations at not more than 25% of the LEL at all times in all parts of the oven. In properly ventilated continuous ovens, a S_f coefficient of 4 (25% of the LEL) is used. In batch ovens, with good air distribution, the existence of peak drying rates requires a S_f coefficient of 10 or 12 to maintain safe concentrations at all times. In non-recirculating or improperly ventilated batch or continuous ovens, larger S_f coefficients may be necessary.

3. B is a constant which takes into account the fact that the lower explosive limit of a solvent vapor or air mixture decreases at elevated temperatures. B = 1 for temperatures up to 250 F; B = 0.7 for temperatures above 250 F.

EXAMPLE PROBLEM

A batch of enamel dipped shelves is baked in a recirculating oven at 350 F for 60 minutes. Volatiles in the enamel applied to the shelves consist of two pints of xylene. What oven ventilation rate, in cfm, is required to dilute the xylene vapor concentration within the oven to a safe limit at all times?

For xylene, the LEL = 1.0%; sp gr = 0.88; MW = 106; S_f = 10; B = 0.7. From Equation 2.12:

$$Q = \frac{(403)(0.88)(2/60)(100)(10)}{(106)(1.0)(0.7)} = 159 \text{ cfm}$$

Since the above equation is at standard conditions, the airflow rate must be converted from 70 F to 350 F (operating conditions):

$$Q_A = (cfm_{STP})(\text{Ratio of Absolute Temperature})$$

$$= (cfm_{STP})\frac{(460F + 350F)}{(460F + 70F)}$$

$$Q_A = 159\left(\frac{810}{530}\right)$$

$$= 243 \text{ cfm}$$

EXAMPLE PROBLEM

In many circumstances, solvent evaporation rate is non-uniform due to the process temperature or the manner of solvent use.

A 6 ft diameter muller is used for mixing resin sand on a 10-minute cycle. Each batch consists of 400 pounds of sand, 19 pounds of resin, and 8 pints of ethyl alcohol (the ethyl alcohol evaporates in the first two minutes). What ventilation rate is required?

For ethyl alcohol, LEL = 3.28%; sp gr = 0.789; MW = 46.07; S_f = 4; B = 1

$$Q = \frac{(403)(0.789)(3/2)(100)(4)}{(46.07)(3.28)(1)} = 3367 \text{ cfm}$$

Another source of data is the National Board of Fire Underwriters' Pamphlet #86, *Standard for Class A Ovens and Furnaces*.[2.3] This contains a more complete list of solvents and their properties. In addition, it lists and describes a number of safeguards and interlocks which must always be considered in connection with fire dilution ventilation. See also Reference 2.4.

2.6 FIRE DILUTION VENTILATION FOR MIXTURES

It is common practice to regard the entire mixture as consisting of the components requiring the highest amount of dilution per unit liquid volume and to calculate the required air quantity on that basis. (This component would be the one with the highest value for sp gr/(MW)(LEL).)

2.7 VENTILATION FOR HEAT CONTROL

Ventilation for heat control in a hot industrial environment is a specific application of general industrial ventilation. The primary function of the ventilation system is to prevent the acute discomfort, heat-induced illness, and possible injury of those working in or generally occupying a designated hot industrial environment. Heat-induced occupational illnesses, injuries, or reduced productivity may occur in situations where the total heat load may exceed the defenses of the body and result in a heat stress situation. It follows, therefore, that a heat control ventilation system or other engineering control method must follow a physiological evaluation in terms of potential heat stress for the occupant in the hot industrial environment.

Due to the complexity of conducting a physiological evaluation, the criteria presented here are limited to general considerations. It is strongly recommended, however, that the NIOSH Publication No. 86-113, *Criteria for a Recommended Standard, Occupational Exposure to Hot Environments*,[2.5] be reviewed thoroughly in the process of developing the heat control ventilation system.

The development of a ventilation system for a hot industrial environment usually includes the control of the ventilation airflow rate, velocity, temperature, humidity, and airflow path through the space in question. This may require inclusion of certain phases of mechanical air-conditioning engineering design which is outside the scope of this manual. The necessary engineering design criteria that may be required are available in appropriate publications of the American Society of Heating, Refrigeration and Air-Conditioning Engineers (ASHRAE) handbook series.

2.8 HEAT BALANCE AND EXCHANGE

An essential requirement for continued normal body function is that the deep body core temperature be maintained within the acceptable range of about 37 C (98.6 F) ± 1 C (1.8 F). To achieve this, body temperature equilibrium requires a constant exchange of heat between the body and the environment. The rate and amount of the heat exchange are governed by the fundamental laws of thermodynamics of heat exchange between objects. The amount of heat that must be exchanged is a function of (1) the total heat produced by the body (metabolic heat), which may range from about 1 kilocalorie (kcal) per kilogram (kg) of body weight per hour (1.16 watts) at rest to 5 kcal/kg body weight/hour (7 watts) for moderately hard industrial work; and (2) the heat gained, if any, from the environment. The rate of heat exchange with the environment is a function of air temperature and humidity, skin temperature, air velocity, evaporation of sweat, radiant temperature, and type, and amount, and characteristics of the clothing worn, among other factors. Respiratory heat loss is of little consequence in human defenses against heat stress.

The basic heat balance equation is:

$$\Delta S = (M - W) \pm C \pm R - E \qquad [2.13]$$

where: ΔS = change in body heat content

(M−W) = total metabolism − external work performed

C = convective heat exchange

R = radiative heat exchange

E = evaporative heat loss

To solve the equation, measurement of metabolic heat production, air temperature, air water vapor pressure, wind velocity, and mean radiant temperature are required.

The major modes of heat exchange between man and the environment are convection, radiation, and evaporation. Other than for brief periods of body contact with hot tools, equipment, floors, etc., which may cause burns, conduction plays a minor role in industrial heat stress. Because of the typically small areas of contact between either body surfaces or its clothing and hot or cold objects, heat exchange by thermal conduction is usually not evaluated in a heat balance equation for humans. The effect of heat exchange by thermal conduction in human thermal regulation is important only when large areas of the body are in contact with surfaces that are at temperatures different from average skin temperature (nominally 95 F), as when someone is prone or supine for long periods. It is important, also, when even small body areas are in contact with objects that provide steep thermal gradients for heat transfer, as when someone is standing on very cold or very hot surfaces.

The equations for calculating heat exchange by convection, radiation, and evaporation are available in Standard International (SI) units, metric units, and English units. In SI units heat exchange is in watts per square meter of body surface (W/m^2). The heat exchange equations are available in both metric and English units for both the seminude individual and the worker wearing conventional long-sleeved work shirt and trousers. The values are in kcal/h or British thermal units per hour (Btu/h) for the "standard worker" defined as one who weighs 70 kg (154 lbs) and has a body surface area of $1.8 \ m^2$ ($19.4 \ ft^2$).

2.8.1 Convection: The rate of convective heat exchange between the skin of a person and the ambient air immediately surrounding the skin is a function of the difference in temperature between the ambient air (t_a), the mean weighted skin temperature (t_{sk}) and the rate of air movement over the skin (V_a). This relationship is stated algebraically for the "standard worker" wearing the customary one layer work clothing ensemble as:

$$C = 0.65 \ V_a^{0.6} \ (t_a - t_{sk}) \qquad \text{[2.14]}$$

where: C = convective heat exchange, Btu/h

V_a = air velocity, fpm

t_a = air temperature, F

t_{sk} = mean weighted skin temperature, usually assumed to be 95 F

When $t_a > 95$ F there will be a gain in body heat from the ambient air by convection. When $t_a < 95$ F, heat will be lost from the body to the ambient air by convection.

2.8.2 Radiation: Infrared radiative heat exchange between the exposed surfaces of a person's skin and clothing varies as a function of the difference between the fourth power of the absolute temperature of the exposed surfaces and that of the surface of the radiant source or sink, the exposed areas and their emissivities. Heat is gained by thermal radiation if the facing surface is warmer than the average temperature of the exposed skin and clothing, and *vice versa*. A practical approximation for infrared radiant heat exchange for a person wearing conventional clothing is:

$$R = 15.0 \ (t_w - t_{sk}) \qquad \text{[2.15]}$$

where: R = radiant heat exchange, Btu/h

t_w = mean radiant temperature, F

t_{sk} = mean weighted skin temperature

2.8.3 Evaporation: The evaporation of water (sweat) or other liquids from the skin or clothing surfaces results in a heat loss from the body. Evaporative heat loss for humans is a function of airflow over the skin and clothing surfaces, the water vapor partial pressure gradient between the skin surface and the surrounding air, the area from which water or other liquids are evaporating and mass transfer coefficients at their surfaces.

$$E = 2.4V_a^{0.6} \ (\rho_{sk} - \rho_a) \qquad \text{[2.16]}$$

where: E = evaporative heat loss, Btu/h

V_a = air velocity, fpm

ρ_a = water vapor pressure of ambient air, mmHg

ρ_{sk} = water vapor pressure on the skin, assumed to be 42 mmHg at a 95 F skin temperature

2.9 ADAPTIVE MECHANISM OF THE BODY

Even people in generally good health can adjust physiologically to thermal stress only over a narrow range of environmental conditions. Unrestricted blood flow to the skin, an unimpeded flow of dry, cool air over the skin surface and sweating are prime defenses in heat stress. Although heat produced by muscle activity reduces the impact of cold stress, it can add substantially to the total challenge during heat stress. Diminished health status, medications, limited prior thermal exposure, among other factors, increase danger to thermal stresses.

The reflex control of blood flow is the body's most effective and important first line of defense in facing either cold or heat stress. Reducing blood flow to the skin of the hands, feet, fingers, and toes is an important measure for reducing heat loss in a cold environment. Blood flow to the skin, however, increases many-fold during heat stress. Its effect is to increase rates of heat distribution in the body and maximize conductive, convective, radiative, and evaporative heat losses to the environment (Figure 2-4). Its cost is often to reduce perfusion of other organs, especially the brain, and reduce systemic arterial blood pressure leading to reduced consciousness, collapse, heat exhaustion, and other heat-induced illnesses.

Reflex sweating during the physical activities of exercise, work, and/or heat stress brings often large volumes of body water and electrolytes (salts) to the skin surface. Heat is lost when the water in sweat evaporates. Whether the electrolytes remain on the skin surface or are deposited in clothing, they are nonetheless permanently lost to the body. The electrolyte content of a typical American diet usually provides adequate electrolyte replacement for these losses. Electrolyte replacement fluids, however, may be necessary for people on salt-restricted diets and those who commonly sustain periods of prolonged and profuse sweating. It is essential for everyone that the lost body water and electrolytes are replaced in the same volume and proportion as lost in sweat. Muscle spasms, cramps, gas-

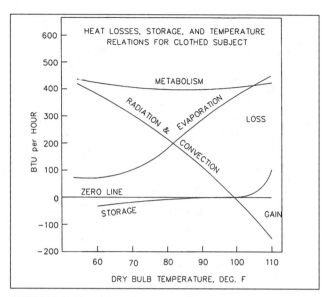

FIGURE 2–4. Heat losses, storage, and temperature relations

trointestinal disturbances, and general malaise, among other signs and symptoms, commonly develop when they are not.

2.10 ACCLIMATIZATION

People in general good health normally develop heat acclimatization in a week or so after intermittently working or exercising in a heat stress. Its effect is to improve the comfort and safety of the heat exposure. It occurs because of an increase in total circulating blood volume, an improved ability to maintain systemic arterial blood pressure during heat stress, a developed ability to produce larger volumes of more dilute sweat, the rate of production of which is more precisely matched to the heat load. Heat acclimatization rapidly diminishes even after a day or so of discontinued activity in the heat—most is lost after about a week.

2.11 ACUTE HEAT DISORDERS

A variety of heat disorders can be distinguished clinically when individuals are exposed to excessive heat. A brief description of these disorders follows.

2.11.1 Heatstroke (also called "Sunstroke"): Heat stroke is a **life-threatening** condition which without exception demands immediate emergency medical care and hospitalization. Before medical care arrives, move the person to a shaded area, check for other injuries, ensure there is an unobstructed airway, remove or loosen clothing, and flood the body surface with free-flowing, tepid (not cold) water. Vigorous fanning helps cooling. Heat stroke develops when body heat gains from exercise, work, and/or a hot environment overwhelm normal thermoregulatory defenses. Characteristically, sweating has ceased, the skin is hot and dry, and deep body temperature is above about 104 F. The person may be either diaphoretic, semiconscious, unconscious or agitated, delirious, and in convulsions. Demand medical care even if consciousness returns—lethal effects may develop in the next 24 to 72 hours.

2.11.2 Heat Exhaustion (Also Called "Exercise-induced Heat Exhaustion", "Heat Syncope"): Heat exhaustion most commonly occurs in people who are not heat acclimatized and who are in poor physical condition, obese, inappropriately dressed for a heat stress and exercising, or working energetically in the heat at unaccustomed and/or demanding tasks. It is characterized by lightheadedness, dizziness, vision disturbances, nausea, vague flu-like symptoms, tinnitus, weakness, and occasionally, collapse. The person's deep body temperature is typically in a normal range or only slightly elevated; the skin is moist and cool but may be reddened by its high rate of blood flow. Heat exhaustion develops when there is reflex demand for blood flow to the skin to dissipate body heat and a simultaneous reflex demand for blood flow to exercising muscles to meet metabolic needs of increased activity. These peripheral distributions of blood volume reduce systemic arterial pressure and brain blood flow, causing most of the symptoms of heat exhaustion. Rest in a cool environment where there is freely flowing, dry air usually remediates symptoms quickly. Although heat exhaustion is debilitating and uncomfortable, it is not often a long-term health threat. There are considerable dangers, of course, for anyone operating machinery when consciousness is impaired because of heat exhaustion or for any other reason.

2.11.3 Heat Cramps ("Muscle Cramps") and Heat Rash ("Prickly Heat", "Miliaria Rubia"): Spontaneous, involuntary, painful, and prolonged muscle contractions commonly occur in otherwise healthy people when both body water and electrolyte levels have not been restored after extended periods of heavy sweating during exercise and/or heat stress. Full recovery can be expected in about 24 hours with the use of electrolyte replacement fluids and rest. Heat rash is an acute, inflammatory skin disease characterized by small red, itchy or tingling lesions, commonly in areas of skin folds or where there is abrasive clothing. It commonly disappears when these areas are kept dry, unabraded and open to free flowing, dry air.

2.12 ASSESSMENT OF HEAT STRESS AND HEAT STRAIN

Heat Stress is defined by environmental measurements of air temperature, humidity, airflow rate, the level of radiant heat exchange, and evaluation of a person's metabolic heat production rate from exercise and/or work. Heat stress is the load on thermoregulation. *Heat Strain* is defined as the cost to each person facing heat stress. Although all people working at the same intensity in the same environment face the same level of heat stress, each is under a unique level of heat strain. Almost any environmental thermal exposure will be comfortable and safe for some, but endangering, even lethal to others. Because disabilities, danger, and death arise directly from heat strain, no measure of heat stress is a reliable indicator of a particular person's heat strain, or the safety of the exposure.

TABLE 2-2. Estimating Energy Cost of Work by Task Analysis

A. Body position and movement	kcal/min*	
Sitting	0.3	
Standing	0.6	
Walking	2.0 - 3.0	
Walking uphill	Add 0.8 /meter rise	

B. Type of work kcal/min	Average kcal/min	Range
Hand work – light	0.4	0.2 - 1.2
Hand work – heavy	0.9	
Work one arm – light	1.0	0.7 - 2.5
Work one arm – heavy	1.7	
Work both arms – light	1.5	1.0 - 3.5
Work both arms – heavy	2.5	
Work whole body – light	3.5	2.5 - 15.0
Work whole body – moderate	5.0	
Work whole body – heavy	7.0	
Work whole body – very heavy	9.0	

C. Basal metabolism	1.0	

D. Sample calculation**		
Assembling work with heavy hand tools		
1. Standing	0.6	
2. Two-arm work	3.5	
3. Basal metabolism	1.0	
TOTAL	5.1 kcal/min	

*For standard worker of 70 kg body weight (154 lbs) and 1.8 m^2
body surface (19.4 ft^2).

**Example of measuring metabolic heat production of a worker when
performing initial screening.

2.12.1 Evaluation of Heat Stress: Dry-bulb air temperature (DB: so-called "dry-bulb" temperature) is measured by calibrated thermometers, thermistors, thermocouples, and similar temperature-sensing devices which themselves do not produce heat and which are protected from the effects of thermal conduction, evaporation, condensation, and radiant heat sources and sinks. Relative humidity is evaluated psychrometrically as a function of the steady state difference between "dry-bulb" temperature and that indicated by the temperature of a sensor covered with a freely evaporating, water-saturated cotton wick. Such a measure reports "NWB" (natural wet-bulb temperature) when the wetted sensor is affected only by prevailing air movement, and "WB" (when it is exposed to forced convection). Free air movement is measured with an unobstructed anemometer. Infrared radiant "heat transfer" is typically measured by a temperature sensor at the center of a 6-inch, hollow, copper sphere painted flat ("matte") black. Such a measure reports "GT" (globe temperature) (Figure 2-5). A person's metabolic heat production is usually evaluated from an estimated level of average physical activity (Table 2-2).

Although there are a number of different indices for evaluating heat stress, none is reliable as a sole indicator of heat strain for a specific person. "Dry-bulb" temperature is the least valu-

able measure of heat stress because it provides no information about ambient relative humidity, or heat exchange by convection or radiation, and gives no estimate of the metabolic heat production. "Wet-bulb, Globe Temperature" (WBGT) is often used as an index of heat stress. When there is a source of radiant heat transfer (solar radiation, hot surfaces of machinery):

$$WBGT = 0.7\,t_{nwb} + 0.2\,t_g + 0.1\,t_a \qquad [2.17]$$

where t_{nwb} = natural wet-bulb temperature
t_g = globe temperature

When radiant heat transfer is negligible:

$$WBGT = 0.7\,t_{nwb} + 0.3\,t_g \qquad [2.18]$$

WBGT evaluates more factors contributing to heat stress than does the measure of DB alone. It does not, however, effectively evaluate the importance of mass and energy transfer from human skin by convection which is essential for the removal of heat from the skin surface and the formation of water vapor from secreted sweat. Nor does WBGT evaluate the importance of metabolic heat production in the heat stress. Under many environmental conditions, heat produced by metabolism is the predominant, sometimes lethal, stressor.

2.12.2 Evaluation of Heat Strain: The incidence and severity of heat strain will vary greatly among people, even though all are exposed to the same level of heat stress. Paying attention to the early signs and symptoms of heat strain is the best first line of defense against debilitating heat-induced discomfort and injuries. It is dangerous, inappropriate, and irresponsible to consider a heat stress as safe for all when some exposed to it show heat strain signs and symptoms, while others do not. Acute heat strain is indicated by:

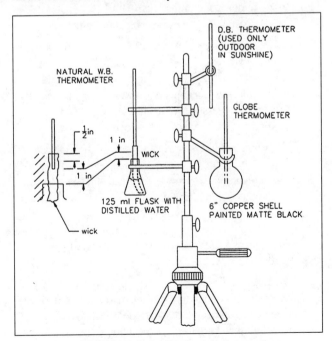

FIGURE 2–5. Determination of wet-bulb globe temperature

Visible Sweating: Thermoregulatory reflexes normally fine-tune with precision the rate of sweating to the rate at which body heat must be lost to maintain homeostasis. Normally, there is no liquid water on the skin surface in a tolerable heat stress because water brought to the skin surface by sweating readily forms invisible water vapor in the process of evaporative cooling. Although an all too common occurrence in the workplace, liquid sweat either on the skin surface, or soaked into clothing, is a sure sign of heat strain. It indicates the level of sweating required to keep body temperature in a normal range cannot be matched by the rate of water evaporation from the skin surface to the environment. It is necessary either to increase the airflow rate over skin and clothing surfaces, lower ambient temperature and relative humidity, reduce radiative heat gain, and/or reduce metabolic heat production if progressive heat disabilities are to be avoided. Visible sweating is an indisputable sign of heat strain.

Discontinued Sweating: A hot, dry skin for someone exposed to heat stress is a dangerous sign. It indicates either suppression of sweating, as perhaps by prescription, or even over-the-counter medications, or an entry level into heat stroke. The appearance of a hot, dry skin for someone in a heat stress demands immediate attention and corrective actions.

Elevated Heart Rate: Short term increases in heart rate are normal for episodic increases in work load. In a heat stress, however, a sustained heart rate greater than 160/min for those younger than about 35 years, or 140/min for those who are older, is a sign of heat strain.

Elevated Deep Body Temperature: A sustained deep body temperature greater than 100.4 F (38 C) is a sign of heat strain in someone exposed to heat stress.

Decreased Systemic Arterial Blood Pressure: A fall in blood pressure of more than about 40 Torr in about 3.5 minutes for someone working in a heat stress indicates a heat-induced disability. Reduced consciousness, feeling of weakness, vision disturbances, and other signs and symptoms are likely to follow.

Personal Discomfort: Heat strain may be indicated by people exposed to heat stress by severe and sudden fatigue, nausea, dizziness, lightheadedness, or fainting. Others may complain of irritability, mental confusion, clumsiness for otherwise competently executed skills, forgetfulness, general malaise and the development of sometimes vague, flu-like symptoms, and paradoxical chills and shivering.

Infrequent Urination: Urinating less frequently than normal and the voiding of a small volume of dark-colored urine is a sign of whole body dehydration. Such dehydration compromises the body's ability to maintain a large enough circulating blood volume so that normal blood pressure is maintained in the face of the combined stressors of exercise and heat exposure. People who work or exercise in the heat need to develop the habit of drinking adequate volumes of water at frequent enough intervals to maintain the same patterns of urination they have when not heat stressed. Those who sweat heavily for long periods need also to evaluate with their physicians a possible need for using electrolyte replacement fluids.

2.13 WORKER PROTECTION

There is improved safety, comfort, and productivity when those working in the heat are:

1. In generally good physical condition, not obese, heat acclimatized, experienced in the heat stressing job. They also need to know how to select clothing and maintain whole body hydration and electrolyte levels to provide the greatest comfort and safety.

2. In areas that are well-ventilated and shielded from infrared radiant heat sources.

3. Knowledgeable about the effects of their medications affecting cardiovascular and peripheral vascular function, blood pressure control, body temperature maintenance, sweat gland activity, metabolic effects, and levels of attention or consciousness.

4. Appropriately supervised when there is a history of abuse or recovery from abuse of alcohol or other intoxicants.

5. Provided accurate verbal and written instructions, frequent training programs, and other information about heat stress and strain.

6. Able to recognize the signs and symptoms of heat strain in themselves and others exposed to heat stress and know the appropriately effective steps for their remediation (Figures 2-6 and 2-7).

2.14 VENTILATION CONTROL

The control method presented here is limited to a general engineering approach. Due to the complexity of evaluating a potential heat stress producing situation, it is essential that the accepted industrial hygiene method of recognition, evaluation, and control be utilized to its fullest extent. In addition to the usual time limited exposures, it may be necessary to specify additional protection which may include insulation, baffles, shields, partitions, personal protective equipment, administrative control, and other measures to prevent possible heat stress. Ventilation control measures may require a source of cooler replacement air, an evaporative or mechanically cooled source, a velocity cooling method, or any combination thereof. Specific guidelines, texts, and other publications or sources should be reviewed for the necessary data to develop the ventilation system.

2.15 VENTILATION SYSTEMS

Exhaust ventilation can be used to remove excessive heat and/or humidity if a replacement source of cooler air is available. If it is possible to enclose the heat source, such as in the case of ovens or certain furnaces, a gravity or forced air stack may be all that is necessary to prevent excessive heat from entering the workroom. If a partial enclosure or local hood is indicated, control velocities, as shown in Chapters 3 and 10, can be estimated from the volume of air to be exhausted.

Many operations do not lend themselves to local exhaust. General ventilation may be the only alternative. To determine the required general ventilation, the designer must estimate the acceptable temperature or humidity rise. The first step in determining the required volumetric flow is to determine the sensible and latent heat load. Next, determine the volumetric flow to dissipate the sensible heat and the volumetric flow to dissipate the latent heat. The required general ventilation is the larger of the two volumetric flows.

The sensible heat rise can be determined by the following:

$$H_s = Q_s \times \rho \times c_p \times \Delta T \times (60 \text{ min/hr}) \qquad [2.19]$$

where: H_s = Sensible heat gain, BTU/hr

Q_s = Volumetric flow for sensible heat, cfm

ρ = Density of the air, lbm/ft^3

c_p = Specific heat of the air, BTU/lbm-deg F

ΔT = Change in temperature, deg F

For air c_p = 0.24 BTU/lbm-deg F and ρ = 0.075 lbm/ft^3; consequently, the equation becomes

$$H_s = 1.08 \times Q_s \times \Delta T$$

or

$$Q_s = H_s \div (1.08 \times \Delta T) \qquad [2.20]$$

In order to use this equation, it is necessary to first estimate the heat load. This will include sun load, people, lights, and motors as well as other particular sources of heat. Of these, sun load, lights, and motors are all completely sensible. The people heat load is part sensible and part latent. In the case of hot processes which give off both sensible and latent heat, it will be necessary to estimate the amounts or percentages of each. In using the above equation for sensible heat, one must decide the amount of temperature rise which will be permitted. Thus, in a locality where 90 F outdoor dry-bulb may be expected, if it is desired that the inside temperature not exceed 100 F, or a 10 degree rise, a certain airflow rate will be necessary. If an inside temperature of 95 F is required, the airflow rate will be doubled.

For latent heat load, the procedure is similar although more difficult. If the total amount of water vapor is known, the heat load can be estimated from the latent heat of vaporization, 970 BTU/lb. In a manner similar to the sensible heat calculations, the latent heat gain can be approximated by:

$$H_l = Q_l \times \rho \times c_l \times \Delta h \times (60 \text{ min/hr}) \times (1 \text{ lb/7000 grains})$$

Where: H_l = Latent heat gain, BTU/hr

Q_l = Volumetric flow for latent heat, cfm

ρ = Density of the air, lbm/ft^3

c_l = Latent heat of vaporization, BTU/lbm

Δh = Change in absolute humidity of the air, grains-water/lbm-dry air

For air, c_l is approximately 970 BTU/lb and ρ = 0.075 lbm/ft^3. Consequently, the equation becomes

$$H_l = 0.62 \times Q_l \times \Delta h$$

or

$$Q_l = H_l \div (0.62 \times \Delta h) \qquad [2.21]$$

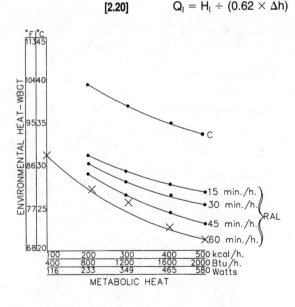

C = CEILING LIMIT
RAL = RECOMMENDED ALERT LIMIT
*FOR "STANDARD WORKER" OF 70 kg (154 lbs) BODY
WEIGHT AND 1.8 m^2 (19.4 ft^2) BODY SURFACE.

FIGURE 2–6. Recommended heat-stress alert limits, heat-unacclimatized workers

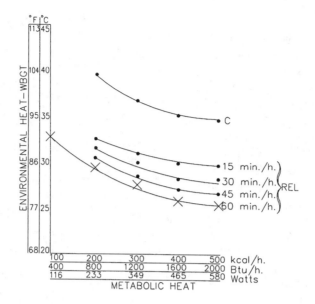

C = CEILING LIMIT
REL = RECOMMENDED EXPOSURE LIMIT
*FOR "STANDARD WORKER" OF 70 kg (154 lbs) BODY WEIGHT AND
1.8 m² (19.4 ft²) BODY SURFACE.

FIGURE 2–7. Recommended heat-stress exposure limits, heat-unacclimatized workers

If the rate of moisture released, M in pounds per hours, is known, then

$$M = Q_l \times \rho \times \Delta h \times (1\ lb/7000\ gr) \times (60\ min/hr)$$
$$= Q_l \times \rho \times \Delta h \div (116.7)$$

or

$$Q_1 = 116.7 \times M \div (\rho \times \Delta h) \qquad [2.22]$$

The term "grains-water per pound-air difference" is taken from the psychrometric chart or tables and represents the difference in moisture content of the outdoor air and the conditions acceptable to the engineer designing the exhaust system. The air quantities calculated from the above two equations should not be added to arrive at the required quantity. Rather, the higher quantity should be used since both sensible and latent heat are absorbed simultaneously. Furthermore, in the majority of cases the sensible heat load far exceeds the latent heat load so the design can be calculated only on the basis of sensible heat.

The ventilation should be designed to flow through the hot environment in a manner that will control the excess heat by removing it from that environment. Figures 2-8 and 2-9 illustrate this principle.

2.16 VELOCITY COOLING

If the air dry-bulb or wet-bulb temperatures are lower than 95 - 100 F, the worker may be cooled by convection or evaporation. When the dry-bulb temperature is higher than 95 - 100 F, increased air velocity may add heat to the worker by convection; if the wet-bulb temperature is high also, evaporative heat loss may not increase proportionately and the net result will be an increase in the worker's heat burden. Many designers consider that supply air temperature should not exceed 80 F for practical heat relief.

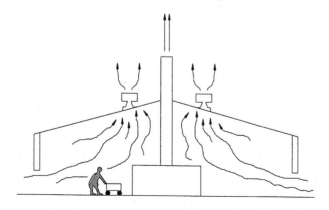

FIGURE 2–8. Good natural ventilation and circulation

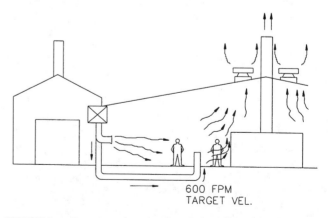

FIGURE 2–9. Good mechanically supplied ventilation

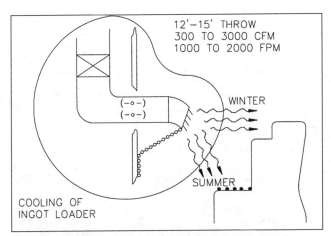

FIGURE 2-10. Spot cooling with volume and directional control

Current practice indicates that air velocities in Table 2-3 can be used successfully for direct cooling of workers. For best results provide directional control of the air supply (Figure 2-10) to accommodate daily and seasonal variations in heat exposure and supply air temperature.

2.17 RADIANT HEAT CONTROL

Since radiant heat is a form of heat energy which needs no medium for its transfer, radiant heat cannot be controlled by any of the above means. Painting or coating the surface of hot bodies with materials having low radiation emission characteristics is one method of reducing radiation.

For materials such as molten masses of metal or glass which cannot be controlled directly, radiation shields are effective. These shields can consist of metal plates, screens, or other material interposed between the source of radiant heat and the workers. Shielding reduces the radiant heat load by reflecting the major portion of the incident radiant heat away from the operator and by re-emitting to the operator only a portion of that radiant heat which has been absorbed. Table 2-4 indicates the percentage of both reflection and emission of radiant heat associated with some common shielding materials. Additional ventilation will control the sensible heat load but will have only a minimal effect, if any, upon the radiant heat load. See Figure 2-11.

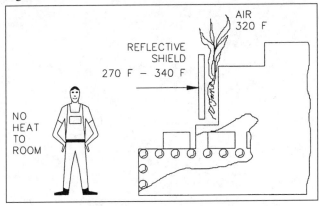

FIGURE 2-11. Heat shielding

TABLE 2-3. Acceptable Comfort Air Motion at the Worker

	Air Velocity, fpm*
Continuous Exposure	
Air conditioned space	50–75
Fixed work station, general ventilation or spot cooling: Sitting	75–125
Standing	100–200
Intermittent Exposure, Spot Cooling or Relief Stations	
Light heat loads and activity	1000–2000
Moderate heat loads and activity	2000–3000
High heat loads and activity	3000–4000

*Note: Velocities greater than 1000 fpm may seriously disrupt the performance of nearby local exhaust systems. Care must be taken to direct air motion to prevent such interference.

2.18 PROTECTIVE SUITS FOR SHORT EXPOSURES

For brief exposures to very high temperatures, insulated aluminized suits and other protective clothing may be worn. These suits reduce the rate of heat gain by the body but provide no means of removing body heat; therefore, only short exposures may be tolerated.

2.19 RESPIRATORY HEAT EXCHANGERS

For brief exposure to air of good quality but high temperature, a heat exchanger on a half-mask respirator face piece is available. This device will bring air into the respiratory passages at a tolerable temperature but will not remove contaminants nor furnish oxygen in poor atmospheres.

TABLE 2-4. Relative Efficiencies of Common Shielding Materials

Surface of Shielding	Reflection of Radiant Heat Incident Upon Surface	Emission of Radiant Heat from Surface
Aluminum, bright	95	5
Zinc, bright	90	10
Aluminum, oxidized	84	16
Zinc, oxidized	73	27
Aluminum paint, new, clean	65	35
Aluminum paint, dull, dirty	40	60
Iron, sheet, smooth	45	55
Iron, sheet, oxidized	35	65
Brick	20	80
Lacquer, black	10	90
Lacquer, white	10	90
Asbestos board	6	94
Lacquer, flat black	3	97

2.20 REFRIGERATED SUITS

Where individuals must move about, cold air may be blown into a suit or hood worn as a portable enclosure. The usual refrigeration methods may be used with insulated tubing to the suit. It may be difficult, however, to deliver air at a sufficiently low temperature. If compressed air is available, cold air may be delivered from a vortex tube worn on the suit. Suits of this type are commercially available.

2.21 ENCLOSURES

In certain hot industries, such as in steel mills, it is unnecessary and impractical to attempt to control the heat from the process. If the operation is such that remote control is possible, an air conditioned booth or cab can be utilized to keep the operators reasonably comfortable in an otherwise intolerable atmosphere.

2.22 INSULATION

If the source of heat is a surface giving rise to convection, insulation at the surface will reduce this form of heat transfer.

Insulation by itself, however, will not usually be sufficient if the temperature is very high or if the heat content is high.

REFERENCES

2.1   U.S. Department of Health, Education and Welfare, PHS, CDC, NIOSH: The Industrial Environment—Its Evaluation and Control, 1973.

2.2   Air Force AFOSH Standard 161.2.

2.3   National Board of Fire Underwriters: Pamphlet #86, Standards for Class A Ovens and Furnaces.

2.4   Feiner, B.; Kingsley, L.: "Ventilation of Industrial Ovens." Air Conditioning, Heating and Ventilating, December 1956, pp. 82-89.

2.5   U.S. Department of Health and Human Services, PHS, CDC, NIOSH: Occupational Exposure to Hot Environments, Revised Criteria, 1986.

Chapter 3

LOCAL EXHAUST HOODS

3.1 INTRODUCTION

Local exhaust systems are designed to capture and remove process emissions prior to their escape into the workplace environment. The local exhaust hood is the point of entry into the exhaust system and is defined herein to include all suction openings regardless of their physical configuration. The primary function of the hood is to create an air flow field which will effectively capture the contaminant and transport it into the hood. Figure 3-1 provides nomenclature associated with local exhaust hoods.

3.2 CONTAMINANT CHARACTERISTICS

3.2.1 Inertial Effects: Gases, vapors, and fumes will not exhibit significant inertial effects. Also, fine dust particles, 20 microns or less in diameter (which includes respirable particles), will not exhibit significant inertial effects. These materials will move solely with respect to the air in which they are mixed. In such cases, the hood needs to generate an air flow pattern and capture velocity sufficient to control the motion of the contaminant-laden air plus extraneous air currents caused by room cross-drafts, vehicular traffic, etc.

3.2.2 Effective Specific Gravity: Frequently, the location of exhaust hoods is mistakenly based on a supposition that the contaminant is "heavier than air" or "lighter than air." In most health hazard applications, this criterion is of little value (see Figure 3-2). Hazardous fine dust particles, fumes, vapors, and gases are truly airborne, following air currents and are not subject to appreciable motion either upward or downward because of their own density. Normal air movement will assure an even mixture of these contaminants. Exception to these observations may occur with very hot or very cold operations or where a contaminant is generated at very high levels and control is achieved before the contaminant becomes diluted.

3.2.3 Wake Effects: As air flows around an object a phenomenon known as "boundary layer separation" occurs. This results in the formation of a turbulent wake on the downstream side of the object similar to what is observed as a ship moves through the water. The wake is a region of vigorous mixing and recirculation. If the object in question is a person who is working with, or close to, a contaminant generating source, recirculation of the contaminant into the breathing zone is likely. An important consideration in the design of ventilation for contaminant control is minimizing this wake around the human body and, to the extent possible, keeping contaminant sources out of these recirculating regions (see also Section 3.4.6.)

3.3 HOOD TYPES

Hoods may be of a wide range of physical configurations but can be grouped into two general categories: enclosing and exterior. The type of hood to be used will be dependent on the physical characteristics of the process equipment, the contaminant generation mechanism, and the operator/equipment interface (see Figure 3-3).

3.3.1 Enclosing Hoods: Enclosing hoods are those which completely or partially enclose the process or contaminant generation point. A complete enclosure would be a laboratory glove box or similar type of enclosure where only minimal openings exist. A partial enclosure would be a laboratory hood or paint spray booth. An inward flow of air through the enclosure opening will contain the contaminant within the enclosure and prevents its escape into the work environment.

The enclosing hood is preferred wherever the process configuration and operation will permit. If complete enclosure is not feasible, partial enclosure should be used to the maximum extent possible (see Figure 3-3.)

3.3.2 Exterior Hoods: Exterior hoods are those which are located adjacent to an emission source without enclosing it. Examples of exterior hoods are slots along the edge of the tank or a rectangular opening on a welding table.

Where the contaminant is a gas, vapor, or fine particulate and is not emitted with any significant velocity, the hood orientation is not critical. However, if the contaminant contains large particulates which are emitted with a significant velocity, the hood should be located in the path of the emission. An example would be a grinding operation (see VS-80-11).

If the process emits hot contaminated air, it will rise due to thermal buoyancy. Use of a side draft exterior hood (located horizontally from the hot process) may not provide satisfactory capture due to the inability of the hood induced air flow to overcome the thermally induced air flow. This will be especially true for very high temperature processes such as a melting furnace. In such cases a canopy hood located over the process may be indicated (see Section 3.9).

A variation of the exterior hood is the push-pull system (Section 3.8). In this case, a jet of air is pushed across a contaminant source into the flow field of a hood. Contaminant control is primarily achieved by the jet. The function of the exhaust hood is to receive the jet and remove it. The advantage of the push-pull system is that the push jet can travel in a controlled manner over much greater distances than air can be drawn by an exhaust hood alone. The push-pull system is used successfully for some plating and open surface vessel operations but has potential application for many other processes. However, the push portion of the system has potential for increasing operator exposure if not properly designed, installed, or operated. Care must be taken to ensure proper design, application, and operation.

3.4 HOOD DESIGN FACTORS

Capture and control of contaminants will be achieved by the inward air flow created by the exhaust hood. Air flow toward the hood opening must be sufficiently high to maintain control of the contaminant until it reaches the hood. External air motion may disturb the hood-induced air flow and require higher air flow rates to overcome the disturbing effects. Elim-

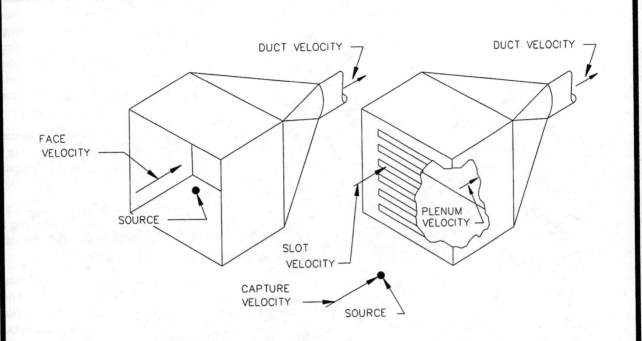

CAPTURE VELOCITY—   AIR VELOCITY AT ANY POINT IN FRONT OF THE HOOD OR AT THE HOOD
OPENING NECESSARY TO OVERCOME OPPOSING AIR CURRENTS AND TO
CAPTURE THE CONTAMINATED AIR AT THAT POINT BY CAUSING IT TO FLOW
INTO THE HOOD.

FACE VELOCITY—   AIR VELOCITY AT THE HOOD OPENING.

SLOT VELOCITY—   AIR VELOCITY THROUGH THE OPENINGS IN A SLOT—TYPE HOOD. IT IS
USED PRIMARILY AS A MEANS OF OBTAINING UNIFORM AIR DISTRIBUTION
ACROSS THE FACE OF THE HOOD.

PLENUM VELOCITY—   AIR VELOCITY IN THE PLENUM. FOR GOOD AIR DISTRIBUTION
WITH SLOT—TYPES OF HOODS, THE MAXIMUM PLENUM VELOCITY
SHOULD BE 1/2 OF THE SLOT VELOCITY OR LESS.

DUCT VELOCITY—   AIR VELOCITY THROUGH THE DUCT CROSS SECTION. WHEN SOLID MATERIAL IS
PRESENT IN THE AIR STREAM, THE DUCT VELOCITY MUST BE EQUAL TO OR
GREATER THAN THE MINIMUM AIR VELOCITY REQUIRED TO MOVE THE
PARTICLES IN THE AIR STREAM.

AMERICAN CONFERENCE OF GOVERNMENTAL INDUSTRIAL HYGIENISTS	HOOD NOMENCLATURE LOCAL EXHAUST	
	DATE *4—96*	FIGURE *3—1*

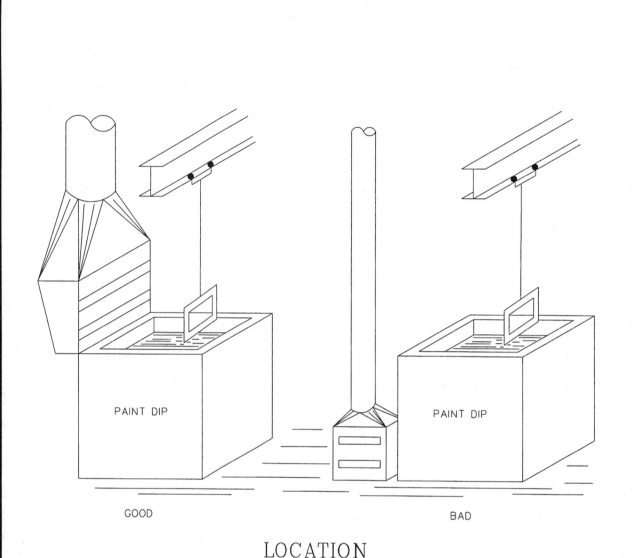

GOOD

BAD

LOCATION

SOLVENT VAPORS IN HEALTH HAZARD CONCENTRATIONS ARE NOT APPRECIABLY HEAVIER THAN AIR.
EXHAUST FROM THE FLOOR USUALLY GIVES FIRE PROTECTION ONLY.

Example: Density of air   1.0
            Density of 100% amyl acetate vapor   4.49
            Density lowest explosive mixture   1.038
            Density T.L.V. mixture   1.0003

AMERICAN CONFERENCE OF GOVERNMENTAL INDUSTRIAL HYGIENISTS	EFFECTS OF SPECIFIC GRAVITY	
	DATE 2—00	FIGURE 3—2

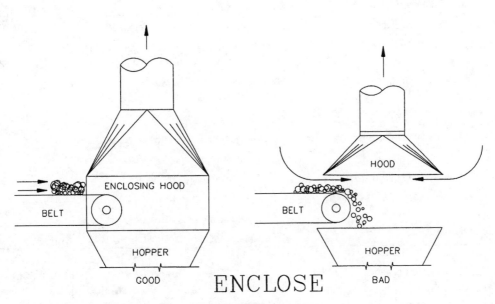

ENCLOSE

ENCLOSE THE OPERATION AS MUCH AS POSSIBLE. THE MORE COMPLETELY ENCLOSED THE
SOURCE, THE LESS AIR REQUIRED FOR CONTROL.

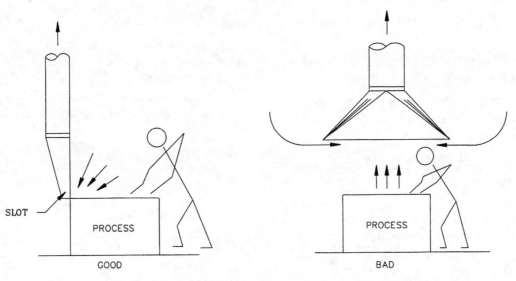

DIRECTION OF AIR FLOW

LOCATE THE HOOD SO THE CONTAMINANT IS REMOVED AWAY FROM THE BREATHING
ZONE OF THE OPERATOR.

AMERICAN CONFERENCE OF GOVERNMENTAL INDUSTRIAL HYGIENISTS	ENCLOSURE AND OPERATOR/ EQUIPMENT INTERFACE	
	DATE 4—96	FIGURE 3—3

TABLE 3-1. Range of Capture Velocities[3.1,3.2]

Condition of Dispersion of Contaminant	Example	Capture Velocity, fpm
Released with practically no velocity into quiet air.	Evaporation from tanks; degreasing, etc.	50-100
Released at low velocity into moderately still air.	Spray booths; intermittent container filling; low speed conveyor transfers; welding; plating; pickling	100-200
Active generation into zone of rapid air motion.	Spray painting in shallow booths; barrel filling; conveyor loading; crushers	200-500
Released at high initial velocity into zone at very rapid air motion.	Grinding; abrasive blasting; tumbling	500-2000

In each category above, a range of capture velocity is shown. The proper choice of values depends on several factors:

Lower End of Range	Upper End of Range
1. Room air currents minimal or favorable to capture.	1. Disturbing room air currents.
2. Contaminants of low toxicity or of nuisance value only.	2. Contaminants of high toxicity.
3. Intermittent, low production.	3. High production, heavy use.
4. Large hood-large air mass in motion.	4. Small hood-local control only.

ination of sources of external air motion is an important factor in achieving effective control without the need for excessive air flow and its associated cost. Important sources of air motion are

- Thermal air currents, especially from hot processes or heat-generating operations.
- Motion of machinery, as by a grinding wheel, belt conveyor, etc.
- Material motion, as in dumping or container filling.
- Movements of the operator.
- Room air currents (which are usually taken at 50 fpm minimum and may be much higher).
- Rapid air movement caused by spot cooling and heating equipment.

The shape of the hood, its size, location, and rate of air flow are important design considerations.

3.4.1 Capture Velocity:
The minimum hood-induced air velocity necessary to capture and convey the contaminant into the hood is referred to as capture velocity. This velocity will be a result of the hood air flow rate and hood configuration.

Exceptionally high air flow hoods (example, large foundry side-draft shakeout hoods) may require less air flow than would be indicated by the capture velocity values recommended for small hoods. This phenomenon may be ascribed to:

- The presence of a large air mass moving into the hood.
- The fact that the contaminant is under the influence of the hood for a much longer time than is the case with small hoods.
- The fact that the large air flow rate affords considerable dilution as described above.

Table 3-1 offers capture velocity data. Additional information is found in Chapter 10.

3.4.2 Hood Flow Rate Determination:
Within the bounds of flanges, baffles, adjacent walls, etc., air will move into an opening under suction from all directions. For an enclosure, the capture velocity at the enclosed opening(s) will be the exhaust flow rate divided by the opening area. The capture velocity at a given point in front of the exterior hood will be established by the hood air flow through the geometric surface which contains the point.

As an example, for a theoretical unbounded point suction source, the point in question would be on the surface of a sphere whose center is the suction point (Figure 3-4).

The surface area of a sphere is $4\pi X^2$. Using $V = Q/A$ (Equation 1.3), the velocity at point X on the sphere's surface can be given by

$$Q = V (4\pi X^2) = 12.57VX^2 \qquad [3.1]$$

where: Q = air flow into suction point, cfm
         V = velocity at distance X, fpm
         A = $4\pi X^2$ = area of sphere, ft^2
         X = radius of sphere, ft

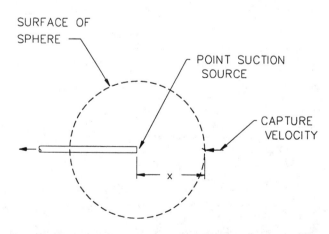

FIGURE 3-4. Point suction source

Similarly, if an unbounded line source were considered, the surface would be that of a cylinder and the flow rate (neglecting end effects) would be

$$Q = V(2\pi X^2) = 6.28\ VXL \qquad \text{[3.2]}$$

where: L = length of line source, ft

Equations 3.1 and 3.2 illustrate, on a theoretical basis, the relationship between distance, flow, and capture velocity and can be used for gross estimation purposes. In actual practice, however, suction sources are not points or lines, but rather have physical dimensions which cause the flow surface to deviate from the standard geometric shape. Velocity contours have been determined experimentally. Flow[3.3] for round hoods, and rectangular hoods which are essentially square, can be approximated by

$$Q = V(10X^2 + A) \qquad \text{[3.3]}$$

where: Q = air flow, cfm

V = centerline velocity at X distance from hood, fpm

X = distance outward along axis in ft. (NOTE: equation is accurate only for limited distance of X, where X is within 1.5 D)

A = area of hood opening, ft^2

D = diameter of round hoods or side of essentially square hoods, ft

Where distances of X are greater than 1.5 D, the flow rate increases less rapidly with distance than Equation 3.3 indicates.[3.4-3.5]

It can be seen from Equation 3.3 that velocity decreases inversely with the square of the distance from the hood (see Figure 3-5.)

Figures 3-6 and 3-7 show flow contours and streamlines for plane and flanged circular hood openings. Flow contours are lines of equal velocity in front of a hood. Similarly, streamlines are lines perpendicular to velocity contours. (The tangent to a streamline at any point indicates the direction of air flow at that point.)

Flow capture velocity equations for various hood configurations are provided in Figures 3-8, 3-9, 3-10, and 3-11.

3.4.3 Effects of Flanges and Baffles:
A flange is a surface at and parallel to the hood face which provides a barrier to unwanted air flow from behind the hood. A baffle is a surface which provides a barrier to unwanted air flow from the front or sides of the hood.

If the suction source were located on a plane, the flow area would be reduced (1/2 in both cases), thereby decreasing the flow rate required to achieve the same velocity. A flange around a hood opening has the same effect of decreasing the required flow rate to achieve a given capture velocity. In practice, flanging can decrease flow rate (or increase velocity) by approximately 25% (see Figures 3-6, 3-7, and 3-11). For most

applications the flange width should be equal to the square root of the hood area ($\sqrt{A}$).

Baffles can provide a similar effect. The magnitude of the effort will depend on the baffle location and size.

Figure 3-11 illustrates several hood types and gives the velocity/flow formulas which apply.

A summary of other equations for hood velocity and the impact of cross-drafts on hood performance can be found in Reference 3.25.

3.4.4 Air Distribution:
Slot hoods are defined as hoods with an opening width to length ratio (W/L) of 0.2 or less. Slot hoods are most commonly used to provide uniform exhaust air flow and an adequate capture velocity over a finite length of contaminant generation, e.g. an open tank or over the face of a large hood such as a side-draft design. The function of the slot is solely to provide uniform air distribution. Slot velocity does not contribute toward capture velocity. A high slot velocity simply generates high pressure losses. Note that the capture velocity equation (Figure 3-11) shows that capture velocity is related to the exhaust volume and the slot length, not to the slot velocity.

Slot hoods usually consist of a narrow exhaust opening and a plenum chamber. Uniform exhaust air distribution across the slot is obtained by sizing slot width and plenum depth so that velocity through the slot is much higher than in the plenum. Splitter vanes may be used in the plenum; however, in most industrial exhaust systems, vanes are subject to corrosion

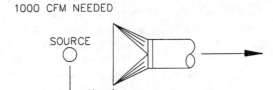

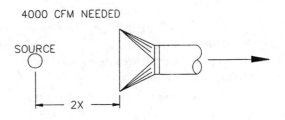

LOCATION
PLACE HOOD AS CLOSE TO THE SOURCE OF CONTAMINANT AS POSSIBLE. THE REQUIRED VOLUME VARIES WITH THE SQUARE OF THE DISTANCE FROM THE SOURCE.

FIGURE 3–5. Flow rate as distance from hood

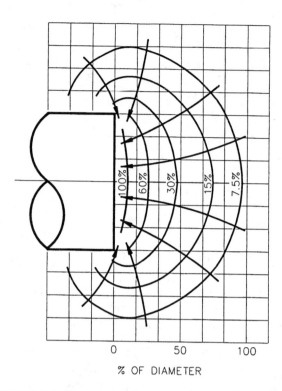

FIGURE 3–6. Velocity contours — plain circular opening — % of opening velocity

and/or erosion and provide locations for material to accumulate. Adjustable slots can be provided but are subject to tampering and maladjustment. The most practical hood is the fixed slot and unobstructed plenum type. The design of the slot and plenum is such that the pressure loss through the slot is high compared with the pressure loss through the plenum. Thus, all portions of the slot are subjected to essentially equal suction and the slot velocity will be essentially uniform.

There is no straight forward method for calculating the pressure drop from one end to the other of a slot-plenum combination. A very useful approximation, applicable to most hoods, is to design for a maximum plenum velocity equal to one-half of the slot velocity. For most slot hoods a 2,000 fpm slot velocity and 1,000 fpm plenum velocity is a reasonable choice for uniformity of flow and moderate pressure drop. Centered exhaust take-off design results in the smallest practical plenum size since the air approaches the duct from both directions. Where large, deep plenums are possible, as with foundry shake-out hoods, the slot velocity may be as low as 1,000 fpm with a 500 fpm plenum velocity.

3.4.5 Rectangular and Round Hoods: Air distribution for rectangular and round hoods is achieved by air flow within the hood rather than by pressure drop as for the slot hood. The plenum (length of hood from face to tapered hood to duct connection) should be as long as possible. The hood take-off should incorporate a 60° to 90° total included tapered angle. Multiple take-offs may be required for long hoods. End take-off configurations require large plenum sizes because all of the air must pass in one direction.

Figures 3-12 and 3-13 provide a number of distribution techniques.

3.4.6 Worker Position Effect: The objective of industrial ventilation is to control the worker's exposure to toxic airborne pollutants in a safe, reliable manner. As one of the main engineering controls, local exhaust ventilation is designed to be near the point of contaminant generation. Often, consideration is not given to how the workers will position themselves with respect to the air flow. Studies[3.6-3.9] show that the position of the worker with respect to the flow direction is an important parameter in determining the breathing zone concentration.

Figure 3-14, Position 2, shows a worker oriented with his back to the air flow. Immediately downstream of the worker a zone of reverse flow and turbulent mixing occurs due to boundary layer separation. Contaminant released into this region (e.g., from a hand-held or proximal source) will be mixed into the breathing zone resulting in exposure. Figure 3-14, Position 1, shows a worker oriented at 90° to the flow direction; here, the reverse flow zone forms to the side and there is less opportunity for the entrainment of contaminant into the breathing zone.

Studies suggest that this phenomenon is important when large booth-type hoods are employed, or in situations where there is a reasonably uniform air flow. Exposure studies[3.10]

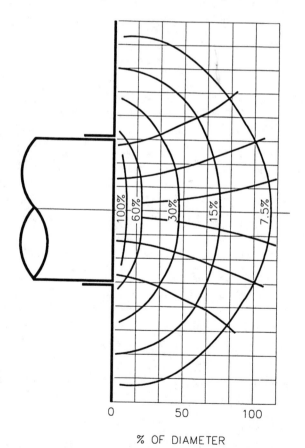

FIGURE 3–7. Velocity contours — flanged circular opening — % of opening velocity

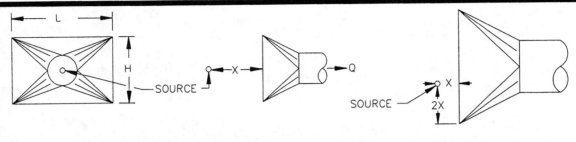

FREELY SUSPENDED HOOD

$$Q = V(10X^2 + A)$$

LARGE HOOD

LARGE HOOD, X SMALL--MEASURE X PERPENDICULAR TO HOOD FACE, NOT LESS THAN 2X FROM HOOD EDGE.

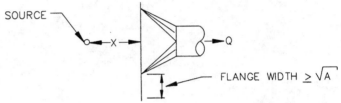

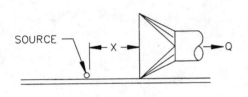

HOOD ON BENCH OR FLOOR

$$Q = V(5X^2 + A)$$

HOOD WITH WIDE FLANGE

$$Q = V \, 0.75(10X^2 + A)$$

SUSPENDED HOODS
(SMALL SIDE-DRAFT HOODS)

Q = REQUIRED EXHAUST AIR FLOW, CFM.
X = DISTANCE FROM HOOD FACE TO FARTHEST POINT OF CONTAMINANT RELEASE, FT.
A = HOOD FACE AREA, FT^2.
V = CAPTURE VELOCITY, FPM, AT DISTANCE X.

NOTE: AIR FLOW RATE MUST INCREASE AS THE SQUARE OF DISTANCE OF THE SOURCE FROM THE HOOD. BAFFLING BY FLANGING OR BY PLACING ON BENCH, FLOOR, ECT. HAS A BENEFICIAL EFFECT.

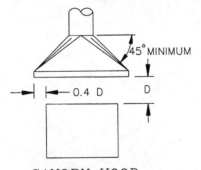

CANOPY HOOD

Q = 1.4 PDV(P=PERIMETER OF TANK, FT).
NOT RECOMMENDED IF WORKERS MUST BEND OVER SOURCE. V RANGES FROM 50 TO 500 FPM DEPENDING ON CROSSDRAFTS. SIDE CURTAINS ON TWO OR THREE SIDES TO CREATE A SEMI-BOOTH OR BOOTH ARE DESIRABLE.

AMERICAN CONFERENCE OF GOVERNMENTAL INDUSTRIAL HYGIENISTS	*FLOW/CAPTURE VELOCITY*	
	DATE *1-88*	FIGURE *3-8*

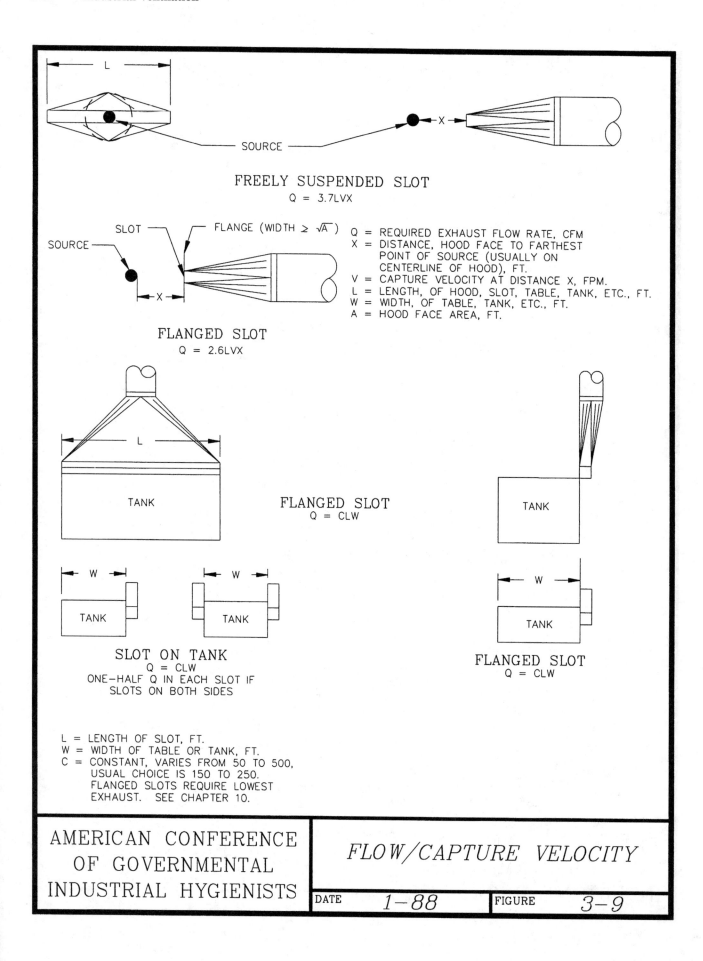

FREELY SUSPENDED SLOT
Q = 3.7LVX

FLANGED SLOT
Q = 2.6LVX

Q = REQUIRED EXHAUST FLOW RATE, CFM
X = DISTANCE, HOOD FACE TO FARTHEST POINT OF SOURCE (USUALLY ON CENTERLINE OF HOOD), FT.
V = CAPTURE VELOCITY AT DISTANCE X, FPM.
L = LENGTH, OF HOOD, SLOT, TABLE, TANK, ETC., FT.
W = WIDTH, OF TABLE, TANK, ETC., FT.
A = HOOD FACE AREA, FT.

FLANGED SLOT
Q = CLW

SLOT ON TANK
Q = CLW
ONE—HALF Q IN EACH SLOT IF SLOTS ON BOTH SIDES

FLANGED SLOT
Q = CLW

L = LENGTH OF SLOT, FT.
W = WIDTH OF TABLE OR TANK, FT.
C = CONSTANT, VARIES FROM 50 TO 500, USUAL CHOICE IS 150 TO 250. FLANGED SLOTS REQUIRE LOWEST EXHAUST. SEE CHAPTER 10.

AMERICAN CONFERENCE OF GOVERNMENTAL INDUSTRIAL HYGIENISTS

FLOW/CAPTURE VELOCITY

DATE *1—88*

FIGURE *3—9*

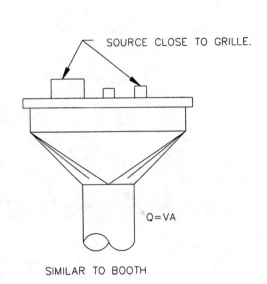

SOURCE CLOSE TO GRILLE.

SIMILAR TO BOOTH

$Q = VA$

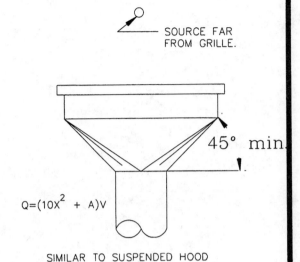

SOURCE FAR FROM GRILLE.

45° min.

SIMILAR TO SUSPENDED HOOD

$Q = (10X^2 + A)V$

DOWNDRAFT HOODS

NOT RECOMMENDED FOR HOT OR HEAT-PRODUCING OPERATIONS IF DOWNDRAFT AREA IS LARGE, SEE "CAPTURE VELOCITY" IN THIS SECTION.

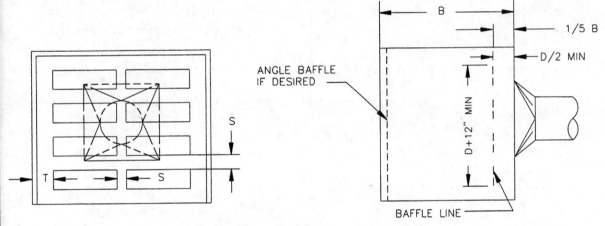

ANGLE BAFFLE IF DESIRED

BAFFLE LINE

B

1/5 B

D/2 MIN

D+12" MIN

S

T

S

BOOTH-TYPE HOODS

$Q = AV$ (A=FACE AREA, FT^2; V=FACE VELOCITY, FPM).
BAFFLES ARE OPTIONAL FOR AIR DISTRIBUTION; NOT REQUIRED IF A WATER WALL BOOTH OR
   IF OTHER MEANS FOR DISTRIBUTION IS PROVIDED.
S VARIES FROM 4 INCHES TO 8 INCHES, DEPENDING ON SIZE OF BOOTH.
T VARIES FROM 6 INCHES TO 12 INCHES, DEPENDING ON SIZE OF BOOTH.
INCREASE THE NUMBER OF PANELS WITH SIZE OF BOOTH.

AMERICAN CONFERENCE OF GOVERNMENTAL INDUSTRIAL HYGIENISTS	*FLOW/CAPTURE VELOCITY*	
	DATE *1-88*	FIGURE *3-10*

HOOD TYPE	DESCRIPTION	ASPECT RATIO,W/L	AIR FLOW
L X W	SLOT	0.2 OR LESS	$Q = 3.7$ LVX
X	FLANGED SLOT	0.2 OR LESS	$Q = 2.6$ LVX
W L X $A = WL (Ft^2)$	PLAIN OPENING	0.2 OR GREATER AND ROUND	$Q = V(10X^2 + A)$
X	FLANGED OPENING	0.2 OR GREATER AND ROUND	$Q = 0.75V(10X^2 + A)$
H W	BOOTH	TO SUIT WORK	$Q = VA = VWH$
D	CANOPY	TO SUIT WORK	$Q = 1.4$ PVD SEE FIG. VS−99−03 P = PERIMETER D = HEIGHT ABOVE WORK
W L X	PLAIN MULTIPLE SLOT OPENING 2 OR MORE SLOTS	0.2 OR GREATER	$Q = V(10X^2 + A)$
W L X	FLANGED MULTIPLE SLOT OPENING 2 OR MORE SLOTS	0.2 OR GREATER	$Q = 0.75V(10X^2 + A)$

AMERICAN CONFERENCE OF GOVERNMENTAL INDUSTRIAL HYGIENISTS	*HOOD TYPES*	
	DATE *4−96*	FIGURE *3−11*

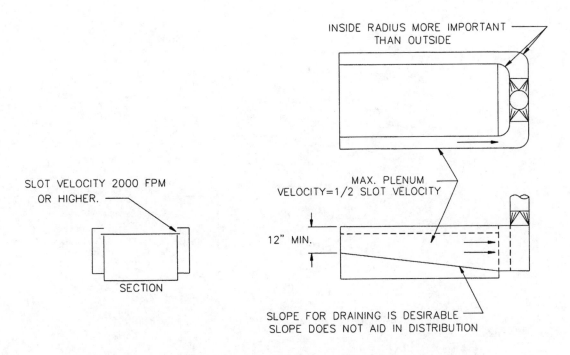

SLOT VELOCITY 2000 FPM OR HIGHER.

SECTION

INSIDE RADIUS MORE IMPORTANT THAN OUTSIDE

MAX. PLENUM VELOCITY=1/2 SLOT VELOCITY

12" MIN.

SLOPE FOR DRAINING IS DESIRABLE
SLOPE DOES NOT AID IN DISTRIBUTION

DISTRIBUTION BY SLOT RESISTANCE

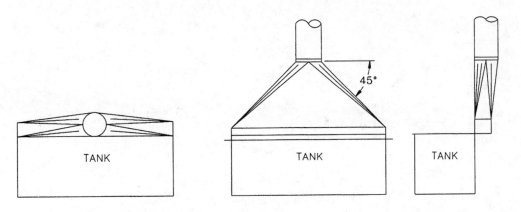

45°

TANK   TANK   TANK

DISTRIBUTION BY FISH TAIL

WITH LOW PLENUM VELOCITIES AND HIGH SLOT VELOCITIES, GOOD DISTRIBUTION IS OBTAINED.
SLOTS OVER 10 FEET TO 12 FEET IN LENGTH USUALLY NEED MULTIPLE TAKE-OFFS.

AMERICAN CONFERENCE OF GOVERNMENTAL INDUSTRIAL HYGIENISTS	*DISTRIBUTION TECHNIQUES*	
	DATE *1-88*	FIGURE *3-12*

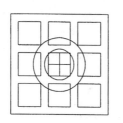
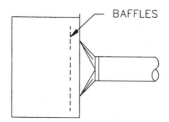

DISTRIBUTION BY BAFFLES
SEE FIG. 3-10

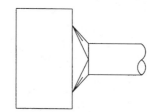

LONG BOOTHS — DISTRIBUTION BY MULTIPLE TAKE-OFFS AND TAPERS

BOOTH CANOPY

(SAME PRINCIPLES APPLY TO CANOPY TYPE)

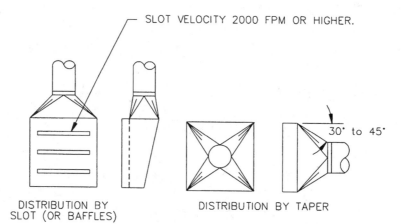

SLOT VELOCITY 2000 FPM OR HIGHER.

30° to 45°

DISTRIBUTION BY
SLOT (OR BAFFLES)

DISTRIBUTION BY TAPER

SIDE–DRAFTS AND SUSPENDED HOODS

AMERICAN CONFERENCE OF GOVERNMENTAL INDUSTRIAL HYGIENISTS	*DISTRIBUTION TECHNIQUES*	
	DATE *1–88*	FIGURE *3–13*

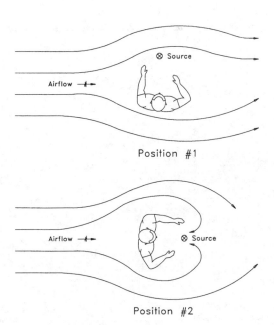

Position #1

Position #2

FIGURE 3–14. Worker position effect

using a tailor's mannequin to simulate an operator in a booth-type hood used for the transfer of powders showed, in all cases, that exposures for Position 1 were less than those in Position 2 by at least a factor of 2000.

A second case study[3.6] cites women using a spray and brush application of a chloroform-based adhesive significantly exposed despite working in a ventilated booth. A 50% reduction in exposure was found when the workers stood side-on to the air flow (Position 1). Subsequent modification of spray practices resulted in a determination that a 30° angle to the air flow and holding the nozzle in the downstream hand seemed optimal. No alterations to the actual design or air flow of the booth were needed to achieve acceptable exposure levels.

The preceding discussion assumes that the worker is not in the wake of an upstream object and that the contaminant source has negligible momentum. In cases where the contaminant source has significant momentum (e.g., high-pressure compressed air paint spray operations), the effect of position on exposure may be reversed—i.e., Position #1 in Figure 3-14 may produce higher exposures. This is associated with the deflection of the spray upstream of the worker and subsequent recirculation through the breathing zone. Further research and field studies are needed to evaluate the tendency for reverse flow to occur in more complex situations. Although the importance of boundary layer separation effects with smaller local exhaust hoods has not been thoroughly explored, three studies[3.11-3.13] suggest that the 90° orientation is beneficial even in this instance. It is recommended that the side orientation (i.e., Position 1) be the preferred orientation in situations where feasible. Down-draft configurations may provide similar benefits under certain conditions.

It is recommended that the side orientation (e.g., Position 1) be investigated as a preferred work practice where feasible. It is important to assess the exposure with personal sampling pumps to confirm the benefits of one position vs. another as other factors may complicate the issue.

3.5 HOOD LOSSES

Plain duct openings, flanged duct openings, canopies, and similar hoods have only one significant energy loss. As air enters the duct, a vena contract is formed and a small energy loss occurs first in the conversion of static pressure to velocity pressure (see Figure 3-15.) As the air passes through the vena contracta, the flow area enlarges to fill the duct and velocity pressure converts to static pressure. At this point the uncontrolled slow down of the air from the vena contracta to the downstream duct velocity results in the major portion of the

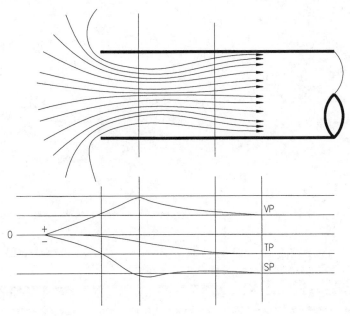

FIGURE 3–15. Air flow at the vena contracta

HOOD TYPE	DESCRIPTION	HOOD ENTRY LOSS (F_h) COEFFICIENT
	PLAIN OPENING	0.93
	FLANGED OPENING	0.49
	TAPER OR CONE HOOD	SEE CHAPTER 10
	BELL MOUTH INLET	0.04
	ORIFICE	SEE CHAPTER 10
	TYPICAL GRINDING HOOD	(STRAIGHT TAKEOFF) 0.65 (TAPERED TAKEOFF) 0.40

AMERICAN CONFERENCE OF GOVERNMENTAL INDUSTRIAL HYGIENISTS

HOOD LOSS COEFFICIENTS

| DATE | 4—96 | FIGURE | 3—16 |

entry loss. The more pronounced the vena contracta, the greater will be the energy loss and hood static pressure.

Compound hoods are hoods which have two or more points of significant energy loss and must be considered separately and added together to arrive at the total loss for the hood. Common examples of hoods having double entry losses are lot-type hoods and multiple opening, lateral draft hoods commonly used on plating, paint dipping and degreasing tanks, and foundry side-draft shakeout ventilation.

The hood entry loss (h_e) can be expressed, therefore, in terms of hood loss coefficients (F_s and F_h) which, when multiplied by the slot or duct velocity pressure (VP), will give the entry loss (h_e) in inches of water. The hood static pressure is equal to the hood entry loss plus the velocity pressure in the duct. The hood entry loss represents the energy necessary to overcome the losses due to air moving through and into the duct. The velocity pressure represents the energy necessary to accelerate the air from rest to duct velocity (see Chapter 1, Section 1.6, "Acceleration of Air and Hood Entry Losses".) This may be expressed as:

$$SP_h = h_e + VP_d \qquad [3.4]$$

$$SP_h = (F_s)(VP_s) + (F_h)(VP_d) + VP_d \qquad [3.5]$$

where: h_e = overall hood entry loss = $h_s + h_h$, "wg

F_s = loss coefficient for slot

F_h = loss coefficient for duct entry

VP_s = slot or opening velocity pressure, "wg

VP_d = duct velocity pressure, "wg

One exception can occur when the slot velocity (or other hood entry velocity is higher than is the duct velocity. In such case, the acceleration velocity pressure used in determining SP is the higher slot or opening velocity pressure.

Figures 3-16 and 5-15 give hood entry loss coefficients for several typical hood types.

3.5.1 Simple Hood: A simple hood is shown in Figure 3-17. If the hood face velocity for such a simple hood is less than 1000 fpm, h_s will be negligible and the loss will be dependent on h_h only. If the hood face velocity is greater than 1000 fpm, both h_s and h_h should be considered. Face velocities greater than 1000 fpm will usually only occur with relatively small hood face areas (0.25 to 0.50 ft^2).

EXAMPLE PROBLEM

Given: Face Velocity (V_f) = Q/A_f = 250 fpm

Duct Velocity (V_d) = Q/A_d = 3000 fpm

$VP_d = (V_d/4005)^2 = 0.56$ "wg

$F_h = 0.25$ as shown in Figure 5-15

$SP_h = h_e + VP_d = h_h + VP_d = F_hVP_d + VP_d$

$= (0.25)(0.56) + 0.56$

$= 0.70$ "wg

3.5.2 Compound Hoods: Figure 3-18 illustrates a double entry loss hood. This is a single slot hood with a plenum and a transition from the plenum to the duct. The purpose of the plenum is to give uniform velocity across the slot opening. Air enters the slot, in this case a sharp-edged orifice, and loses energy due to the vena contract at this point. The air then continues through the plenum where the greater portion of the slot velocity is retained because the air stream projects itself across the plenum in a manner similar to the "blowing" supply stream show in Figure 1-7. (The retention of velocity in the plenum is characteristic of most local exhaust hoods because of the short plenum length.) In the case of very large hoods or exhausted closed rooms, however, the velocity loss must be taken into account. Finally, the air converges into the duct through the transition where the second significant energy loss occurs. For this type hood, both h_s and h_h must be considered.

EXAMPLE PROBLEM

Given: Slot Velocity (V_s) = 2000 fpm

Duct Velocity (V_d) = 3500 fpm

(V_d is greater than V_s; therefore, use VP_d as the acceleration VP)

$VP_s = (V_s/4005)^2 = 0.25$ "wg

F_s for slot = 1.78 from Figure 5-15

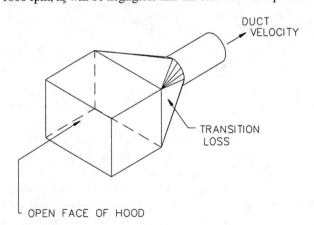

FIGURE 3–17. Simple hood

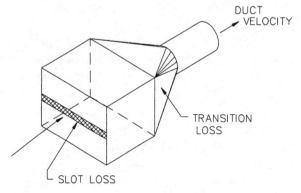

FIGURE 3–18. Compound hood

TABLE 3-2. Range of Minimum Duct Design Velocities

Nature of Contaminant	Examples	Design Velocity
Vapors, gases, smoke	All vapors, gases and smoke	Any desired velocity (economic optimum velocity usually 1000-2000 fpm)
Fumes	Welding	2000-2500
Very fine light dust	Cotton lint, wood flour, litho powder	2500-3000
Dry dusts & powders	Fine rubber dust, Bakelite molding powder dust, jute lint, cotton dust, shavings (light), soap dust, leather shavings	3000-4000
Average industrial dust	Grinding dust, buffing lint (dry), wool jute dust (shaker waste), coffee beans, shoe dust, granite dust, silica flour, general material handling, brick cutting, clay dust, foundry (general), limestone dust, packaging and weighing asbestos dust in textile industries	3500-4000
Heavy dusts	Sawdust (heavy and wet), metal turnings, foundry tumbling barrels and shake-out, sand blast dust, wood blocks, hog waste, brass turnings, cast iron boring dust, lead dust	4000-4500
Heavy or moist	Lead dusts with small chips, moist cement dust, asbestos chunks from transite pipe cutting machines, buffing lint (sticky), quick-lime dust	4500 and up

$$VP_d = (V_d/4005)^2 = 0.76 \text{ "wg}$$
$$F_h = 0.25 \text{ as shown in Figure 5-15}$$
$$SP_h = h_e + VP_d = h_s + h_h + VP_d$$
$$= F_s VPd + F_h VP_d + VP_d$$
$$= (1.78)(0.25) + (0.25)(0.76) + 0.76$$
$$= 1.40 \text{ "wg}$$

3.6 MINIMUM DUCT VELOCITY

The velocity pressure, VP_d, utilized to determine hood losses in the previous examples is determined from the air velocity in the duct immediately downstream of the hood to duct connection. This velocity is determined by the type of material being transported in the duct.

For systems handling particulate, a minimum design velocity is required to prevent settling and plugging of the duct. On the other hand, excessively high velocities are wasteful of power and may cause rapid abrasion of ducts.[3.14-3.21] Minimum recommended design velocities are higher than theoretical and experimental values to protect against practical contingencies such as:

1. Plugging or closing one or more branch will reduce the total flow rate in the system and correspondingly will reduce the velocities in at least some sections of the duct system.

2. Damage to ducts, by denting for example, will increase the resistance and decrease the flow rate and velocity in the damaged portion of the system.

3. Leakage of ducts will increase flow rate and velocity downstream of the leak but will decrease airflow upstream and in other parts of the system.

4. Corrosion or erosion of the fan wheel or slipping of a fan drive belt will reduce flow rates and velocities.

5. Velocities must be adequate to pick up or re-entrain dust which may have settled due to improper operation of the exhaust system.

The designer is cautioned that for some conditions such as sticky materials, condensing conditions in the presence of dust, strong electrostatic effects, etc., velocity alone may not be sufficient to prevent plugging and other special measures may be necessary.

Some typical duct velocities are provided in Table 3-2. The use of minimum duct velocity is treated in detail in Chapter 5.

3.7 SPECIAL HOOD REQUIREMENTS

3.7.1 Ventilation of Radioactive and High Toxicity Processes: Ventilation of radioactive and high toxicity processes requires a knowledge of the hazards, the use of extraordinarily effective control methods, and adequate maintenance which includes monitoring. Only the basic principles can be covered here. For radioactive processes, reference should be made to the standards and regulations of the nuclear regulatory agencies.

Local exhaust hoods should be of the enclosing type with the maximum enclosure possible. Where complete or nearly complete enclosure is not possible, control velocities from 50 to 100% higher than the minimum standards in this manual should be used. If the enclosure is not complete and an operator must be located at an opening, such as in front of a laboratory hood, the maximum control velocity should not exceed 125 fpm. Air velocities higher than this value will create eddies in front of the operator which may pull contaminant from the hood into the operator's breathing zone. Replacement air should be introduced at low velocity and in a direction which does not cause disruptive cross-drafts at the hood opening.

3.7.2 For Laboratory Operations: Glove boxes should be used for high activity alpha or beta emitters and highly toxic and biological materials. The air locks used with the glove box should be exhausted if they open directly to the room.

For low activity radioactive laboratory work, a laboratory fume hood may be acceptable. For such hoods, an average face velocity of 80-100 fpm is recommended. See Section 10.35, VS-35-01, -02, -04 and -20.

For new buildings it is frequently necessary to estimate the air conditioning early — before the detailed design and equipment specifications are available. For early estimating, the guidelines provided in Section 10.35 for hood air flow and replacement air flow can be used.

3.8 PUSH-PULL VENTILATION

Push-pull ventilation consists of a push nozzle and an exhaust hood to receive and remove the push jet. Push-pull is used most commonly on open surface vessels such as plating tanks[3.22] but may be effectively used elsewhere (see VS-70-10). The advantage of push-pull is that a push jet will maintain velocity over large distances, 20-30 ft or more, whereas the velocity in front of an exhaust hood decays very rapidly as the distance from the hood increases. Properly used, the push jet intercepts contaminated air and carries it relatively long distances into the exhaust hood thus providing control where it may be otherwise difficult or impossible.

It is to be noted that the criteria provided in paragraphs 3.8, 3.8.1, 3.8.2, 3.8.3, and VS-70-10, VS-70-11, and VS-70-12 apply to manual open surface tank plating or automated plating systems which do not have significant obstructions to the push jet. Plating operations which are automated and which employ large parts containers and/or plating system mechanisms which would significantly obstruct and deflect the jet flow will require careful analysis to determine the method of application or applicability of push-pull. If not suitable, other control measures such as enclosure or direct airflow over the operation may be appropriate.

3.8.1 Push Jet: Ambient air is entrained in the push jet and results in a jet flow at the exhaust hood several times greater than the push nozzle flow rate. The jet velocity will decay with distance from the nozzle. The entrainment ratio for a long thin slot (or pipe) type nozzle may be approximated by:[3.23]

$$\frac{Q_x}{Q_o} = 1.2 \sqrt{\left(\frac{ax}{b_o}\right) + 0.41} \qquad \textbf{[3.6]}$$

The velocity ratio may be approximated by:[3.23]

$$\frac{V_x}{V_o} = \frac{1.2}{\sqrt{\frac{ax}{b_o} + 0.41}} \qquad \textbf{[3.7]}$$

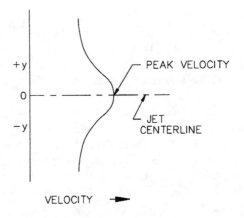

(a) FREE PLANE JET

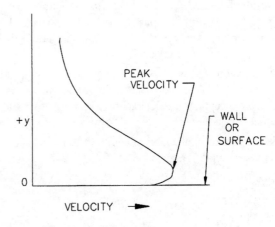

(b) PLANE WALL JET

FIGURE 3–19. Jet velocity profile

where: Q_o = the push nozzle supply flow

Q_x = the jet flow rate at a distance x from the nozzle

V_o = the push nozzle exit air velocity

V_x = the peak push jet velocity at a distance x

a = a coefficient characteristic of the nozzle (0.13 for slots and pipes)

x = distance from the nozzle

b_o = the slot width*

[*For pipes with holes, b_o is the width of a slot with area equivalent to the area of the holes. If the nozzle is freely suspended, the b_o is ½ the slot width. If the nozzle is positioned at or close to a surface (wall, plating tank, etc.) b_o is the full slot width.]

Typical jet velocity profiles are shown in Figure 3-19.

Obstructions in the jet path should be minimized near the jet. Objects with small cross-sections, such as parts hangers, will cause serious problems; however, large flat surface objects should be avoided. At further distances from the nozzle where the jet has expanded, larger objects may be acceptable if they are located within the jet.

The nozzle may be constructed as a long thin slot, a pipe with holes or individual nozzles. The total nozzle exit area should not exceed 50% of the nozzle plenum cross-sectional area to assure even flow distribution. Slot width can range from 0.125 to 0.25 inch for short push length such as plating tanks (4 to 8 ft). Hole size should be 0.25 inch on 3 to 8 diameter spacing. The nozzle momentum factor, which is proportional to nozzle exit flow per foot of nozzle length times nozzle exit velocity ($Q_o \times V_o$) must be sufficient to result in an effective jet, but not so strong so that the exhaust hood is overpowered. A $Q_o V_o$ range should be approximately 50,000 to 75,000 per foot of nozzle length for short distances of 4 to 8 feet.

3.8.2 Pull Hood: The pull hood will accept and remove the push jet flow. The same design considerations regarding flow distribution, hood entry losses, etc., used for a normal pull only hood should be used. The hood pull flow should be approximately 1.5 to 2.0 times the push flow which reaches the hood. If design criteria specifying pull flow rate are not available, Equation 3.6 can be used.

The hood opening height should be the same as the width of the expanded jet, if possible. However, smaller opening heights are acceptable if the hood flow rate meets the 1.5 to 2.0 times jet flow criteria.

Each push pull application will necessitate special attention. Wherever possible, a pilot system should be evaluated prior to final installation.

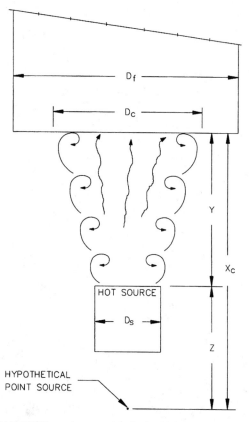

FIGURE 3–20. Dimensions used to design high-canopy hoods for hot sources (Ref. 3.24)

3.8.3 Push-Pull System Design: Specific design criteria have been developed experimentally for plating, cleaning, or other open surface vessels and are provided in VS-70-10, VS-70-11 and VS-70-12. Where such specific design criteria are not available, the criteria provided in Sections 3.8.1 and 3.8.2 can be used. When designing with Equation 3.7, a push jet velocity (V_x) of 150 to 200 fpm at the exhaust hood face should be specified.

3.9 HOT PROCESSES

Design of hooding for hot processes requires different considerations than design for cold processes.[3.24] When significant quantities of heat are transferred to the air above and around the process by conduction and convection, a thermal draft is created which causes an upward air current with air velocities as high as 400 fpm. The design of the hood and exhaust rate must take this thermal draft into consideration.

3.9.1 Circular High Canopy Hoods: As the heated air rises, it mixes turbulently with the surrounding air. This results in an increasing air column diameter and volumetric flow rate. The diameter of the column (see Figure 3-20) can be approximated by:

$$D_c = 0.5X_c^{0.88} \qquad \text{[3.8]}$$

where: D_c = column diameter at hood face

$X_c = y + z$ = the distance from the hypothetical point source to the hood face, ft

y = distance from the process surface to the hood face, ft

z = distance from the process surface to the hypothetical point source, ft

"z" can be calculated from:

$$z = (2 D_s)^{1.138} \qquad \text{[3.9]}$$

where: D_s = diameter of hot source, ft.

The velocity of the rising hot air column can be calculated from:

$$V_f = 8 (A_s)^{0.33} \frac{(\Delta t)^{0.42}}{X_c^{0.25}} \qquad \text{[3.10]}$$

where: V_f = velocity of hot air column at the hood face, fpm

A_s = area of the hot source, ft^2

Δ_t = the temperature difference between the hot source and the ambient air, F

$X_c = y + z$ = the distance from the hypothetical point source to the hood face, ft.

The diameter of the hood face must be larger than the diameter of the rising hot air column to assure complete capture. The hood diameter is calculated from:

$$D_f = D_c + 0.8y \qquad \text{[3.11]}$$

where: D_f = diameter of the hood face, ft.

Total hood airflow rate is

$$Q_t = V_f A_c = V_r (A_f - A_c) \qquad [3.12]$$

where: Q_t = total volume entering hood, cfm

V_f = velocity of hot air column at the hood face, fpm

A_c = area of the hot air column at the hood face, ft^2

V_r = the required air velocity through the remaining hood area, fpm

A_f = total area of hood face, ft^2.

EXAMPLE PROBLEM

Given: 4.0 ft diameter melting pot (D_a)

1000 F metal temperature

100 F ambient temperature

Circular Canopy hood located 10 ft above pot (y)

Calculate xc:

$$x_c = y + z = y + (2D_s)^{1.138}$$

$$x_c = 10 + (2 \times 4)^{1.138}$$

$$x_c = 10.7 \text{ ft}$$

Calculate the diameter of the hot air column at the hood face:

$$D_c = 0.5 \, x_c^{0.88}$$

$$D_c = 0.5(20.7)^{0.88}$$

$$D_c = 7.2 \text{ ft}$$

Calculate the velocity of the hot air column at the hood face:

$$V_f = 8(A_s)^{0.33} \frac{(\Delta t)^{0.42}}{(x)^{0.25}}$$

$$A_s = 0.25\pi D_c^2$$

$$A_s = 0.25\pi(4.2)^2$$

$$A_s = 12.6 \text{ ft}^2$$

$$\Delta t = 1000 - 100 = 900 \text{ F}$$

$$V_f = 8(1.26)^{0.33} \frac{(900)^{0.42}}{(20.7)^{0.25}}$$

$$V_f = (8)(2.31) \frac{(17.4)}{(2.13)}$$

$$V_f = 151 \text{ fpm}$$

Calculate diameter of hood face:

$$D_f = Dc + 0.8y$$

$$D_f = 7.2 + 0.8 \times 10$$

$$D_f = 15.2 \text{ ft}$$

Calculate total hood airflow rate

$$Q_f = V_f A_c + V_r(A_f - A_c)$$

$$A_c = 0.25\pi D_c^2$$

$$A_c = 0.25\pi(7.2)^2$$

$$A_c = 41 \text{ ft}^2$$

$$A_f = 0.25\pi D_f^2$$

$$A_f = 0.25\pi(7.2)^2$$

$$A_f = 181 \text{ ft}^2$$

$$Q_f = 151(41) + 100(181 - 41)$$

$$Q_f = 10,290 \text{ cfm}$$

3.9.2 Rectangular High Canopy Hoods: Hot air column from sources which are not circular may be better controlled by a rectangular canopy hood. Hood air flow calculations are performed in the same manner as for circular hoods except the dimensions of the hot air column at the hood (and the hood dimensions) are determined by considering both the length and width of the source. Equations 3.8, 3.9, and 3.11 are used individually to determine length and width of the hot air column and the hood. The remaining values are calculated in the same manner as for the circular hood.

EXAMPLE PROBLEM

Given: 2.5' x 4' rectangular melting furnace

700 F metal temperature

80 F ambient temperature

Rectangular canopy hood located 8' above furnace (y)

Calculate X_c for each furnace dimension.

$$X_{c2.5} = y + Z_{2.5} = y + (2D_{s2.5})^{1.138}$$

$$= 8 + (2 \times 2.5)^{1.138}$$

$$= 14.2 \text{ ft}$$

$$X_{c4} = 8 + (2 \times 4)^{1.138}$$

$$= 18.7 \text{ ft}$$

Calculate the width of the hot air column at the hood face.

$$D_{c2.5} = 0.5 \, X_{c2.5}^{0.88}$$

$$= 0.5(14.2)^{0.88}$$

$$= 5.2 \text{ ft}$$

$$D_{c4.0} = 0.5(18.7)^{0.88}$$

$$= 6.6 \text{ ft}$$

Calculate the velocity of the hot air column at the hood face.

$$V_f = 8(A_s)^{0.33} \frac{(\Delta t)^{0.42}}{(x_c)^{0.25}}$$

$$A_s = 2.5 \times 4 = 10 \text{ ft}^2$$

$$\Delta t = 700 - 80 = 620 \text{ F}$$

$$x_c = X_{c2.5} = 14.2 \text{ ft}$$

Note: $X_{c2.5}$ is used rather than $x_{c4.0}$ as it is smaller and as such will yield a slightly larger V_f which results in a margin of safety.

$$V_f = 8(10)^{0.33} \frac{(620)^{0.42}}{(14.2)^{0.25}}$$

$$= 8(2.1) \frac{(14.9)}{1.9}$$

$$= 132 \text{ fpm}$$

Calculate hood face dimensions.

Hood width $= D_{c2.5} + 0.8y$

$$= (5.2) + 0.8(8)$$

$$= 11.6 \text{ ft}$$

Hood length $= D_{c4.0} + 0.8y$

$$= 6.6 + 0.8(8)$$

$$= 13.0 \text{ ft}$$

Calculate the total hood airflow rate.

$$Q_f = V_f A_c + V_r (A_f - A_c)$$

$$A_c = (D_{c2.5})(D_{c4.0})$$

$$= (5.2)(6.6)$$

$$= 34 \text{ ft}^2$$

$$A_f = (\text{hood length})(\text{hood width})$$

$$= (11.6)(13.0)$$

$$= 151 \text{ ft}^2$$

$$Q_f = (151)(34) + 100(151 - 34)$$

$$= 5134 + 11,700$$

$$= 16,834 \text{ cfm}$$

3.9.3 Low Canopy Hoods: If the distance between the hood and the hot source does not exceed approximately the diameter of the source or 3 ft, whichever is smaller, the hood may be considered a low canopy hood. Under such conditions, the diameter or cross-section of the hot air column will be approximately the same as the source. The diameter or side dimensions of the hood therefore need only be 1 ft larger than the source.

The total flow rate for a circular low canopy hood is

$$Q_t = 4.7 (D_f)^{2.33} (\Delta_t)^{0.41} \qquad \text{[3.13]}$$

where: Q_t = total hood air flow, cfm

D_f = diameter of hood, ft

Δt = difference between temperature of the hot source, and the ambient, F.

The total flow rate for a rectangular low hood is

$$\frac{Q_t}{L} = 6.2 \, b^{1.33} \, \Delta t^{0.42} \qquad \text{[3.14]}$$

where: Q_t = total hood air flow, cfm

L = length of the rectangular hood, ft

b = width of the rectangular hood, ft

Δt = difference between temperature of the hot source and the ambient, F.

REFERENCES

3.1.   Brandt, A.D.: Industrial Health Engineering, John Wiley and Sons, New York (1947).

3.2.   Kane, J.M.: "Design of Exhaust Systems." Health and Ventilating 42:68 (November 1946).

3.3.   Dalla Valle, J.M.: Exhaust Hoods. Industrial Press, New York (1946).

3.4.   Silverman, L.: "Velocity Characteristics of Narrow Exhaust Slots." J. Ind. Hg. Toxicol. 24:267 (November 1942).

3.5.   Silverman, L.: "Center-line Characteristics of Round Openings Under Suction." J. Ind. Hyg. Toxicol. 24:259 (November 1942).

3.6.   Piney, M.; Gill, F.; Gray, C.; et al.: "Air Contaminant Control: the Case History Approach - Learning From the Pat and Looking to the Future", Ventilation '88, J. H. Vincent, Ed., Pergammon Press, Oxford, U.K., 1989.

3.7.   Ljungqvist, B.: "Some Observations on the Interaction Between Air Movements and the |Dispersion of Pollution", Document D8:1979, Swedish Council for Building Research, Stockholm, Sweden, 1979.

3.8.   Kim, T.; Flynn, M. R.: "Airflow Pattern Around a Worker in a Uniform Freestream", Am. Ind. Hyg. Assoc. J., 52:7 (1991), pp. 187-296.

3.9.   George, D. K.; Flynn, M. R.; Goodman, R.: "The Impact of Boundary Layer Separation on Local Exhaust Design and Worker Exposure, Appl. Occup. and Env. Hyg., 5:501-509, (1990).

3.10. Heriot, N. R.; Wilkinson, J.: "Laminar Flow Booths for the Control of Dust", Filtration and Separation, 16:2:159-164, 1979.

3.11. Flynn, M. R.; Shelton, W. K.: "Factors Affecting the Design of Local Exhaust Ventilation for the Control of Contaminants from Hand-held Sources", Appl. Occup. and Env. Hyg., 5:707-714, (1990).

3.12. Tum Suden, K. D.; Flynn, M. R.; Goodman, R.: "Computer Simulation in the Design of Local Exhaust Hoods for Shielded Metal Arc Welding", Am. Ind. Hyg. Assoc. J., 51(3):115-126, (1990).

3.13. American Welding Society, "Fumes and Gases in the Welding Environment", F. Y. Speight and H. C. Campbell, Eds., Miami, FL (1979).

3.14. American Society of Mechanical Engineers: Power Test Code 19.2.4, "Liquid Column Gages" (1942).

3.15. Hemeon, W.C.L.: Plant and Process Ventilation. Industrial Press, New York (1963).

3.16. Alden, J.L.: Design of Industrial Exhaust System. Industrial Press, New York (1939).

3.17.   Rahjans, G.S.; Thompkins, R.W.: "Critical Velocities of Mineral Dusts." Canadian Mining J. (October 1967).

3.18.   Djamgowz, O.T.; Ghoneim, S.A.A.: "Determining the Pick-Up Air Velocity of Mineral Dusts." Canadian Mining J. (July 1974).

3.19.   Baliff, J.L.; Greenburg, L.; Stern, A.C.: "Transport Velocities for Industrial Dusts _ An Experimental Study." Ind. Hyg. Q. (December 1948).

3.20.   Dalla Valle, J.M.: "Determining Minimum Air Velocities for Exhaust Systems. Heating, Piping and Air Conditioning (1932).

3.21.   Hatch, T.F.: Economy in the Design of Exhaust Systems

3.22.   Hughes, R.T.: "Design Criteria for Plating Tank Push-Pull Ventilation." Ventilation '86. Elsiever Press, Amsterdam (1986).

3.23.   Baturin, V.V.: Fundamentals Industrial Ventilation. Pergamon Press, New York (1972).

3.24.   U.S. Public Health Service: Air Pollution Engineering Manual. Publication No. 999-AP-40 (1973).

3.25.   Burgess, W.A.; Ellenbecker, M. J.; Treitman, R.D.: *Ventilation for Control of the Work Environment*, John Wiley & Sons, New York, 1989.

3.26.   Braconnier, R.: "Bibliographic Review of Velocity Fields in the Vicinity of Local Exhaust Hoods." Am. Ind. Hyg. Assoc. J, 49(4):185-198 (1988).

LOCAL EXHAUST HOOD CENTERLINE VELOCITY

A3.1 INTRODUCTION

Velocity characteristics of local exhaust hoods have been studied by many individuals during the past sixty years. These empirical studies provide, many times as best, an approximation of the actual situation. Review of a number of these studies is provided in Reference A3.1

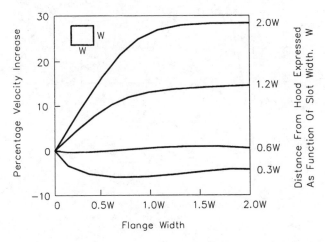

FIGURE 3A-1. Effect of flange width on velocity in front of square hood

The works of DallaValle and Silverman have been the basis for the centerline velocity equations presented in this manual. They are simple in format and have provided acceptable approximations for use in hood design and evaluation and are retained as a recommended method of determining exhaust hood centerline velocity. However, additional methods developed by Fletcher[A3.2] and Yousefi[A3.3] have found use by the European Community.

A3.2 FLETCHER

The Fletcher centerline velocity equations for freely suspended non-flanged hoods are provided as follows

$$\frac{V_x}{V_o} = \frac{1}{0.93 + 8.58a^2}$$

$$Q = V_x A (0.93 + 8.58a^2)$$

$$a = \frac{x}{\sqrt{A}} \left(\frac{W^{-B}}{L} \right)$$

$$B = 0.2 \left(\frac{x}{\sqrt{A}} \right)^{-1/3}$$

where: Q = hood flow rate, cfm

X = distance from hood along centerline, ft

V_o = average velocity at hood face, fpm

V_x = average velocity at centerline distance x (fpm)

A = hood face area, ft^2

W = hood face width, ft

L = hood face length, ft

The effects of hood flanges on centerline velocities calculated from the Fletcher equations are shown in Figures A3-1, A3-2 and A3-3. The figures show the percent increase in centerline velocity in terms of hood dimensions.[A3.4]

Example A3-1 (Fletcher)

X = 1 ft

V^x = 100 fpm

W = 0.5 ft

L = 2 ft

Find Q for an unflanged rectangular hood.

$$\frac{V_x}{V_o} = \frac{1}{0.93 + 8.58a^2}$$

$$B = 0.2 \left(\frac{x}{\sqrt{A}} \right)^{-1/3}$$

$$a = \frac{x}{\sqrt{A}} \left(\frac{W^{-B}}{L} \right) = 1.32$$

$$\frac{V_x}{V_o} = 0.063$$

$$V_o = 1587 \text{ fpm}$$

$$Q = VA - 1587 \text{ cfm}$$

A3.3 YOUSEFI

The Yousefi centerline equations for freely suspended non-flanged hoods are provided as follows:

A3.3.1 Rectangular Unflanged Hoods

$$\frac{V}{V_o} = \frac{1.8\left(\frac{x}{HR}\right)^{-2.04}}{1+0.16\left(\frac{x}{HR}\right)^{=2.04}}$$

A3.3.2 Circular Unflanged Hoods

$$\frac{V}{V_o} = \frac{1}{9.78+3.497\left(\frac{x^2}{A}\right)^{-1.56}}$$

A3.3.3 All Shape Flanged Hoods

$$\frac{V_x}{V_o} = \frac{1.022\left(\frac{x}{HR}\right)^{-1.56}}{1+1.825\left(\frac{x}{HR}\right)^{-1.56}}$$

where: x = distance from hood along centerline, ft

V_o = average velocity at hood face, fpm

A = hood face area, ft^2

HR = hydraulic radius = (wl)/2)(w+1)

L = hood length

V_x = average velocity at centerline distance x, fpm

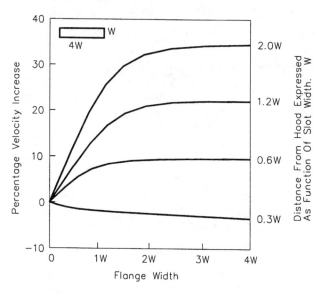

FIGURE 3A-2. Effect of flange width on velocity in front of a 4:1 aspect ratio hood

Example A3-2:

$$x = 1 \text{ ft}$$
$$W = 0.5 \text{ ft}$$
$$L = 2.0 \text{ ft}$$
$$V_x = 100 \text{ fpm}$$

Find Q for an unflanged rectangular hood.

$$HR = (wl)/2(W+1) = 0.2$$

$$\frac{V}{V_o} = \frac{1.8\left(\frac{x}{HR}\right)^{-2.04}}{1+0.16\left(\frac{x}{HR}\right)^{-2.04}} = 0.675$$

$$V_o = 1481 \text{ fpm}$$

$$Q = VA = 1481 \text{ cfm}$$

Example A3-3 (DalleValle)

$$X = 1 \text{ ft}$$
$$W = 0.5 \text{ ft}$$
$$L = 2.0 \text{ ft}$$
$$V_x = 100 \text{ fpm}$$
$$A = V_x(10x^2+A) = 1100 \text{ cfm}$$

A comparison of the Fletcher, Yousefi and DallaValle velocity characteristics for the example hood are shown in Figure A3-4.

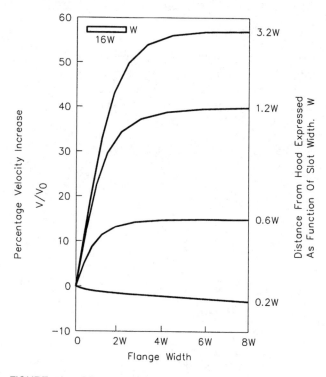

FIGURE 3A-3. Effect of flange width on velocity in front of a 16:1 aspect ratio hood

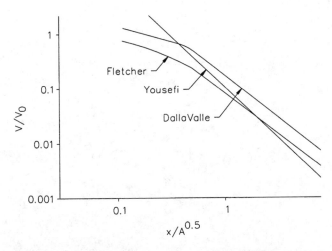

FIGURE 3A-3. Effect of flange width on velocity in front of a 16:1 aspect ratio hood

REFERENCES

A3.1   Branconnier, R.: Bibliographic Review of Velocity Fields in the Vicinity of Local Exhaust Hood Openings; Am. Ind. Hyg. Assoc. J. (49)(April, 1988).

A3.2   Fletcher, B.: Centerline Velocity Characteristics of Rectangular Unflanged Hoods and Slots Under Suction, Ann. Occu. Hyg., Vol. 20, pp 141-146.

A3.3   Yousefi, V.; Annegarn, H.J.: Aerodynamic Aspects of Exhaust Ventilation; Ventilation '91, 3rd International Symposium on Ventilation for Contaminant Control; American Conference of Governmental Industrial Hygienists, Inc., Cincinnati, OH.

A3.4   Fletcher, B.: Effect of Flanges on the Velocity in Frnt of Exhaust Ventilation Hoods; Ann. Occup. Hyg., Vol. 21, pp 265-269.

Chapter 4
AIR CLEANING DEVICES

4.1 INTRODUCTION

Air cleaning devices remove contaminants from an air or gas stream. They are available in a wide range of designs to meet variations in air cleaning requirements. Degree of removal required, quantity and characteristics of the contaminant to be removed, and conditions of the air or gas stream will all have a bearing on the device selected for any given application. In addition, fire safety and explosion control must be considered in all selections. (See NFPA publications.)

For particulate contaminants, air cleaning devices are divided into two basic groups: AIR FILTERS and DUST COLLECTORS. Air filters are designed to remove low dust concentrations of the magnitude found in atmospheric air. They are typically used in ventilation, air-conditioning, and heating systems where dust concentrations seldom exceed 1.0 grains per thousand cubic feet of air and are usually well below 0.1 grains per thousand cubic feet of air. (One pound equals 7000 grains. A typical atmospheric dust concentration in an urban area is 87 micrograms per cubic meter or 0.038 grains per thousand cubic feet of air.)

Dust collectors are usually designed for the much heavier loads from industrial processes where the air or gas to be cleaned originates in local exhaust systems or process stack gas effluents. Contaminant concentrations will vary from less than 0.1 to 100 grains or more for each cubic foot of air or gas. Therefore, dust collectors are, and must be, capable of handling concentrations 100 to 20,000 times greater than those for which air filters are designed.

Small, inexpensive versions of all categories of air cleaning devices are available. The principles of selection, application, and operation are the same as for larger equipment. However, due to the structure of the market that focuses on small, quickly available, and inexpensive equipment, much of the available equipment is of light duty design and construction. One of the major economies of unit collectors implies recirculation, for which such equipment may or may not be suitable. For adequate prevention of health hazards, fires, and explosions, application engineering is just as essential for unit collectors as it is for major systems.

4.2 SELECTION OF DUST COLLECTION EQUIPMENT

Dust collection equipment is available in numerous designs utilizing many different principles and featuring wide variations in effectiveness, first cost, operating and maintenance cost, space, arrangement, and materials of construction. Consultation with the equipment manufacturer is the recommended procedure in selecting a collector for any problem where extensive previous plant experience on the specific dust problem is not available. Factors influencing equipment selection include the following:

4.2.1 Contaminant Characteristics: Contaminants in exhaust systems cover an extreme range in concentration and particle size. Concentrations can range from less than 0.1 to much more than 100,000 grains of dust per cubic foot of air. In low pressure conveying systems, the dust ranges from 0.5 to 100 or more microns in size. Deviation from mean size (the range over and under the mean) will also vary with the material.

4.2.2 Efficiency Required: Currently, there is no accepted standard for testing and/or expressing the "efficiency" of a dust collector. It is virtually impossible to accurately compare the performance of two collectors by comparing efficiency claims. The only true measure of performance is the actual mass emission rate, expressed in terms such as mg/m^3 or grains/ft^3. Evaluation will consider the need for high efficiency–high cost equipment requiring minimum energy high voltage electrostatic precipitators, high efficiency–moderate cost equipment such as fabric or wet collectors, or the lower cost primary units such as the dry centrifugal group. If either of the first two groups is selected, the combination with primary collectors should be considered.

When the cleaned air is to be discharged outdoors, the required degree of collection can depend on plant location; nature of contaminant (its salvage value and its potential as a health hazard, public nuisance, or ability to damage property); and the regulations of governmental agencies. In remote locations, damage to farms or contribution to air pollution problems of distant cities can influence the need for and importance of effective collection equipment. Many industries, originally located away from residential areas, failed to anticipate the construction of residential building which frequently develops around a plant. Such lack of foresight has required installation of air cleaning equipment at greater expense than initially would have been necessary. Today, the remotely located plant must comply, in most cases, with the same regulations as the plant located in an urban area. With present emphasis on public nuisance, public health, and preservation and improvement of community air quality, management can continue to expect criticism for excessive emissions of air contaminants whether located in a heavy industry section of a city or in an area closer to residential zones.

The mass rate of emission will also influence equipment selection. For a given concentration, the larger the exhaust volumetric flow rate, the greater the need for better equipment. Large central steam generating stations might select high efficiency electrostatic precipitators or fabric collectors for their pulverized coal boiler stacks while a smaller industrial pulverized fuel boiler might be able to use slightly less efficient collectors.

A safe recommendation in equipment selection is to select the collector that will allow the least possible amount of contaminant to escape and is reasonable in first cost and maintenance while meeting all prevailing air pollution regulations. For some applications even the question of reasonable cost and maintenance must be sacrificed to meet established standards for air pollution control or to prevent damage to health or property.

It must be remembered that visibility of an effluent will be a function of the light reflecting surface area of the escaping material. Surface area per pound increases inversely as the square of particle size. This means that the removal of 80% or more of the dust on a weight basis may remove only the coarse particles without altering the stack appearance.

4.2.3 Gas Stream Characteristics: The characteristics of the carrier gas stream can have a marked bearing on equipment selection. Temperature of the gas stream may limit the material choices in fabric collectors. Condensation of water vapor will cause packing and plugging of air or dust passages in dry collectors. Corrosive chemicals can attack fabric or metal in dry collectors and when mixed with water in wet collectors can cause extreme damage.

4.2.4 Contaminant Characteristics: The contaminant characteristics will also affect equipment selection. Chemicals emitted may attack collector elements or corrode wet type collectors. Sticky materials, such as metallic buffing dust impregnated with buffing compounds, can adhere to collector elements, plugging collector passages. Linty materials will adhere to certain types of collector surfaces or elements. Abrasive materials in moderate to heavy concentrations will cause rapid wear on dry metal surfaces. Particle size, shape, and density will rule out certain designs. For example, the parachute shape of particles like the "bees wings" from grain will float through centrifugal collectors because their velocity of fall is less than the velocity of much smaller particles having the same specific gravity but a spherical shape. The combustible nature of many finely divided materials will require specific collector designs to assure safe operation.

4.2.5 Energy Considerations: The cost and availability of energy makes essential the careful consideration of the total energy requirement for each collector type which can achieve the desired performance. An electrostatic precipitator, for example, might be a better selection at a significant initial cost penalty because of the energy savings through its inherently lower pressure drop.

4.2.6 Dust Disposal: Methods of removal and disposal of collected materials will vary with the material, plant process, quantity involved, and collector design. Dry collectors can be unloaded continuously or in batches through dump gates, trickle valves, and rotary locks to conveyors or containers. Dry materials can create a secondary dust problem if careful thought is not given to dust-free material disposal or to collector dust bin locations suited to convenient material removal. See Figures 4-1, 4-2, and 4-3 for some typical discharge arrangements and valves.

Wet collectors can be arranged for batch removal or continual ejection of dewatered material. Secondary dust problems are eliminated although disposal of wet sludge can be a material handling problem. Solids carry-over in waste water can create a sewer or stream pollution problem if waste water is not properly clarified.

Material characteristics can influence disposal problems. Packing and bridging of dry materials in dust hoppers, and floating or slurry forming characteristics in wet collectors are examples of problems that can be encountered.

4.3 DUST COLLECTOR TYPES

The four major types of dust collectors for particulate contaminants are Electrostatic Precipitators, Fabric Collectors, Wet Collectors, and Dry Centrifugal Collectors.

4.3.1 Electrostatic Precipitators: In electrostatic precipitation, a high potential electric field is established between discharge and collecting electrodes of opposite electrical charge. The discharge electrode is of small cross-sectional area, such as a wire or a piece of flat stock, and the collection electrode is large in surface area such as a plate.

The gas to be cleaned passes through an electrical field that develops between the electrodes. At a critical voltage, the gas molecules are separated into positive and negative ions. This is called "ionization" and takes place at, or near, the surface of the discharge electrode. Ions having the same polarity as the discharge electrode attach themselves to neutral particles in the gas stream as they flow through the precipitator. These charged particles are then attracted to a collecting plate of opposite polarity. Upon contact with the collecting surface, dust particles lose their charge and then can be easily removed by washing, vibration, or gravity.

The electrostatic process consists of:

1. Ionizing the gas
2. Charging the dust particles
3. Transporting the particles to the collecting surface
4. Neutralizing, or removing the charge from the dust particles
5. Removing the dust from the collecting surface.

The two basic types of electrostatic precipitators are "Cottrell," or single-stage, and "Penny," or two-stage (see Figures 4-4 and 4-5).

The "Cottrell," single-stage, precipitator (Figure 4-4) combines ionization and collection in a single stage. Because it operates at ionization voltages from 40,000 to 75,000 volts DC, it may also be called a high voltage precipitator and is used extensively for heavy duty applications such as utility boilers, larger industrial boilers, and cement kilns. Some precipitator designs use sophisticated voltage control systems and rigid electrodes instead of wires to minimize maintenance problems.

The "Penny," or two-stage, precipitator (Figure 4-5) uses DC voltages from 11,000 to 15,000 for ionization and is frequently referred to as a low voltage precipitator. Its use is limited to low concentrations, normally not exceeding 0.025 grains per cubic foot. It is the most practical collection technique for the many hydrocarbon applications where an initially clear exhaust

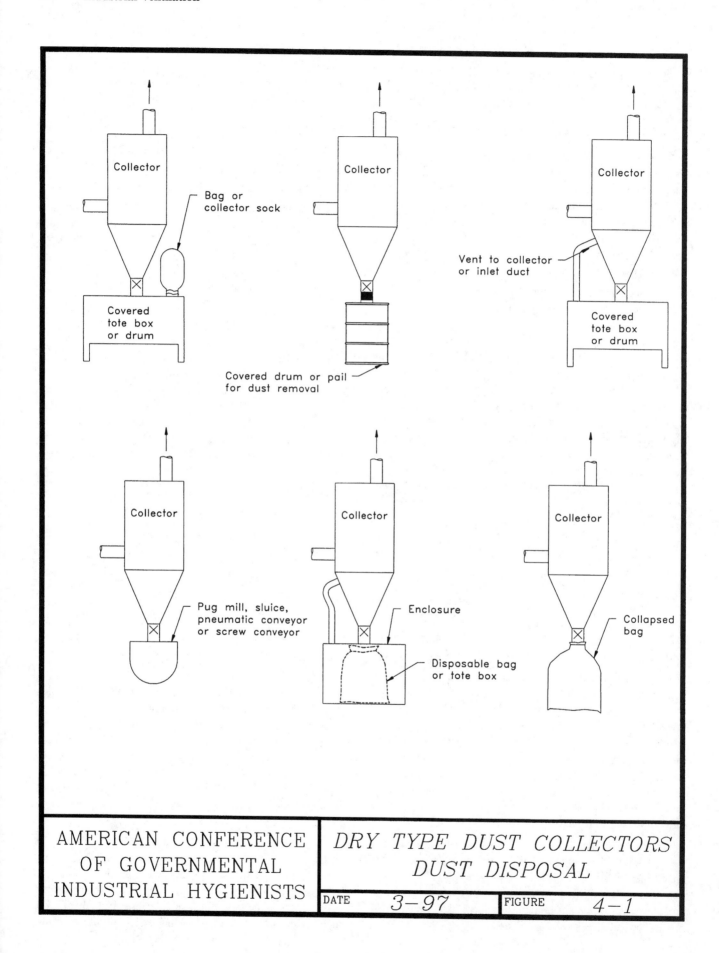

Bag or collector sock

Collector

Covered tote box or drum

Collector

Covered drum or pail for dust removal

Collector

Vent to collector or inlet duct

Covered tote box or drum

Collector

Pug mill, sluice, pneumatic conveyor or screw conveyor

Collector

Enclosure

Disposable bag or tote box

Collector

Collapsed bag

AMERICAN CONFERENCE OF GOVERNMENTAL INDUSTRIAL HYGIENISTS

DRY TYPE DUST COLLECTORS DUST DISPOSAL

DATE   3-97   FIGURE   4-1

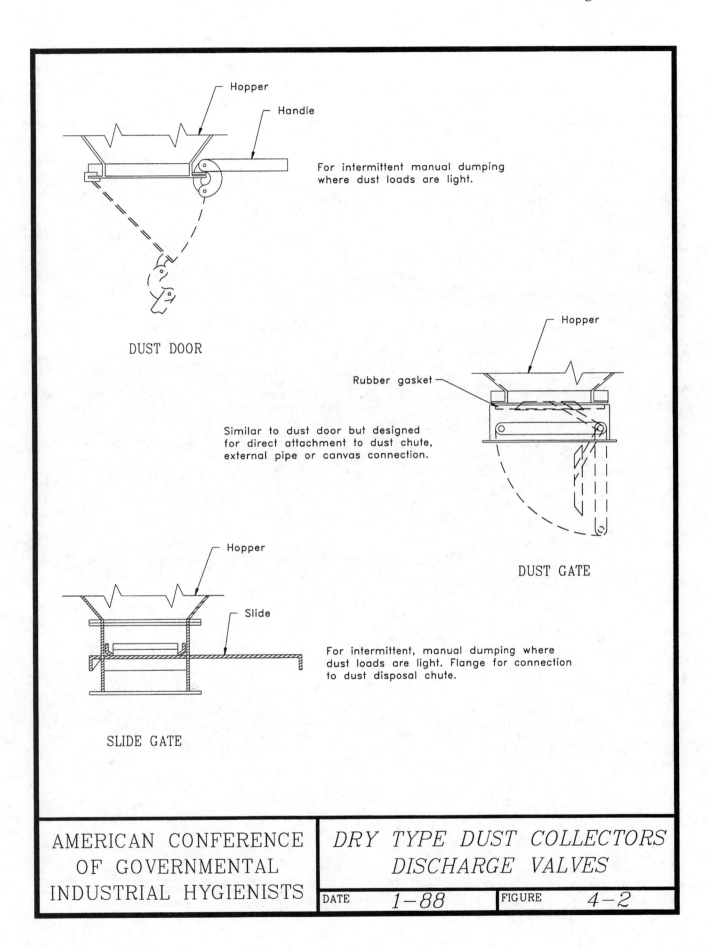

Hopper

Handle

For intermittent manual dumping where dust loads are light.

DUST DOOR

Hopper

Rubber gasket

Similar to dust door but designed for direct attachment to dust chute, external pipe or canvas connection.

DUST GATE

Hopper

Slide

For intermittent, manual dumping where dust loads are light. Flange for connection to dust disposal chute.

SLIDE GATE

AMERICAN CONFERENCE OF GOVERNMENTAL INDUSTRIAL HYGIENISTS	DRY TYPE DUST COLLECTORS DISCHARGE VALVES
	DATE 1-88 FIGURE 4-2

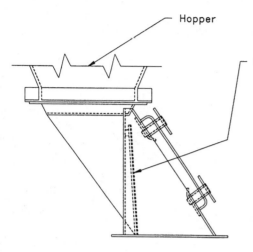

Hopper

Curtain

For continuous removal of collected dust where hopper is under negative pressure. Curtain is kept closed by pressure differential until collected material builds up sufficient height to overcome pressure.

TRICKLE VALVE

Motor driven multiple blade rotary valve provide air lock while continuously dumping collected material. Can be used with hoppers under either positive or negative pressure. Flanged for connection to dust disposal chute.

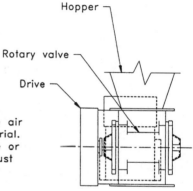

Hopper

Rotary valve

Drive

ROTARY LOCK

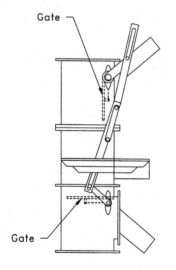

Gate

Motor driven, double gate valve for continuous removal of collected dust. Gates are sequenced so only one is open at a time in order to provide air seal. Flanged for connection to dust disposal chute.

Gate

DOUBLE DUMP VALVE

AMERICAN CONFERENCE OF GOVERNMENTAL INDUSTRIAL HYGIENISTS	*DRY TYPE DUST COLLECTORS DISCHARGE VALVES*	
	DATE *1-88*	FIGURE *4-3*

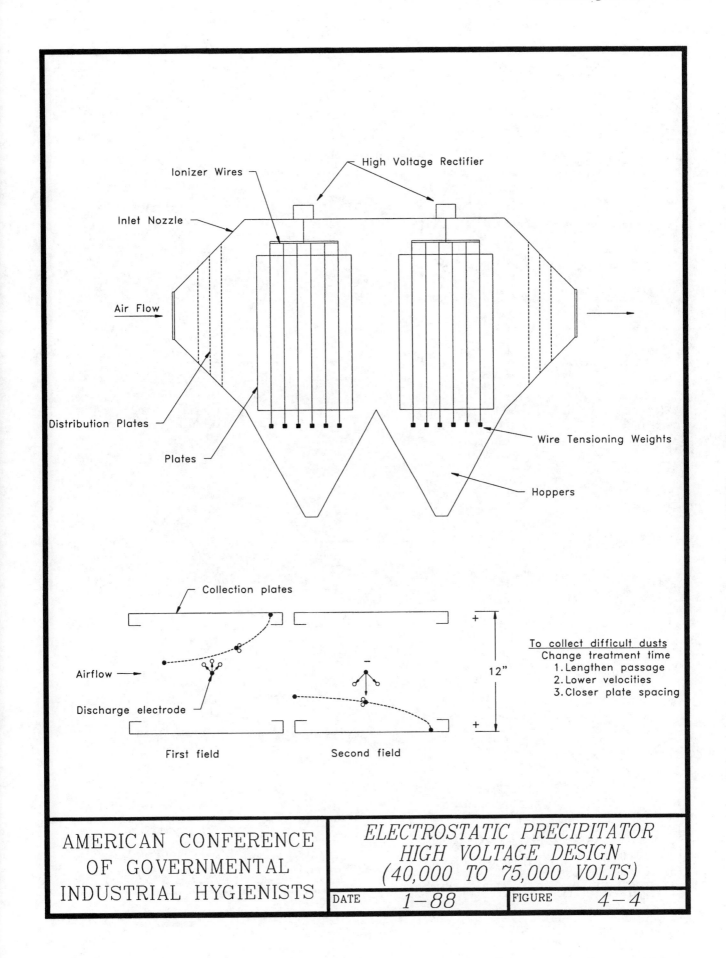

High Voltage Rectifier

Ionizer Wires

Inlet Nozzle

Air Flow

Distribution Plates

Plates

Wire Tensioning Weights

Hoppers

Collection plates

Airflow

Discharge electrode

First field

Second field

12"

To collect difficult dusts
Change treatment time
1. Lengthen passage
2. Lower velocities
3. Closer plate spacing

AMERICAN CONFERENCE
OF GOVERNMENTAL
INDUSTRIAL HYGIENISTS

ELECTROSTATIC PRECIPITATOR
HIGH VOLTAGE DESIGN
(40,000 TO 75,000 VOLTS)

DATE   1—88

FIGURE   4—4

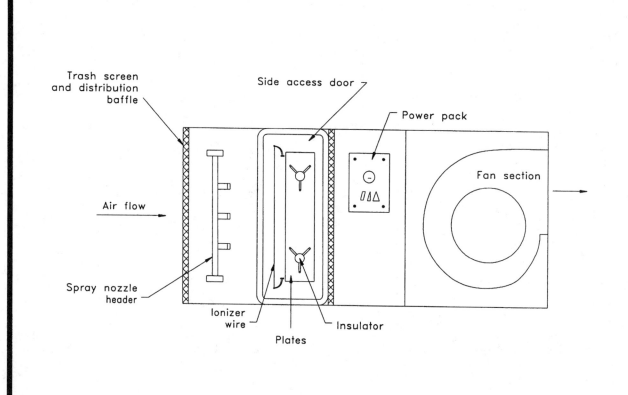

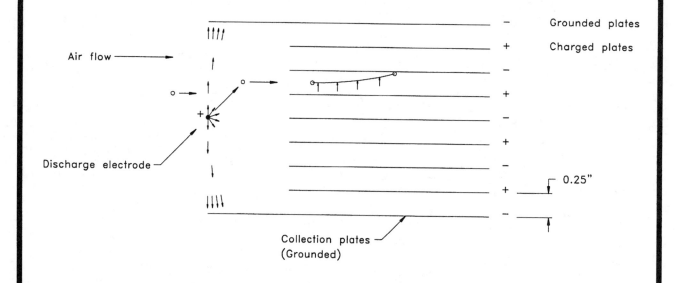

stack turns into a visible emission as vapor condenses. Some applications include plasticizer ovens, forge presses, die-casting machines, and various welding operations. Care must be taken to keep the precipitator inlet temperature low enough to insure that condensation has already occurred.

For proper results, the inlet gas stream should be evaluated and treated where necessary to provide proper conditions for ionization. For high-voltage units a cooling tower is sometimes necessary. Low voltage units may use wet scrubbers, evaporative coolers, heat exchangers, or other devices to condition the gas stream for best precipitator performance.

The pressure drop of an electrostatic precipitator is extremely low, usually less than 1 "wg; therefore, the energy requirement is significantly less than for other techniques.

4.3.2 Fabric Collectors: Fabric collectors remove particulate by straining, impingement, interception, diffusion, and electrostatic charge. The "fabric" may be constructed of any fibrous material, either natural or man-made, and may be spun into a yarn and woven or felted by needling, impacting, or bonding. Woven fabrics are identified by thread count and weight of fabric per unit area. Non-woven (felts) are identified by thickness and weight per unit area. Regardless of construction, the fabric represents a porous mass through which the gas is passed unidirectionally such that dust particles are retained on the dirty side and the cleaned gas passes through.

The ability of the fabric to pass air is stated as "permeability" and is defined as the cubic feet of air that is passed through one square foot of fabric each minute at a pressure drop of 0.5 "wg. Typical permeability values for commonly used fabrics range from 25 to 40 cfm.

A non-woven (felted) fabric is more efficient than a woven fabric of identical weight because the void areas or pores in the non-woven fabric are smaller. A specific type of fabric can be made more efficient by using smaller fiber diameters, a greater weight of fiber per unit area and by packing the fibers more tightly. For non-woven construction, the use of finer needles for felting also improves efficiency. While any fabric is made more efficient by these methods, the cleanability and permeability are reduced. A highly efficient fabric that cannot be cleaned represents an excessive resistance to airflow and is not an economical engineering solution. Final fabric selection is generally a compromise between efficiency and permeability.

Choosing a fabric with better cleanability or greater permeability but lower inherent efficiency is not as detrimental as it may seem. The efficiency of the fabric as a filter is meaningful only when new fabric is first put into service. Once the fabric has been in service any length of time, collected particulate in contact with the fabric acts as a filter aid, improving collection efficiency. Depending on the amount of particulate and the time interval between fabric reconditioning, it may well be that virtually all filtration is accomplished by the previously collected particulate—or dust cake—as opposed to the fabric itself. Even immediately after cleaning, a residual and/or redeposited dust cake provides additional filtration surface and higher collection efficiency than obtainable with new fabric. While the collection efficiency of new, clean fabric is easily determined by laboratory test and the information is often published, it is not representative of operating conditions and therefore is of little importance in selecting the proper collector.

Fabric collectors are not 100% efficient, but well-designed, adequately sized, and properly operated fabric collectors can be expected to operate at efficiencies in excess of 99%, and often as high as 99.9+% on a mass basis. The inefficiency, or penetration, that does occur is greatest during or immediately after reconditioning. Fabric collector inefficiency is frequently a result of by-pass due to damaged fabric, faulty seals, or sheet metal leaks rather than penetration of the fabric. Where extremely high collection efficiency is essential, the fabric collector should be leak tested for mechanical leaks.

The combination of fabric and collected dust becomes increasingly efficient as the dust cake accumulates on the fabric surface. At the same time, the resistance to airflow increases. Unless the air moving device is adjusted to compensate for the increased resistance, the gas flow rate will be reduced. Figure 4-6 shows how efficiency, resistance to flow and flow rate change with time as dust accumulates on the fabric. Fabric collectors are suitable for service on relatively heavy dust concentrations. The amount of dust collected on a single square yard of fabric may exceed five pounds per hour. In virtually all applications, the amount of dust cake accumulated in just a few hours will represent sufficient resistance to flow to cause an unacceptable reduction in airflow.

In a well-designed fabric collector system, the fabric or filter mat is cleaned or reconditioned before the reduction in airflow is critical. The cleaning is accomplished by mechanical agitation or air motion, which frees the excess accumulation of dust from the fabric surface and leaves a residual or base cake. The residual dust cake does not have the same characteristics of efficiency or resistance to airflow as new fabric.

Commercially available fabric collectors employ fabric configured as bags or tubes, envelopes (flat bags), rigid elements, or pleated cartridges. Most of the available fabrics, whether woven or non-woven, are employed in either bag or envelope configuration. The pleated cartridge arrangement uses a paper-like fiber in either a cylindrical or panel configuration. It features extremely high efficiency on light concentrations. Earlier designs employed cellulose based media. Today, more conventional media, such as polypropolene or spun-bonded polyester, are frequently used.

The variable design features of the many fabric collectors available are:

1. Type of fabric (woven or non-woven)

2. Fabric configuration (bags or tubes, envelopes, cartridges)

3. Intermittent or continuous service

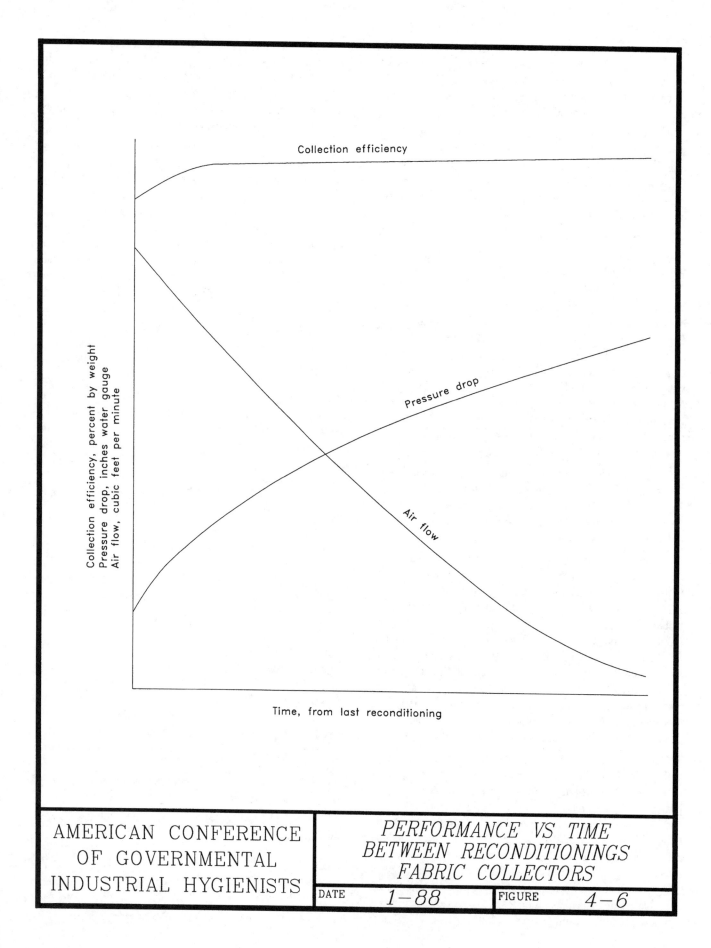

Collection efficiency, percent by weight
Pressure drop, inches water gauge
Air flow, cubic feet per minute

Collection efficiency

Pressure drop

Air flow

Time, from last reconditioning

AMERICAN CONFERENCE
OF GOVERNMENTAL
INDUSTRIAL HYGIENISTS

PERFORMANCE VS TIME
BETWEEN RECONDITIONINGS
FABRIC COLLECTORS

DATE 1-88   FIGURE 4-6

4. Type of reconditioning (shaker, pulse-jet/reverse-air)

5. Housing configuration (single compartment, multiple compartment)

At least two of these features will be interdependent. For example, non-woven fabrics are more difficult to recondition and therefore require high-pressure cleaning.

A fabric collector is selected for its mechanical, chemical, and thermal characteristics. Table 4-1 lists those characteristics for some common filter fabrics.

Fabric collectors are sized to provide a sufficient area of filter media to allow operation without excessive pressure drop. The amount of filter area required depends on many factors, including:

1. Release characteristics of dust

2. Porosity of dust cake

3. Concentration of dust in carrier gas stream

4. Type of fabric and surface finish, if any

5. Type of reconditioning

6. Reconditioning interval

7. Airflow pattern within the collector

8. Temperature and humidity of gas stream

Because of the many variables and their range of variation, fabric collector sizing is a judgment based on experience. The sizing is usually made by the equipment manufacturer, but at times may be specified by the user or a third party. Where no experience exists, a pilot installation is the only reliable way to determine proper size.

The sizing or rating of a fabric collector is expressed in terms of airflow rate versus fabric media area. The resultant ratio is called "air to cloth ratio" with units of cfm per square foot of fabric. This ratio represents the average velocity of the gas stream through the filter media. The expression "filtration velocity" is used synonymously with air to cloth ratio for rating fabric collectors. For example, an air to cloth ratio of 7:1 (7 cfm/sq ft) is equivalent to a filtration velocity of 7 fpm.

Table 4-2 compares the various characteristics of fabric collectors. The different types will be described in detail later. Inspection of Table 4-2 now may make the subsequent discussion more meaningful. The first major classification of fabric collectors is intermittent or continuous duty. Intermittent duty fabric collectors cannot be reconditioned while in operation. By design, they require that the gas flow be interrupted while the fabric is agitated to free accumulated dust cake. Continuous duty collectors do not require shut down for reconditioning.

Intermittent duty fabric collectors may use a tube, cartridge, or envelope configuration of woven fabric and will generally employ shaking or vibration for reconditioning. Figure 4-7 shows both tube and envelope shaker collector designs. For the tube type, dirty air enters the open bottom of the tube and dust is collected on the inside of the fabric. The bottoms of the tubes are attached to a tube sheet and the tops are connected to a shaker mechanism. Since the gas flow is from inside to outside, the tubes tends to inflate during operation and no other support of the fabric is required.

Gas flow for envelope type collectors is from outside to inside, therefore, the envelopes must be supported during operation to prevent collapsing. This is normally done by inserting wire mesh or fabricated wire cages into the envelopes. The opening of the envelope from which the cleaned air exits is attached to a tube sheet and, depending on design, the other end may be attached to a support member or cantilevered without support. The shaker mechanism may be located in either the dirty air or cleaned air compartments.

Periodically (usually at 3- to 6-hour intervals) the airflow must be stopped to recondition the fabric. Figure 4-8 illustrates the system airflow characteristics of an intermittent-duty fabric collector. As dust accumulates on the fabric, resistance to flow increases and airflow decreases until the fan is turned off and the fabric reconditioned. Variations in airflow due to changing pressure losses is sometimes a disadvantage and, when coupled with the requirement to periodically stop the airflow, may preclude the use of intermittent collectors. Reconditioning seldom requires more than two minutes but must be done without airflow through the fabric. If reconditioning is attempted with airflowing it will be less effective and the flexing of the woven fabric will allow a substantial amount of dust to escape to the clean air side.

The filtration velocity for large intermittent duty fabric collectors seldom exceeds 6 fpm and normal selections are in the 2 fpm to 4 fpm range. Lighter dust concentrations and the ability to recondition more often allow the use of higher filtration velocities. Ratings are usually selected so that the pressure drop across the fabric will be in the 2 to 5 "wg range between start and end of operating cycle.

With multiple-section, continuous-duty, automatic fabric collectors the disadvantage of stopping the airflow to permit fabric reconditioning and the variations in airflow with dust cake build-up can be overcome. The use of sections or compartments, as indicated in Figure 4-7, allows continuous operation of the exhaust system because automatic dampers periodically remove one section from service for fabric reconditioning while the remaining compartments handle the total gas flow. The larger the number of compartments, the more constant the pressure loss and airflow. Either tubes or envelopes may be used and fabric reconditioning is usually accomplished by shaking or vibrating.

Figure 4-8 shows airflow versus time for a multiple-section collector. Each individual section or compartment has an airflow versus time characteristic like that of the intermittent collector, but the total variation is reduced because of the multiple compartments. Note the more constant airflow characteristic of the five-compartment unit as opposed to the three-compart-

TABLE 4-1. Chacteristics of Filter Fabrics*

Generic Names	Example Trade Name Fabrics**	Max. Temp. F		Resistance to Physical Action					Resistance to Chemicals				
		Continuous	Intermittent	Dry Heat	Moist Heat	Abrasion	Shaking	Flexing	Mineral Acid	Organic Acid	Alkalies	Oxidizing	Solvents
Cotton	Cotton	180	—	G	G	F	G	G	P	G	F	F	E
Polyester	Dacron(1)												
	Fortrel(2)												
	Vycron(3)												
	Kodel(4)												
	Enka												
	Polyester(5)	275	—	G	F	G	E	E	G	G	F	G	E
Acrylic	Orlon(1)												
	Acrilan(6)												
	Creslan(7)												
	Dralon T(8)												
	Zefran(9)	275	285	G	G	G	G	E	G	G	F	G	E
Modacrylic	Dynel(10)												
	Verel(4)	160	—	F	F	F	P-F	G	G	G	G	G	G
Nylon (Polyamide)	Nylon 6,6(1,2,6)	225	—	G	G	E	E	E	P	F	G	F	E
	Nylon 6(11,5,12)												
	Nomex(11)	400	450	E	E	E	E	E	P-F	E	G	G	E
Polyimide	P-84(18)	500	580	E	P	G	G	E	P-F	G	F	G	E
Polypropylene	Herculon(13)												
	Reevon(14)												
	Vectra(15)	200	250	G	F	E	E	G	E	E	E	G	G
Teflon (Flurocarbon)	Teflon TFE(1)	500	550	E	E	P-F	G	G	E	E	E	E	E
	Teflon FEP(1)	450	—	E	E	P-F	G	G	E	E	E	E	E
Expanded PTFE	Rastex(18)	500	550	E	E	P-F	G	G	E	E	E	E	E
Vinyon	Vinyon(16)												
	Clevylt(17)	350	—	F	F	F	G	G	E	E	G	G	P
Glass	Glass	500	600	E	E	P	P	F	E	E	F	E	E
Fiberglass	Fiberglass(19)	550	550	E	E	P	P	G	G	G	G	E	G

*E = excellent; G = good; F = fair; P = poor

**Registered Trademarks

(1) Du Pont; (2) Celanese; (3) Beaunit; (4) Eastman; (5) American Enka; (6) Chemstrand; (7) American Cyanamid; (8) Farbenfabriken Bayer AG; (9) Dow Chemical; (10) Union Carbide; (11) Allied Chemical; (12) Firestone; (13) Hercules; (14) Alamo Polymer; (15) National Plastic; (16) FMC; (17) Societe Rhovyl; (18) Lenzing; (19) Huyglas

ment design. Since an individual section is out of service only a few minutes for reconditioning and remaining sections handle the total gas flow during that time, it is possible to clean the fabric more frequently than with the intermittent type. This permits the multiple-section unit to handle higher dust concentrations. Compartments are reconditioned in fixed sequence with the ability to adjust the time interval between cleaning of individual compartments.

One variation of this design is the low-pressure, reverse-air collector which does not use shaking for fabric reconditioning. Instead, a compartment is isolated for cleaning and the tubes collapsed by means of a low pressure secondary blower, which draws air from the compartment in a direction opposite to the primary airflow. This is a "gentle" method of fabric reconditioning and was developed primarily for the fragile glass cloth used for high temperature operation. The reversal of airflow and tube deflation is accomplished very gently to avoid damage to the glass fibers. The control sequence usually allows the deflation and re-inflation of tubes several times for complete removal of excess dust. Tubes are 6 to 11 inches in diameter and can be as long as 30 feet. For long tubes, stainless steel rings may be sewn on the inside to help break up the dust cake during deflation. A combination of shaking and reverse airflow has also been utilized.

When shaking is used for fabric reconditioning, the filtration velocity usually is in the 1 fpm to 4 fpm range. Reverse air collapse type reconditioning generally necessitates lower filtration velocities since reconditioning is not as complete. They are seldom rated higher than 3 fpm. The air to cloth ratio or filtration velocity is based on *net* cloth area available when a compartment is out of service for reconditioning.

Reverse-jet, continuous-duty, fabric collectors may use envelopes or tubes of non-woven (felted) fabric, pleated cartridges of non-woven mat (paper-like) in cylindrical or panel configuration, or rigid elements such as sintered polyethylene. They differ from the low pressure reverse air type in that they employ a brief burst of high pressure air to recondition the fabric. Woven fabric is not used because it allows excessive dust penetration during reconditioning. The most common designs use compressed air at 80 to 100 psig, while others use an integral pressure blower at a lower pressure but higher secondary flow rate. Those using compressed air are generally called pulse-jet collectors and those using pressure blowers are called fan-pulse collectors.

All designs collect dust on the outside and have airflow from outside to inside the fabric. All recondition the media by introducing the pulse of cleaning air into the opening where cleaned air exits from the tube, envelope, or cartridge. In many cases, a venturi shaped fitting is used at this opening to provide additional cleaning by inducing additional airflow. The venturi also directs or focuses the cleaning pulse for maximum efficiency.

Figure 4-9 shows typical pulse-jet collectors. Under normal operation (airflow from outside to inside) the fabric shape will tend to collapse, therefore, a support cage is required. The injection of a short pulse of high pressure air induces a secondary flow from the clean air compartment in a direction opposite to the normal airflow. Reconditioning is accomplished by the pulse of high pressure air which stops forward airflow, then rapidly pressurizes the media, breaking up the dust cake and freeing accumulated dust from the fabric. The secondary or induced air acts as a damper, preventing flow in the normal direction during reconditioning. The entire process, from injection of the high pressure pulse and initiation of secondary flow until the secondary flow ends, takes place in approximately one second. Solenoid valves which control the pulses of compressed air may be open for a tenth of a second or less. An adequate flow rate of clean and dry compressed air of sufficient pressure must be supplied to ensure effective reconditioning.

Reverse-jet collectors normally clean no more than 10% of the fabric at any one time. Because such a small percentage is cleaned at any one time and because the induced secondary

TABLE 4-2. Summary of Fabric Type Collectors and Their Characteristics

	INTERRUPTABLE OPERATION Light to Moderate Loading	INTERRUPTABLE OPERATION Heavy Loading		CONTINUOUS OPERATION Any Loanding	
Fabric Reconditioning Requirement	Intermittent	Continuous			
Type of Reconditioning	Shaker	Shaker	Reverse Air (Low Pressure)	Reverse Pulse - (High Pressure) Pulse Jet of Fan Pulse	
Collector Configuration	Single Compartment	Multiple Compartments with inlet or outlet dampers for each		Single Compartment	
Fabric Configuration	Tube, Cartridge or Envelope	Tube or Envelope	Tube	Tube or Envelope	Pleated Cartridge
Type of Fabric	Woven	Woven		Non-Woven (Felt)	Non-Woven
Airflow	Highly Variable	Slightly Variable		Virtually Constant	Virtually Constant
Normal Rating (filtration velocity, fpm)	1 to 6 fpm	1 to 3 fpm	1 to 3 fpm	5 to 12 fpm	<1 to 7 fpm

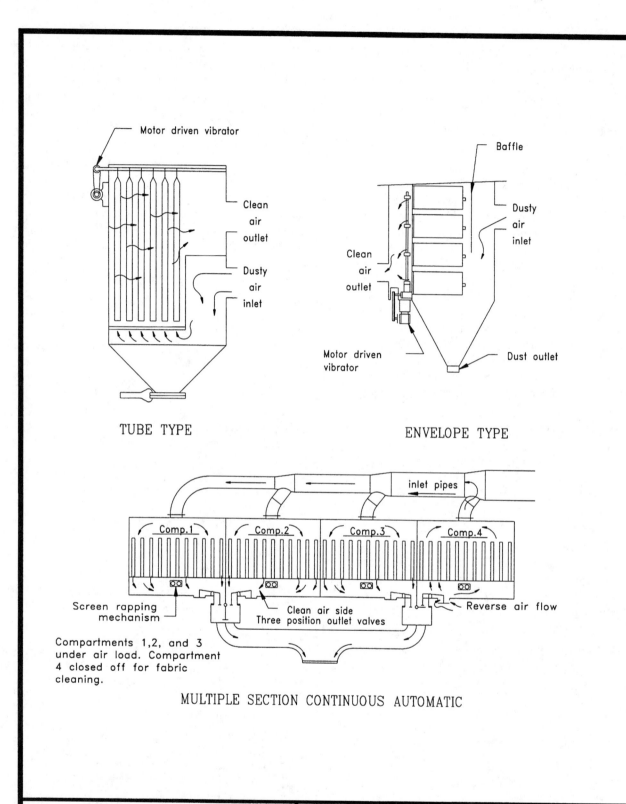

TUBE TYPE

ENVELOPE TYPE

Compartments 1,2, and 3
under air load. Compartment
4 closed off for fabric
cleaning.

MULTIPLE SECTION CONTINUOUS AUTOMATIC

AMERICAN CONFERENCE
OF GOVERNMENTAL
INDUSTRIAL HYGIENISTS

FABRIC COLLECTORS

| DATE | 6-00 | FIGURE | 4-7 |

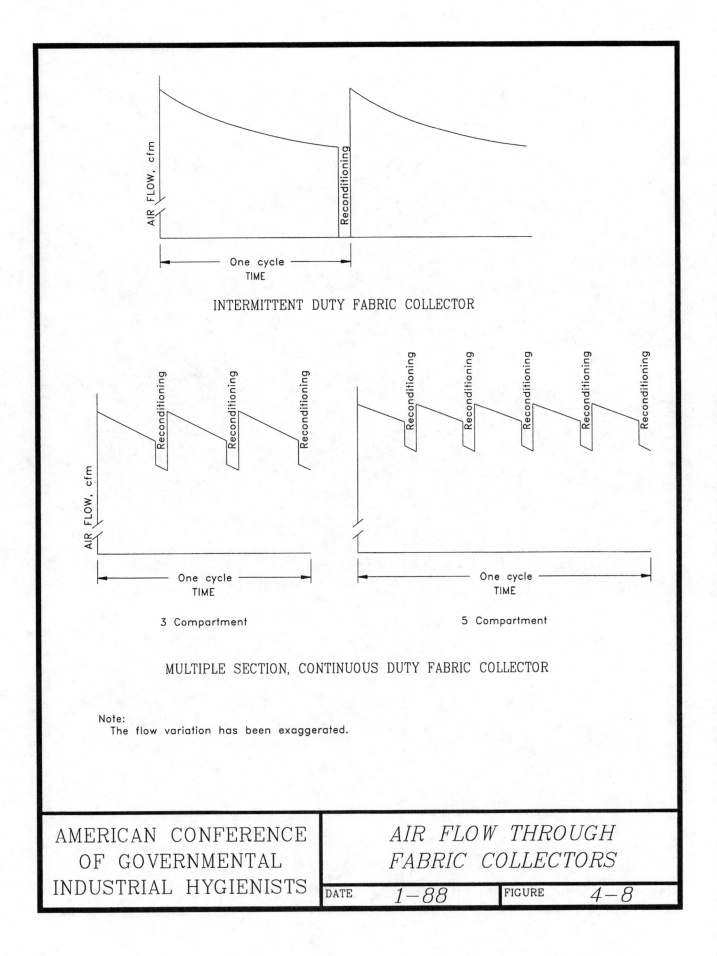

INTERMITTENT DUTY FABRIC COLLECTOR

3 Compartment

5 Compartment

MULTIPLE SECTION, CONTINUOUS DUTY FABRIC COLLECTOR

Note:
The flow variation has been exaggerated.

AMERICAN CONFERENCE OF GOVERNMENTAL INDUSTRIAL HYGIENISTS	AIR FLOW THROUGH FABRIC COLLECTORS	
	DATE 1-88	FIGURE 4-8

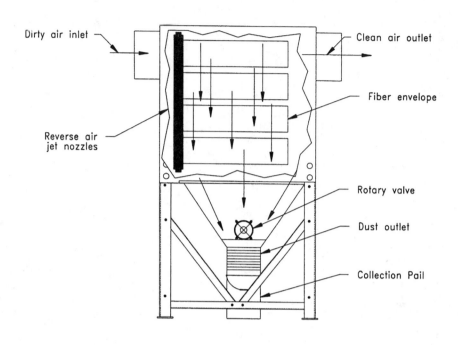

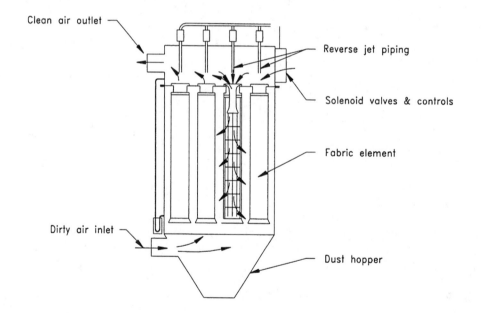

AMERICAN CONFERENCE OF GOVERNMENTAL INDUSTRIAL HYGIENISTS	*FABRIC COLLECTORS PULSE JET TYPE*	
	DATE	*1-88*
	FIGURE	*4-9*

flow blocks normal flow during that time, reconditioning can take place while the collector is in service and without the need for compartmentation and dampers. The cleaning intervals are adjustable and are considerably more frequent than the intervals for shaker or reverse-air collectors. An individual element may be pulsed and reconditioned as often as once a minute to every six minutes.

Due to this very short reconditioning cycle, higher filtration velocities are possible with reverse-jet collectors. However, with all reverse-jet collectors, accumulated dust that is freed from one fabric surface may become reintrained and redeposited on an adjacent surface, or even on the original surface. This phenomenon of redeposition tends to limit filtration velocity to something less than might be anticipated with cleaning intervals of just a few minutes.

Laboratory tests[4.1] have shown that for a given collector design redeposition increases with filtration velocity. Other test work[4.2] indicates clearly that redeposition varies with collector design and especially with flow patterns in the dirty air compartment. EPA sponsored research[4.3] has shown that superior performance results from downward flow of the dirty air stream. This downward airflow reduces redeposition since it aids gravity in moving dust particles toward the hopper.

Filtration velocities of 5 to 12 fpm are normal for reverse-jet collectors. The pleated cartridge type of reverse-jet collector is limited to filtration velocities in the 7 fpm range. The pleat configuration may produce very high approach velocities and greater redeposition.

4.3.3 Wet Collectors: Wet collectors, or scrubbers, are commercially available in many different designs, with pressure drops from 1.5 "wg to as much as 100 "wg. There is a corresponding variation in collector performance. It is generally accepted that, for well-designed equipment, efficiency depends on the energy utilized in air to water contact and is independent of operating principle. Efficiency is a function of total energy input per cfm whether the energy is supplied to the air or to the water. This means that well-designed collectors by different manufacturers will provide similar efficiency if equivalent power is utilized.

Wet collectors have the ability to handle high-temperature and moisture-laden gases. The collection of dust in a wetted form minimizes a secondary dust problem in disposal of collected material. Some dusts represent explosion or fire hazards when dry. Wet collection minimizes the hazard; however, the use of water may introduce corrosive conditions within the collector and freeze protection may be necessary if collectors are located outdoors in cold climates. Space requirements are nominal. Pressure losses and collection efficiency vary widely for different designs.

Wet collectors, especially the high-energy types, are frequently the solution to air pollution problems. It should be realized that disposal of collected material in water without clarification or treatment may create water pollution problems.

Wet collectors have one characteristic not found in other collectors—the inherent ability to humidify. Humidification, the process of adding water vapor to the air stream through evaporation, may be either advantageous or disadvantageous depending on the situation. Where the initial air stream is at an elevated temperature and not saturated, the process of evaporation reduces the temperature and the volumetric flow rate of the gas stream leaving the collector. Assuming the fan is to be selected for operation on the clean air side of the collector, it may be smaller and will definitely require less power than if there had been no cooling through the collector. This is one of the obvious advantages of humidification; however, there are other applications where the addition of moisture to the gas stream is undesirable. For example, the exhaust of humid air to an air-conditioned space normally places an unacceptable load on the air conditioning system. High humidity can also result in corrosion of finished goods. Therefore, humidification effects should be considered before designs are finalized. While all wet collectors humidify, the amount of humidification varies for different designs. Most manufacturers publish the humidifying efficiency for their equipment and will assist in evaluating the results.

Chamber or Spray Tower: Chamber or spray tower collectors consist of a round or rectangular chamber into which water is introduced by spray nozzles. There are many variations of design, but the principal mechanism is impaction of dust particles on the liquid droplets created by the nozzles. These droplets are separated from the air stream by centrifugal force or impingement on water eliminators.

The pressure drop is relatively low (on the order of 0.5 to 1.5 "wg), but water pressures range from 10 to 400 psig. The high pressure devices are the exception rather than the rule. In general, this type of collector utilizes low pressure supply water and operates in the lower efficiency range for wet collectors. Where water is supplied under high pressure, as with fog towers, collection efficiency can reach the upper range of wet collector performance.

For conventional equipment, water requirements are reasonable, with a maximum of about 5 gpm per thousand scfm of gas. Fogging types using high water pressure may require as much as 10 gpm per thousand scfm of gas.

Packed Towers: Packed towers (see Figure 4-10) are essentially contact beds through which gases and liquid pass concurrently, counter-currently, or in cross-flow. They are used primarily for applications involving gas, vapor, and mist removal. These collectors can capture solid particulate matter but they are not used for that purpose because dust plugs the packing and requires unreasonable maintenance.

Water rates of 5 to 10 gpm per thousand scfm are typical for packed towers. Water is distributed over V-notched ceramic or plastic weirs. High temperature deterioration is avoided by using brick linings, allowing gas temperatures as high as 1600 F to be handled direct from furnace flues.

The airflow pressure loss for a four foot bed of packing, such as ceramic saddles, will range from 1.5 to 3.5 "wg. The face velocity (velocity at which the gas enters the bed) will typically be 200 to 300 fpm.

Wet Centrifugal Collectors: Wet centrifugal collectors (see Figure 4-11) comprise a large portion of the commercially available wet collector designs. This type utilizes centrifugal force to accelerate the dust particle and impinge it upon a wetted collector surface. Water rates are usually 2 to 5 gpm per thousand scfm of gas cleaned. Water distribution can be from nozzles, gravity flow or induced water pickup. Pressure drop is in the 2 to 6 "wg range.

As a group, these collectors are more efficient than the chamber type. Some are available with a variable number of impingement sections. A reduction in the number of sections results in lower efficiency, lower cost, less pressure drop, and smaller space. Other designs contain multiple collecting tubes. For a given airflow rate, a decrease in the tube size provides higher efficiency because the centrifugal force is greater.

Wet Dynamic Precipitator: The wet dynamic precipitator (see Figure 4-12) is a combination fan and dust collector. Dust particles in the dirty air stream impinge upon rotating fan blades wetted with spray nozzles. The dust particles impinge into water droplets and are trapped along with the water by a metal cone while the cleaned air makes a turn of 180 degrees and escapes from the front of the specially shaped impeller blades. Dirty water from the water cone goes to the water and sludge outlet and the cleaned air goes to an outlet section containing a water elimination device.

Orifice Type: In this group of wet collector designs (see Figure 4-12) the airflow through the collector is brought in contact with a sheet of water in a restricted passage. Water flow may be induced by the velocity of the air stream or maintained by pumps and weirs. Pressure losses vary from 1 "wg or less for a water wash paint booth to a range of 3 to 6 "wg for most of the industrial designs. Pressure drops as high as 20 "wg are used with some designs intended to collect very small particles.

Venturi: The venturi collector (see Figure 4-11) uses a venturi-shaped constriction to establish throat velocities considerably higher than those used by the orifice type. Gas velocities through venturi throats may range from 12,000 to 24,000 fpm. Water is supplied by piping or jets at or ahead of the throat at rates from 5 to 15 gpm per thousand scfm of gas.

The collection mechanism of the venturi is impaction. As is true for all well-designed wet collectors, collection efficiency increases with higher pressure drops. Specific pressure drops are obtained by designing for selected velocities in the throat. Some venturi collectors are made with adjustable throats allowing operation over a range of pressure drops for a given flow rate or over a range of flow rates with a constant pressure drop. Systems are available with pressure drops as low as 5 "wg for moderate collection efficiency and as high as 100 "wg for collection of extremely fine particles.

The venturi itself is a gas conditioner causing intimate contact between the particulates in the gas and the multiple jet streams of scrubbing water. The resulting mixture of gases, fume-dust agglomerates and dirty water must be channeled through a separation section for the elimination of entrained droplets as shown in Figure 4-11.

4.3.4 Dry Centrifugal Collectors: Dry centrifugal collectors separate entrained particulate from an air stream by the use or combination of centrifugal, inertial, and gravitational force. Collection efficiency is influenced by:

1. Particle size, weight, and shape. Performance is improved as size and weight become larger and as the shape becomes more spherical.

2. Collector size and design. The collection of fine dust with a mechanical device requires equipment designed to best utilize mechanical forces and fit specific application needs.

3. Velocity. Pressure drop through a cyclone collector increases approximately as the square of the inlet velocity. There is, however, an optimum velocity that is a function of collector design, dust characteristics, gas temperature and density.

4. Dust Concentration. Generally, the performance of a mechanical collector increases as the concentration of dust becomes greater.

Gravity Separators: Gravity separators consist of a chamber or housing in which the velocity of the gas stream is made to drop rapidly so that dust particles settle out by gravity. Extreme space requirements and the usual presence of eddy currents nullify this method for removal of anything but extremely coarse particles.

Inertial Separators: Inertial separators depend on the inability of dust to make a sharp turn because its inertia is much higher than that of the carrier gas stream. Blades or louvers in a variety of shapes are used to require abrupt turns of 120 degrees or more. Well-designed inertial separators can separate particles in the 10 to 20 micron range with about 90% efficiency.

Cyclone Collector: The cyclone collector (see Figure 4-13) is commonly used for the removal of coarse dust from an air stream, as a precleaner to more efficient dust collectors and/or as a product separator in air conveying systems. Principal advantages are low cost, low maintenance, and relatively low pressure drops (in the 0.75 to 1.5 "wg range). It is not suitable for the collection of fine particles.

High Efficiency Centrifugals: High efficiency centrifugals (see Figure 4-13) exert higher centrifugal forces on the dust particles in a gas stream. Because centrifugal force is a function of peripheral velocity and angular acceleration, improved dust separation efficiency has been obtained by:

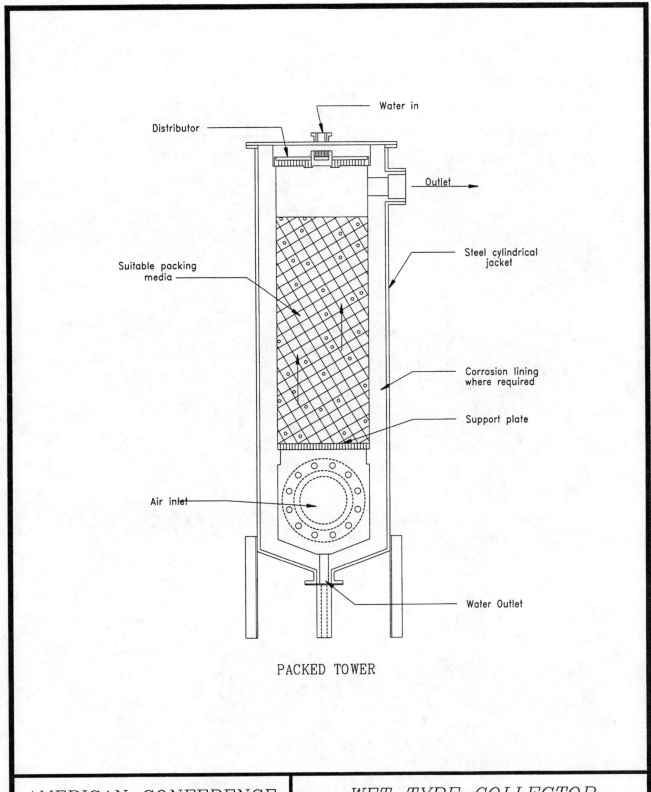

Water in

Distributor

Outlet

Steel cylindrical jacket

Suitable packing media

Corrosion lining where required

Support plate

Air inlet

Water Outlet

PACKED TOWER

AMERICAN CONFERENCE OF GOVERNMENTAL INDUSTRIAL HYGIENISTS	WET TYPE COLLECTOR (FOR GASEOUS CONTAMINANT)
	DATE 1-88 FIGURE 4-10

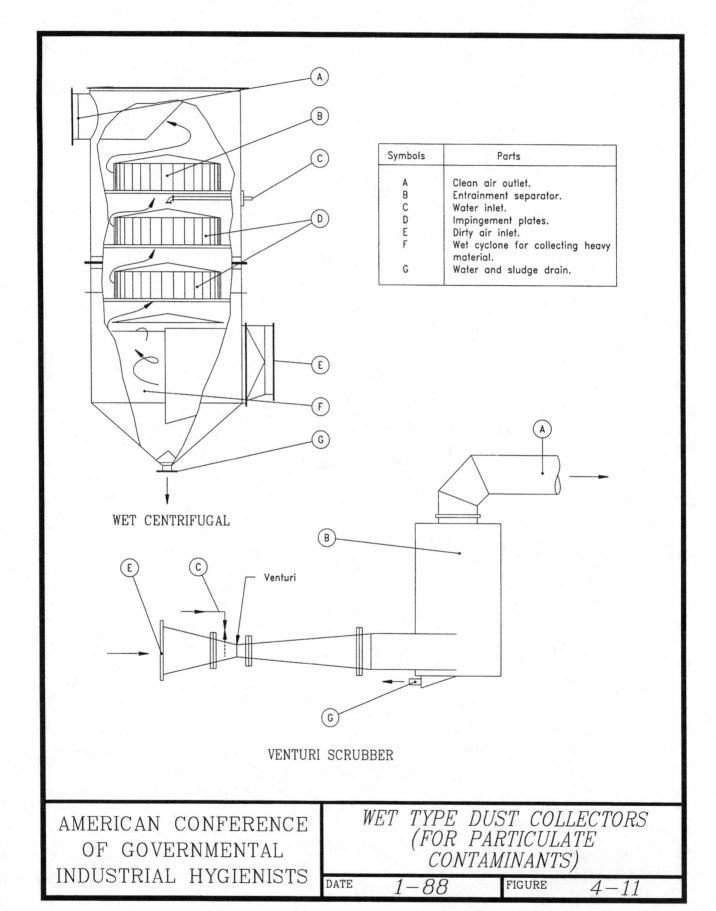

Symbols	Parts
A	Clean air outlet.
B	Entrainment separator.
C	Water inlet.
D	Impingement plates.
E	Dirty air inlet.
F	Wet cyclone for collecting heavy material.
G	Water and sludge drain.

WET CENTRIFUGAL

VENTURI SCRUBBER

AMERICAN CONFERENCE OF GOVERNMENTAL INDUSTRIAL HYGIENISTS	WET TYPE DUST COLLECTORS (FOR PARTICULATE CONTAMINANTS)	
	DATE *1-88*	FIGURE *4-11*

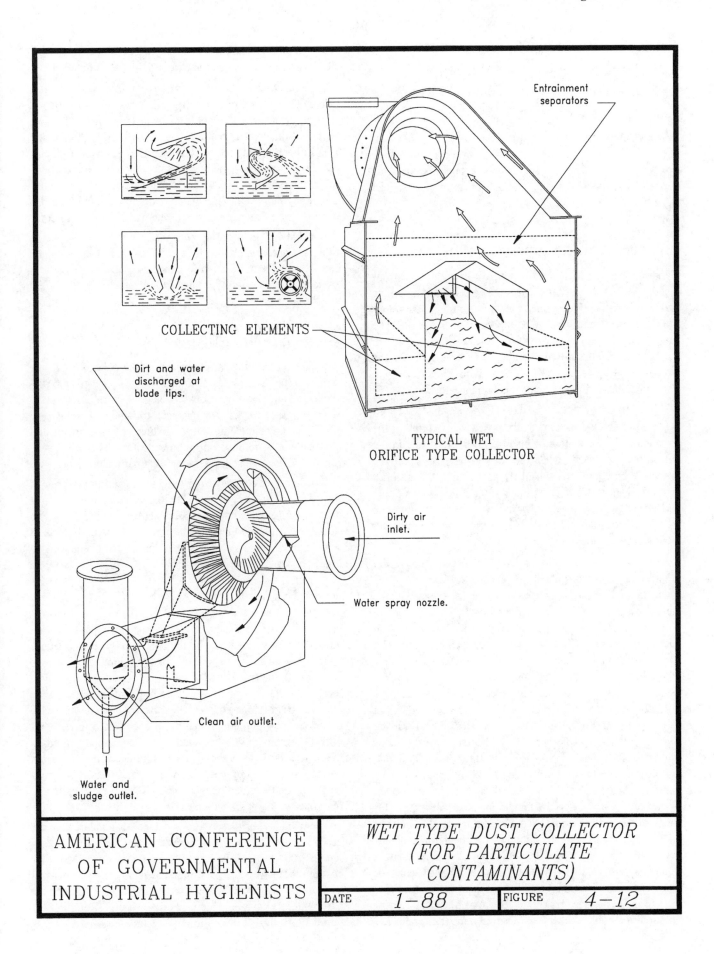

Entrainment separators

COLLECTING ELEMENTS

TYPICAL WET
ORIFICE TYPE COLLECTOR

Dirt and water
discharged at
blade tips.

Dirty air
inlet.

Water spray nozzle.

Clean air outlet.

Water and
sludge outlet.

AMERICAN CONFERENCE OF GOVERNMENTAL INDUSTRIAL HYGIENISTS	*WET TYPE DUST COLLECTOR (FOR PARTICULATE CONTAMINANTS)*	
	DATE *1-88*	FIGURE *4-12*

1. Increasing the inlet velocity

2. Making the cyclone body and cone longer

3. Using a number of small diameter cyclones in parallel

4. Placing units in series.

While high efficiency centrifugals are not as efficient on small particles as electrostatic, fabric, and wet collectors, their effective collection range is appreciably extended beyond that of other mechanical devices. Pressure losses of collectors in this group range from 3 to 8 "wg.

4.4 ADDITIONAL AIDS IN DUST COLLECTOR SELECTION

The collection efficiencies of the five basic groups of air cleaning devices have been plotted against mass mean particle size (Figure 4-14). The graphs were found through laboratory and field testing and were not compiled mathematically. The number of lines for each group indicates the range that can be expected for the different collectors operating under the same principle. Variables, such as type of dust, velocity of air, water rate, etc., will also influence the range for a particular application.

Deviation lines shown in the upper right hand corner of the chart allow the estimation of mass mean material size in the effluent of a collector when the inlet mean size is known. Space does not permit a detailed explanation of how the slopes of these lines were determined, but the following example illustrates how they are used. The deviation lines should not be used for electrostatic precipitators but can be used for the other groups shown at the bottom of the figure.

Example: A suitable collector will be selected for a lime kiln to illustrate the use of the chart. Referring to Figure 4-14, the concentration and mean particle size of the material leaving the kiln can vary between 3 and 10 grains per cubic foot, with 5 to 10 microns the range for mass mean particle size. Assume an inlet concentration of 7.5 grains per cubic foot and a mean inlet size of 9 microns. Projection of this point vertically downwardly to the collection efficiency portion of the chart will indicate that a low resistance cyclone will be less than 50% efficient; a high efficiency centrifugal will be 60 to 80% efficient and a wet collector, fabric arrester and electrostatic precipitator will be 97+% efficient. A precleaner is usually feasible for dust concentrations over 5 grains per cubic foot unless it is undesirable to have the collected dust separated by size. For this example a high efficiency centrifugal will be selected as the precleaner. The average efficiency is 70% for this group, therefore the effluent from this collector will have a concentration of 7.5 (100 - 0.70) = 2.25 grains per cubic foot. Draw a line through the initial point with a slope parallel to the deviation lines marked "industrial dust." Where deviation is not known, the average of this group of lines normally will be sufficiently accurate to predict the mean particle size in the collector effluent. A vertical line from the point of intersection between the 2.25 grains per cubic foot horizontal and the deviation line to the base of the chart will indicate a mean effluent particle size of 6.0 microns.

A second high efficiency centrifugal in series would be less than 50% efficient on this effluent. A wet collector, fabric arrester, or electrostatic would have an efficiency of 94% or better. Assume that a good wet collector will be 98% efficient. The effluent would then be 2.25 (1.00 - 0.98) = 0.045 grains per cubic foot. Using the previous deviation line and its horizontal intersection of 0.045 grains per cubic foot yields a vertical line intersecting the mean particle size chart at 1.6 microns, the mean particle size of the wet collector effluent.

In Table 4-3, an effort has been made to report types of dust collectors used for a wide range of industrial processes. While many of the listings are purely arbitrary, they may serve as a guide in selecting the type of dust collector most frequently used.

4.5 CONTROL OF MIST, GAS AND VAPOR CONTAMINANTS

Previous discussion has centered on the collection of dust and fume or particulate existing in the solid state. Only the packed tower was singled out as being used primarily to collect mist, gas, or vapor. The character of a mist aerosol is very similar, aerodynamically, to that of a dust or fume aerosol, and the mist can be removed from an air stream by applying the principles that are used to remove solid particulate.

Standard wet collectors are used to collect many types of mists. Specially designed electrostatic precipitators are frequently employed to collect sulfuric acid or oil mist. Even fabric and centrifugal collectors, although not the types previously mentioned, are widely used to collect oil mist generated by high speed machining.

4.6 GASEOUS CONTAMINANT COLLECTORS

Industrial processes produce tremendous quantities of gaseous contaminants. In order to better understand the specific problems associated with the control of gaseous contaminants it would serve one well to look at the properties of gases and vapors. The terms "gas" and "vapor" are commonly incorrectly used interchangeably. Matter that takes both the shape and volume of its container is said to be in a gaseous state. Gas molecules contain enough energy to continue to move apart until they bounce off the sides of the container(s) holding them. The term gas describes those substances that exist in a gaseous state at room temperature. For example, air is a mixture of gases including oxygen and nitrogen. One characteristic property of a gas is its great compressibility.

The word "vapor" describes a substance that, although in the gaseous state, is generally a liquid or solid at room temperature. Steam, the gaseous form of water, is a vapor. Moist air contains water vapor. Partial pressure relationships described by Dalton's Law explain how water vapor and dry air coexist at room temperature and atmospheric pressure. (Refer to Section 5.13 for further discussion of Psychrometric Principles.)

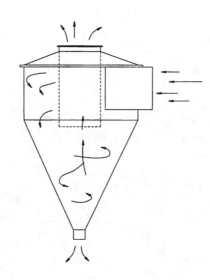

LOW PRESSURE CYCLONE

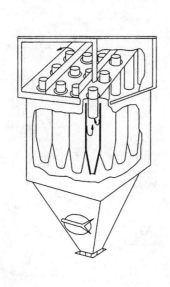
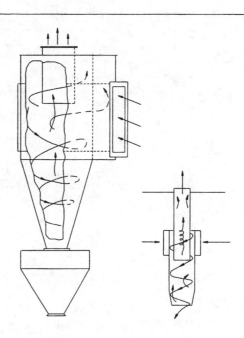

HIGH EFFICIENCY CENTRIFUGALS

AMERICAN CONFERENCE OF GOVERNMENTAL INDUSTRIAL HYGIENISTS	*DRY TYPE CENTRIFUGAL COLLECTORS*	
	DATE *3-97*	FIGURE *4-13*

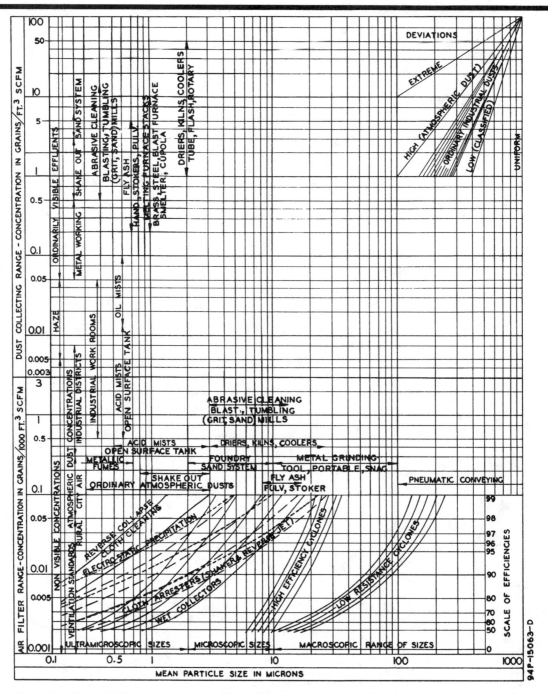

RANGE OF PARTICLE SIZES, CONCENTRATION, & COLLECTOR PERFORMANCE
COMPILED BY S. SYLVAN APRIL 1952 : COPYRIGHT 1952 AMERICAN AIR FILTER CO. INC.
ACKNOWLEDGEMENTS OF PARTIAL SOURCES OF DATA REPORTED :
  1 FRANK W.G. – AMERICAN AIR FILTER – SIZE AND CHARACTERISTICS OF AIR BORNE SOLIDS – 1931
  2 FIRST AND DRINKER – ARCHIVES OF INDUSTRIAL HYGIENE AND OCCUPATIONAL MEDICINE – APRIL 1952
  3 TAFT INSTITUTE AND AAF LABORATORY TEST DATA – 1961 – '63
  4 REVERSE COLLAPSE CLOTH CLEANING ADDED 1964

AMERICAN CONFERENCE OF GOVERNMENTAL INDUSTRIAL HYGIENISTS	*RANGE OF PARTICLE SIZE*	
	DATE *1–88*	FIGURE *4–14*

Numerous techniques have been developed to control gaseous contaminants. The more commonly used techniques include Absorption, Adsorption, Incineration/Oxidation, and more recently, Biofiltration. Lesser known control methods include Corona Reactors, Direct Electric Arcing, Plasma Treatment, and Condensation.

4.6.1 Absorption: Absorption is a mass transfer process where transfer occurs through a phase boundary and the absorbed molecule is held within the absorbing medium. Absorbers remove soluble or chemically reactive gases from the gas stream through intimate contact with a suitable liquid so that one or more of the gas stream components will dissolve in the liquid. While all designs utilize intimate contact between the gaseous contaminant and the absorbent, they vary widely in configuration and performance. Removal may be by absorption if the gas solubility and vapor pressure promote absorption or chemical reaction. There are both dry and wet absorbers. In wet absorbers, water is the most frequently used absorbent, but additives are frequently required and occasionally other chemical solutions must be used. Typical wet absorber designs include packed scrubbers, staged devices, and high energy contactors (venturi scrubbers).

Variants of the packed scrubber are available in four configurations. They are the Horizontal Cocurrent Scrubber, the Vertical Cocurrent Scrubber, the Crossflow Scrubber, and the Countercurrent Scrubber. The horizontal cocurrent scrubber depends on the gas velocity to carry the liquid into the packed bed and operates as a wetted entrainment separator with limited gas and liquid contact time. A vertical cocurrent scrubber may be operated at pressure drops of 1 to 3 inches of water per foot of packing depth. Contact time is a function of packing depth in this configuration.[4.4]

Crossflow Scrubbers use a horizontal gas stream movement with the liquid scrubbing medium flowing down through the gas stream. Absorption efficiency for this design is generally somewhere between that of cocurrent and countercurrent flow scrubbers.

Countercurrent scrubbers have the gas flowing up through a downward liquid flow. The efficiency of countercurrent scrubbers is maximized because the exit gas is in contact with the fresh scrubbing liquor where the highest driving forces exist to aid the mass transfer process. Packed Towers are countercurrent scrubbers. The packed tower unit was previously discussed in Section 4.3.3. It consists of a cylindrical shell, a packed section held on a support plate, a liquid distributor, possibly a liquid redistributor, access manholes, gas inlet and outlet, and possibly a sump with recirculation pump and overflow. There are a wide variety of packing materials available. Packings providing more surface area per unit volume are generally regarded as superior. There are tradeoffs to consider when selecting a packing material which will impact the overall equipment height and pressure drop requirements to meet specific contaminant collection removal characteristics.[4.5]

Staged or "stagewise" equipment utilizes a group of horizontal metal plates arranged in a vertical series and generally placed in a cylindrical housing. Each horizontal plate is a stage. The plates can be sieves, bubble type or ballasts. Gas flow is countercurrent to the liquid flow in all cases. In each of these designs the liquid is kept on the tray surface by a dam at the entrance to a downcomer or sealed conduit allowing overflow liquid to pass to the tray below.[4.6]

High Energy Contactors (Venturi Scrubbers, Figure 4-11) were also described in Section 4.3.3. Although used predominately as particulate control devices they can simultaneously function as absorbers. Venturi scrubbers are cocurrent devices and their absorption characteristics are maximized when operating at low velocities with high liquid to gas ratios.

Dry Absorption systems include Dry Scrubbers, Spray Dryers and Fluid Bed Reactors. Dry Scrubbers involve injection of a dry solvent directly into a process gas stream. Spray Dryers inject a wet solvent into a hot gas stream where the liquid evaporates leaving a dry solvent in contact with the gas. Fluid Bed Reactors employ a bed of granulated solvent fluidized within a vessel and the process gas flows through the fluidized bed. All dry absorption systems must include an appropriate particulate removal device.

4.6.2 Adsorption: Adsorption is also a mass transfer process which removes contaminants by adhesion of molecules of one phase to the surface or interfaces of a solid second phase. Relatively weak adsorption, where the forces involved are intermolecular, is known as van der Waals Adsorption. Strong adsorption where the forces involved are valence forces, is known as activated adsorption or chemisorption. No chemical reaction is involved as adsorption is a physical process which is normally thought of as reversible. Activated carbon, activated alumina, silica gel, Fuller's earth, and molecular sieves are popular adsorbents.

4.6.3 Incineration/Oxidation: These two terms, Incineration and Oxidation, are used interchangeably to describe the process of combustion. Combustion is a chemical process in which oxygen reacts with various elements or chemical compounds resulting in the release of light and heat. The combustion process readily converts volatile organic compounds (VOCs), organic aerosols, and most odorous materials to carbon dioxide and water vapor. It is a very effective means of eliminating VOCs. Typical applications for incineration devices include odor control, reduction in plume opacity, reduction in reactive hydrocarbon emissions, and reduction of explosion hazards. The equipment used for control of gaseous contaminants by combustion may be divided into three categories: Thermal Oxidizers, Direct Combustors, or Catalytic Oxidizers.

Thermal Oxidizers, or afterburners, may be used where the contaminant is combustible. The contaminated air stream is introduced to an open flame or heating device followed by a residence chamber where combustibles are oxidized producing carbon dioxide and water vapor. Most combustible contaminants can be oxidized at temperatures between 1,000 F and 1,500 F. The residence chamber must provide sufficient dwell time and turbulence to allow complete oxidation. Thermal oxidizers are often equipped with heat exchangers where combustion gas is used to preheat the incoming contaminated gas. If gasoline is the contaminant, heat exchanger efficiencies are limited to 25 to 35% and preheat temperatures are maintained below 277 C (530 F) to minimize the possibility of ignition occurring in the heat exchanger. Flame arrestors are always installed between the vapor source and the thermal oxidizer. Burner capacities in the combustion chamber range from 0.5 to 2.0 GJ (0.5 to 2 M Btu.) per hour. Operating temperatures range from 760 to 871 C (1,400 to 1,600 F), and gas residence times are typically 1 second or less. This condition causes the molecular structure to break down into simple carbon dioxide and water vapor.

Regenerative Thermal Oxidation (RTO) units are distinguished from other thermal incinerators by their ability to recover heat at high efficiency. RTOs employ three, five, seven, or more chambers that store and recycle heat energy. RTO technology uses high temperature to convert VOCs into carbon dioxide and water vapor.

In RTO, a contaminated process air enters a combustion chamber after being preheated through a ceramic bed, where the air is raised to a required temperature and held there for a specified period of time. The heat recovery chambers are outfitted with stoneware or ceramic beds that absorb most of the heat energy from the combustion chamber. The flow is then reversed, allowing the next contaminated batch of air to enter the combustion chamber through the stoneware bed that was heated from the last batch. The level of heat recovery varies, depending on the specific design of the system.

Using a Flameless Thermal Oxidation process, VOC-laden exhaust gas typically enters a single or multiple module thermal oxidation unit (or an RTO). The VOC gas stream is alternatively directed using valves to the top or bottom air plenum and is transported through a porous gravel heat exchange bed. In the gravel media, it is flamelessly oxidized and converted to carbon dioxide and water vapor. Reversal of the gas stream keeps the high temperature band centered in the gravel media. For start-up, natural gas/propane is injected into the heat transfer media to bring the temperature up to 982 C (1,800 F). For low concentration streams of VOC exhaust, supplemental fuel is needed to maintain the proper oxidation temperature. For VOC streams above a concentration of 3.8%, the reaction is self-sustaining. The process attains greater than 98% VOC destruction and 95% heat recovery.

Direct Combustors (flares) differ from thermal oxidizers by introducing the contaminated gases and auxiliary air directly into the burner as fuel. Auxiliary fuel, usually natural gas or oil, is generally required for ignition and may or may not be required to sustain burning and all of the waste gases react at the burner.

Catalytic oxidation is a relatively new alternative for the treatment of VOCs in air streams resulting from remedial operations. It is very similar to thermal oxidation, except that with a catalyst present, the same reaction occurs at a lower temperature. Catalysts are substances which alter the rate of a chemical reaction without themselves being consumed in the reaction. VOCs are thermally destroyed at temperatures typically ranging from 315 to 538 C (600 to 1,000 F) by using a solid catalyst. First, the contaminated air is directly preheated (electrically or, more frequently, using natural gas or propane) to reach a temperature necessary to initiate the catalytic oxidation of the VOCs. Then the preheated VOC-laden air is passed through a bed of solid catalysts where the VOCs are rapidly oxidized.

In most cases, the process can be enhanced to reduce auxiliary fuel costs by using an air-to-air heat exchanger to transfer heat from the exhaust gases to the incoming contaminated air. Typically, about 50% of the heat of the exhaust gases are recovered. Depending on VOC concentrations, the recovered heat may be sufficient to sustain oxidation without additional fuel. Catalyst systems used to oxidize VOCs typically use metal oxides such as nickel oxide, copper oxide, manganese dioxide, or chromium oxide. Noble Metals such as platinum and palladium may also be used. However, in a majority of remedial applications, non-precious metals (e.g., nickel, copper, or chromium) are used. Most commercially available catalysts are proprietary.

To use either thermal or catalytic oxidation, the combustible contaminant concentration must be below the lower explosive limit. Equipment specifically designed for control of gaseous or vapor contaminants should be applied with caution when the air stream also contains solid particles. Solid particulate can plug absorbers, adsorbers, and catalysts and, if noncombustible, will not be converted in thermal oxidizers and direct combustors.

4.6.4 Biofiltration: [4.7,4.8] Biofiltration process involves drawing air through a pretreatment unit to adjust its temperature and moisture content and then through a filter in which the contaminants are transferred to microorganisms selected for their efficiency in treating those specific contaminants.

It is an emerging air pollution control technology suited for cleaning VOCs and other gases such as ammonia and hydrogen sulfide. These gases are considered responsible for odors associated with livestock and poultry production. Successful and common applications of biofilters in agricultural facilities, rendering plants, wastewater treatment plants, chemical, and food processing plants have been reported in Europe and Japan. In the United States, common applications are reported in water treatment plants. Some chemical manufacturing plants are also reported to be using biofilters. Few, if any, are currently being used in livestock and poultry facilities.

The most commonly used of the lesser known gaseous contaminant control methods referred to above is condensation. It has been widely used for recovery of and/or removal of gaseous specific constituents in a bulk gas flow. Specific examples would include the selective distillation of various hydrocarbons in refining processes and the drying of air. In order to remove a selected contaminant from a gas stream by this method the dew point of the pollutant must be significantly higher than that of the non-contaminant gases. This technique has been successfully applied as a control method for removal of some VOCs.

Application of the Corona Reactor, Direct Electric Arcing, and Plasma Treatment techniques are largely experimental at this date. All of these techniques target VOCs and some inorganic gases such as hydrogen sulfide, mercaptans, trichloroethylene, and carbon tetrachloride.

Air streams containing both solid particles and gaseous contaminants may require appropriate control devices in series.

4.7 UNIT COLLECTORS

Unit collector is a term usually applied to small fabric collectors having capacities in the 200-2000 cfm range. They have integral air movers, feature small space requirements and simplicity of installation. In most applications cleaned air is recirculated, although discharge ducts may be used if the added resistance is within the capability of the air mover. One of the primary advantages of unit collectors is a reduction in the amount of duct required, as opposed to central systems, and the addition of discharge ducts to unit collectors negates that advantage.

When cleaned air is to be recirculated, a number of precautions are required (see Chapter 7).

Unit collectors are used extensively to fill the need for dust collection from isolated, portable, intermittently used, or frequently relocated dust producing operations. Typically, a single collector serves a single dust source with the energy saving advantage that the collector must operate only when that particular dust producing machine is in operation.

Figure 4-15 shows a typical unit collector. Usually they are the intermittent duty, shaker-type in envelope configuration. Woven fabric is nearly always used. Automatic fabric cleaning is preferred. Manual methods without careful scheduling and supervision are unreliable.

4.8 DUST COLLECTING EQUIPMENT COST

The variations in equipment cost, especially on an installed basis, are difficult to estimate. Comparisons can be misleading if these factors are not carefully evaluated.

4.8.1 Price Versus Capacity: All dust collector prices per cfm of gas will vary with the gas flow rate. The smaller the flow rate, the higher the cost per cfm. The break point, where price per cfm cleaned tends to level off, will vary with the design. See the typical curves shown on Figure 4-16.

4.8.2 Accessories Included: Careful analysis of components of equipment included is very important. Some collector designs include exhaust fan, motor, drive, and starter. In other designs, these items and their supporting structure must be obtained by the purchaser from other sources. Likewise, while dust storage hoppers are integral parts of some dust collector designs, they are not provided in other types. Duct connections between elements may be included or omitted. Recirculating water pumps and/or settling tanks may be required but not included in the equipment price.

4.8.3 Installation Cost: The cost of installation can equal or exceed the cost of the collector. Actual cost will depend on the method of shipment (completely assembled, sub-assembled, or completely knocked down), the location (which may require expensive rigging), and the need for expensive supporting steel and access platforms. Factory installed media will reduce installation cost. The cost can also be measurably influenced by the need for water and drain connections, special or extensive electrical work, and expensive material handling equipment for collection material disposal. Items in the latter group will often also be variable, decreasing in cost per cfm as the flow rate of gas to be cleaned increases.

4.8.4 Special Construction: Prices shown in any tabulation must necessarily assume standard or basic construction. The increase in cost for corrosion resisting material, special high temperature fabrics, insulation, and/or weather protection for outdoor installations can introduce a multiplier of one to four times the standard cost.

A general idea of relative dust collector cost is provided in Figure 4-16. The additional notes and explanations included in these data should be carefully examined before they are used for estimating the cost of specific installations. For more accurate data, the equipment manufacturer or installer should be asked to provide estimates or a past history record for similar control problems utilized. Table 4-4 lists other characteristics that must be evaluated along with equipment cost.

Price estimates included in Figure 4-16 are for equipment of standard construction in normal arrangement. Estimates for exhausters and dust storage hoppers have been included, as indicated in Notes 1 and 2, where they are normally furnished by others.

4.9 SELECTION OF AIR FILTRATION EQUIPMENT

Air filtration equipment is available in a wide variety of designs and capability. Performance ranges from a simple throwaway filter for the home furnace to the "clean room" in the electronics industry, where the air must be a thousand times as clean as in a hospital surgical suite. Selection is based on efficiency, dust holding capacity, and pressure drop. There are five basic methods of air filtration.

4.9.1 Straining: Straining occurs when a particle is larger than the opening between fibers and cannot pass through. It is a very ineffective method of filtration because the vast major-

TABLE 4-3. Dust Collector Selection Guide

Operation	Concentration Note 1	Particle Sizes Note 2	Dry Centrifugal Collector	Wet Collector	Fabric Collector	Low-Volt Electrostatic	Hi-Volt Electrostatic	See Remark No.
CERAMICS								
a. Raw product handling	light	fine	S	O	O	N	N	1
b. Fettling	light	fine-medium	S	S	O	N	N	2
c. Refractory sizing	heavy	coarse	N	S	O	N	N	3
d. Glaze & vitr. enamel spray	moderate	medium	N	O	O	N	N	
CHEMICALS								49
a. Material handling	light-moderate	fine-medium	S	O	O	N	N	4
b. Crushing, grinding	moderate-heavy	fine-coarse	O	S	O	N	N	5
c. Pneumatic conveying	very heavy	fine-coarse	O	S	O	N	N	6
d. Roasters, kilns, coolers	heavy	mid-coarse	O	O	O	N	N	7
COAL, MINING AND POWER PLANT								49
a. Material handling	moderate	medium	O	S	O	N	N	8
b. Bunker ventilation	light	fine	S	S	O	N	N	9
c. Dedusting, air cleaning	heavy	medium-coarse	S	O	O	N	N	10
d. Drying	moderate	fine	N	O	O	N	N	11
FLY ASH								
a. Coal burning—chain grate	light	fine	S	S	O	N	O	12
b. Coal burning—stoker fired	moderate	fine-coarse	S	S	O	N	O	
c. Coal burning—pulverized fuel	moderate	fine	S	S	O	N	O	13
d. Wood burning	varies	coarse	S	S	O	N	S	14
FOUNDRY								
a. Shakeout	light-moderate	fine	N	O	O	N	N	15
b. Sand handling	moderate	fine-medium	N	O	O	N	N	16
c. Tumbling mills	heavy	medium-coarse	N	S	O	N	N	17
d. Abrasive cleaning	moderate-heavy	fine-medium	N	S	O	N	N	18
GRAIN ELEVATOR, FLOUR AND FEED MILLS								49
a. Grain handling	light	medium	O	S	O	N	N	19
b. Grain dryers	light	coarse	S	S	O	N	N	20
c. Flour dust	moderate	medium	O	S	O	N	N	21
d. Feed mill	moderate	medium	O	S	O	N	N	22
METAL MELTIN49								50
a. Steel blast furnace	heavy	varied	N	O	S	N	S	23
b. Steel open hearth	moderate	fine-coarse	N	O	S	N	S	24
c. Steel electric furnace	light	fine	N	S	O	N	S	25
d. Ferrous cupola	moderate	varied	N	O	O	N		26
e. Non-ferrous reverberatory	varied	fine	N	S	O	N	N	27
f. Non-ferrous crucible	light	fine	N	S	O	N	N	28
METAL MINING AND ROCK PRODUCTS								
a. Material handling	moderate	fine-medium	N	O	O	N	N	29
b. Dryers, kilns	moderate	medium-coarse	O	O	O	N	O	30
c. Rock dryer	moderate	fine-medium	N	S	S	N	S	31
d. Cement kiln	heavy	fine-medium	N	N	O	N	S	32
e. Cement grinding	moderate	fine	N	N	O	N	N	33
f. Cement clinker cooler	moderate	coarse	O	N	O	N	N	34

| | | Collector Types Used in Industry | | | | | |
Operation	Concentration Note 1	Particle Sizes Note 2	Dry Centrifugal Collector	Wet Collector	Fabric Collector	Low-Volt Electrostatic	Hi-Volt Electrostatic	See Remark No.
METAL WORKING								49
a. Production grinding, scratch brushing, abrasive cut off	light	coarse	O	O	O	N	N	35
b. Portable and swing frame	light	medium	S	O	O	N	N	
c. Buffing	light	varied	S	O	O	N	N	36
d. Tool room	light	fine	S	S	S	N	N	37
e. Cast iron machining	moderate	varied	O	O	O	S	N	38
PHARMACEUTICAL AND FOOD PRODUCTS								
a. Mixers, grinders, weighing, blending, bagging, packaging	light	medium	O	O	O	N	N	39
b. Coating pans	varied	fine-medium	N	O	O	N	N	40
PLASTICS								49
a. Raw material processing	(See comments under Chemicals)		O	S	O	N	N	41
b. Plastic finishing	light-moderate	varied	S	S	O	N	N	42
c. Extrusion	light	fine	N	S	N	O	N	
RUBBER PRODUCTS								49
a. Mixers	moderate	fine	S	O	S	N	N	43
b. Batchout rolls	light	fine	S	O	S	S	N	
c. Talc dusting and dedusting	moderate	medium	S	S	O	N	N	44
d. Grinding	moderate	coarse	O	O	O	N	N	45
WOODWORKING								49
a. Woodworking machines	moderate	varied	O	S	O	N	N	46
b. Sanding	moderate	fine	S	S	O	N	N	47
c. Waste conveying, hogs	heavy	varied	O	S	S	N	N	48

Note 1: Light: less than 2 gr/ft^3; Moderage: 2 to 5 gr/ft^3; Heavy: 5 gr/ft^3 and up.
Note 2: Fine: 50% less than 5 microns; Medium: 50% 5 to 15 microns; Coarse: 50% 15 microns and larger.
Note 3: O = often; S = seldom; N = never.

Remarks Referred to in Table 4-3

1. Dust released from bin filling, conveying, weighing, mixing, pressing forming. Refractory products, dry pan and screen operations more severe.

2. Operations found in vitreous enameling, wall and floor tile, pottery.

3. Grinding wheel or abrasive cut-off operation. Dust abrasive.

4. Operations include conveying, elevating, mixing, screening, weighing, packaging. Category covers so many different materials that recommendation will vary widely.

5. Cyclone and high efficiency centrifugals often act as primary collectors followed by fabric or wet type.

6. Cyclones used as product collector followed by fabric arrester for high over-all collection efficiency.

7. Dust concentration determines need for dry centrifugal; plant location, product value determines need for final collectors. High temperatures are usual and corrosive gases not unusual.

8. Conveying, screening, crushing, unloading.

9. Remove from other dust producing points. Separate collector usually.

10. Heavy loading suggests final high efficiency collector for all except very remote locations.

11. Difficult problem but collectors will be used more frequently with air pollution emphasis.

12. Public nuisance from boiler blow-down indicates collectors are needed.

13. Large installations in residential areas require electrostatic in addition to dry centrifugal.

14. Cyclones used as spark arresters in front of fabric collectors.

15. Hot gases and steam usually involved.

16. Steam from hot sand, adhesive clay bond involved.

17. Concentration very heavy at start of cycle.

18. Heaviest load from airless blasting due to higher cleaning speed. Abrasive shattering greater with sand than with grit or shot. Amounts removed greater with sand castings, less with forging scale removal, least when welding scale is removed.

19. Operations such as car unloading, conveying, weighing, storing.

20. Collection equipment expensive but public nuisance complaints becoming more frequent.

Remarks Referred to in Table 4-3 (continued)

21. Operations include conveyors, cleaning rolls, sifters, purifiers, bins and packaging.

22. Operations include conveyors, bins, hammer mills, mixers, feeders and baggers.

23. Primary dry trap and wet scrubbing usual. Electrostatic is added where maximum cleaning required.

24. Use of this technique declining.

25. Air pollution standards will probably require increased usage of fabric arresters.

26. CAUTION! Recent design improvements such as coke-less, plasma-fired type, have altered emission characteristics.

27. Zinc oxide loading heavy during zinc additions. Stack temperatures high.

28. Zinc oxide plume can be troublesome in certain plant locations.

29. Crushing, screening, conveying involved. Wet ores often introduce water vapor in exhaust air.

30. Dry centrifugals used as primary collectors, followed by final cleaner.

31. Industry is aggressively seeking commercial uses for fines.

32. Collectors usually permit salvage of material and also reduce nuisance from settled dust in plant area.

33. Salvage value of collected material high. Same equipment used on raw grinding before calcining.

34. Coarse abrasive particles readily removed in primary collector types.

35. Roof discoloration, deposition on autos can occur with cyclones and less frequently with high efficiency dry centrifugal. Heavy duty air filters sometimes used as final cleaners.

36. Linty particles and sticky buffing compounds can cause pluggage and fire hazard in dry collectors.

37. Unit collectors extensively used, especially for isolated machine tools.

38. Dust ranges from chips to fine floats including graphitic carbon. Low voltage ESP applicable only when a coolant is used.

39. Materials vary widely. Collector selection depends on salvage value, toxicity, sanitation yardsticks.

40. Controlled temperature and humidity of supply air to coating pans makes recirculation desirable.

41. Plastic manufacture allied to chemical industry and varies with operations involved.

42. Operations and collector selection similar to woodworking. See Item 13.

43. Concentration is heavy during feed operation. Carbon black and other fine additions make collection and dust-free disposal difficult.

44. Salvage of collected material often dictates type of high efficiency collector.

45. Fire hazard from some operations must be considered.

46. Bulking material. Collected material storage and bridging from splinters and chips can be a problem.

47. Dry centrifugals not effective on heavy concentration of fine particles from production sanding.

48. Dry centrifugal collectors required. Wet or fabric collectors may be used for final collectors.

49. See NFPA publications for fire hazards, e.g., zirconium, magnesium, aluminum, woodworking, plastics, etc.

---

ity of particles are far smaller than the spaces between fibers. Straining will remove lint, hair, and other large particles.

4.9.2 Impingement: When air flows through a filter, it changes direction as it passes around each fiber. Larger dust particles, however, cannot follow the abrupt changes in direction because of their inertia. As a result, they do not follow the air stream and collide with a fiber. Filters using this method are often coated with an adhesive to help fibers retain the dust particles that impinge on them.

4.9.3 Interception: Interception is a special case of impingement where a particle is small enough to move with the air stream but, because its size is very small in relation to the fiber, makes contact with a fiber while following the tortuous airflow path of the filter. The contact is not dependent on inertia and the particle is retained on the fiber because of the inherent adhesive forces that exist between the particle and fiber. These forces, called van der Waals (J. D. van der Waals, 1837-1923) forces, enable a fiber to trap a particle without the use of inertia.

4.9.4 Diffusion: Diffusion takes place on particles so small that their direction and velocity are influenced by molecular collisions. These particles do not follow the air stream, but behave more like gases than particulate. They

move across the direction of airflow in a random fashion. When a particle does strike a fiber, it is retained by the van der Waals forces existing between the particle and the fiber. Diffusion is the primary mechanism used by most extremely efficient filters.

4.9.5 Electrostatic: A charged dust particle will be attracted to a surface of opposite electrical polarity. Most dust particles are not electrically neutral, therefore, electrostatic attraction between dust particle and filter fiber aids the collection efficiency of all barrier type air filters. Electrostatic filters establish an ionization field to charge dust particles so that they can be collected on a surface that is grounded or of opposite polarity. This concept was previously discussed in Section 4.3.1.

Table 4-5 shows performance versus filter fiber size for several filters. Note that efficiency increases as fiber diameter decreases because more small fibers are used per unit volume. Note also that low velocities are used for high efficiency filtration by diffusion.

The wide range in performance of air filters makes it necessary to use more than one method of efficiency testing. The industry-accepted methods in the United States are ASHRAE Arrestance, ASHRAE Efficiency, and DOP. For ASHRAE Arrestance, a measured quantity of 72% standardized air

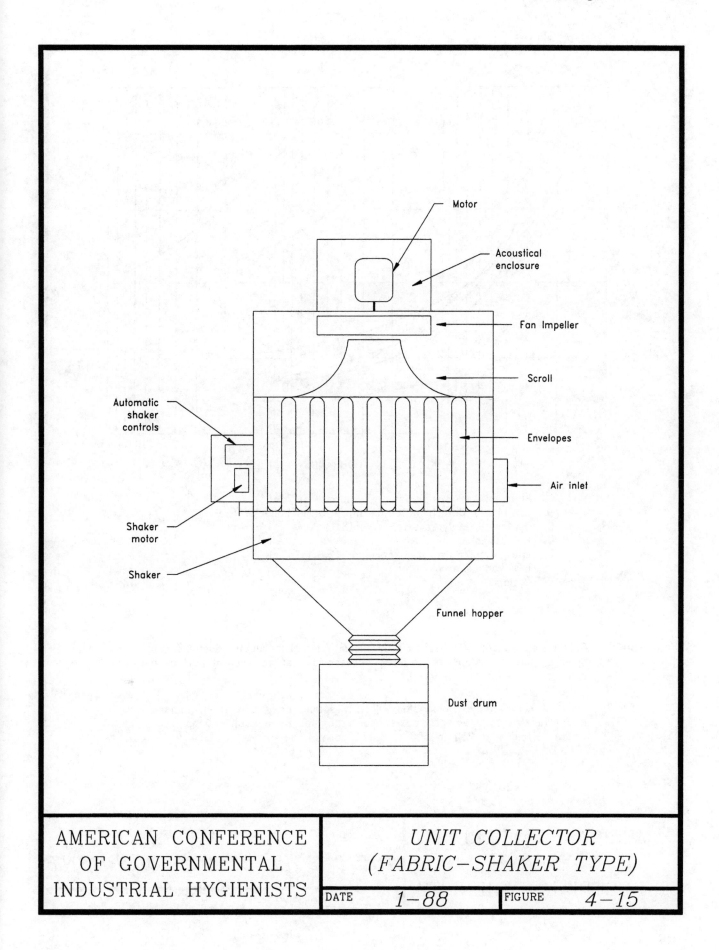

Motor

Acoustical
enclosure

Fan Impeller

Scroll

Automatic
shaker
controls

Envelopes

Air inlet

Shaker
motor

Shaker

Funnel hopper

Dust drum

AMERICAN CONFERENCE OF GOVERNMENTAL INDUSTRIAL HYGIENISTS	*UNIT COLLECTOR (FABRIC–SHAKER TYPE)*	
	DATE *1–88*	FIGURE *4–15*

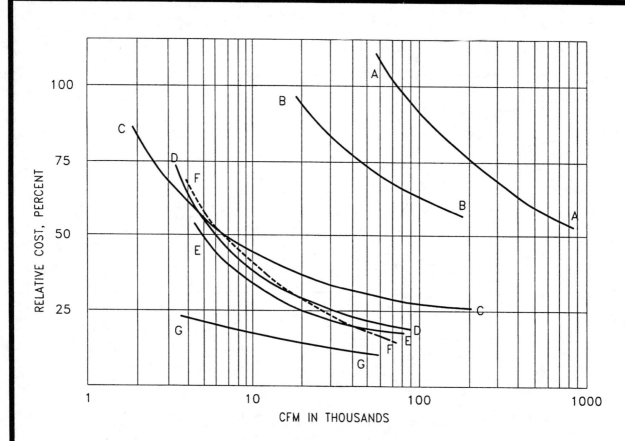

A. High voltage precipitator (minimum cost range)
B. Continuous duty high temperature fabric collector (2.0:1)
C. Continuous duty reverse pulse (8:1)
D. Wet collector
E. Intermittent duty fabric collector (2.0:1)
F. Low voltage precipitator
G. Cyclone

Note 1:   Cost based on collector section only. Does not include ducts, dust disposal devices, pumps, exhausters or other accessories not an integral part of the collector.

Note 2:   Price of high voltage precipitator will vary substantially with applications and efficiency requirements. Costs shown are for fly ash aplications where velocities of 200 to 300 fpm are normal.

AMERICAN CONFERENCE OF GOVERNMENTAL INDUSTRIAL HYGIENISTS	COST ESTIMATES OF DUST COLLECTING EQUIPMENT	
	DATE *1–88*	FIGURE *4–16*

TABLE 4-4. Comparison of Some Important Dust Collector Characteristics

Type	Higher Efficiency Range on Particles Greater than Mean Size in Microns	Pressure Loss inches	H2 O Gal. Per 1000 cfm	Space	Sensitivity to Q Change		Humid Air Influence	Max. Temp. F Standard Construction Note 4
					Pressure	Efficiency		
Electrostatic:	0.25	½	—	Large	Negligible	Yes	Improves Efficiency	500
Fabric:								
Intermittent—Shaker	0.25	3-6	—	Large	As cfm	Negligible	May Make Reconditioning Difficult	See Table 4-1
Continuous—Shaker	0.25	3-6	—	Large	As cfm	Negligible		
Continuous—Reverse Air	0.25	3-6 (Note 1)	—	Large	As cfm	Negligible		
Continuous—Reverse Pulse	0.25	3-6	—	Moderate	As cfm	Negligible		
Glass, Reverse Flow	0.25	3-8	—	Large	As cfm	Negligible		500
Wet:								
Packed Tower	1-5	1.5-3.5	5-10	Large	As cfm	Yes	None	Unlimited
Wet Centrifugal	1-5	2.5-6	3-5	Moderate	As $(cfm)^2$	Yes		
Wet Dynamic	1-2	Note 2	½ - 1	Small	Note 2	No		
Orifice Types	1-5	2½ - 6	10-40	Small	As cfm or less	Varies with Design		
Higher Efficiency:								
Fog Tower	0.5-5	2-4	5-10	Moderate	As $(cfm)^2$	Slightly	None	Note 3
Venturi	0.5-2	10-100	5-15	Moderate	As $(cfm)^2$	Yes	None	Unlimited
Dry Centrifugal:								
Low Pressure Cyclone	20-40	0.75-1.5	—	Large	As $(cfm)^2$	Yes	May Cause condensation and plugging	400
High Eff. Centrifugal	10-30	3-6	—	Moderate	As $(cfm)2$	Yes		400
Dry Dynamic	10-20	Note 2	—	Small	Note 2	No		400

Note 1: Pressure loss is that for fabric and dust cake. Pressure losses associated with outlet connections to be added by system designer..
Note 2: A function of the mechanical efficiency of these combined exhausters and dust collectors.
Note 3: Precooling of high temperature gases will be necessary to prevent rapid evaporation of fine droplets.
Note 4: See NFPA requirements for fire hazards, e.g., zirconium, magnesium, aluminum, woodworking, etc.

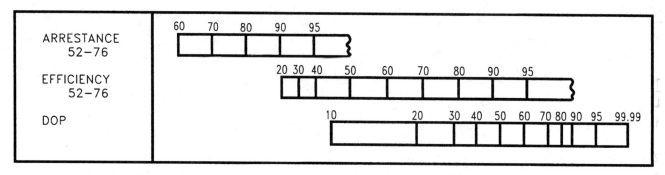

FIGURE 4–17. Comparison between various methods of measuring air cleaning capability

cleaner test dust, 23% carbon black, and 5% cotton lint is fed to the filter. The efficiency by weight on this specific test dust is the ASHRAE Arrestance. ASHRAE Efficiency is a measure of the ability of a filter to prevent staining or discoloration. It is determined by light reflectance readings taken before and after the filter in a specified test apparatus. Atmospheric dust is used for the test. Both ASHRAE tests are described in ASHRAE Publication 52-76.[4.9]

In a DOP Test, 0.3 micron particles of dioctylphthalate (DOP) are drawn through a HEPA (High Efficiency Particulate Air) filter. Efficiency is determined by comparing the downstream and upstream particle counts. To be designated as a HEPA filter, the filter must be at least 99.97% efficient, i.e., only three particles of 0.3 micron size can pass for every ten thousand particles fed to the filter. Unlike both ASHRAE tests, the DOP test is not destructive, so it is possible to repair leaks and retest a filter that has failed.

The three tests are not directly comparable; however, Figure 4-17 shows the general relationship. Table 4-6 compares several important characteristics of commonly used air filters. Considerable life extension of an expensive final filter can be obtained by the use of one or more cheaper, less efficient, prefilters. For example, the life of a HEPA filter can be increased 25% with a throwaway prefilter. If the throwaway filter is followed by a 90% efficient extended surface filter, the life of the HEPA filter can be extended nearly 900%. This concept of "progressive filtration" allows the final filters in clean rooms to remain in place for ten years or more.

TABLE 4-5. Media Velocity vs. Fiber Size

Filter Type	Filter Size (microns)	Velocity (fpm)	Media Filtration Mechanism
Panel Filters	25-50	250-625	Impingement
Automatic Roll Filters	25-50	500	Impingement
Extended Surface Filters	0.75-2.5	20-25	Interception
HEPA Filters	0.5-6.3	5	Diffusion

The European Committee of the Construction of Air Handling Equipment has developed a method for testing air filters in general ventilation. Although their method, called Eurovent 4/5, is based directly on ASHRAE Standard 52-76, some wording and definitions have been amended to suit the needs of Eurovent. Eurovent 4/5 aims to establish a uniform comparative testing procedure for air filters having volumetric flow rates greater than 0.236 m³/s (500 cfm) and an average dust spot efficiency up to 98%.

The wide range of filter efficiency is segregated into 14 grades of filters from EU1 to EU14.

4.10 RADIOACTIVE AND HIGH TOXICITY OPERATIONS

There are three major requirements for air cleaning equipment to be utilized for radioactive or high toxicity applications:

1. High efficiency

2. Low maintenance

3. Safe disposal

High efficiency is essential because of extremely low tolerances for the quantity and concentration of stack effluent and the high cost of the materials handled. Not only must the efficiency be high, it must also be verifiable because of the legal requirement to account for all radioactive material.

The need for low maintenance is of special importance when exhausting any hazardous material. For many radioactive processes, the changing of bags in a conventional fabric collector may expend the daily radiation tolerances of 20 or more persons. Infrequent, simple, and rapid maintenance requirements are vital. Another important factor is the desirability of low residual build up of material in the collector since dose rates increase with the amount of material and reduce the allowable working time.

Disposal of radioactive or toxic materials is a serious and very difficult problem. For example, scalping filters loaded with radioactive dust are usually incinerated to reduce the quantity of material that must be disposed of in special burial grounds. The incinerator will require an air cleaning device, such as a wet collector of very special design, to avoid unacceptable pollution of air and water.

With these factors involved, it is necessary to select an air cleaning device that will meet efficiency requirements without causing too much difficulty in handling and disposal.

TABLE 4-6. Comparison of Some Important Air Filter Characteristics

Type	Pressure Drop "wg (Notes 1 & 2)		ASHRAE Performance (Note 4)		Face Velocity fpm	Maintenance (Note 5)	
	Initial	Final	Arrestance	Efficiency		Labor	Material
Low/Medium Efficiency							
1. Glass Throwaway (2" deep)	0.1	0.5	77%	NA Note 6	300	High	High
2. High Velocity (permanent units) (2" deep)	0.1	0.5	73%	NA Note 6	500	High	Low
3. Automatic (viscous)	0.4	0.4	80%	NA Note 6	500	Low	Low
Medium/High Efficiency							
1. Extended Surface (dry)	0.15-0.60	0.5-1.25	90-99%	25-95%	300-625	Medium	Medium
2. Electrostatic							
a. Dry Agglomerator/ Roll Media	0.35	0.35	NA Note 7	90%	500	Medium	Low
b. Dry Agglomerator/ Extended Surface Media	0.55	1,25	NA Note 7	95%+	530	Medium	Medium
c. Automatic Wash Type	0.25	0.25	NA Note 7	85-955	400-600	Low	Low
Ultra High Efficiency							
1. HEPA	0.5-1.0	1.0-3.0	Note 3	Note 3	250-500	High	High

Note 1:Pressure drop values shown constitute a range or average, whichever is applicable.

Note 2:Final pressure drop indicates point at which filter or filter media is removed and the media is either cleaned or replaced. All others are cleaned in place, automatically, manually, or media renewed automatically. Therefore, pressure drop remains approximately constant.

Note 3:95–99.97% by particle count, DOP test.

Note 4:ASHRAE Standard 52-76 defines (a) Arrestance as a measure of the ability to remove injected synthetic dust, calculated as a percentage on a weight basis and (b) Efficiency as a measure of the ability to remove atmospheric dust determined on a light-transmission (dust spot) basis.

Note 5:Compared to other types within efficiency category.

Note 6:Too low to be meaningful.

Note 7:Too high to be meaningful.

Filter units especially designed for high efficiency and low maintenance are available. These units feature quick change-out through a plastic barrier which is intended to encapsulate spent filters, thereby eliminating the exposure of personnel to radioactive or toxic material. A filtration efficiency of 99.97% by particle count on 0.3 micron particles is standard for this type of unit.

For further information on this subject, see Reference 4.10.

4.11 EXPLOSION VENTING

There is a wide range of dusts which are combustible and capable of producing an explosion. Explosions occur when the right concentration of finely divided dust is suspended in air and exposed to a sufficient source of ignition. A dust collector, by its very operation, maintains a cloud of finely divid-ed particles suspended in air. If a source of ignition initiates the combustion of the dust cloud, the gases in the cloud will rapidly expand due to heat developed during the combustion. If a dust collector vessel constricts this expansion, a rapid pressure build up inside the collector casing will cause a violent rupture. When dust particles are known to be combustible, precautions for an explosion must be taken and suitable protection provided to reduce the risk of property damage and personal injury.

To begin taking precautions, sources of possible ignition must be identified and controlled to minimize the risk of a dust cloud explosion. Usual causes of explosions include static discharge, hot surfaces on machinery and sparks and flames from processes. After identifying possible sources of ignition, preventive measures should be taken. Static grounding of the equipment and spark traps are typical preventive measures.

The addition of an inert gas to replace oxygen in a dust collector can prevent an explosion by ensuring the minimum oxygen content required for ignition is never reached. Inerting can be very effective in closed loop systems but is not economical in typical local exhaust systems because of the constant loss of expensive inerting gas. Should ignition occur, protective measures must be taken to limit the damage. Typical protective measures include: explosion suppression, explosion containment, and explosion venting.

Explosion suppression requires the early detection of an explosion, usually within the first 20 milliseconds. Once ignition is detected, an explosion suppression device injects a pressurized chemical suppressant into the collector to displace the oxygen and impede combustion. These are typically used in conjunction with fast acting isolation valves on the inlet and outlet ducts. These systems can be very useful when toxic dusts are being handled.

Explosion containment uses specialized dust collectors designed to withstand the maximum pressure generated and contain the explosion. Most pressure capabilities of commercially available dust collectors are not sufficient to contain an explosion in progress.

Explosion venting, the most common protection, is afforded by fitting pressure relief vents to the collector housing. As pressure increases quickly leading up to an explosion, a relief vent opens to allow the rapidly expanding gases to escape. This effectively limits the maximum pressure build up to less than the bursting pressure of the vessel. The necessary area for such a relief vent is a function of the vessel volume, vessel strength, the opening pressure of the relief vent and the rate of pressure rise characteristic of the dust in question. Most standard dust collectors will require reinforcing to withstand the reduced maximum pressure experienced during an explosion.

To choose the most reliable, economical, and effective means of explosion control, an evaluation of the specifics of the exhaust system and the degree of protection required is necessary.

NAPA 68-1994, *Guide for Explosion Venting*,[4.11] is the most commonly recognized standard and should be studied and thoroughly familiar to anyone responsible for the design or evaluation of dust collectors applied to potentially explosive dusts.

REFERENCES:

4.1.   Leith, D.; First, M.K.W.; Feldman, H.: Performance of a Pulse-Jet at High Velocity Filtration II, Filter Cake Redeposition. J. Air Pollut. Control Assoc. 28:696 (July 1978).

4.2.   Beake, E.: "Optimizing Filtration Parameters." J. Air Pollut. Control Assoc. 24:1150 (1974).

4.3.   Leith, D.; Gibson, D. D.; First, M. W.: Performance of Top and Bottom Inlet Pulse-Jet Fabric Filters. J. Air Pollut. Control Assoc. 24:1150 (1974).

4.4.   American Society of Heating, Refrigeration and Air-Conditioning Engineers, Inc.: HVAC Systems and Equipment Handbook, 1996: 1791 Tullie Circle, N.E., Atlanta, GA 30329

4.5   Lund, Herbert F.: Industrial Pollution Control Handbook, McGraw-Hill, 1971.

4.6   Heumann, William L.: Industrial Air Pollution Control Systems, McGraw-Hill, 1997

4.7   Gilliland, G.A.; Ramaswami, R.D.; Patel, D.N.: Removal of volatile organic compounds (VOCs) generated by Forest Product Industries using biofiltration technology. In Proc. Emerging technologies in hazardous waste management VII, ACS Special Symposium: Atlanta, GA, Sept. 17-20, 1995. Editor Tedder, D.W., Washington, DC (United States) American Chemical Society p 921 (1352p) CONF-9509139

4.8   Biofiltration. Air emissions from Wood and Wood-Based Products: Conducting Research and Sharing Information. 22 April 1998. USDA Forest Products Laboratory. 16 Dec 2000. <http.fpl.fs.fed.us/voc/biofilt.html>.

4.9.   American Society of Heating, Refrigerating and Air-Conditioning Engineers: Method of Testing Cleaning Devices Used in General Ventilation for Removing Particulate Matter. ASHRAE Pub. No. 52-76. ASHRAE, Atlanta, GA (May 1976).

4.10.   National Council on Radiation Protection and Measurement: NCRP Report No. 39, Basic Radiation Protection Criteria. NCRP Report No. 39. Publications, Bethesda, MD (January, 1971).

4.11.   National Fire Protection Association: Guide for Explosion Venting. NFPA 68-1978. NFPA, Quincy, MA (1978).

Chapter 5
EXHAUST SYSTEM DESIGN PROCEDURE

5.1 INTRODUCTION

The duct system that connects the hoods, air cleaning device(s), and fan must be properly designed. This process is much more involved than merely connecting pieces of duct. If the system is not carefully designed in a manner that inherently ensures that the design flow rates will be realized, contaminant control may not be achieved. Duct systems require large amounts of air to move relatively small amounts of contaminant. For that reason they are one of the least efficient items in the plant or process. Careful design can provide the required system goals utilizing the least amount of power. In addition, the designer must consider initial capital costs, reliability, maintenance, and equipment life.

The results of the following design procedure will determine the duct sizes, material thickness, and the fan operating point (system flow rate and required pressure) required by the system. Chapter 6 describes how to select a fan based on these results.

The reader will note the revision to consider density changes in almost all calculations. This is a change from previous editions and includes a more comprehensive Calculation sheet. The user of the calculation methods will need to consider the changes in density of the air due to elevation, temperature, moisture, and static pressure. If "Standard Air" is considered, a simple insertion of "1" for the value of the density factor will yield the same results. Not all problems or calculations will require the consideration for density change but it is strongly recommended that the designer investigate this before beginning the design process. Similarly, if the design involves gases other than air, the designer will need to consider the density of the fluid involved. This could be the case where there are large concentrations of combustion products or other process gasses. In these cases the calculation methods below may not be appropriate.

5.2 PRELIMINARY STEPS

Coordinate design efforts with all personnel involved, including the equipment or process operator as well as maintenance, health, safety, fire, and environmental personnel. The designer should have, at a minimum, the following data available at the start of the design calculations:

1. A layout of the operations, workroom, building (if necessary), etc. The available location(s) for the air cleaning device and fan should be determined. An important aspect that must be considered at this time is to locate the system exhaust point (where the air exits the system) so that the discharged air will not re-enter the work space, either through openings in the building perimeter or through replacement air unit intakes. (See Figures 5-31 and 5-32.)

2. A line sketch of the duct system layout, including plan and elevation dimensions, fan location, air cleaning device location, etc. Number, letter, or otherwise identify each branch and section of main duct on the line

sketch for convenience. The examples show hoods numbered and other points lettered.

Locate the fan close to pieces of equipment with high losses. This will facilitate balancing and may result in lower operating costs. Locating the fan in the center of the system may yield a smaller static pressure requirement.

Flexible duct is susceptible to sagging and excessive bending, which increases static pressure losses. Usually, these additional SP losses cannot be predicted accurately. Use hard duct whenever possible and keep flexible duct lengths as straight and short as possible.

3. A design or sketch of the desired hood for each operation with direction and elevation of outlet for duct connection.

4. Information about the details of the operation(s), specifically toxicity, ergonomics, physical and chemical characteristics, required flow rate, minimum required duct velocity, entry losses, and required capture velocities.

Information about the elevation of the plant above sea level and also the temperature and moisture conditions from each process and duct branch.

6. The method and location of the replacement air distribution devices on the hood's performance. The type and location of these fixtures can dramatically lower contaminant control by creating undesirable turbulence at the hood (see Chapter 7.) Perforated plenums or perforated duct provide better replacement air distribution with fewer adverse effects on hood performance.

5.3 DESIGN PROCEDURE

A simple exhaust system is comprised of a hood, duct segment, and special fittings leading to and from an exhaust fan. A complex system is merely an arrangement of several simple exhaust systems connected to a common duct. There are two general classes of duct system designs: tapered systems and plenum systems. The duct in a tapered system gradually gets larger as additional flows are merged together, thus keeping duct velocities nearly constant. If the system transports particulate (dust, mist, or condensable vapors), the tapered system maintains the minimum velocity required to prevent settling. The duct in a plenum system (see Section 5.7) is generally larger than that in a tapered system and the velocity in it is usually low. Any particulate in the air stream can settle out in the large ducts. Certain mist control systems are designed this way to encourage settling of droplets in the duct. Figures 5-4 and 5-5 illustrate design alternatives. Regardless of which system is used, the following procedure will result in a workable system design. Moisture must also be considered because of the possibility of condensation below the dew point temperature. This could cause dusts to adhere to duct walls and plug collection devices.

The design procedure is a continuing process and does not end with the first system calculations. They may be repeated several times including the original conceptual design, final drive speed specification from "as-built" drawings, as well as a tool for the air balance technician. In addition, the designer must not consider this only a simple tool to size ducts and fan. It should be used to identify ducts with very high velocities that could wear prematurely and to analyze the branches with the highest pressure drop so system pressure could be reduced. For example, a small branch duct in a large volume system may represent the highest static pressure loss (determining leg). By increasing the flow at the hood, making the duct larger and reducing the friction losses in the duct, the overall system pressure may go down with very little increase in flow. The result is less system horsepower required.

Similarly, the system design usually only considers the conditions at initial start-up and installation. After the system is in use it will lose some effectiveness as dust coats the duct (changing friction losses) and fan impellers and collectors show wear. The designer must consider the conditions during the operating life of the system. For instance, where volumes, face velocities, or transport velocities are selected from a range of values, the upper end of the range may want to be considered if the system cannot be shut down for normal maintenance.

The system itself is dynamic. Readings taken at start-up and commissioning may not be repeated again as the system ages and the readings themselves are open to interpretation (see Chapter 9). The calculation method should be considered a

tool to determine duct sizes and fan requirements rather than a prediction of exact operating conditions in all branches throughout the life of the system.

1. Select or design each exhaust hood based on the toxicity, physical, and chemical characteristics of the material and the ergonomics of the process and determine its design flow rate, minimum duct velocity, and entry losses (see Chapters 3 and 10). Note that minimum duct velocity is only important for systems transporting particulate, condensing vapors, or mist and to prevent explosive concentrations building up in the duct (see Section 5.18 for a discussion on economic velocities for non-particulate systems.)

2. Start with the duct segment that has the greatest number of duct segments between it and the fan. A duct segment is defined as the constant diameter round (or constant area rectangular) duct that separates points of interest such as hoods, entry points, fan inlet, etc. The calculation sheet includes asterisks next to certain lines. These describe the requirements for input information. For example, the asterisk at Line 3 indicates that the designer must input the air volume for that branch.

3. Determine the airflow requirement at each hood. The airflow rate is determined using two components. The first uses the duct velocity required to capture and convey the contaminant into a hood or to maintain the contaminant within an enclosure or enclosing hood. Recommendations for these values are included in

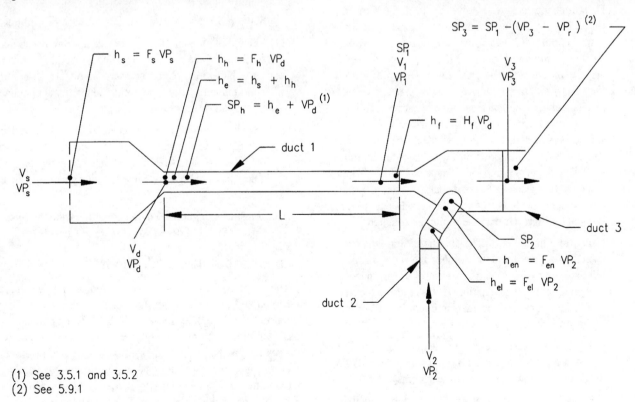

(1) See 3.5.1 and 3.5.2
(2) See 5.9.1

FIGURE 5–1. System duct calculation parameter location

Chapter 3 and/or Chapter 10. The second is the volume of contaminants generated inside the hood enclosure—defined in SCFM @ 0.75 lbs/ft^3. Note that this may differ from the actual contaminants being generated and the designer will be required to re-state these contaminants in terms of SCFM of air. The calculation sheet uses SCFM as a start point (Line 3.) Because the face velocities and volume going into the hood are at local conditions (ACFM), it is best to return these flows to standard conditions before starting the duct calculations. This allows for one density factor in all of the calculations for that branch.

4. Calculate the branch density factor (Line 7) considering the effects of elevation, temperature, and moisture for the air stream coming from the hood. Use these actual conditions (ACFM) for sizing duct. *Note: if "Standard Air" only is being considered, then SCFM will equal ACFM, df = 1, and all references to temperature, elevation, and moisture can be eliminated. (Lines 2, 5, 6, 7, 8, and 14 can be skipped.) Note 2: density factor should also consider the absolute pressure inside the duct. For most calculation purposes, we will consider this only at the fan inlet where the effects are usually the greatest and the information is needed to specify the fan. If more detailed system calculation is considered or if there are very low pressures throughout the system (<-20 "wg), then the designer may opt to consider these effects in all ducts.*

5. Determine the duct area by dividing the design flow rate (in ACFM) by the minimum duct velocity. *Note: If the system contains air with lower density due to elevation, moisture, and temperature, then a higher transport velocity may want to be considered. This is especially the case if the density factor is below 0.8.* Convert the resultant cross-sectional area into a tentative duct diameter. A commercially available duct size (see Table 5-8) should be selected. If solid particulate or condensable vapor is being transported through the system, a minimum velocity is required (See Chapters 3 and 10). If the tentative duct diameter is not a standard size, select the next smaller size to ensure that the actual duct velocity is equal to or greater than the minimum required.

6. Using the line sketch, determine the design length for each duct segment and the number and type of fittings (elbows, entries and other special fittings) needed. Design length is the centerline distance along the duct (the distance between the intersection of the centerlines of the straight duct components).

7. Calculate the pressure losses for the duct segments that merge at a common junction point (see Section 5.4 for the details on how to calculate these items).

8. Calculate the condition of the air at each branch by considering moisture, heat, and mass flow in the mixture from the two branches and balancing mass, moisture, and heat. Review these conditions to ensure that the air is safely above the dew point. Use the new air conditions for sizing the next segment.

9. Determine the material type and thickness (gauge) for each duct segment based upon the air stream characteristics

10. Directly after each junction point, there will be one and only one SP, *regardless of the path taken to reach that point.* If not ensured by the design process, the system will "self-balance" by reducing the flow rate in the higher-resistance duct segment(s) and increasing the flow rate in the lower-resistance duct segment(s) until there is a single SP in the duct downstream of each junction point.

SP balance at any junction point can be achieved by either one of two fundamental design methods:

1. Adjust the flow rate through the hood(s) until the static pressures at each junction point are the same, or

2. Increase the resistance in the low resistance duct segment(s) by means of some artificial device such as a blast gate, orifice plate, or other obstruction in the segment or a reduction in duct size.

3. Investigate whether system static pressure can be reduced by increasing flow at one or both hoods and increasing duct sizes. Consider the effect on total system horsepower and capital costs.

Section 5.5 discusses the details of these procedures.

11. Select both the air cleaning device and fan based upon final calculated system flow rate in ACFM, temperature, elevation, static pressure, moisture condition, contaminant loading, physical and chemical characteristics, and overall system resistance.

12. Check the duct sizes designed against the available space and resolve any interference problems (i.e., will the elbow or duct size desired actually fit in the available space). This may cause a redesign of part of the system.

13. Consider fan inlet and outlet conditions and the System Effects that will de-rate the fan. (See Chapter 6.)

5.4 DUCT SEGMENT CALCULATIONS

The Velocity Pressure Method is based on the fact that all frictional and dynamic (fitting) losses in ducts and hoods are functions of the velocity pressure and can be calculated by a loss coefficient multiplied by the velocity pressure. Loss coefficients for hoods, straight ducts, elbows, branch entries, contractions, and expansions are shown in Figures 5-15 through 5-18. Figure 5-1 shows the application of these coefficients. For convenience, loss coefficients for round elbows and entries are also presented on the calculation sheet (see Figure 5-3).

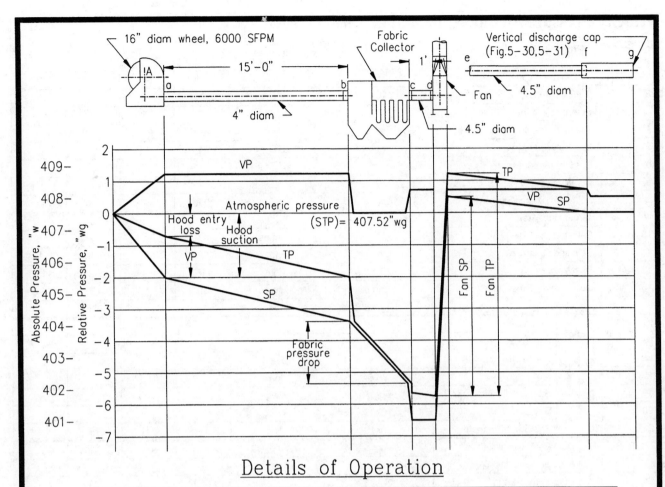

Details of Operation

NO.		HOOD NO.	VS-PRINT	REQUIRED AIR-FLOW, cfm
1	16" Diameter Grinding wheel, 2" Wide	A	80–11	390

Dimensions

No. of Branch or Main	Straight Run, Ft	CFM Required	Elbows	Entries
ab	15	390	--	--
bc	Collector	390	--	--
cd	1	390	--	--
ef	10	390	--	--
fg	Stack Head	390	--	--

AMERICAN CONFERENCE OF GOVERNMENTAL INDUSTRIAL HYGIENISTS	PROBLEM 1	
	DATE 1-88	FIGURE 5-2

Velocity Pressure Method Calculation Sheet

Elevation ___0___ (z)

Project _____ Problem 1 — Figure 5-3 _____   Designer _____

						a-b	b-c	c-d	e-f
1*		Duct Segment Identification							
2*	T	Dry-Bulb Temperature			F	70	70	70	70
3*	Q_{std}	Standard Volumetric Flow Rate			scfm	390	390	390	390
4*	V_t	Minimum Transport Velocity			fpm	4000		4000	4000
5*	m_{H2O}	Lbs Water per Minute			#H2O/min				
6*	m_{da}	Lbs Dry Air per Minute			#da/min				
7	df	Density Factor	Eqn 2			1	1	1	1
8	Q_{act}	Actual Volumetric Flow Rate	Eqn 3		acfm	390	390	390	390
9	A_t	Target Duct Area	(3/4std)(8/4nstd)		ft²				
10	d	Selected Duct Diameter			inches	4.0		4.5	4.5
11	A	Selected Duct Area			ft²	0.0975		0.1104	0.1104
12	V_d	Duct Velocity	(3/11std)(8/11nstd)		fpm	4469		3531	3531
13	VP_d	Duct Velocity Pressure	Eqn 5		"wg	1.25		0.78	0.78
14	h	Total Heat	branch balance		btu/#da				
15*	A_s	HOOD LOSSES / SLOT	Slot Area		ft²				
16*	F_s		Slot Loss Coefficient						
17*			Acceleration Factor		0 or 1				
18	V_s		Slot Velocity	8/15	fpm				
19	VP_s		Slot Velocity Pressure	Eqn 5	"wg				
20			Slot Loss in VP	16+17					
21			Slot Static Pressure	20x19	"wg				
22*	F_h		Duct Entry Coefficient			0.65		0.5	
23*			Acceleration Factor	1 or 0		1		1	
24			Duct Entry Loss in VP	22+23		1.65		1.5	
25			Duct Entry Loss	24x13	"wg	2.05		1.17	
26			Other Losses		"wg				
27	SP_h		Hood Static Pressure	21+25+26	"wg	2.05		1.17	
28*	L	DUCT LOSSES	Straight Duct Length		ft	15		1	10
29*	H_f		Duct Friction Factor	Eqn 8		0.0703		0.0620	0.0620
30*			No. of 90 Degree Elbows						
31*	F_{el}		Elbow Loss Coefficient	Table 6					
32*	F_{en}		Branch Entry Coefficient	Table 7					
33*			Special Fitting Coefficient						
34	h_f		Duct Friction Loss in VP	28x29		1.05		0.06	0.62
35			Elbow Loss in VP	30x31					
36			Branch Entry Loss in VP	32					
37			Duct Loss in VP	33+34+35+36		1.05		0.06	0.62
38			Duct Loss	37x13	"wg	1.31		0.05	0.4838
39*			Other Losses		"wg		2.0		
40	VP_r		Resultant Velocity Pressure	Eqn 9	"wg				
41			Loss from Velocity Increase	13-40 (if>0)	"wg				
42			Duct Pressure Loss	27+38+39+41	"wg	-3.36		-1.22	+0.48
43*	SP_{gov}	Governing Static Pressure			"wg				
44	SP_{cum}	Cumulative Static Pressure			"wg	-3.36	-5.36	-6.58	+0.48
45	Q_{corr}	Corrected Volumetric Flow Rate	Eqn 10		acfm				
46	V_{corr}	Corrected Velocity	45 / 11		fpm				
47	VP_{corr}	Corrected Velocity Pressure	Eqn 5		"wg				

* Data Input
** Shaded lines 5, 6, 7, 8 & 14 used for non-standard calculations
*** std is for standard calculations and nst is for non-standard calculations

Date_____

The right-hand reference column contains:

1

$$\omega = \#H_2O/\#Dry\ Air$$

2

$$df = df_e * df_p * df_t * df_m$$

$$df_e = [1 - (6.73*10^{-6})(z)]^{5.258}$$

$$df_p = (407 + SP)/(407)$$

$$df_t = (530)/(T + 460)$$

$$df_m = (1 + \omega)/(1 + 1.607\omega)$$

3

$$Q_{act} = Q_{std}\ ((1 + \omega)/df)$$

4

$$V = 4005\sqrt{VP/df}$$

5

$$VP = df(V/4005)^2$$

6

90° Round Elbow Loss Coefficients
(5 Piece)

R/D	Coefficient
1.5	0.24
2.0	0.19
2.5	0.17

7

Branch Entry Loss Coefficients

Angle	Coefficient
15°	0.09
30°	0.18
45°	0.28

8

$$H_f^{(galvanized)} = 0.0307(V^{0.533}/Q^{0.612})$$

$$H_f^{(black\ iron)} = 0.0425(V^{0.465}/Q^{0.602})$$

$$H_f^{(flexible)} = 0.0311(V^{0.604}/Q^{0.639})$$

9

$$VP_f = (Q_1/Q_3)(VP_1) + (Q_2/Q_3)(VP_2)$$

10

$$Q_{corr} = Q_{design}\sqrt{SP_{gov}/SP_{duct}}$$

11

$$FAN\ SP = SP_{out} - SP_{in} - VP_{in}$$

Row labels (far right of grid): 1*, 2*, 3*, 4*, 5*, 6*, 7, 8, 9, 10, 11, 12, 13, 14*, 15*, 16*, 17*, 18, 19, 20, 21, 22*, 23*, 24, 25, 26, 27, 28*, 29*, 30*, 31*, 32*, 33*, 34, 35, 36, 37, 38, 39*, 40, 41, 42, 43*, 44, 45, 46, 47

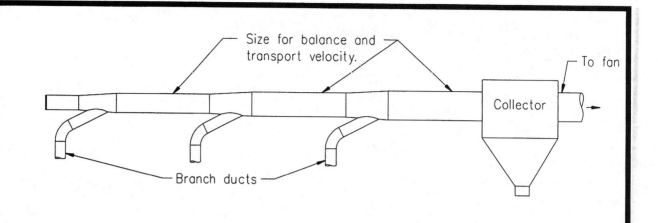

TAPERED DUCT SYSTEM
Maintains transport velocity

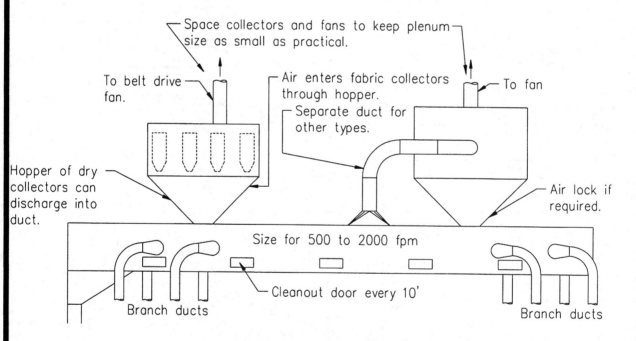

EXTENDED PLENUM SYSTEM
Self cleaning type

NOTE: Design plenum velocities are at the most 1/2 the branch duct design velocities and typically less than 2000 fpm.

AMERICAN CONFERENCE OF GOVERNMENTAL INDUSTRIAL HYGIENISTS	*PLENUM vs CONVENTIONAL SYSTEM*	
	DATE *1-95*	FIGURE *5-4*

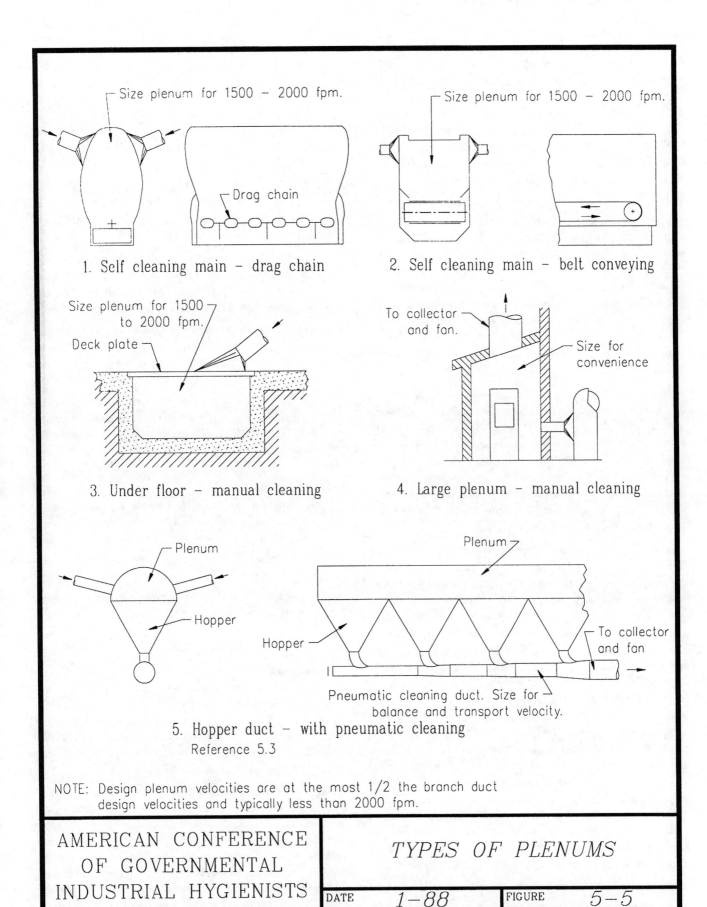

Size plenum for 1500 – 2000 fpm.

Drag chain

1. Self cleaning main – drag chain

Size plenum for 1500 – 2000 fpm.

2. Self cleaning main – belt conveying

Size plenum for 1500 to 2000 fpm.

Deck plate

3. Under floor – manual cleaning

To collector and fan.

Size for convenience

4. Large plenum – manual cleaning

Plenum

Hopper

Plenum

Hopper

To collector and fan

Pneumatic cleaning duct. Size for balance and transport velocity.

5. Hopper duct – with pneumatic cleaning
Reference 5.3

NOTE: Design plenum velocities are at the most 1/2 the branch duct design velocities and typically less than 2000 fpm.

AMERICAN CONFERENCE OF GOVERNMENTAL INDUSTRIAL HYGIENISTS	*TYPES OF PLENUMS*	
	DATE *1–88*	FIGURE *5–5*

Friction charts for this method are presented as Tables 5-5 and 5-6. These charts give the loss coefficients per foot of galvanized and commercial steel, aluminum, PVC, and stainless steel duct. The equations for these charts are listed on these tables and also on the calculation sheet (see Figure 5-3).[1,5] These equations and the resultant tables have been designed to be no more than 4% different from the "exact" values of the Colebrook-White equation and were designed to err on the high side over the normal velocity range of exhaust ventilation systems.

For convenience, two data sets determined from the same equations used to generate the friction charts are presented in tabular form as well as chart form in the familiar "three' eye chart" (see Figures 5-19a and 5-19b). These tables are possible because, for a specific diameter, the friction loss coefficient changes only slightly with velocity. Each table lists the friction coefficient as a function of diameter for six different velocities. The error in using these data with velocities plus or minus 5 fpm is within 6%. If desired, a linear interpolation between velocity values can be performed.

In Chapter 1, an equation was presented for flexible duct with the wires covered. No data are presented here for this type of material due to the wide variability from manufacturer to manufacturer. Perhaps an even more important reason is that these data are for straight duct losses, and flexible duct, by its very nature, is seldom straight. Typically, bends in flexible duct can produce extremely large losses that cannot be predicted easily. Be very careful to keep the flexible duct as straight and as short as possible.

The following steps will establish the overall pressure loss of a duct segment that starts at a hood. Figure 5-2 shows a simple one hood ventilation system. The use of a calculation sheet can be very beneficial when performing the calculations manually. Figure 5-3 is a calculation sheet which shows the details of the calculations for each component of the system. There is also a profile through the system showing the magnitude and relationships of total, static, and velocity pressures on both the "suction" and the "pressure" sides of the fan on Figure 5-2. It should be noted that VP is always positive. While total and static pressure may be either negative or positive with respect to atmospheric pressure, TP is always greater than SP (TP = SP + VP). Also note that the value for VP can be affected by the air conditions (moisture, heat, elevation) but in this example "Standard Air" with df = 1 is considered.

NOTE: The numbers in the problems presented in this chapter were generated using one of the available computer programs (see Section 5.6). The values presented in the calculation sheets may be different from those determined by other methods. Because of the nature of the calculation sheet, it is also suitable for commercially available spreadsheet software.

1. Determine the *actual* velocity by dividing the flow rate by the area of the commercial duct size chosen. Then determine the corresponding velocity pressure from Table 5-7 (only if "Standard Air") or Equation 1.4 in Chapter 1. In the example, the diameter chosen was 4" (Line 10), the actual velocity is given on Line 12 and the VP corresponding to this actual velocity is given on Line 13.

2. Determine the hood static pressure from the equations in Chapter 3 or available information in Chapter 10. In this example, there are no slots, so the duct entry loss is as given on Lines 22 through 27.

3. Multiply the design duct length by the loss coefficient obtained from the tabulated data of Tables 5-5 or 5-6 (Lines 28 and 29.) The use of galvanized sheet metal duct was assumed throughout this chapter.

4. Determine the number and type of fittings in the duct segment. For each fitting type (see Figures 5-15, 5-16, 5-17, and 5-18), determine the loss coefficient and multiply by the number of fittings (there were none in this example.)

5. Add the results of Steps 3 and 4 above and multiply by the duct VP. This is the actual loss in inches of water for the duct segment (given on Line 38.)

6. Add the result of Step 5 to the hood suction. If there are any additional losses (expressed in inches of water), such as for an air cleaning device, add them in also. This establishes the cumulative energy required, expressed as static pressure, to move the design flow rate through the duct segment (Line 42.) Note that the value on Line 42 is negative.

The calculations listed in the last three columns of Figure 5-3 will be discussed in Section 5.8.3.

5.5 DISTRIBUTION OF AIRFLOW

As discussed previously, a complex exhaust system is actually a group of simple exhaust systems connected to a common main duct. Therefore, when designing a system of multiple hoods and branches, the same rules apply. In a multiple branch system, however, it is necessary to provide a means of distributing airflow between the branches either by balanced design or by the use of blast gates or orifice plates.

Air will always take the path of least resistance. A natural balance at each junction will occur; that is, the exhaust flow rate will distribute itself automatically according to the pressure losses of the available flow paths. The designer must provide distribution such that the design airflow at each hood will never fall below the minimums listed in Chapter 3 and/or 10. To do so, the designer must make sure that all flow paths (ducts) entering a junction will have equal calculated static pressure requirements.

To accomplish this, the designer has a choice of two methods. The object of both methods is the same: to obtain the desired flow rate at each hood in the system while maintaining the desired velocity in each branch and main.

The two methods, labeled Balance by Design Method and Blast Gate Method, are outlined below. Their relative advantages and disadvantages can be found in Table 5-1. The use of orifice plates instead of blast gates may be considered with many of the same advantages and disadvantages. The method of calculating orifice plate openings can be found in other texts. The losses due to blast gates (as a function of insertion depth) are difficult to predict because of the different blade shapes and clearances. Some of this data may be available by the damper manufacturer.

5.5.1 Balance by Design Method: This procedure (see Section 5.10) provides for achievement of desired airflow (a "balanced" system) without the use of blast gates or orifice plates. It is often called the "Static Pressure Balance Method." In this type of design, the calculation usually begins at the hood farthest from the fan in terms of number of duct segments and proceeds, segment by segment, to the fan. At each junction, the static pressure necessary to achieve desired flow in one stream must equal the static pressure in the joining air stream. The static pressures are balanced by suitable choice of duct sizes, elbow radii, etc., as detailed below.

5.5.2 Blast Gate Method: The design procedure depends on the use of blast gates which must be adjusted after installation in order to achieve the desired flow at each hood. At each junction, the flow rates of two joining ducts are achieved by blast gate adjustment which results in the desired static pressure balance.

It is a common practice to design systems on the assumption that only a fraction of the total number of hoods will be used at a time and the flow to the branches not used will be shut off with dampers. For tapered system designs, where particulate is transported, this practice may lead to plugging in the main duct due to settled particulate. This procedure is **not** recommended unless minimum transport velocity can be assured in all ducts during any variation of closed blast gates. It is better to design these systems with individual branch lines all converging very close to the fan inlet so that lengths of duct mains are minimized.

5.5.3 Choice of Methods: The Balance by Design Method will normally be selected where highly toxic materials are controlled to safeguard against tampering with blast gates and consequently subjecting personnel to potentially excessive exposures. This method is highly recommended and sometimes mandatory where explosives, radioactive dusts, and biological materials are exhausted as the possibility of accumulations in the system caused by a blast gate obstruction is eliminated.

It should be noted that the Blast Gate Method will usually require less total flow in the system because volume increases to balance pressures at branches will not occur. With the Blast Gate Method, the static pressure needed to balance the branches will be the difference between the calculated pressures in these branches.

5.5.4 Balance by Design Procedure: The pressure loss of each duct segment is calculated from an exhaust hood to the junction with the next branch based on hood design data, fittings, and total duct length. At each junction, the SP for each parallel path of airflow must be the same. Where the ratio of

TABLE 5-1. Relative Advantages and Disadvantages of the Two Methods

Balance by Design Method	Blast Gate Method
1. Flow rates cannot be changed easily by workers or at the whim of the operator	1. Flow rates may be changed relatively easily. Such changes are desirable where pickup of unnecessary quantities of material may affect the process.
2. There is little degree of flexibility for future equipment changes or additions. The duct is "tailor made" for the job.	2. Depending on the fan and motor selected, there is somewhat greater flexibility for future changes or additions.
3. The choice of exhaust flow rates for a new operation may be incorrect. In such cases, some duct revision may be necessary.	3. Correcting improperly estimated exhaust flow rates is relatively easy within certain ranges.
4. No unusual erosion or accumulation problems will occur.	4. Partially closed blast gates may cause erosion thereby changing resistance or causing particulate accumulation.
5. Duct will not plug if velocities are chosen correctly.	5. Duct may plug if blast gate insertion depth has been adjusted improperly.
6. Total flow rate may be greater than design due to higher air requirements.	6. Balance may be achieved with design flow rate; however, the net energy required may be greater than for the Balance by Design Method.
7. The system must be installed exactly as designed, with all obstructions cleared and length of runs accurately determined.	7. Moderate variations in duct layout are possible.
8. Small ducts chosen for static pressure balance may be required to operate at high velocities causing premature wear.	8. Operators can change blast gate settings possibly putting the system out of balance.

the value of the higher SP to the lower SP is greater than 1.2, redesign of the branch with the lower pressure loss should be considered. This may include a change of duct size, selection of different fittings, and/or modifications to the hood design. Where the ratio of the static pressures of parallel paths are unequal and less than 1.2, balance can be obtained by increasing the airflow through the run with the lower resistance. This change in flow rate is calculated by noting that pressure losses vary with the velocity pressure and therefore as the square of the flow rate, so:

$$Q_{Corrected} = Q_{Design} \sqrt{\frac{SP_{gov}}{SP_{duct}}} \qquad [5.1]$$

where the "governing" SP is the desired SP at the junction point and the "duct" SP is that calculated for the duct segment being designed. Note that the value under the square root is always greater than 1.0.

5.5.5 Blast Gate Procedure: Data and calculations involved are the same as for the balanced design method except that the duct sizes, fittings, and flow rates are not adjusted; the blast gates are set after installation to provide the design flow rates. It should be noted that a change in any of the blast gate settings will change the flow rates in all of the other branches. Readjusting the blast gates during the system balancing process sometimes can result in increases to the actual fan static pressure and increased fan power requirements.

Recent work[5.2] describes a method whereby blast gate settings can be made by means of pressure readings instead of by velocity readings. The biggest advantage of this method is that the process of resetting the insertion depths need not be a repetitive procedure.

5.5.6 System Redesign: Many ventilation systems are changed after installation (processes are changed, operations are relocated, additional equipment is added to the production floor, etc.) When such changes occur, the effect of the proposed change(s) to the ventilation system must be calculated. Often, systems are changed without adequate design, resulting in catastrophic changes to some hood flow rates. The result is that worker safety and health are jeopardized.

5.6 AIDS TO CALCULATIONS

As an alternative to performing these calculations manually, programmable calculators and computers can be used to provide assistance with the design of systems. The Committee does not recommend any specific hardware or software. Many firms have developed their own software, and there are commercially available software packages on the market. Many of these software packages are available through ACGIH.

5.7 PLENUM EXHAUST SYSTEMS

Plenum systems differ from the designs illustrated earlier (see Figures 5-4 and 5-5). Minimum transport velocities are maintained only in the branch ducts to prevent settling of particulate matter; the main duct is oversized and velocities are allowed to decrease far below normal values, many times below 1000 fpm. The function of the main duct is to provide a low pressure loss path for airflow from the various branches to the air cleaner or the fan. This helps to maintain balanced exhaust in all of the branches and often minimizes operating power.

Advantages of the plenum type exhaust system include:

1. Branch ducts can be added, removed, or relocated at any convenient point along the main duct.

2. Branch ducts can be closed off and the flow rate in the entire system reduced as long as minimum transport velocities are maintained in the remaining branches.

3. The main duct can act as a primary separator (settling chamber) for large particulate matter or liquids and refuse material which might be undesirable in the air cleaner or fan.

Limitations of this design include:

1. Sticky, linty materials, such as buffing dust, tend to clog the main duct. It may be expected that the greatest difficulty will be encountered with the drag chain type of cleaning, but the other types will be susceptible to buildup as well.

2. Materials which are subject to direct or spontaneous combustion must be handled with care. Wood dust and oil mist have been handled successfully in systems of this type; buffing dust and lint are subject to this limitation and are not recommended. Explosive dusts such as magnesium, aluminum, titanium, or grain dusts cannot be handled in systems of this type.

5.7.1 Plenum Types: Various types of plenum exhaust systems are used in industry (see Figure 5-5). They include both self-cleaning and manual-cleaning designs. Self-cleaning types include pear-shaped designs which incorporate a drag chain conveyor in the bottom of the duct to convey the dust to a chute, tote box, or enclosure for disposal. Another self-cleaning design uses a rectangular main with a belt conveyor. In these types, the conveyors may be run continuously or on periodic cycles to empty the main duct before considerable buildup and clogging occur. A third type[5.3] of self-cleaning design utilizes a standard conveying main duct system to remove the collected material from a hopper type of main duct above. Such a system is usually run continuously to avoid clogging of the pneumatic air circuit. Manual-cleaning designs may be built into the floor or may be large enclosures behind the equipment to be ventilated. Experience indicates that these should be generously oversized, particularly the underfloor designs, to permit added future exhaust capacity as well as convenient housekeeping intervals.

5.7.2 Design Procedure: Control flow rates, hoods, and duct sizes for all branches are calculated in the same manner as with tapered duct systems. The branch segment with the greatest pressure loss will govern the static pressure required in the main duct. Other branches will be designed to operate at this static pressure or locking dampers can be used to adjust their pressure loss to the same static pressure as the governing branch. Where the main duct is relatively short or where the air cleaners or fans can be spaced along the duct, static pressure losses due to airflow in the main duct can be ignored. For extremely long ducts, it is necessary to calculate the static pressure loss along the main in a manner similar to that used in the balanced and blast gate methods. Design plenum velocities are at most 1/2 the branch velocity design duct velocities and typically less than 1000 fpm. Duct connections to air cleaners, fans, and discharge to outdoors are handled in the normal manner with consideration to transport velocity.

5.8 FAN PRESSURE CALCULATIONS

Exhaust system calculations are based on static pressure; that is, all hood static pressures and balancing or governing pressures at the duct junctions are given as system static pressures which can be measured directly as described in Chapter 9. Most fan rating tables are based on Fan Static Pressure. The system static pressure from the Calculation sheet is the basis for the selection of the Fan Static Pressure. An additional calculation is required to determine the Fan Static Pressure before selecting the fan.

5.8.1 Fan Total Pressure (FTP) is the increase in total pressure through or across the fan and can be expressed by the equation:

$$FTP = TP_{outlet} - TP_{inlet} \qquad [5.2]$$

Some fan manufacturers base catalog ratings on Fan Total Pressure. To select a fan on this basis the Fan Total Pressure is calculated noting that TP = SP + VP:

$$FTP = (SP_{outlet} + VP_{outlet}) - (SP_{inlet} + VP_{inlet}) \qquad [5.3]$$

5.8.2 Fan Static Pressure: The Air Movement and Control Association Test Code defines the Fan Static Pressure (FSP) as follows: "the static pressure of the fan is the total pressure diminished by the fan velocity pressure. The fan velocity pressure is defined as the pressure corresponding to the air velocity at the fan outlet."[5.4] Fan Static Pressure can be expressed by the equation:

$$FSP = FTP - VP_{outlet} \qquad [5.4]$$

or

$$FSP = SP_{outlet} - SP_{inlet} - VP_{inlet} \qquad [5.5]$$

In selecting a fan from catalog ratings, the rating tables should be examined to determine whether they are based on Fan Static Pressure or Fan Total Pressure. Fan system effects (see Chapter 6) should also be considered when selecting a fan. The proper pressure rating can then be calculated keep-

ing in mind the proper algebraic signs; i.e., VP is always positive (+), SP_{inlet} is usually negative (-), and SP_{outlet} is usually positive (+).

The final selection of the fan must also consider the air density. Most fan tables and curves are printed for standard conditions. The final system static pressure calculated and then altered to meet the above FSP requirements must then be adjusted for air density using the following formula:

$$FSP_{specified} = FSP/df \qquad [5.5a]$$

The density factor used is the one calculated at the fan inlet. Note that this includes an adjustment for density caused by the static pressure at the fan inlet.

5.8.3 Completion of the Example on Figure 5-3: To determine the Fan Static Pressure and Fan Total Pressure that the second column (b-c) adds the fabric pressure drop through the bags in the collector. Column 3 (c-d) adds the losses from the clean air plenum to the fan inlet, and the last column determines the pressure losses through the stack.

The FSP and FTP can be calculated from these values. At the outlet of the fan, the SP must be 0.48 "wg. At the inlet to the fan, the SP is -6.56 "wg. The VP at both locations is 0.78 "wg. From Equation 5.3, the system FTP = (0.48 + 0.78) - (-6.56 + 0.78) = 7.04 "wg. From Equation 5.5, the FSP = 0.48 - (-6.56) - 0.78 = 6.26 "wg. The specified FSP or FTP is the one selected from the fan tables after the above calculation 5.5a is completed. (Assume df = 1.)

5.9 CORRECTIONS FOR VELOCITY CHANGES

Variations in duct velocity occur at many locations in exhaust systems because of necessary limitations of available standard duct sizes (area) or due to duct selections based on balanced system design. As noted earlier, small accelerations and decelerations are usually compensated automatically in the system where good design practices and proper fittings are used. There are times, however, when special circumstances require the designer to have a knowledge of the energy losses and regains which occur since these may work to his advantage or disadvantage in the final performance of the system.

5.9.1 Branch Entries to Main Ducts: Sometimes the final main duct velocity exceeds the weighted average of the two velocities in the branches entering the main. Air speed cannot be increased through the fitting without an expenditure of kinetic energy. If the difference is significant between the weighted average of the branch velocities and the final velocity is significant (greater than 0.1 "wg), additional static pressure is required to produce the increased velocity.

At any junction point, energy must be conserved. The energy entering each of the two air streams would be Q(TP) = Q(SP +VP). The first law of thermodynamics states that the sum of these must equal the energy leaving, or

$$Q_1(VP_1 + SP_1) + Q_2(VP_2 + SP_2) =$$
$$Q_3(VP_3 + SP_3) + Losses$$

Note that the overall losses would be:

Losses = $F_1Q_1VP_1 + F_2Q_2VP_2$

where the subscripts refer to the ducts shown in Figure 5-6. In this manual, F_1 is considered to be zero and F_2 is given on Figure 5-18. Assuming we are balanced and the junction losses are included such that $SP_1 = SP_2$ and $Q_3 = Q_1 + Q_2$ (see Figure 5-6), there might be an additional change in static pressure due to the acceleration or deceleration of the gas stream. The following equation shows this effect:

$$SP_3 + VP_3 = SP_1 + \left(\frac{Q_1}{Q_3}\right)VP_1 + \left(\frac{Q_2}{Q_3}\right)VP_2$$

The last two terms on the right are defined as the resultant velocity pressure, VP_r ; this can be simplified to

$$VP_r = \left(\frac{Q_1}{Q_3}\right)VP_1 + \left(\frac{Q_2}{Q_3}\right)VP_2 \qquad \textbf{[5.6]}$$

where: VP_r = resultant velocity pressure of the combined branches

Q_1 = flow rate in branch #1

Q_2 = flow rate in branch #2

Q_3 = combined flow rate leaving the junction

Note that the above equation is valid for all conditions, including merging different density gas streams, as long as the velocity pressures include the density effects. Also note that, if the flow rate through one branch was changed to balance at the branch entry, the corrected velocity pressure and corrected flow rates should be used in Equation 5.6.

The resultant velocity pressure (VP_r) (also called "weighted average velocity pressure") is computed using Equation 5.6. Note that VP_r is not a measurable value in the system. It is a computed value only. VP_3 is less than VP_r, a deceleration has occurred and SP has increased. No adjustment is made in the calculations in this case. However, if VP_3 is greater than VP_r, an acceleration has occurred. The difference between VP_3 and VP_r is the necessary loss in SP required to produce the increase in kinetic energy as air travels from the branches into the main duct. The correction is made as follows:

$$SP_3 = SP_1 - (VP_3 - VP_r) \qquad \textbf{[5.7]}$$

where: SP_3 = SP in main #3

SP_1 = SP at branch #1 = SP at branch #2

VP_3 = velocity pressure in main #3

In the Calculation sheet, this is now shown in Line 40 of the downstream branch where the increase in velocity is considered. If this value is higher than the VP in that branch (Line 13), then the difference is added to the static pressure losses of that branch.

EXAMPLE

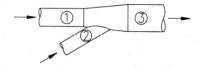

Duct No.	Dia.	Area	Q	V	VP	SP
(1)	10	0.545	1935	3550	0.79	−2.11
(2)	4	0.087	340	3890	0.94	−2.11
Main (3)	10	0.545	2275	4170	1.08	−

FIGURE 5–6. Branch entry velocity correction

With the data shown in Figure 5-6,

$$VP_r = \frac{(1935)(0.79)}{2275} + \frac{(340)(0.94)}{2275} = 0.81 \text{ "wg}$$

$$SP_3 = SP_1 - (VP_3 - VP_r) = -2.11 - (1.08 - 0.81) =$$
$$-2.11 - 0.27 = -2.38 \text{ "wg}$$

Therefore, in this situation, an additional -0.27 "wg should be added to the junction SP to account for losses in pressure due to acceleration of the air stream.

5.9.2 Contractions and Expansions: Contractions are used when the size of the duct must be reduced to fit into tight places, to fit equipment, or to provide a high discharge velocity at the end of the stack. Expansions are used to fit a particular piece of equipment or to reduce the energy consumed in the system by reducing velocity and friction. Expansions are not desirable in transport systems since the duct velocity may become less than the minimum transport velocity and material may settle in the ducts.

Regain of pressure in a duct system is possible because static pressure and velocity pressure are mutually convertible. This conversion is accompanied by some energy loss. The amount of this loss is a function of the geometry of the transition piece (the more abrupt the change in velocity, the greater the loss) and depends on whether air is accelerated or decelerated. Loss is expressed as a loss coefficient multiplied by the velocity pressure in the smaller area duct of the transition piece. One minus the loss coefficient is the efficiency of the energy conversion or regain.

A perfect (no loss) contraction or expansion would cause no change in the total pressure in the duct. There would be an increase or decrease in static pressure corresponding exactly to the decrease or increase in velocity pressure of the air. In practice, the contraction or expansion will not be perfect, and there will be a change in total pressure (see Figure 5-7). In each example, total pressure and static pressure are plotted in order to show their relationship at various points in each system. See Figure 5-18 for design data.

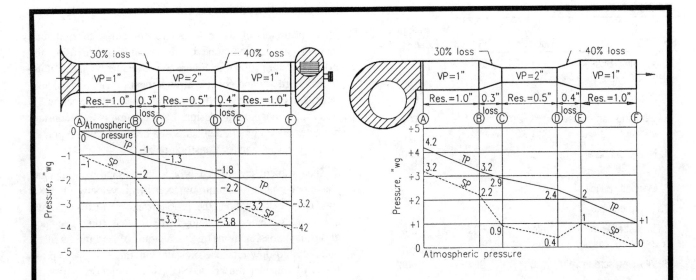

EXAMPLE—DUCT LOCATED ON SUCTION SIDE OF FAN
Velocity changes as indicated. Since all the ductwork is on the suction side of the fan, TP at the fan inlet (point F) is equal to VP at the fan inlet plus the total duct resistance up to that point. This equals −4.2 SP since static pressure on the suction side of the fan is always negative. The duct system is the same as was used in Example 2 and therefore has the same overall resistance of 3.2. If it is again assumed that the inlet and discharge of the fan are equal areas, the total pressure across the fan will be the same as in Example 1 and in each case, the fan will deliver the same air horsepower when handling equal volumes of air.

Static pressure conversion between B and C follows contraction formula (Figure 5-18). There must be sufficient SP at B to furnish the additional VP required at C. In addition, the energy transfer between these two points is accompanied by a loss of 0.3. Since SP at B =−2, SP at C=−2.0+(−1.0)+(−0.3)=−3.3

Static pressure regain between D and E follows the regain formulae (Figure 5-18). If there were no losses in the transition piece, the difference of 1 in velocity pressure would be regained as the static pressure at E, and SP at that point would be −2.8. However, the transition is only 60% efficient (0.4 loss) so the SP at E=−2.8+(−0.4)=−3.2.

EXAMPLE—DUCT LOCATED ON DISCHARGE SIDE OF FAN. Velocity changes as indicated. The ductwork is located all on the fan discharge side of the fan. Total pressure at the fan discharge (point A) is equal to the velocity pressure at the discharge end of the duct (point F) plus the accumulated resistances. These add up to 1.0+1.0+.04+.05+.03+1.0=4.2

Static pressure regain between D and E follows the regain formulae (Figure 5-18). If there were no energy loss in the transition piece, static pressure at D would be 0 because the difference in VP of 1 would show up as static pressure regain. However, the transition is only 60% efficient which means a loss of 0.4, so at point D=0+0.4=0.4

Conversion of static pressure into velocity pressure between B and C follows contraction formulae (Figure 5-18). There must be sufficient static pressure at B to furnish the additional velocity pressure required at C. In addition, transformation of energy between these two points is accompanied by a loss of 0.3. Since SP at C =0.9, SP at B=0.9+0.3+1.0=2.2. Since there is no ductwork on the suction side of the fan, total pressure against which the fan is operating is 4.2".

AMERICAN CONFERENCE OF GOVERNMENTAL INDUSTRIAL HYGIENISTS	*EXPANSIONS AND CONTRACTIONS*	
	DATE *1−95*	FIGURE *5−7*

TABLE 5-2. Details of Operation

No.	Hood No.	VS-Print	Minimum Exhaust, cfm
1. Vibrating Shakeout 4' × 6' grate	1	20-02	9600
2. Shakeout hopper	2	20-03	960
3. Vibrating pan feeder 24" wide	3	20-03	700
4. Incline sand belt 24" × 28' long	5		700
5. Magnetic pulley			
6. Tramp iron box			
7. Bucket elevator 24" × 30" casing	7a(lower) 7b(upper)	50-01	250 250
8. Vibrating screen 24 ft²	8	99-01	1200
9. Sand bin 600 ft³ 18" × 20" opening	9	50-10	500
10. Waste sand box 44" × 54", 6" clearance	10	99-03 (V = 150 fpm)	1225
11. Sand weigh hopper	11	60-02	900
12. Sand muller 6' dia.	12	60-02	
13. Wet dust collector (includes fan)			

DIMENSIONS				
No. of Branch or Main	CFM Required, Minimum	Straight Run, ft	Elbows	Entries
1-A	9600	13	1-90°	
2-B	960	3	1-60°	1-30°
3-B	700	4	1-90° + 1-60°	1-30°
B-A	1660	18	2-90°	1-30°
A-C	11,260	34		
5-D	700	7	1-30° + 1-60°	1-30°
7a-D	250	5		
D-C	950	14	1-90° + 1-60°	1-30°
C-E	12,210	6.5		
8-F	1200	11	2-90°	
9-F	500	4	1-90° + 1-60°	1-30°
F-G	1700	5		
7b-G	250	15	1-60°	1-30°
G-E	1950	6	1-60°	1-30°
E-H	14,160	3.5		
10-J	1225	6	1-45°	
12-J	900	2.5	1-30°	1-30°
J-H	2125	8	1-90° + 1-60°	1-30°
H-K	16,285	9	2-45°	
13	16,285			
14-L	16,285	20		

5.10 SAMPLE SYSTEM DESIGN

A discussion of the calculations for either tapered duct method can best be done by a typical example using the exhaust system shown in Figure 5-8. Calculation sheets illustrate the orderly and concise arrangement of data and calculations (see Figures 5-9). The procedure outlined in Section 5.3 was used to develop the design. Each column is for a constant diameter duct segment that starts at a hood, junction point, air cleaning device, fan, or transition point.

The problem considered is a foundry sand-handling and shake-out system. A minimum conveying velocity of 3,500 fpm is used throughout the problem except in ducts where excess moisture or dust loading increases that value. The operations, hood designations on the diagram, VS-print references, and required flow rates are presented in Table 5-2. This problem will consider the air at "Standard" conditions (70 F, no moisture and the system at sea level; df = 1). This seldom occurs under real conditions and most systems will require some adjustment for non-standard conditions.

5.11 DIFFERENT DUCT MATERIAL FRICTION LOSSES

The friction loss table, Table 5-5, provides average values for galvanized sheet metal duct material (0.0005 feet equivalent sand grain roughness, where the roughness height represents the average height of the roughness elements of the material). Table 5-6 provides the same information for black iron and other materials possessing a roughness height of 0.00015 feet. The values in both tables can be used with no significant error for the majority of designs but special considerations may be desired if environmental conditions could significantly affect the duct design parameters. If the design uses special material such as spiral or flexible duct, operates at a non-standard density, or is very hot, the duct material manufacturer should be consulted to determine anticipated friction loss.

5.12 FRICTION LOSS FOR NON-CIRCULAR DUCTS

Round ducts are strongly recommended for industrial exhaust systems because of a more uniform air velocity to resist settling of material and an ability to withstand higher static pressure. At times, however, the designer must use other duct shapes.

Rectangular duct friction can be calculated by using Table 5-5 or 5-6 in conjunction with Table 5-9 to obtain circular equivalents for rectangular ducts on the basis of equal friction loss. It should be noted that, on this basis, the area of the rectangular duct will be larger than the equivalent round duct; consequently, the actual air velocity in the duct will be reduced. Therefore, it is necessary to use care to maintain minimum transport velocities. Even if the average velocity requirements are met, the flow characteristics in rectangular ducts could yield dead spots and opportunities for material to settle out in corners.

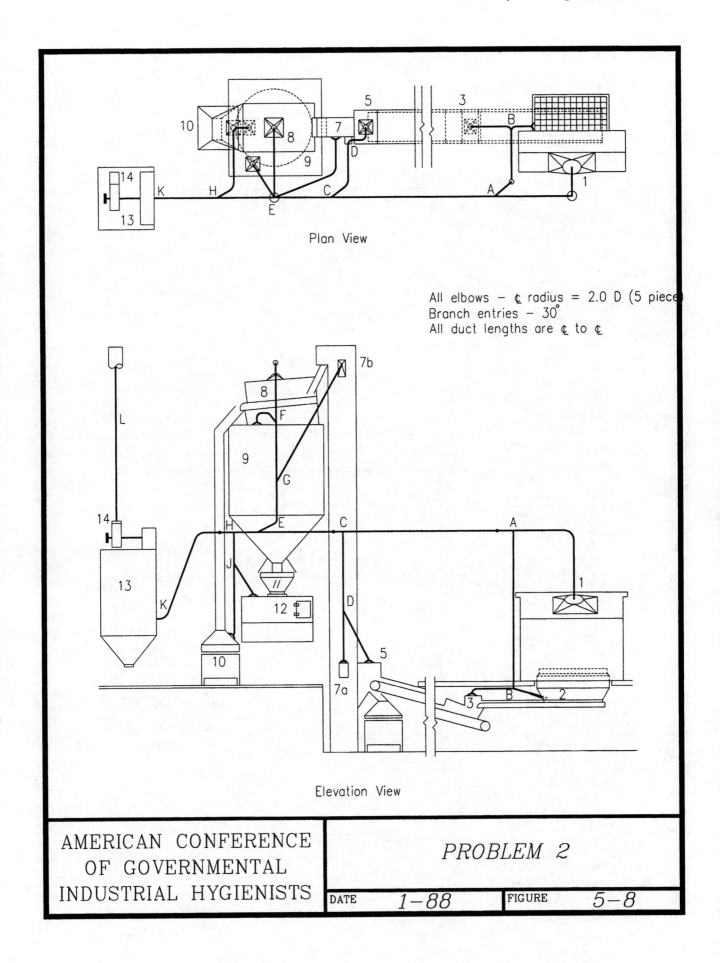

Plan View

All elbows — ¢ radius = 2.0 D (5 piece)
Branch entries — 30°
All duct lengths are ¢ to ¢

Elevation View

AMERICAN CONFERENCE
OF GOVERNMENTAL
INDUSTRIAL HYGIENISTS

PROBLEM 2

| DATE | *1—88* | FIGURE | *5—8* |

Velocity Pressure Method Calculation Sheet

Elevation ___0___ (z)

Project ___Problem 2 Sheet 1 — Figure 5-9___   Designer _____

#	Sym	Description		Formula	Units		2-B	3-B	B-A	1-A
1*		Duct Segment Identification					2-B	3-B	B-A	1-A
2*	T	Dry-Bulb Temperature			F		70	70	70	70
3*	Q_{std}	Standard Volumetric Flow Rate			scfm		960	700	1711	9600
4*	V_t	Minimum Transport Velocity			fpm		4000	4000	4000	4000
5*	m_{H2O}	Lbs Water per Minute			#H₂O/min					
6*	m_{da}	Lbs Dry Air per Minute			#da/min					
7	df	Density Factor		Eqn 2			1	1	1	1
8	Q_{act}	Actual Volumetric Flow Rate		Eqn 3	acfm		960	700	1711	9600
9	A_t	Target Duct Area ***		(3/4std)(8/4nstd)	ft²		6.63	5.86	8.86	20.97
10	d	Selected Duct Diameter			inches		6	5.5	8	20
11	A	Selected Duct Area			ft²		0.1963	0.1650	0.3491	2.1617
12	V_d	Duct Velocity ***		(3/11std)(8/11nstd)	fpm		4889	4243	4902	4400
13	VP_d	Duct Velocity Pressure		Eqn 5	"wg		1.49	1.12	1.5	1.21
14	h	Total Heat		branch balance	btu/#da					
15*	A_s	H	S	Slot Area	ft²					4.8
16*	F_s	O	L	Slot Loss Coefficient						1.78
17*		O	O	Acceleration Factor	0 or 1					0
18	V_s	D	T	Slot Velocity	8/15	fpm				2000
19	VP_s			Slot Velocity Pressure	Eqn 5	"wg				0.25
20		L		Slot Loss in VP	16+17					1.78
21		O		Slot Static Pressure	20x19	"wg				0.44
22*	F_h	S		Duct Entry Coefficient			0.25	0.25		0.25
23*		S		Acceleration Factor	1 or 0		1	1		1
24				Duct Entry Loss in VP	22+23		1.25	1.25		1.25
25		E		Duct Entry Loss	24x13	"wg	1.86	1.40		1.51
26		S		Other Losses		"wg				
27	SP_h			Hood Static Pressure	21+25+26	"wg	1.40	1.40		1.95
28*	L			Straight Duct Length		ft	3	4	18	13
29*	H_f			Duct Friction Factor	Eqn 8		0.0425	0.0478	0.0299	0.0098
30*		D		No. of 90 Degree Elbows			0.67	1.67	2	1
31*	F_{el}	U		Elbow Loss Coefficient	Table 6		0.19	0.19	0.19	0.19
32*	F_{en}	C		Branch Entry Coefficient	Table 7		0.18	0.18	0.18	
33*		T		Special Fitting Coefficient						
34	h_f			Duct Friction Loss in VP	28x29		0.13	0.19	0.54	0.13
35		L		Elbow Loss in VP	30x31		0.13	0.32	0.38	0.19
36		O		Branch Entry Loss in VP	32		0.18	0.18	0.18	
37		S		Duct Loss in VP	33+34+35+36		0.43	0.69	1.10	0.32
38		S		Duct Loss	37x13	"wg	0.65	0.77	1.64	0.38
39*		E		Other Losses		"wg				
40	VP_r	S		Resultant Velocity Pressure	Eqn 9	"wg			1.4	
41				Loss from Velocity Increase	13-40 (if>0)	"wg			0.10	
42				Duct Pressure Loss	27+38+39+41	"wg	-2.51	-2.18	-1.64	-2.34
43*	SP_{gov}	Governing Static Pressure			"wg			-2.18		
44	SP_{cum}	Cumulative Static Pressure			"wg		-2.51	-2.18	-4.25	-2.34
45	Q_{corr}	Corrected Volumetric Flow Rate		Eqn 10	acfm					
46	V_{corr}	Corrected Velocity		45 / 11	fpm					
47	VP_{corr}	Corrected Velocity Pressure		Eqn 5	"wg					

* Data Input
** Shaded lines 5, 6, 7, 8 & 14 used for non-standard calculations
*** std is for standard calculations and nst is for non-standard calculations

Date_____

1-A	A-C	7a-D	5-D	5-D	D-C	D-C	C-E	
1-A	A-C	7a-D	5-D	5-D	D-C	D-C	C-E	1*
70	70	70	70	70	70	70	70	2*
9600	12127	250	700	700	955	955	13130	3*
4000	4000	3500	3500	3500	3500	3500	4000	4*
								5*
								6*
1	1	1	1	1	1	1	1	7
9600	12127	250	700	700	955	955	13130	8
	23.58	3.62	6.05		7.07		24.53	9
18	22	3.5	6	5.5	7	6	24	10
1.7671	2.6398	0.0668	0.79	1.12	0.80	1.47	1.09	11
5432	4594	3742	3565	4243	3573	4864	4179	12
1.84	1.32	0.87	0.79	1.12	0.80	1.47	1.09	13
								14*
4.8								15*
1.78								16*
0								17*
2000								18
0.25								19
1.78								20
0.44								21
0.25		1.0	0.25	0.25				22*
1		1	1	1				23*
1.25		20.	1.25	1.25				24
2.30		1.74	0.99	1.40				25
								26
2.74		1.74	0.99	1.40			14	27
13	34	5	7	7			6.5	28*
0.0110	0.0087	0.0840	0.0436	0.0478	0.0361	0.0425	0.0079	29*
1			1	1	1.67	1.67		30*
0.33			0.19	0.19	0.19	0.19		31*
			0.18	0.18	0.18	0.18		32*
								33*
0.14	0.30	0.42	0.30	0.33	0.51	0.60	0.05	34
0.33			0.19	0.19	0.32	0.32		35
			0.18	0.18	0.18	0.18		36
0.47	0.30	0.42	0.67	0.70	1.01	1.10	0.05	37
0.67	0.39	0.37	0.53	0.79	0.80	1.61	0.06	38
								39*
						1.06		40
						0.41		41
-3.61	-0.39	-2.11	-1.52	-2.19	-0.80	-1.61	-0.06	42
-4.25		-2.19				-4.62		43*
-3.61	-4.64	-2.11						44
								45
								46
								47

1

$$\omega = \#H_2O/\#Dry\ Air$$

2

$$df = df_e \cdot df_p \cdot df_t \cdot df_m$$

$$df_e = [1 - (6.73 \cdot 10^{-6})(z)]^{5.258}$$

$$df_p = (407 + SP)/(407)$$

$$df_t = (530)/(T + 460)$$

$$df_m = (1 + \omega)/(1 + 1.607\omega)$$

3

$$Q_{act} = Q_{std}\,((1 + \omega)/df)$$

4

$$V = 4005\sqrt{VP/df}$$

5

$$VP = df(V/4005)^2$$

6

90° Round Elbow Loss Coefficients
(5 Piece)

R/D	Coefficient
1.5	0.24
2.0	0.19
2.5	0.17

7

Branch Entry Loss Coefficients

Angle	Coefficient
15°	0.09
30°	0.18
45°	0.28

8

$$H_f^{(galvanized)} = 0.0307(V^{0.533}/Q^{0.612})$$

$$H_f^{(black\ iron)} = 0.0425(V^{0.465}/Q^{0.602})$$

$$H_f^{(flexible)} = 0.0311(V^{0.604}/Q^{0.639})$$

9

$$VP_f = (Q_1/Q_3)(VP_1) + (Q_2/Q_3)(VP_2)$$

10

$$Q_{corr} = Q_{design}\sqrt{SP_{gov}/SP_{duct}}$$

11

$$FAN\ SP = SP_{out} - SP_{in} - VP_{in}$$

Velocity Pressure Method Calculation Sheet

Elevation ___0___ (z)

Project_____Problem 2 Sheet 2_____   Designer_____

#	Sym	Description	Formula	Units			8-F	9-F	9-F	F-G
1*		Duct Segment Identification					8-F	9-F	9-F	F-G
2*	T	Dry-Bulb Temperature				F	70	70	70	70
3*	Q_{std}	Standard Volumetric Flow Rate				scfm	1200	500	500	1730
4*	V_t	Minimum Transport Velocity				fpm	3500	3500	3500	3500
5*	m_{H2O}	Lbs Water per Minute				#H₂O/min				
6*	m_{da}	Lbs Dry Air per Minute				#da/min				
7	df	Density Factor	Eqn 2				1	1	1	1
8	Q_{act}	Actual Volumetric Flow Rate	Eqn 3			acfm	1200	500	500	1730
9	A_t	Target Duct Area	(3/4std)(8/4nstd)			ft²	0.342	0.142		0.494
10	d	Selected Duct Diameter				inches	7	5	4.5	9
11	A	Selected Duct Area				ft²	0.2673	0.1364	0.1104	0.4418
12	V_d	Duct Velocity	(3/11std)(8/11nstd)			fpm	4490	3667	4527	3916
13	VP_d	Duct Velocity Pressure	Eqn 5			"wg	1.26	0.84	1.28	0.96
14	h	Total Heat	branch balance			btu/#da				
15*	A_s	Slot Area				ft²				
16*	F_s	Slot Loss Coefficient								
17*		Acceleration Factor				0 or 1				
18	V_s	Slot Velocity		8/15		fpm				
19	VP_s	Slot Velocity Pressure		Eqn 5		"wg				
20		Slot Loss in VP		16+17						
21		Slot Static Pressure		20x19		"wg				
22*	F_h	Duct Entry Coefficient					0.5	0.25	0.25	
23*		Acceleration Factor		1 or 0			1	1	1	
24		Duct Entry Loss in VP		22+23			1.5	1.25	1.25	
25		Duct Entry Loss		24x13		"wg	1.89	1.05	1.60	
26		Other Losses				"wg				
27	SP_h	Hood Static Pressure		21+25+26		"wg	1.89	1.05	1.60	
28*	L	Straight Duct Length				ft	11	4	4	5
29*	H_f	Duct Friction Factor		Eqn 8			0.0354	0.0543	0.0608	0.0263
30*		No. of 90 Degree Elbows					1	1.67	1.67	
31*	F_{el}	Elbow Loss Coefficient		Table 6			0.19	0.19	0.19	
32*	F_{en}	Branch Entry Coefficient		Table 7				0.18	0.18	
33*		Special Fitting Coefficient								
34	h_f	Duct Friction Loss in VP		28x29			0.39	0.22	0.24	0.12
35		Elbow Loss in VP		30x31			0.38	0.32	0.32	
36		Branch Entry Loss in VP		32				0.18	0.18	
37		Duct Loss in VP		33+34+35+36			0.77	0.71	0.74	0.12
38		Duct Loss		37x13		"wg	0.97	0.60	0.95	0.12
39*		Other Losses				"wg				
40	VP_r	Resultant Velocity Pressure		Eqn 9		"wg				1.31
41		Loss from Velocity Increase		13-40 (if>0)		"wg				
42		Duct Pressure Loss		27+38+39+41		"wg	-2.86	-1.65	-2.55	-0.12
43*	SP_{gov}	Governing Static Pressure				"wg				-2.86
44	SP_{cum}	Cumulative Static Pressure				"wg				-2.98
45	Q_{corr}	Corrected Volumetric Flow Rate		Eqn 10		acfm			530	
46	V_{corr}	Corrected Velocity		45 / 11		fpm			4801	
47	VP_{corr}	Corrected Velocity Pressure		Eqn 5		"wg			1.44	

HOOD LOSSES (SLOT, rows 15-27)

DUCT LOSSES (rows 28-42)

* Data Input
** Shaded lines 5, 6, 7, 8 & 14 used for non-standard calculations
*** std is for standard calculations and nst is for non-standard calculations

7b-G	G-E	G-E	E-H	12-J	10-J	10-J	J-H	#	Formula
								1*	$\omega = \#H_2O/\#\text{Dry Air}$
70	70	70	70	70	70	70	70	2*	
250	2017	2017	15308	900	1225	1225	2274	3*	$df = df_e \cdot df_p \cdot df_t \cdot df_m$
3500	3500	3500	4000	4500	3500	3500	4500	4*	$df_e = [1-(6.73 \cdot 10^{-6})(z)]^{5.258}$
								5*	$df_p = (407+SP)/(407)$
								6*	$df_t = (530)/(T+460)$
1	1	1	1	1	1	1	1	7	$df_m = (1+\omega)/(1+1.607\omega)$
250	2017	2017	15308	900	1225	1225	2274	8	
0.071	.0576		3.827	0.20	0.35		0.505	9	$Q_{act} = Q_{std}\,((1+\omega)/df)$
3.5	10	9	26	6	8	7	9	10	
0.0668	0.5454	0.4418	3.687	0.1963	0.3391	0.2673	0.4418	11	$V = 4005\sqrt{VP/df}$
3742	3698	4566	4152	4584	3509	4584	5147	12	
0.87	0.85	1.32	1.07	1.31	0.77	1.31	1.65	13	$VP = df(V/4005)^2$
								14*	
								15*	
								16*	
								17*	90° Round Elbow Loss Coefficients (5 Piece)
								18	
								19	R/D — Coefficient
								20	1.5 — 0.24
								21	2.0 — 0.19
1.0				0.25	0.25	0.25		22*	2.5 — 0.17
1				1	1	1		23*	
2.0				1.25	1.25	1.25		24	Branch Entry Loss Coefficients
1.74				1.64	0.96	1.64		25	
								26	Angle — Coefficient
1.74				1.64	0.96	1.64		27	15° — 0.09
15	6	6	3.5	11	6	6	8	28*	30° — 0.18
0.0840	0.0232	0.0260	0.0072	0.0427	0.0307	0.0354	0.0258	29*	45° — 0.28
0.67	0.67	0.67		0.33	0.5	0.5	1.67	30*	$H_f^{(galvanized)} = 0.0307(V^{0.533}/Q^{0.612})$
0.19	0.19	0.19		0.19	0.19	0.19	0.19	31*	$H_f^{(black\ iron)} = 0.0425(V^{0.465}/Q^{0.602})$
0.18	0.18	0.18		0.18			0.18	32*	$H_f^{(flexible)} = 0.0311(V^{0.604}/Q^{0.639})$
								33*	
1.26	0.14	0.16	0.03	0.47	0.18	0.21	0.21	34	$VP_f = (Q_1/Q_3)(VP_1)+(Q_2/Q_3)(VP_2)$
0.13	0.13	0.13		0.06	0.10	0.10	0.32	35	
0.18	0.18	0.18		0.18			0.18	36	$Q_{corr} = Q_{design}\sqrt{SP_{gov}/SP_{duct}}$
1.57	0.45	0.47	0.03	0.71	0.28	0.31	0.61	37	
1.37	0.38	0.60	0.03	0.94	0.21	0.41	1.01	38	$\text{FAN SP} = SP_{out}-SP_{in}-VP_{in}$
								39*	
	0.98	0.98	1.15				1.47	40	
		0.34					0.18	41	
-3.11	-3.80	-0.94	-.03	-2.58	-1.17	-2.05	-1.19	42	
	-4.70	-4.70				-2.58	-4.73	43*	
-3.11	-3.49	-4.05	-4.73	-2.58	-1.17	-2.05	-3.77	44	
		2178				1374	2492	45	
		4430				5140	5641	46	
		1.52				1.65	1.98	47	

Velocity Pressure Method Calculation Sheet

Elevation ___0___ (z)

Project _____ Problem 2 Sheet 3 _____   Designer _____

1*		Duct Segment Identification			H-K	K-Fan	Fan-L	
2*	T	Dry-Bulb Temperature		F	70	70	70	
3*	Q_{std}	Standard Volumetric Flow Rate		scfm	17800	17800	17800	
4*	V_t	Minimum Transport Velocity		fpm	4500	2600	2600	
5*	m_{H2O}	Lbs Water per Minute		#H$_2$O/min				
6*	m_{da}	Lbs Dry Air per Minute		#da/min				
7	df	Density Factor	Eqn 2		1	1	1	
8	Q_{act}	Actual Volumetric Flow Rate	Eqn 3	acfm	17800	17800	17800	
9	A_t	Target Duct Area	(3/4std)(8/4nstd)	ft^2	3.95	6.85	6.85	
10	d	Selected Duct Diameter		inches	26	35.5	34	
11	A	Selected Duct Area		ft^2	3.687	6.874	6.305	
12	V_d	Duct Velocity	(3/11std)(8/11nstd)	fpm	4828	2590	2823	
13	VP_d	Duct Velocity Pressure	Eqn 5	"wg	1.45	0.42	0.50	
14	h	Total Heat	branch balance	btu/#da				
15*	A_s		Slot Area	ft^2				
16*	F_s	H	Slot Loss Coefficient					
17*		O S	Acceleration Factor		0 or 1			
18	V_s	O L	Slot Velocity	8/15	fpm			
19	VP_s	D O	Slot Velocity Pressure	Eqn 5	"wg			
20		T	Slot Loss in VP	16+17				
21			Slot Static Pressure	20x19	"wg			
22*	F_h	L	Duct Entry Coefficient					
23*		O	Acceleration Factor		1 or 0			
24		S	Duct Entry Loss in VP	22+23				
25		S	Duct Entry Loss	24x13	"wg			
26		E	Other Losses		"wg			
27	SP_h	S	Hood Static Pressure	21+25+26	"wg			
28*	L		Straight Duct Length		ft	9	2	20	
29*	H_f		Duct Friction Factor	Eqn 8		0.0071	0.005	0.0053	
30*		D	No. of 90 Degree Elbows			1			
31*	F_{el}	U	Elbow Loss Coefficient	Table 6		0.19			
32*	F_{en}	C	Branch Entry Coefficient	Table 7					
33*		T	Special Fitting Coefficient						
34	h_f		Duct Friction Loss in VP	28x29		0.06	0.01	0.11	
35		L	Elbow Loss in VP	30x31		0.19			
36		O	Branch Entry Loss in VP	32					
37		S	Duct Loss in VP	33+34+35+36		0.25	0.01	0.11	
38		S	Duct Loss	37x13	"wg	0.37	0.00	0.05	
39*		E	Other Losses		"wg		4.4		
40	VP_r	S	Resultant Velocity Pressure	Eqn 9	"wg	1.20			
41			Loss from Velocity Increase	13-40 (if>0)	"wg	0.25			
42			Duct Pressure Loss	27+38+39+41	"wg	-0.62	-4.5		
43*	SP_{gov}	Governing Static Pressure		"wg				
44	SP_{cum}	Cumulative Static Pressure		"wg	-5.35	-9.85	+0.13	
45	Q_{corr}	Corrected Volumetric Flow Rate	Eqn 10	acfm				
46	V_{corr}	Corrected Velocity	45 / 11	fpm				
47	VP_{corr}	Corrected Velocity Pressure	Eqn 5	"wg				

* Data Input   Date_____

** Shaded lines 5, 6, 7, 8 & 14 used for non-standard calculations

*** std is for standard calculations and nst is for non-standard calculations

									1*	**1**
									2*	$\omega = \#H_2O/\#Dry\ Air$
									3*	
									4*	**2**
									5*	$df = df_e*df_p*df_t*df_m$
									6*	$df_e = [1-(6.73*10^{-6})(z)]^{5.258}$
									7	$df_p = (407+SP)/(407)$
									8	$df_t = (530)/(T+460)$
									9	$df_m = (1+\omega)/(1+1.607\omega)$
									10	
									11	
									12	**3**
									13	$Q_{act} = Q_{std}\ ((1+\omega)/df)$
									14*	
									15*	**4**
									16*	$V = 4005\sqrt{VP/df}$
									17*	**5**
									18	$VP = df(V/4005)^2$
									19	
									20	**6**
									21	90° Round Elbow Loss Coefficients
									22*	(5 Piece)
									23*	
									24	R/D Coefficient
									25	1.5 0.24
									26	2.0 0.19
									27	2.5 0.17
									28*	**7**
									29*	Branch Entry Loss Coefficients
									30*	
									31*	Angle Coefficient
									32*	15° 0.09
									33*	30° 0.18
									34	45° 0.28
									35	**8**
									36	$H_f^{(galvanized)} = 0.0307(V^{0.533}/Q^{0.612})$
									37	$H_f^{(black\ iron)} = 0.0425(V^{0.465}/Q^{0.602})$
									38	
									39*	$H_f^{(flexible)} = 0.0311(V^{0.604}/Q^{0.639})$
									40	**9**
									41	$VP_f = (Q_1/Q_3)(VP_1)+(Q_2/Q_3)(VP_2)$
									42	
									43*	**10**
									44	$Q_{corr} = Q_{design}\sqrt{SP_{gov}/SP_{duct}}$
									45	**11**
									46	$FAN\ SP = SP_{out}-SP_{in}-VP_{in}$
									47	

Occasionally the designer will find it necessary to estimate the air handling ability of odd-shaped ducts. The following procedure[5.5] will be helpful in determining the frictional pressure losses for such ducts. The wetted perimeter in the following discussion is the inside perimeter of the odd-shaped duct corresponding to the cross-sectional area.

1. Find duct cross-sectional area, ft^2 . . . . A
2. Find wetted perimeter, ft . . . . P
3. Calculate hydraulic radius, ft . . . . R (R = A/P)
4. Convert R to inches . . . . r (r = 12R)
5. Calculate equivalent diameter, in . . . . D (D = 4r)
6. Use the proper friction table based on the equivalent diameter and flow rate (or velocity).

5.13 CORRECTIONS FOR NON-STANDARD DENSITY

The example shown in Problem 2 considers only standard air density—something that rarely occurs in real system design. It simplifies the calculations by assuming that air is constantly at standard conditions. Even though the effects of moisture, elevation, and temperature can be small when considered independently, they can have significant, additive effects when considered together.

Fan tables and hood exhaust flow rate requirements assume a *standard air density* of 0.075 lbm/ft^3, which corresponds to sea level pressure, no moisture, and 70 F. Changes in air density can come from several factors, including elevation, temperature, internal duct pressure, changes in apparent molecular weight (moisture content, gas stream constituents, etc.), and amount of suspended particulate. In almost all system design, the change in air density should be considered.

Factors for different temperatures and elevations are listed in Table 5-10. Similarly, internal duct pressures will change air density and can have a significant effect, especially at the fan inlet. If there is excessive moisture in the airstream, the density will decrease. Suspended particulate is assumed to be only a trace impurity in industrial exhaust systems. If there are significant quantities of particulate in the duct system, this addition to the air stream density should be addressed. This field is called material conveying and is beyond the scope of this manual.

The density variation equations of Chapter 1 (Section 1.4) demonstrate that if temperature increases or absolute pressure decreases, the density will decrease if the *mass* flow rate at the hood(s) remains the same; the volume flow rate must change if density changes. It is helpful to remember that a fan connected to a given system will exhaust the same VOLUME flow rate regardless of air density. The mass of air moved, however, will be a function of the density.

5.13.1 Variable Temperature and/or Different Altitude:
Consider an exhaust system at sea level where 5,000 SCFM of air at 70 F is drawn into a hood. The air is then heated to 600 F and the density of the air leaving the heater becomes 0.0375 lbm/ft^3. The flow rate downstream of the heater would be 10,000 actual cubic feet per minute (acfm) at the new density

of 0.0375 lbm/ft^3. This is true because the 50% decrease in density *must* correspond to a twofold increase in the volume flow rate since the mass flow rate has remained constant.

If this temperature effect is ignored and a fan selected for 5,000 cfm is placed in the system, the hood flow rate will be well below that required to maintain contaminant control. The exact operating point of such a system would have to be recalculated based upon the operating point of the incorrectly sized fan.

5.13.2 Elevated Moisture:
When air temperature is under 100 F correction for humidity is minimal and may be ignored if there are no other corrections in the system for density changes. When air temperature exceeds 100 F and moisture content is greater than 0.02 lbs H$_2$O per pound of dry air (Dew Point of 80 F), correction is required to determine fan operating RPM and power. Correction coefficients may be read from the psychrometric charts such as those illustrated in Figures 5-20 through 5-23.

5.13.3 Psychrometric Principles:
The properties of moist air are presented on the psychrometric chart at a single pressure. These parameters define the physical properties of an air/water vapor mixture. *The actual gas flow rate and the density of the gas stream at the inlet of the fan must be known in order to select the fan.* The psychrometric chart provides the information required to calculate changes in the flow rate and density of the gas as it passes through the various exhaust system components. These properties are:

- **Dry-Bulb Temperature** is the temperature observed with an ordinary thermometer. Expressed in degrees Fahrenheit, it may be read directly on the chart and is indicated on the bottom horizontal scale.

- **Wet-Bulb Temperature** is the temperature at which liquid or solid water, by evaporating into air, can bring the air to saturation adiabatically at the same temperature. Expressed in degrees Fahrenheit, it is read directly at the intersection of the constant enthalpy line with the 100% saturation curve.

- **Dew Point Temperature** is that temperature at which the air in an air/vapor mixture becomes saturated with water vapor and any further reduction of dry-bulb temperature causes the water vapor to condense or deposit as drops of water. Expressed in degrees Fahrenheit, it is read directly at the intersection of the saturation curve with a horizontal line representing constant moisture content.

- **Percent Saturation** curves reflect the mass of moisture actually in the air as a percentage of the total amount possible at the various dry-bulb and moisture content combinations. Expressed in percent, it may be read directly from the curved lines on the chart.

- **Density Factor** is a dimensionless quantity which expresses the ratio of the actual density of the mixture to the density of standard air (0.075 lbm/ft^3). The lines representing density factor typically do not appear on low-temperature psychrometric charts when relative humidity or percent saturation curves are presented. A method of calculating the density of the gas defined by a point on the chart (when density factor curves are not presented) is discussed in Section 5.13.4.

- **Moisture Content**, or weight of water vapor, is the amount of water which has been evaporated into the air. In ordinary air, it is very low pressure steam and has been evaporated into the air at a temperature corresponding to the boiling point of water at that low pressure. Moisture content is expressed in grains of water vapor per pound of dry air (7,000 grains = one pound) or pounds of water vapor per pound of dry air and is read directly from a vertical axis.

- **Enthalpy (Total Heat)** as shown on the psychrometric chart is the sum of the heat required to raise the temperature of a pound of air from 0 F to the dry-bulb temperature, plus the heat required to raise the temperature of the water contained in that pound of air from 32 F to the dew point temperature, plus the latent heat of vaporization, plus the heat required to superheat the vapor in a pound of air from the dew point temperature to the dry-bulb temperature. Expressed in BTUs per pound of dry air, it is shown by following the diagonal wet-bulb temperature lines.

- **Humid Volume** is the volume occupied by the air/vapor mixture per pound of dry air and is expressed in cubic feet of mixture per pound of dry air. It is most important to understand the dimensions of this parameter and realize that the reciprocal of humid volume is not density. Humid volume is the parameter used most frequently in determining flow rate changes within a system as a result of mixing gases of different properties or when evaporative cooling occurs within the system.

5.13.4 Density Determination: When the quality of an air/vapor mixture is determined by a point on a psychrometric chart having a family of density factor curves, all that must be done to determine the actual density of the gas at the pressure reference for which the chart is drawn is to multiply the density factor taken from the chart by the density of standard air (0.075 lbm/ft^3). Should relative humidity curves be presented on the chart in lieu of density factor curves, information available through dimensional analysis must be used to determine the actual density of the mixture. This can be done quite easily as follows: The summation of one pound of dry air plus the mass of the moisture contained within that pound of dry air divided by the humid volume will result in the actual density of the mixture.

$$\rho = \frac{1 + \omega}{HV} \qquad [5.8]$$

where: ρ = density of the mix (lbm/ft^3)

   ω = moisture content (lbm H$_2$O/lbm dry air)

   HV = humid volume (ft^3 mix/lbm dry air)

5.13.5 Hood Flow Rate Changes with Density: The control of dust, fumes, and vapors requires an airflow that will achieve the velocity necessary to capture and carry the contaminant into the hood (or contain the contaminant inside an enclosure or enclosing hood) and then convey it through the hood and duct system. In particular, at high elevations, the air providing this containment is already at lower density. To use the methods defined in the Calculation sheet in this Chapter, the air must first be returned to "Standard" conditions and that volume is inserted in Line 3. When the density factor is then calculated for the air leaving the hood, the effects of elevation will then be reinserted with the formulas (in Line 7). This method allows for only one density factor in the calculations. For hoods operating only with consideration for elevation (<100 degrees, little or no moisture), the hood volume can be calculated from VS-plates or Chapter 3 and 5 and inserted directly in Line 8. The density factor must still be used for selection of the fan.

When selecting the capture velocities based on the guidelines in Chapter 3 (Table 3-1), the designer should consider the upper end of the range when working with large dust particles at high temperatures (> 5000 feet above sea level).

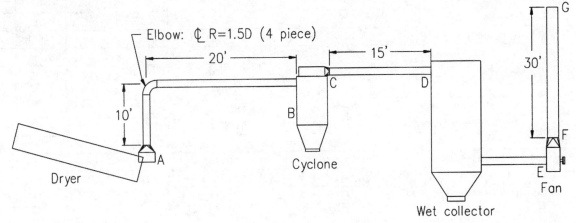

FIGURE 5–10. System layout

Velocity Pressure Method Calculation Sheet   Elevation___575___(z)

Project_____Problem 3 — Figure 5-11_____   Designer_____

						A-B	B-C	C-D	D-E
1*		Duct Segment Identification							
2*	T	Dry-Bulb Temperature			F	500		500	180
3*	Q_{std}	Standard Volumetric Flow Rate			scfm	16000			16000
4*	V_t	Minimum Transport Velocity			fpm	4000		4000	
5*	m_{H2O}	Lbs Water per Minute			#H₂O/min	106.7	106.7	106.7	216
6*	m_{da}	Lbs Dry Air per Minute			#da/min	1200	1200	1200	1200
7	df	Density Factor	Eqn 2			0.513		0.513	0.75
8	Q_{act}	Actual Volumetric Flow Rate	Eqn 3		acfm	33964	33964	33964	25173
9	A_t	Target Duct Area	(3/4std)(8/4nstd)		ft²	8.49		8.49	
10	d	Selected Duct Diameter			inches	38		38	
11	A	Selected Duct Area			ft²	7.876		7.876	
12	V_d	Duct Velocity	(3/11std)(8/11nstd)		fpm	4312		4312	
13	VP_d	Duct Velocity Pressure	Eqn 5		"wg	0.59		0.59	
14	h	Total Heat	branch balance		btu/#da	235		235	235
15*	A_s		Slot Area		ft²		235		
16*	F_s	H	Slot Loss Coefficient						
17*		O S	Acceleration Factor	0 or 1					
18	V_s	O L	Slot Velocity	8/15	fpm				
19	VP_s	D O	Slot Velocity Pressure	Eqn 5	"wg				
20		T	Slot Loss in VP	16+17					
21		L	Slot Static Pressure	20x19	"wg				
22*	F_h	O	Duct Entry Coefficient						
23*		S	Acceleration Factor	1 or 0					
24		S	Duct Entry Loss in VP	22+23					
25		E	Duct Entry Loss	24x13	"wg				
26		S	Other Losses		"wg				
27	SP_h	S	Hood Static Pressure	21+25+26	"wg	2.0			
28*	L		Straight Duct Length		ft	30		15	
29*	H_f		Duct Friction Factor	Eqn 8		0.0045		0.0045	
30*		D	No. of 90 Degree Elbows			1			
31*	F_{el}	U	Elbow Loss Coefficient	Table 6		0.27			
32*	F_{en}	C	Branch Entry Coefficient	Table 7					
33*		T	Special Fitting Coefficient						
34	h_f		Duct Friction Loss in VP	28x29		0.14		0.07	
35		L	Elbow Loss in VP	30x31		0.27			
36		O	Branch Entry Loss in VP	32					
37		S	Duct Loss in VP	33+34+35+36		0.41		0.067	
38		S	Duct Loss	37x13	"wg	0.24		0.04	
39*		E	Other Losses		"wg		2.25		20.0
40	VP_r	S	Resultant Velocity Pressure	Eqn 9	"wg				
41			Loss from Velocity Increase	13-40 (if>0)	"wg				
42			Duct Pressure Loss	27+38+39+41	"wg	-2.24	-2.27	-0.04	-20.0
43*	SP_{gov}	Governing Static Pressure		"wg				
44	SP_{cum}	Cumulative Static Pressure		"wg	-2.24	-4.49	-4.53	-24.53
45	Q_{corr}	Corrected Volumetric Flow Rate	Eqn 10	acfm				
46	V_{corr}	Corrected Velocity	45 / 11	fpm				
47	VP_{corr}	Corrected Velocity Pressure	Eqn 5	"wg				

* Data Input
** Shaded lines 5, 6, 7, 8 & 14 used for non-standard calculations
*** std is for standard calculations and nst is for non-standard calculations

E-F	G-H	Line	Formula
E-F	G-H	1*	1 $\omega = \#H_2O/\#Dry\ Air$
180	180	2*	
16000	16000	3*	
4000		4*	2 $df = df_e * df_p * df_t * df_m$
216	216	5*	$df_e = [1 - (6.73 * 10^{-6})(z)]^{5.258}$
1200	1200	6*	$df_p = (407 + SP)/(407)$
0.71	0.75	7	$df_t = (530)/(T + 460)$
26592	25173	8	
		9	
34	34	10	$df_m = (1 + \omega)/(1 + 1.607\omega)$
6.305	6.305	11	
4218	3993	12	3 $Q_{act} = Q_{std}((1 + \omega)/df)$
0.79	0.75	13	
235	235	14*	
		15*	4 $V = 4005\sqrt{VP/df}$
		16*	
		17*	5 $VP = df(V/4005)^2$
		18	
		19	
		20	6 90° Round Elbow Loss Coefficients (5 Piece)
		21	
		22*	
		23*	
		24	
		25	
		26	
		27	
5	30	28*	7 Branch Entry Loss Coefficients
0.0057	0.0052	29*	
		30*	
		31*	
		32*	
		33*	
0.03	0.16	34	8
		35	$H_f^{(galvanized)} = 0.0307(V^{0.533}/Q^{0.612})$
		36	
0.03	0.16	37	$H_f^{(black\ iron)} = 0.0425(V^{0.465}/Q^{0.602})$
	0.12	38	
		39*	$H_f^{(flexible)} = 0.0311(V^{0.604}/Q^{0.639})$
		40	9
		41	$VP_f = (Q_1/Q_3)(VP_1) + (Q_2/Q_3)(VP_2)$
-0.03	+0.12	42	
		43*	10 $Q_{corr} = Q_{design}\sqrt{SP_{gov}/SP_{duct}}$
-24.58	+0.12	44	
		45	11
		46	FAN SP = $SP_{out} - SP_{in} - VP_{in}$
		47	

6 90° Round Elbow Loss Coefficients (5 Piece)

R/D	Coefficient
1.5	0.24
2.0	0.19
2.5	0.17

7 Branch Entry Loss Coefficients

Angle	Coefficient
15°	0.09
30°	0.18
45°	0.28

Date_____

The example shown in Figure 5-10 illustrates the effect of elevation moisture, and temperature and a method of calculation. A calculation sheet showing the calculation is provided in Figure 5-11.

EXAMPLE PROBLEM 3

Given: The exit flow rate from a 60" x 24' dryer is 16,000 scfm plus removed moisture. The plant is located at 575 feet above sea level. Exhaust air temperature is 500 F. The drier delivers 60 tons/hr of dried material with capacity to remove 5% moisture. Required suction at the dryer hood is -2.0 "wg; minimum conveying velocity must be 4000 fpm (see Figure 5-10.)

It has been determined that the air pollution control system should include a cyclone for dry product recovery and a high-energy wet collector. These devices have the following operating characteristics:

- *Cyclone:* Pressure loss is 4.5 "wg at rated flow rate of 35,000 scfm. The pressure loss across any cyclone varies directly with any change in density and as the square of any change in flow rate from the rated conditions.

- *High-Energy Wet Scrubber:* The manufacturer has determined that a pressure loss of 20 "wg is required in order to meet existing air pollution regulations and has sized the collector accordingly. The humidifying efficiency of the wet collector is 90%.

NOTE: As a practical matter, a high energy scrubber as described in this example would have essentially 100% humidifying efficiency. The assumption of 90% humidifying efficiency along with a high pressure drop allows discussion of multiple design considerations in one example and was therefore adopted for instructional purposes.

- *Fan:* A size #34 "XYZ" fan with the performance shown in Table 5-3 has been recommended.

REQUIRED:
Size the duct and select fan RPM and motor size.

SOLUTION:
Step 1: Find the actual gas flow rate that must be exhausted from the dryer. This flow rate must include both the air used for drying and the water, as vapor, which has been removed from the product. Since it is actual flow rate, it must be corrected from standard air conditions to reflect the actual moisture, temperature, and pressures that exist in the duct.

Step 1A: Find the amount (weight) of water vapor exhausted.

Dryer Discharge = 60 tons/hr of dried material (given)

Since the dryer has capacity to remove 5% moisture, the Dryer Discharge is 95% x dryer feed rate.

60 tons/hr dried material = (0.95) (dryer feed)

$$\text{dryer feed} = \frac{60 \text{ tons/hr}}{0.95} = 63.2 \text{ tons/hr}$$

Moisture removed = (feed rate) − (discharge rate)

= 63.2 tons/hr − 60 tons/hr

= 6400 lbs/hr or 106.7 lbm/min

Step 1B: Find the amount (weight) of dry air exhausted.

Dry air exhausted = 16,000 scfm at 70 F and 29.92 "Hg (0.075 lbs/ft^3 density)

Exhaust rate, lbs/min = (16,000 scfm)(0.075 lbs/ft^3)

= 1200 lbs/min dry air

Step 1C: Knowing the water-to-dry air ratio and the temperature of the mixture, it is possible to determine other quantities of the air-to-water mixture. This can be accomplished by the use of psychrometric charts (see Figures 5-20 to 5-23) which are most useful tools when working with humid air.

TABLE 5-3. FAN RATING TABLE

Fan Size #34							Inlet Diameter=34								Max. safe RPM=1700							
	20" SP		22" SP		24" SP		26" SP		28" SP		30" SP		32" SP		34" SP		36" SP		38" SP		40"SP Typical	
CFM	RPM	BHP	RPM	BHP	RPM	BHP	RPM	BHP	RPM	BHP	RPM	BHP	RPM	BHP	RPM	BHP	RPM	BHP	RPM	BHP	RPM	BHP
14688	1171	73.3	1225	81.4	1277	89.8	1326	98.3	1374	107	1421	116	1466	125	1510	134	1552	143	1594	153	1634	162
16524	1181	81.8	1234	90.2	1286	98.8	1335	107	1382	116	1428	126	1472	135	1516	145	1557	155	1600	165	1639	175
18360	1191	90.2	1244	99.5	1294	108	1344	118	1391	127	1437	137	1481	146	1524	157	1565	167	1606	178	1645	188
20196	1204	99.9	1256	109	1306	119	1354	129	1400	139	1446	149	1490	160	1532	170	1574	181	1615	191	1654	202
22032	1217	110	1268	120	1318	130	1366	141	1412	151	1456	162	1499	173	1542	184	1584	196	1624	207	1663	218
23868	1230	120	1282	131	1331	142	1378	154	1424	165	1468	176	1511	187	1553	199	1594	211	1633	223	1672	235
25704	1245	131	1296	143	1345	155	1391	167	1437	179	1481	191	1524	203	1565	215	1606	227	1645	239	1683	252
27540	1261	143	1311	156	1359	168	1406	181	1450	193	1494	206	1537	219	1578	232	1618	245	1658	258	1695	271
29376	1277	156	1327	169	1374	182	1421	196	1465	209	1508	222	1550	236	1591	249	1631	263	1670	277		
31212	1295	170	1344	184	1391	197	1436	211	1480	225	1523	239	1564	253	1605	268	1644	282	1683	297		
33048	1313	184	1361	198	1407	213	1453	228	1496	242	1538	257	1580	272	1620	287	1659	302	1697	317		
34884	1331	198	1379	214	1425	229	1469	245	1513	260	1555	276	1595	291	1635	307	1674	323				

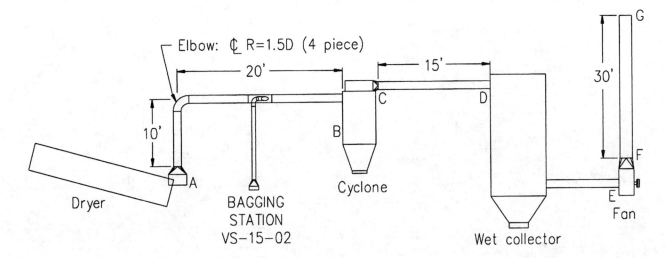

FIGURE 5–12. System layout

ω = 0.089 lbs H_2O/lb dry air

Dry-Bulb temperature = 500 F (given)

The intersection of the 500 F Dry-Bulb temperature line and the 0.089 lbs H_2O/lb dry air line can be located on the psychrometric chart (see Figure 5-14). Point #1 completely defines the quality of the air and water mixture. Other data relative to this specific mixture can be read as follows:

Dew Point Temperature: 122 F

Wet-Bulb Temperature: 145 F

Humid volume, ft^3 of mix/lb of dry air: 27.5 ft^3/lb dry air

Enthalpy, BTU/lb of dry air: 235 BTU/lb dry air

Density factor, df: 0.53

The system is designed at an elevation of 575 feet above sea level; this alters the df further to a value of 0.513. The density factor, Dry-Bulb temperature, mass of air and water, SCFM and enthalpy are entered in the appropriate lines on the Calculation sheet.

Step 2: Proceed with the system design using the calculation methods from pervious Problems 1 and 2.

When considering the loss through the cyclone (B-C), the value is inserted in Line 39. The pressure loss of the cyclone is provided by the manufacturer. In this example, the cyclone pressure loss is 4.5 "wg at a rated flow of 35,000 scfm. The pressure loss through a cyclone, as with duct, varies as the square of the change in flow rate and directly with the change in density.

Therefore, the actual loss through the cyclone would be

$$(4.5) \left[\frac{33,964}{35,000} \right]^2 (0.53) = -2.25" \text{ wg}$$

and the static pressure at the cyclone outlet would be -4.49 "wg.

Information for calculation of changes in flow rate, density, etc., across the wet collector should be provided by the equipment manufacturer. An important characteristic of wet collectors is their ability to humidify a gas stream. The humidification process is generally assumed to be adiabatic (without gain or loss of heat to the surroundings). Therefore, water vapor is added to the mixture, but the enthalpy, expressed in BTU/lb dry air, remains unchanged. During the process of humidification, the point on the psychrometric chart that defines the quality of the mixture to the left, along a line of constant enthalpy, toward saturation.

All wet collectors do not have the same ability to humidify. If a collector is capable of taking an air stream to complete adiabatic saturation, it is said to have a humidifying efficiency of 100%. The humidifying efficiency of a given device may be expressed by either of the following equations:

$$\eta_n = \frac{T_i - T_o}{T_i - T_s} \times 100$$

where: η_n = humidifying efficiency, %

T_i = Dry-Bulb temperature at collector inlet, F

T_o = Dry-Bulb temperature at collector outlet, F

T_s = adiabatic saturation temperature, F

or

$$\eta_n = \frac{\omega_i - \omega_o}{\omega_i - \omega_s} \times 100$$

where: ω_i = moisture content in lb H_2O/lb dry air at inlet

ω_o = moisture content in lb H_2O/lb dry air at outlet

ω_s = moisture content in lb H_2O/lb dry air at adiabatic saturation conditions

The designer must find the quality of the air to water mixture at Point 2, the collector outlet.

Velocity Pressure Method Calculation Sheet

Elevation ___575___ (z)

Project _____ Problem 4 — Figure 5-13 _____   Designer _____

#	Sym	Description	Formula	Units			A-B1	B2-B1	B1-B	B-C
1*		Duct Segment Identification					A-B1	B2-B1	B1-B	B-C
2*	T	Dry-Bulb Temperature		F			500	70	475	475
3*	Q_{std}	Standard Volumetric Flow Rate		scfm			16000	1500	17500	17500
4*	V_t	Minimum Transport Velocity		fpm			1000	3500	4000	
5*	m_{H2O}	Lbs Water per Minute		#H$_2$O/min			106.7		106.7	106.7
6*	m_{da}	Lbs Dry Air per Minute		#da/min			1200	112.5	1312.5	1312.5
7	df	Density Factor	Eqn 2				0.513	0.98	0.54	0.54
8	Q_{act}	Actual Volumetric Flow Rate	Eqn 3	acfm			33964	1530	35000	35000
9	A_t	Target Duct Area	(3/4std)(8/4nstd)	ft^2			8.49	0.428	8.75	
10	d	Selected Duct Diameter		inches			38	8	38	
11	A	Selected Duct Area		ft^2			7.876	0.349	7.876	
12	V_d	Duct Velocity	(3/11std)(8/11nstd)	fpm			4312	4383	444	
13	VP_d	Duct Velocity Pressure	Eqn 5	"wg			0.59	1.17	0.66	
14	h	Total Heat	branch balance	btu/#da			235	16.6	216	216
15*	A_s	Slot Area		ft^2						
16*	F_s	Slot Loss Coefficient								
17*		Acceleration Factor		0 or 1						
18	V_s	Slot Velocity	8/15	fpm						
19	VP_s	Slot Velocity Pressure	Eqn 5	"wg						
20		Slot Loss in VP	16+17							
21		Slot Static Pressure	20x19	"wg						
22*	F_h	Duct Entry Coefficient						0.25		
23*		Acceleration Factor	1 or 0					1		
24		Duct Entry Loss in VP	22+23					1.25		
25		Duct Entry Loss	24x13	"wg				1.46		
26		Other Losses		"wg						
27	SP_h	Hood Static Pressure	21+25+26	"wg			2.0	1.46		
28*	L	Straight Duct Length		ft			20	60	10	
29*	H_f	Duct Friction Factor	Eqn 8				0.0045	0.030	0.0045	
30*		No. of 90 Degree Elbows					1	0.67		
31*	F_{el}	Elbow Loss Coefficient	Table 6				0.27	0.27		
32*	F_{en}	Branch Entry Coefficient	Table 7					0.18		
33*		Special Fitting Coefficient								
34	h_f	Duct Friction Loss in VP	28x29				0.09	1.84	0.05	
35		Elbow Loss in VP	30x31				0.27	0.18		
36		Branch Entry Loss in VP	32					0.18		
37		Duct Loss in VP	33+34+35+36				0.36	2.20	0.05	
38		Duct Loss	37x13	"wg			0.21	2.57	0.03	
39*		Other Losses		"wg						2.43
40	VP_r	Resultant Velocity Pressure	Eqn 9	"wg					0.62	
41		Loss from Velocity Increase	13-40 (if>0)	"wg					0.04	
42		Duct Pressure Loss	27+38+39+41	"wg			-2.21	-4.03	-0.07	-2.43
43*	SP_{gov}	Governing Static Pressure		"wg				-4.03		
44	SP_{cum}	Cumulative Static Pressure		"wg			Add	-4.03	-4.10	-6.53
45	Q_{corr}	Corrected Volumetric Flow Rate	Eqn 10	acfm			Blast			
46	V_{corr}	Corrected Velocity	45 / 11	fpm			Gate			
47	VP_{corr}	Corrected Velocity Pressure	Eqn 5	"wg						

Rows 15–21 labeled "HOOD LOSSES" with "SLOT" sub-section; rows 22–27 "HOOD LOSSES"; rows 28–42 "DUCT LOSSES".

Date_____

*   Data Input
** Shaded lines 5, 6, 7, 8 & 14 used for non-standard calculations
*** std is for standard calculations and nst is for non-standard calculations

Line	C-D	D-E	E-F	G-H
1*	C-D	D-E	E-F	G-H
2*	475	175	175	175
3*	17500	17500	17500	17500
4*	4000		4000	4000
5*	106.7	210	210	210
6*	1312.5	1312.5	1312.5	1312.5
7	0.54	0.75	0.70	0.75
8	35000	27066	29000	27066
9	8.75			
10	38		34	34
11	7.876		6.305	6.305
12	4444		4599	4293
13	0.66		0.92	0.86
14*	216	216	216	216
15*				
16*				
17*				
18				
19				
20				
21				
22*				
23*				
24				
25				
26				
27				
28*	15		5	30
29*	0.0045		0.0051	0.0046
30*				
31*				
32*				
33*				
34	0.07		0.03	0.14
35				
36				
37	0.07		0.03	0.14
38	0.04		0.03	0.12
39*		20.0		
40				
41				
42	-0.04	-20.0	-0.03	+0.12
43*				
44	-6.57	-26.57	-26.60	+0.12
45				
46				
47				

1

$$\omega = \#H_2O/\#Dry\ Air$$

2

$$df = df_e {}^*df_p {}^*df_t {}^*df_m$$

$$df_e = [1-(6.73{}^*10^{-6})(z)]^{5.258}$$

$$df_p = (407+SP)/(407)$$

$$df_t = (530)/(T+460)$$

$$df_m = (1+\omega)/(1+1.607\omega)$$

3

$$Q_{act} = Q_{std}\ ((1+\omega)/df)$$

4

$$V = 4005\sqrt{VP}/df$$

5

$$VP = df(V/4005)^2$$

6

90° Round Elbow Loss Coefficients
(5 Piece)

R/D	Coefficient
1.5	0.24
2.0	0.19
2.5	0.17

7

Branch Entry Loss Coefficients

Angle	Coefficient
15°	0.09
30°	0.18
45°	0.28

8

$$H_f^{(galvanized)} = 0.0307(V^{0.533}/Q^{0.612})$$

$$H_f^{(black\ iron)} = 0.0425(V^{0.465}/Q^{0.602})$$

$$H_f^{(flexible)} = 0.0311(V^{0.604}/Q^{0.639})$$

9

$$VP_f = (Q_1/Q_3)(VP_1)+(Q_2/Q_3)(VP_2)$$

10

$$Q_{corr} = Q_{design}\sqrt{SP_{gov}/SP_{duct}}$$

11

$$FAN\ SP = SP_{out}-SP_{in}-VP_{in}$$

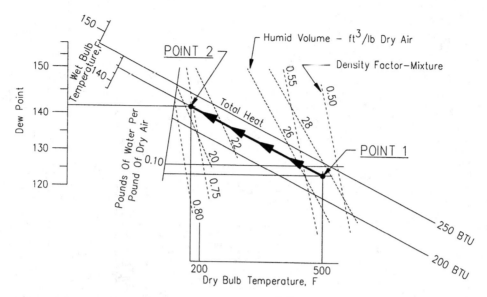

FIGURE 5–14. Psychrometric chart for humid air (see Figures 5–17 through 5–20)

Humidifying Efficiency = 90% (given). Dry-bulb Temperature at Collector Inlet = 500 F (given). Adiabatic saturation temperature = 145 F from inspection of Psychrometric Chart.

$$90 = \frac{(500 - t_o)}{(500 - 145)} \times 100$$

where: $t_o = 180$ F

Then the air leaving the collector will have a Dry-Bulb temperature of 180 F and an enthalpy of 235 BTU/lb of dry air as the humidifying process does not change the total heat or enthalpy.

The point of intersection of 180 F Dry-Bulb and 235 BTU/lb dry air on the psychrometric chart defines the quality of the air leaving the collector and allows other data to be read from the chart as follows:

Dew Point Temperature	143 F
Wet-Bulb Temperature	145 F
Humid Volume, ft³/lb dry air	20.5 ft³/lb dry air
Enthalpy, BTU/lb dry air	235 BTU/lb dry air
Density factor, df	0.76

Density factor is recalculated at 0.75 to consider elevation. Required information is placed in the calculation sheet. (Formulas on calculation can be used to obtain the density factor, knowing Dry-Bulb temperature, elevation, and moisture content.) With that information, the ACFM can be calculated going into the scrubber.

The wet collector loss was stated to be 20 "wg, the static pressure at the wet collector outlet would be -24.45 "wg.

Step 3: Previously, in low-pressure exhaust systems, where the negative pressure at the fan inlet was less than 20 "wg, the effect of the negative pressure was usually ignored. In practical system design, the other factors that affect density (temperature, moisture, elevation) can be additive so that the inlet pressure can be significant when specifying the fan. Systems designed at air temperatures less than 100 F and near sea level (df = 1) can still ignore fan inlet pressure if the values are between 0 and -20 "wg. However, as the pressures decrease, or the magnitude of negative pressures increases, it is understood that gases expand to occupy a larger volume. Unless this larger volume is anticipated and the fan sized to handle the larger flow rate, it will have the effect of reducing the amount of air that is pulled into the hood at the beginning of the system. From the characteristic equation for the ideal gas laws, PQ = wRT (where w = the mass flow rate in lbm/min), the pressure flow rate relationship is

$$P_1Q_1 = P_2Q_2$$

or

$$\frac{P_1}{P_2} = \frac{Q_2}{Q_1}$$

Up to this point the air has been considered to be at standard atmospheric pressure which is 14.7 PSI A, 29.92 "Hg or 407 "wg. The pressure within the duct at Point E is -24.48 "wg and minus or negative only in relation to the pressure outside the duct which is 407 "wg. Therefore, the absolute pressure within the duct is 407 "wg - 24.48 "wg = 382.52 "wg.

$$\frac{407}{382.52} = \frac{Q_2}{24,600 \text{ cfm}}$$

Q_2, the value at the fan inlet = 26,592 acfm

Step 4: Pressure also affects the density of the air. From PQ = wRT the relationship

$$\frac{(w_1 / Q_1)\, RT_1}{(w_2 / Q_2)\, RT_2} = \frac{P_1}{P_2}$$

can be derived. Density factor is directly proportional to the density and the equation can be rewritten

$$\frac{P_1}{P_2} = \frac{df_2}{df_1}$$

Substitute

$$\frac{407}{382.6} = \frac{0.76}{df_2}$$

$$df_2 = 0.71$$

The duct from the wet collector to the fan can now be sized. The flow rate leaving the wet collector was 26,592 acfm. As the fan selected has a 34-inch diameter inlet (area = 6.305 ft^2), it is logical to make the duct from the wet collector to the fan a 34-inch diameter.

After the system calculation has been completed, the fan can be selected.

$$\text{Actual FSP} = SP_{out} - SP_{in} - VP_{in}$$
$$= + 0.12 - (-24.58) - 0.79$$
$$= 23.81 \text{ "wg}$$

Step 5: Specified fan static pressure is determined by dividing the actual fan static pressure by the density factor at the fan inlet (Equation 5.5a). This is necessary since fan rating tables are based on standard air.

$$\text{Specified FSP} = \frac{23.76}{0.71} \times 33.46\text{" wg}$$

Step 6: Interpolating the fan rating table (Table 5-3) for 26,592 cfm at 33.67 "wg yields a fan speed of 1570 RPM at 220 BHP.

Since actual density is less than standard air density, the actual required power is determined by multiplying by the density factor, or (220 BHP)(0.71) = 156 BHP. If a damper is installed in the duct to prevent overloading of the motor, at cold start the motor need only be a 200 HP (see Chapter 6.)

A second example is included where a new hood connection is added to the original duct system (Figure 5-12). This is not good practice under almost all cases. The original design is always compromised and there can be cases where material can drop out in the duct, airflow will be reduced to other connections, and/or the fan can operate in an unstable manner. If the addition of a duct is made, the system calculation principles still apply. Losses can be calculated for the added flows required at the fan and transport velocities must be considered for all ducts in the system. The following example should not in any way be considered an endorsement of this practice. It is included only to show that calculations and system adjustments can be made

to get the system into balance (if suitable resources are available in the duct, fan, motor, and collection device.)

In this case, a hood similar to the bagging hood show in VS-15-02 is connected through a properly sized branch and tapped into the 38" duct coming from the dryer. When the decision is made to proceed on this basis, many factors must be considered:

1. Mixing hot and moist air streams with cold air can cause condensation in duct or collectors. Under normal conditions, the Dry-Bulb temperature should be at least 35 F above the dew point and preferably 50 F. The system must also consider start-up and shut down when the system is especially susceptible to condensation.

2. Downstream velocities may be high enough to cause premature wear of duct and other parts.

3. Sufficient volume and transport velocities must be maintained through all duct system components and at all hoods.

EXAMPLE PROBLEM 4

A new calculation sheet (Figure 5-13) shows the alterations that must be made. A new sketch inserting a new branch duct with a new numbering method is made. The designer in this case has chosen to keep all duct the same size, i.e., no size increase in the main duct between the dryer and the cyclone. All calculations are done the same way as previous examples except a calculation must be done for the mixing of the ambient air from the bagging station with the hot moist air from the dryer.

Knowing that mass and energy must be conserved, the conditions from downstream of the fitting can be calculated using the formula:

$$(m_{da} \times h)_1 + (m_{da} \times h)_2 = (m_{da} \times h)_3$$

The mass of dry air (Line 6) and enthalpy (Line 14) are known for the two branches and the mass is known for that downstream duct since it is the sum of the two branches.

$$(1200 \times 235)_1 + (112.5 \times 16.6)_2 = (1312.5 \times h)_3$$

$$h_3 = 216 \text{ BTU/lb dry air}$$

The mass of air and water downstream will be the summation of the two values from the new hood and the dryer (Lines 5 and 6 on the calculation sheet). Using this information, the conditions in duct B_1-B can be determined from the psychrometric chart as:

Dew Point Temperature	142 F
Dry-Bulb Temperature	475 F
Density factor, df	0.56

Density factor is recalculated at 0.54 to consider elevation. Required information is placed in the calculation sheet. Note that the static pressure requirement for the new branch is -4.03" at junction B_1 and the requirement at the same junction for the dryer is only -2.21 "wg. Normally there would be a change in duct design or selection of new volumes to increase the flow to the dryer and balance the pressure from each branch. In this case, the dryer is sensitive to the static pressure from the duct and cannot be altered. This is a good example where dampers or orifice plates can be used to balance the system.

The remainder of the calculation process is identical to the first example and volume at the fan inlet is now required to be 27,066 ACFM. After the system calculation has been completed, the new fan conditions can be determined:

$$FSP = SP_{out} - SP_{in} - VP_{in}$$
$$= +0.12 - (-26.60) - 0.92$$
$$= 25.80 \text{ "wg}$$

The fan will now be asked to operate at increased volume and pressure to meet the design requirements but with a significant increase in horsepower. The fan speed is recalculated at 1648 RPM and the horsepower required under cold conditions is now 266.

The fan will now be asked to operate at increased volume and pressure but if a 250 HP motor was originally selected, it will not be large enough for a cold start-up. In that case, design changes will have to be made to damper the fan at start-up until sufficient heat is in the system to reduce the power requirements.

5.14 AIR CLEANING EQUIPMENT

Dusts, fumes, and toxic or corrosive gases should not be discharged to the atmosphere. Each exhaust system handling such materials should be provided with an adequate air cleaner as outlined in Chapter 4. As a rule, the exhaust fan should be located on the clean air side of such equipment. An exception is in the use of cyclone cleaners where the hopper discharge is not tightly sealed and better performance is obtained by putting the fan ahead of the collector.

5.15 EVASÉ DISCHARGE

An evasé discharge is a gradual enlargement at the outlet of the exhaust system (see Figure 5-18). The purpose of the evasé is to reduce the air discharge velocity efficiently; thus, the available velocity pressure can be regained and credited to the exhaust system instead of being wasted. Practical considerations usually limit the construction of an evasé to approximately a $10°$ angle ($5°$ side angle) and a discharge velocity of about 2,000 fpm (0.25 "wg velocity pressure) for normal exhaust systems. Further streamlining or lengthening the evasé yields diminishing returns.

It should be noted, however, that for optimum vertical dispersion of contaminated air many designers feel that the discharge velocity from the stack should not be less than 3,000-3,500 fpm. When these considerations prevail, the use of an evasé is questionable.

The following example indicates the application of the evasé fitting. It is not necessary to locate the evasé directly after the outlet of the fan. It should be noted that, depending upon the evasé location, the static pressure at the fan discharge may be below atmospheric, i.e., negative (-), as shown in this example.

EXAMPLE

Duct No.	Dia.	Q	V	VP	SP
1 Fan Inlet	20	8300	3800	0.90	7.27
2 Fan Discharge = 16.5 x 19.5		8300	3715	0.86	
3 Round Duct Connection	20		3800	0.90	
4 Evasé Outlet	28		1940	0.23	0

To calculate the effect of the evasé, see Figure 5-18 for expansion at the end of the duct where the Diameter Ratio, $D_4/D_3 = 28/20 = 1.4$ and Taper length $L/D = 40/20 = 2$.

$$R = 0.52 \times 70\% \text{ (since the evasé is within 5 diameters of the fan outlet)}$$

$$VP_3 = 0.9 \text{ as given}$$

$$SP_4 = 0 \text{ (since the end of the duct is at atmospheric pressure)}$$

$$SP_3 = SP_4 - R(VP_3)$$
$$= 0 - (0.52)(0.70)(0.90")$$
$$= -0.33 \text{ "wg}$$

$$FSP = SP_{outlet} - SP_{inlet} - VP_{inlet}$$
$$= -0.33 - (-7.27) - 0.9 = 6.04 \text{ "wg}$$

5.16 EXHAUST STACK OUTLETS

The final component of the ventilation system is the exhaust stack, an extension of the exhaust duct above the roof. There are two reasons for the placement of an exhaust stack on a ventilation system. First, the air exhausted by a local exhaust system should escape the building envelope. Second, once it has escaped the building envelope, the stack should provide sufficient dispersion so that the plume does not cause an unacceptable situation when it reaches the ground. This brief description of stack design will address only the first concern.

When placing an exhaust stack on the roof of a building, the designer must consider several factors. The most important is the pattern of the air as it passes the building. Even in the case of a simple building design with a perpendicular wind, the airflow patterns over the building can be complex to analyze. Figure 5-31 shows the complex interaction between the building and the wind at height H. A stagnation zone is formed on the upwind wall. Air flows away from the stagnation zone resulting in a down draft near the ground. Vortices are formed by the wind action resulting in a recirculation zone along the front of the roof or roof obstructions, down flow along the downwind side, and forward flow along the upwind side of the building.

Figure 5-31 also shows a schematic of the critical zones formed within the building cavity. A recirculation zone is formed at the leading edge of the building. A recirculation zone is an area where a relatively fixed amount of air moves in a circular fashion with little air movement through the boundary. A stack discharging into the recirculation zone can contaminate the zone. Consequently, all stacks should penetrate the recirculation zone boundary.

The high turbulence region is one through which the air passes; however, the flow is highly erratic with significant downward flow. A stack that discharges into this region will contaminate anything downwind of the stack. Consequently, all stacks should extend high enough that the resulting plume does not enter the high turbulence region upwind of an air intake.

Because of the complex flow patterns around simple buildings, it is almost impossible to locate a stack that is not influenced by vortices formed by the wind. Tall stacks are often used to reduce the influence of the turbulent flow, to release the exhaust air above the influence of the building and to prevent contamination of the air intakes. Selection of the proper location is made more difficult when the facility has several supply and exhaust systems and when adjacent buildings or terrain cause turbulence around the facility itself.

When locating the stack and outdoor air inlets for the air handling systems, it is often desirable to locate the intakes upwind of the source. However, often there is no true upwind position. The wind in all locations is variable. Even when there is a natural prevailing wind, the direction and speed are constantly changing. If stack design and location rely on the direction of the wind, the system will clearly fail.

The effect of wind on stack height varies with speed:

- At very low wind speeds, the exhaust jet from a vertical stack will rise above the roof level resulting in significant dilution at the air intakes.
- Increasing wind speed will decrease plume rise and consequently decrease dilution.
- Increasing wind speed will increase turbulence and consequently increase dilution.

The prediction of the location and form of the recirculation cavity, high turbulence region, and roof wake is difficult. However, for wind perpendicular to a rectangular building, the height (H) and the width (W) of the upwind building face determine the airflow patterns. The critical dimensions are shown in Figure 5-31B. According to Wilson,[5.6] the critical dimensions depend on a scaling coefficient (R) which is given by:

$$R = B_s^{0.67} \times B_l^{0.33} \qquad [5.9]$$

where B_s is the smaller and B_l is the larger of the dimensions H and W. When B_l is larger than 8 B_s, use $B_l = 8 B_s$ to calculate

the scaling coefficient. For a building with a flat roof, Wilson[5.7] estimated the maximum height (H_c), center (X_c), and lengths (L_c) of the recirculation region as follows:

$$H_c = 0.22 R \qquad [5.10]$$
$$X_c = 0.5 R \qquad [5.11]$$
$$L_c = 0.9 R \qquad [5.12]$$

In addition, Wilson estimated the length of the building wake recirculation region by:

$$L_r = 1.0 R \qquad [5.13]$$

The exhaust air from a stack often has not only an upward momentum due to the exit velocity of the exhaust air but buoyancy due to its density as well. For the evaluation of the stack height, the effective height is used (see Figure 5-32). The effective height is the sum of the actual stack height (H_s), the rise due to the vertical momentum of the air, and any wake downwash effect that may exist. A wake downwash occurs when air passing a stack forms a downwind vortex. The vortex will draw the plume down, reducing the effective stack height (see Figure 5-32). This vortex effect is eliminated when the exit velocity is greater than 1.5 times the wind velocity. If the exit velocity exceeds 3000 fpm, the momentum of the exhaust air reduces the potential downwash effect.

The ideal design extends the stack high enough that the expanding plume does not meet the wake region boundary. More realistically, the stack is extended so that the expanding plume does not intersect the high turbulence region or any recirculation cavity. According to Wilson,[5.6] the high turbulence region boundary (Z_2) follows a 1:10 downward slope from the top of the recirculation cavity.

To avoid entrainment of exhaust gas into the wake, stacks must terminate above the recirculation cavity. The effective stack height to avoid excessive reentry can be calculated by assuming that the exhaust plume spreads from the effective stack height with a slope of 1:5 (see Figure 5-31). The first step is to raise the effective stack height until the lower edge of the 1:5 sloping plume avoids contact with all recirculation zone boundaries. The zones can be generated by roof top obstacles such as air handling units, penthouses or architectural screens. The heights of the cavities are determined by Equations 5.10, 5.11, and 5.12 using the scaling coefficient for the obstacle. Equation 5.13 can be used to determine the length of the wake recirculation zone downwind of the obstacle.

If the air intakes, including windows and other openings, are located on the downwind wall, the lower edge of the plume with a downward slope of 1:5 should not intersect with the recirculation cavity downwind of the building. The length of the recirculation cavity (L_r) is given by Equation 5.13. If the air intakes are on the roof, the downward plume should not intersect the high turbulence region above the air intakes. When the intake is above the high turbulence boundary, extend a line from the top of the intake to the stack with a slope of 1:5.

TABLE 5-4. Typical Physical and Chemical Properties of Fabricated Plastics and Other Materials

Chemical Type	Trade Names	Max. Opr. Temp., F	Flam-mability	Gasoline	Mineral Oil	Strong Alk.	Weak Alk.	Strong Acid	Weak Acid	Salt Solution	Solvents
Urea Formaldehyde	Beetle Plaskon Sylplast	170	Self Ext.	Good	Good	Unacc.	Fair	Poor	Poor	—	Good
Melamine Formaldehyde	Cymel Plaskon Resimene	210-300	Self Ext.	Good	Good	Poor	Good	Poor	Good	—	Good
Phenolic	Bakelite Durite Durez G.E. Resinox	250-450	Self Ext.	Fair	—	Poor	Fair	Poor	Fair	—	Fair
Alkyd	Plaskon	—	Self Ext.	Good	—	Unac.	Poor	—	Good	—	Good
Silicone	Bakelite G.E.	550	—	Good	Good	—	—	Good	Good	—	Unac.
Epoxy	Epiphem Araldite Maraset Renite Tool Plastik Epon Resin	50-200	Self Ext.	Good	—	Good	Good	Good	Good	—	Good
Cast Phenolic	Marblette	—	Self Ext.	—	—	Unac.	Fair	Good	Good	—	Good to
Allyl & Polyester	Laminac Bakelite Plaskon Glykon Paraplex	300-450	Self Ext.	—	—	Poor	Fair	Poor	Fair	—	Fair
Acrylic	Lucite Plexiglas Wascoline	140-200	0.5-2.0 in/min	—	—	—	Good	—	Good	—	Good to Unac.
Polyethylene	Tenite Irrathene	140-200	Slow Burning	—	—	—	—	—	—	—	Unac.
Tetrafluoroethylene	Teflon	500	Non-Fl.	Good	—	Good	Good	Good	Good	—	Good
Chlortrifluoroethylene	Kel F										
Polyvinyl Formal &	Vinylite Butyral Saflex Butvar Formuaré	— Butacite	Slow	Good Burning	Good	Good	Good	Unac.	Unac.	—	Unac.
Vinyl Chloride Polyner & Copolyner	Krene Bakelite Vinyl Dow pvc Vygen	130-175	Slow Burning	—	—	Good	Good	Good	Good	—	Unac.
Vinylidene Chloride	Saran	160-200	Self Ext.	Good	Good	Good	Good	Good	Good	—	Fair
Styrene	Bakelite Catalin Styron Dylene Luxtrex	150-165	0.5-2.0 in/min	Unac.	Fair	Good	Good	—	—	Good	Fair
Polystyrene Reinforced with fibrous glass				Unac.	Fair	Good	Good	—	—	Good	Poor
Cellulose Acetate	Celanese Acetate Tenite	Thermo Plastic	0.5-2.0 in/min	Good	Good	Unac.	Unac.	Unac.	Fair	—	Poor
Nylon	Plaskon Zytol Tynex	250	Self Ext.	Good	Good	Good	Good	—	Good	—	Good
Glass	Pyrex	450	Non-Fl.	Good	Good	Good	Good	Good	Good	Good	Good

NOTE: Each situation must be thoroughly checked for compatability of materials during the design phase of if usage is changed.

When the intake is below the high turbulence region boundary, extend a vertical line to the boundary, then extend back to the stack with a slope of 1:5. This allows the calculation of the necessary stack height. The minimum stack height can be determined for each air intake. The maximum of these heights would be the required stack height.

In large buildings with many air intakes, the above procedure will result in very tall stacks. An alternate approach is to estimate the amount of dilution that is afforded by stack height, distance between the stack and the air intake, and internal dilution that occurs within the system itself. This approach is presented in the "Airflow Around Buildings" chapter in the *Fundamentals* volume of the 1993 *ASHRAE Handbook*.[5.8]

5.16.1: Stack Design Considerations

1. Discharge velocity and gas temperature influence the effective stack height.

2. Wind can cause a downwash into the wake of the stack reducing the effective stack height. Stack velocity should be at least 1.5 times the wind velocity to prevent downwash.

3. A good stack velocity is 3000 fpm because it:

   - Prevents downwash for winds up to 2000 fpm (22 mph). Higher wind speeds have significant dilution effects.

   - Increases effective stack height.

   - Allows selection of a smaller centrifugal exhaust fan to provide a more stable operation point on the fan curve (see Chapter 6).

   - Provides conveying velocity if there is dust in the exhaust or there is a failure of the air cleaning device.

4. High exit velocity is a poor substitute for stack height. For example, a flush stack requires a velocity over 8000 fpm to penetrate the recirculation cavity boundary.

5. The terminal velocity of rain is about 2000 fpm. A stack velocity above 2600 fpm will prevent rain from entering the stack when the fan is operating.

6. Locate stacks on the highest roof of the building when possible. If not possible, a much higher stack is required to extend beyond the wake of the high bay, penthouse, or other obstacle.

7. The use of an architectural screen should be avoided. The screen becomes an obstacle and the stack must be raised to avoid the wake effect of the screen.

8. The best stack shape is a straight cylinder. If a drain is required, a vertical stack head is preferred (see Figure 5-33). In addition, the fan should be provided with a drain hole and the duct should be slightly sloped toward the fan.

9. Rain caps should not be used. The rain cap directs the air toward the roof, increases the possibility of reentry, and causes exposures to maintenance personnel on the roof. Moreover, rain caps are not effective. A field study[5.9] with a properly installed standard rain cap showed poor performance. A 12-inch diameter stack passed 16% of all rain and as high as 45% during individual storms.

10. Separating the exhaust points from the air intakes can reduce the effect of reentry by increasing dilution.

11. In some circumstances, several small exhaust systems can be manifolded to a single exhaust duct to provide internal dilution thereby reducing reentry.

12. A combined approach of vertical discharge, stack height, remote air intakes, proper air cleaning device, and internal dilution can be effective in reducing the consequences of reentry.

13. A tall stack is not an adequate substitute for good emission control. The reduction achieved by properly designed air cleaning devices can have a significant impact on the potential for reentry.

5.17 AIR BLEED DESIGN

Bleed-ins are used at the ends of branch ducts to provide additional airflow rates to transport heavy material loads as in woodworking at saws and jointers or at the ends of a main duct to maintain minimum transport velocity when the system has been oversized deliberately to provide for future expansion. Some designers use bleed-ins also to introduce additional air to an exhaust system to reduce air temperature and to assist in balancing the system.

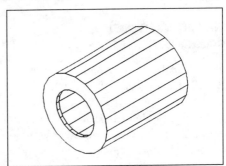

EXAMPLE

End cap bleed-in (see sketch). Consider it to be an orifice or slot. From Figure 5-15, $h_e = 1.78$ VP.

1. Calculate SP for branch duct to junction (X).

2. Determine flow rate in main duct according to design or future capacity or determine Q bleed-in directly from temperature or moisture considerations.

3. Q bleed-in = (Q main duct) − (Q branch)

4. SP bleed-in = SP branch as calculated = $(h_e + 1$ VP$)$ = $(1.78 + 1.0)$ VP

5. VP, bleed-in $= \dfrac{SP}{(1.78 + 1.0)} = \dfrac{SP}{2.78}$

6. Velocity, bleed-in from VP and Table 5-7a.

7. Area bleed-in $= \dfrac{Q \text{ bleed-in}}{V \text{ bleed-in}}$

5.18 OPTIMUM ECONOMIC VELOCITY

In systems which are intended to carry dust, a minimum conveying velocity is necessary to ensure that the dust will not settle in the duct. Also, when a system is installed in a quiet area, it may be necessary to keep velocities below some maximum to avoid excessive duct noise. When axial flow fans are used, duct velocities of 1,000 to 1,500 fpm are preferred. In a gas or vapor exhaust system installed in a typical factory environment where none of these restrictions apply, the velocity may be selected to yield the lowest annual operating cost.

To determine the optimum economic velocity, the system must first be designed at any assumed velocity and the total initial costs of duct material, fabrication, and installation estimated.[5.10]

This optimum economic velocity may range from under 2,000 fpm to over 4,000 fpm. Lengthy expected service periods and system operating times tend to lower the optimum while high interest rates and duct costs tend to raise the optimum. In general, a velocity of 2,500 to 3,000 fpm will not result in equivalent total annual costs much in excess of the true optimum.

5.19 CONSTRUCTION GUIDELINES FOR LOCAL EXHAUST SYSTEMS

Ducts are specified most often for use in the low static pressure range (-10 "wg to +10 "wg); but higher static pressures are occasionally encountered. The duct conveys air or gas which is sometimes at high temperatures and often contaminated with abrasive particulate or corrosive aerosols. Whether conditions are mild or severe, correct design and competent installation of ducts and hoods are necessary for proper functioning of any ventilation system. The following minimum specifications are recommended.

Exhaust systems should be constructed with materials suitable for the conditions of service and installed in a permanent and workmanlike manner. To minimize friction loss and turbulence, the interior of all ducts should be smooth and free from obstructions—especially at joints.

5.19.1 Materials: Ducts are constructed of black iron, which has been welded, flanged and gasketed, or of welded galvanized sheet steel unless the presence of corrosive gases, vapors, and mists or other conditions make such material impractical. Arc welding of black iron lighter than 18 gauge is not recommended. Galvanized construction is not recommended for temperatures exceeding 400 F. The presence of corrosive gases, vapor and mist may require the selection of corrosive resistant metals, plastics or coatings. It is recommended that a specialist be consulted for the selection of materials best suited for applications when corrosive atmospheres are anticipated. Table 5-4 provides a guide for selection of materials for corrosive conditions.

5.19.2 CONSTRUCTION

1. There are four classifications for exhaust systems on noncorrosive applications:

    A. ***Class 1***—Light Duty: Includes nonabrasive applications, e.g., replacement air, general ventilation, gaseous emissions control.

    B. ***Class 2***—Medium Duty: Includes applications with moderately abrasive particulate in light concentrations, e.g., buffing and polishing, woodworking, grain dust.

    C. ***Class 3***—Heavy Duty: Includes applications with high abrasive in low concentrations (e.g., abrasive cleaning operations, dryers and kilns, boiler breeching, sand handling).

    D. ***Class 4***—Extra Heavy Duty: Includes applications with highly abrasive particles in high concentrations, e.g., materials conveying high concentrations of particulate in all examples listed under Class 3 (usually used in heavy industrial plants such as steel mills, foundries, mining, and smelting).

2. For most conditions, round duct is recommended for industrial ventilation, air pollution control, and dust collecting systems. Compared to non-round duct, it provides for lower friction loss and its higher structural integrity allows lighter gauge materials and fewer reinforcing members. Round duct should be constructed in accordance with the Reference 5.11. Metal thickness required for round industrial duct varies with classification, static pressure, reinforcement, and span between supports. Metal thicknesses required for the four classes are based on design and use experience.

3. Rectangular ducts should only be used when space requirements preclude the use of round construction. Rectangular ducts should be as nearly square as possible to minimize resistance, and they should be constructed in accordance with Reference 5.12.

4. For many applications, spiral wound duct is adequate and less expensive than custom construction. However, spiral wound duct should not be used for Classes 3 and 4 because it does not withstand abrasion well. Elbows, branch entries, and similar fittings should be

fabricated, if necessary, to achieve good design. Special considerations concerning use of spiral duct are as follows:

A. Unless flanges are used for joints, the duct should be supported close to each joint, usually within 2 inches. Additional supports may be needed. See Reference 5.11.

B. Joints should be sealed by methods shown to be adequate for the service.

C. Systems may be leak tested after installation at the maximum expected static pressure. The acceptable leakage criteria, often referred to as leakage class, should be carefully selected based on the hazards associated with the contaminant.

5. The following formula[5.11] can be used for specifying ducts to be constructed of metals other than steel. For a duct of infinite length, the required thickness may be determined from:

$$\frac{t}{D} = \sqrt[3]{0.035714\, p\, \frac{(1 - v^2)}{E}\, (52 + D)}$$

where:　t = the thickness of the duct in inches

　　　　D = the diameter of the duct in inches

　　　　p = the intensity of the negative pressure on the duct in psi

　　　　E = modulus of elasticity in psi

　　　　v = Poisson's ratio

The above equation for Class 1 ducts incorporates a safety coefficient which varies linearly with the diameter (D), beginning at 4 for small ducts and increasing to 8 for duct diameters of 60 inches. This safety coefficient has been adopted by the sheet metal industry to provide for lack of roundness; excesses in negative pressure due to particle accumulation in the duct and other manufacturing or assembly imperfections unaccounted for by quality control; and tolerances provided by design specifications.

Additional metal thickness must be considered for Classes 2, 3, and 4. The designer is urged to consult the SMACNA standards for complete engineering design procedures.

6. Hoods should be a minimum of two gauges heavier than straight sections of connecting branches, free of sharp edges or burrs, and reinforced to provide necessary stiffness.

7. Longitudinal joints or seams should be welded. All welding should conform to the standards established by the American Welding Society (AWS) structural code.[5.13] Double lock seams are limited to Class 1 applications.

8. Duct systems subject to wide temperature fluctuations should be provided with expansion joints. Flexible materials used in the construction of expansion joints should be selected with temperature and corrosion conditions considered.

9. Elbows and bends should be a minimum of two gauges heavier than straight lengths of equal diameter and have a centerline radius of at least two and preferably two and one-half times the pipe diameter (see Figure 5-24). Large centerline radius elbows are recommended where highly abrasive dusts are being conveyed.

10. Elbows of 90° should be of a five piece construction for round ducts up to six inches and of a seven piece construction for larger diameters. Bends less than 90° should have a proportional number of pieces. Prefabricated elbows of smooth construction may be used (see Figure 5-25 for heavy duty elbows).

11. Where the air contaminant includes particulate that may settle in the ducts, clean-out doors should be provided in horizontal runs, near elbows, junctions, and vertical runs. The spacing of clean-out doors should not exceed 12 feet for ducts of 12 inches diameter and less but may be greater for larger duct sizes (see Figure 5-26). Removable caps should be installed at all terminal ends and the last branch connection should not be more than six inches from the capped end.

12. Transitions in mains and sub-mains should be tapered. The taper should be at least five units long for each one unit change in diameter or 30° included angle (see Figure 5-28).

13. All branches should enter the main at the center of the transition at an angle not to exceed 45° with 30° preferred. To minimize turbulence and possible particulate fall out, connections should be to the top or side of the main with no two branches entering at opposite sides (see Figure 5-29).

14. Where condensation may occur, the duct system should be liquid tight and provisions made for proper sloping and drainage.

15. A straight duct section of at least six equivalent duct diameters should be used when connecting to a fan (see Figure 5-30). Elbows or other fittings at the fan inlet will seriously reduce the volume discharge (see Figures 6-23, 6-24 and AMCA 201[5.14]). The diameter of the duct should be approximately equal to the fan inlet diameter.

16. Discharge stacks should be vertical and terminate at a point where height or air velocity limit re-entry into supply air inlets or other plant openings (see Figures 5-31 and 5-32).

5.19.3 System Details

1. Provide duct supports of sufficient capacity to carry the weight of the system plus the weight of the duct half filled with material and with no load placed on the connecting equipment. (See SMACNA standards[5.11, 5.12]).

2. Provide adequate clearance between ducts and ceilings, walls and floors for installation and maintenance.

3. Install fire dampers, explosion vents, etc., in accordance with the National Fire Protection Association Codes and other applicable codes and standards.

4. Minimize the use of blast gates or other dampers. However, if blast gates are used for system adjustment, place each in a vertical section midway between the hood and the junction. To reduce tampering, provide a means of locking dampers in place after the adjustments have been made. (See Figure 5-27 for types.)

5. Allow for vibration and expansion. If no other considerations make it inadvisable, provide a flexible connection between the duct and the fan. The fan housing and drive motor should be mounted on a common base of sufficient weight to dampen vibration, or on a properly designed vibration isolator.

6. Exhaust fans handling explosive or flammable atmospheres require special construction (see Section 6.3.9).

7. Do not allow hoods and duct to be added to an existing exhaust system unless specifically provided for in the original design or unless the system is modified.

8. Locate fans and filtration equipment such that maintenance access is easy. Provide adequate lighting in penthouses and mechanical rooms.

5.19.4 Codes: Where federal, state, or local laws conflict with the preceding, the more stringent requirement should be followed. Deviation from existing regulations may require approval.

5.19.5 Other Types of Duct Materials

1. Avoid use of flexible ducts. Where required, use a noncollapsible type that is no longer than necessary. Refer to the manufacturer's data for friction and bend losses.

2. Commercially available seamless tubing for small duct sizes (i.e., up to 6 inches) may be more economical on an installed cost basis than other types.

3. Plastic pipe may be the best choice for some applications (e.g., corrosive conditions at low temperature). See Table 5-4. For higher temperatures consider fiberglass or a coated duct.

4. Friction losses for non-fabricated duct will probably be different than shown in Tables 5-5 and 5-6. For specific information, consult manufacturer's data.

5.19.6 Testing: The exhaust system should be tested and evaluated (see Chapter 9). Openings for sampling should be provided in the discharge stack or duct to test for compliance with air pollution codes or ordinances.

REFERENCES

5.1   Loeffler, J.J.: "Simplified Equations for HVAC Duct Friction Factors," ASHRAE Journal, January 1980, pp. 76-79.

5.2   Guffey, S.E.: "Air-Flow Redistribution in Exhaust Ventilation Systems Using Dampers and Static Pressure Ratios," Applied Occupational and Environmental Hygiene, Volume 8, Number 3, March 1993.

5.3   The Kirk and Blum Mfg. Co.: Woodworking Plants, pp. W-9, Cincinnati, OH.

5.4   Air Movement and Control Association, Inc.: AMCA Standard 210-74. 30 West University Drive, Arlington Heights, IL 60004.

5.5   Constance, J.A.: "Estimating Air Friction in Triangular Ducts," Air Conditioning, Heating and Ventilating, 60, 6, June 1963, pp. 85-86.

5.6   Wilson, D.J.: "Contamination of Air Intakes from Roof Exhaust Vents," ASHRAE Transactions, 82:1024-38, 1976.

5.7   Wilson, D.J.: "Flow Patterns Over Flat Roof Buildings and Application to Exhaust Stack Design," ASHRAE Transactions, 85:284-95, 1979.

5.8   American Society of Heating, Refrigerating and Air-Conditioning Engineers, 1993 ASHRAE Handbook, Fundamentals Volume, 14:1-14,18, 1993.

5.9   Clark, J.: "The Design and Location of Building Inlets and Outlets to Minimize Wind Effect and Building Reentry," Journal of the American Industrial Hygiene Society, 26:262, 1956.

5.10   Lynch, J.R.: "Computer Design of Industrial Exhaust Systems," Heating, Piping and Air Conditioning, September, 1968.

5.11   Sheet Metal and Air Conditioning Contractors' National Assoc., Inc.: Round Industrial Duct Construction Standards. 8224 Old Courthouse Rd., Tysons Corner, Vienna, VA 22180 (1982).

5.12   Sheet Metal and Air Conditioning Contractors' National Assoc., Inc., Rectangular Industrial Duct Construction Standards. 8224 Old Courthouse Rd., Tysons Corner, Vienna, VA 22180 (1980).

5.13   American Welding Society: (AWS D1.1-72). P.O. Box 351040, Miami, FL 33135.

5.14   Air Movement & Control Associations, Inc.: AMCA Publication 201. 30 West University Drive, Arlington Heights, IL 60004. Publication 201.

5.15   Wright, Jr. D.K.: "A New Friction Chart for Round Ducts," ASHVE Transactions, Vol. 51, 1945, p. 303.

5.16   Clarke, J.H.: "Air Flow Around Buildings," Heating, Piping and Air Conditioning, 39, 5, May 1967, pp. 145-154.

5.17   American Society of Heating, Refrigerating and Air-Conditioning Engineers: 1989 Fundamentals Volume, p. 32.31

5.18   Bryant, D.: Industrial Health Engineering, 1947. John Wiley & Sons, New York.

5.19   American Society of Heating, Refrigerating and Air-Conditioning Engineers: Heating, Ventilating, Air Conditioning Guide, 37th ed., 1959. ASHRAE, Atlanta, GA.

5.20   American Society of Heating, Refrigerating and Air Conditioning Engineers: 1993 ASHRAE Handbook, Fundamentals, Chapter 5, 34 13:33 (1993), Atlanta, GA.

TABLE 5-5 Tabulated Friction Loss Factors

Galvanized Sheet Metal Duct						
Diameter	Friction Loss, No. VP per foot					
inches	1000 fpm	2000 fpm	3000 fpm	4000 fpm	5000 fpm	6000 fpm
0.5	1.0086	0.9549	0.9248	0.9040	0.8882	0.8755
1	0.4318	0.4088	0.3959	0.3870	0.3802	0.3748
1.5	0.2629	0.2489	0.2410	0.2356	0.2315	0.2282
2	0.1848	0.1750	0.1695	0.1657	0.1628	0.1605
2.5	0.1407	0.1332	0.1290	0.1261	0.1239	0.1221
3	0.1125	0.1065	0.1032	0.1009	0.0991	0.0977
3.5	0.0932	0.0882	0.0854	0.0835	0.0821	0.0809
4	0.0791	0.0749	0.0726	0.0709	0.0697	0.0687
4.5	0.0685	0.0649	0.0628	0.0614	0.0603	0.0595
5	0.0602	0.0570	0.0552	0.0540	0.0530	0.0523
5.5	0.0536	0.0507	0.0491	0.0480	0.0472	0.0465
6	0.0482	0.0456	0.0442	0.0432	0.0424	0.0418
7	0.0399	0.0378	0.0366	0.0358	0.0351	0.0346
8	0.0339	0.0321	0.0311	0.0304	0.0298	0.0294
9	0.0293	0.0278	0.0269	0.0263	0.0258	0.0255
10	0.0258	0.0244	0.0236	0.0231	0.0227	0.0224
11	0.0229	0.0217	0.0210	0.0206	0.0202	0.0199
12	0.0206	0.0195	0.0189	0.0185	0.0182	0.0179
13	0.0187	0.0177	0.0171	0.0168	0.0165	0.0162
14	0.0171	0.0162	0.0157	0.0153	0.0150	0.0148
15	0.0157	0.0149	0.0144	0.0141	0.0138	0.0136
16	0.0145	0.0137	0.0133	0.0130	0.0128	0.0126
17	0.0135	0.0127	0.0123	0.0121	0.0119	0.0117
18	0.0126	0.0119	0.0115	0.0113	0.0111	0.0109
19	0.0118	0.0111	0.0108	0.0105	0.0103	0.0102
20	0.0110	0.0104	0.0101	0.0099	0.0097	0.0096
21	0.0104	0.0098	0.0095	0.0093	0.0092	0.0090
22	0.0098	0.0093	0.0090	0.0088	0.0086	0.0085
23	0.0093	0.0088	0.0085	0.0083	0.0082	0.0081
24	0.0088	0.0084	0.0081	0.0079	0.0078	0.0077
25	0.0084	0.0080	0.0077	0.0075	0.0074	0.0073
26	0.0080	0.0076	0.0073	0.0072	0.0070	0.0069
27	0.0076	0.0072	0.0070	0.0069	0.0067	0.0066
28	0.0073	0.0069	0.0067	0.0066	0.0064	0.0063
29	0.0070	0.0066	0.0064	0.0063	0.0062	0.0061
30	0.0067	0.0064	0.0062	0.0060	0.0059	0.0058
31	0.0065	0.0061	0.0059	0.0058	0.0057	0.0056
32	0.0062	0.0059	0.0057	0.0056	0.0055	0.0054

TABLE 5-5 Tabulated Friction Loss Factors (continued)

Galvanized Sheet Metal Duct						
Diameter	Friction Loss, No. VP per foot					
inches	1000 fpm	2000 fpm	3000 fpm	4000 fpm	5000 fpm	6000 fpm
33	0.0060	0.0057	0.0055	0.0054	0.0053	0.0052
34	0.0058	0.0055	0.0053	0.0052	0.0051	0.0050
35	0.0056	0.0053	0.0051	0.0050	0.0049	0.0048
36	0.0054	0.0051	0.0049	0.0048	0.0047	0.0047
37	0.0052	0.0049	0.0048	0.0047	0.0046	0.0045
38	0.0050	0.0048	0.0046	0.0045	0.0044	0.0044
39	0.0049	0.0046	0.0045	0.0044	0.0043	0.0042
40	0.0047	0.0045	0.0043	0.0042	0.0042	0.0041
41	0.0046	0.0043	0.0042	0.0041	0.0040	0.0040
42	0.0045	0.0042	0.0041	0.0040	0.0039	0.0039
43	0.0043	0.0041	0.0040	0.0039	0.0038	0.0038
44	0.0042	0.0040	0.0039	0.0038	0.0037	0.0036
45	0.0041	0.0039	0.0038	0.0037	0.0036	0.0036
46	0.0040	0.0038	0.0037	0.0036	0.0035	0.0035
47	0.0039	0.0037	0.0036	0.0035	0.0034	0.0034
48	0.0038	0.0036	0.0035	0.0034	0.0033	0.0033
49	0.0037	0.0035	0.0034	0.0033	0.0032	0.0032
50	0.0036	0.0034	0.0033	0.0032	0.0032	0.0031
52	0.0034	0.0032	0.0031	0.0031	0.0030	0.0030
54	0.0033	0.0031	0.0030	0.0029	0.0029	0.0028
56	0.0031	0.0030	0.0029	0.0028	0.0028	0.0027
58	0.0030	0.0028	0.0027	0.0027	0.0026	0.0026
60	0.0029	0.0027	0.0026	0.0026	0.0025	0.0025
62	0.0028	0.0026	0.0025	0.0025	0.0024	0.0024
64	0.0027	0.0025	0.0024	0.0024	0.0023	0.0023
66	0.0026	0.0024	0.0023	0.0023	0.0023	0.0022
68	0.0025	0.0023	0.0023	0.0022	0.0022	0.0021
70	0.0024	0.0023	0.0022	0.0021	0.0021	0.0021
72	0.0023	0.0022	0.0021	0.0021	0.0020	0.0020
74	0.0022	0.0021	0.0020	0.0020	0.0020	0.0019
76	0.0022	0.0020	0.0020	0.0019	0.0019	0.0019
78	0.0021	0.0020	0.0019	0.0019	0.0018	0.0018
80	0.0020	0.0019	0.0019	0.0018	0.0018	0.0018
82	0.0020	0.0019	0.0018	0.0018	0.0017	0.0017
84	0.0019	0.0018	0.0017	0.0017	0.0017	0.0017
86	0.0019	0.0018	0.0017	0.0017	0.0016	0.0016
88	0.0018	0.0017	0.0017	0.0016	0.0016	0.0016
90	0.0018	0.0017	0.0016	0.0016	0.0015	0.0015

TABLE 5-6 Tabulated Friction Loss Factors

Diameter	Friction Loss, No. VP per foot					
inches	1000 fpm	2000 fpm	3000 fpm	4000 fpm	5000 fpm	6000 fpm
0.5	0.8757	0.7963	0.7533	0.7242	0.7024	0.6851
1	0.3801	0.3457	0.3270	0.3143	0.3049	0.2974
1.5	0.2333	0.2121	0.2007	0.1929	0.1871	0.1825
2	0.1650	0.1500	0.1419	0.1364	0.1323	0.1291
2.5	0.1261	0.1147	0.1085	0.1043	0.1012	0.0987
3	0.1013	0.0921	0.0871	0.0837	0.0812	0.0792
3.5	0.0841	0.0765	0.0724	0.0696	0.0675	0.0658
4	0.0716	0.0651	0.0616	0.0592	0.0574	0.0560
4.5	0.0621	0.0565	0.0535	0.0514	0.0499	0.0486
5	0.0547	0.0498	0.0471	0.0453	0.0439	0.0428
5.5	0.0488	0.0444	0.0420	0.0404	0.0392	0.0382
6	0.0440	0.0400	0.0378	0.0364	0.0353	0.0344
7	0.0365	0.0332	0.0314	0.0302	0.0293	0.0286
8	0.0311	0.0283	0.0267	0.0257	0.0249	0.0243
9	0.0270	0.0245	0.0232	0.0223	0.0216	0.0211
10	0.0238	0.0216	0.0204	0.0197	0.0191	0.0186
11	0.0212	0.0193	0.0182	0.0175	0.0170	0.0166
12	0.0191	0.0174	0.0164	0.0158	0.0153	0.0149
13	0.0173	0.0158	0.0149	0.0143	0.0139	0.0136
14	0.0158	0.0144	0.0136	0.0131	0.0127	0.0124
15	0.0146	0.0133	0.0125	0.0121	0.0117	0.0114
16	0.0135	0.0123	0.0116	0.0112	0.0108	0.0106
17	0.0125	0.0114	0.0108	0.0104	0.0101	0.0098
18	0.0117	0.0106	0.0101	0.0097	0.0094	0.0092
19	0.0110	0.0100	0.0094	0.0091	0.0088	0.0086
20	0.0103	0.0094	0.0089	0.0085	0.0083	0.0081
21	0.0097	0.0088	0.0084	0.0080	0.0078	0.0076
22	0.0092	0.0084	0.0079	0.0076	0.0074	0.0072
23	0.0087	0.0079	0.0075	0.0072	0.0070	0.0068
24	0.0083	0.0075	0.0071	0.0068	0.0066	0.0065
25	0.0079	0.0072	0.0068	0.0065	0.0063	0.0062
26	0.0075	0.0068	0.0065	0.0062	0.0060	0.0059
27	0.0072	0.0065	0.0062	0.0059	0.0058	0.0056
28	0.0069	0.0063	0.0059	0.0057	0.0055	0.0054
29	0.0066	0.0060	0.0057	0.0055	0.0053	0.0052
30	0.0063	0.0058	0.0054	0.0052	0.0051	0.0050
31	0.0061	0.0055	0.0052	0.0050	0.0049	0.0048
32	0.0059	0.0053	0.0050	0.0048	0.0047	0.0046

Black Iron, Aluminum, Stainless Steel, PVC Ducts

TABLE 5-6 Tabulated Friction Loss Factors (continued)

Diameter	Friction Loss, No. VP per foot					
inches	1000 fpm	2000 fpm	3000 fpm	4000 fpm	5000 fpm	6000 fpm
33	0.0056	0.0051	0.0049	0.0047	0.0045	0.0044
34	0.0054	0.0050	0.0047	0.0045	0.0044	0.0043
35	0.0053	0.0048	0.0045	0.0043	0.0042	0.0041
36	0.0051	0.0046	0.0044	0.0042	0.0041	0.0040
37	0.0049	0.0045	0.0042	0.0041	0.0039	0.0038
38	0.0048	0.0043	0.0041	0.0039	0.0038	0.0037
39	0.0046	0.0042	0.0040	0.0038	0.0037	0.0036
40	0.0045	0.0041	0.0039	0.0037	0.0036	0.0035
41	0.0043	0.0040	0.0037	0.0036	0.0035	0.0034
42	0.0042	0.0038	0.0036	0.0035	0.0034	0.0033
43	0.0041	0.0037	0.0035	0.0034	0.0033	0.0032
44	0.0040	0.0036	0.0034	0.0033	0.0032	0.0031
45	0.0039	0.0035	0.0033	0.0032	0.0031	0.0030
46	0.0038	0.0034	0.0033	0.0031	0.0030	0.0030
47	0.0037	0.0034	0.0032	0.0030	0.0030	0.0029
48	0.0036	0.0033	0.0031	0.0030	0.0029	0.0028
49	0.0035	0.0032	0.0030	0.0029	0.0028	0.0027
50	0.0034	0.0031	0.0029	0.0028	0.0027	0.0027
52	0.0033	0.0030	0.0028	0.0027	0.0026	0.0026
54	0.0031	0.0028	0.0027	0.0026	0.0025	0.0024
56	0.0030	0.0027	0.0026	0.0025	0.0024	0.0023
58	0.0029	0.0026	0.0025	0.0024	0.0023	0.0022
60	0.0027	0.0025	0.0024	0.0023	0.0022	0.0021
62	0.0026	0.0024	0.0023	0.0022	0.0021	0.0021
64	0.0025	0.0023	0.0022	0.0021	0.0020	0.0020
66	0.0024	0.0022	0.0021	0.0020	0.0020	0.0019
68	0.0024	0.0021	0.0020	0.0020	0.0019	0.0018
70	0.0023	0.0021	0.0020	0.0019	0.0018	0.0018
72	0.0022	0.0020	0.0019	0.0018	0.0018	0.0017
74	0.0021	0.0019	0.0018	0.0018	0.0017	0.0017
76	0.0021	0.0019	0.0018	0.0017	0.0017	0.0016
78	0.0020	0.0018	0.0017	0.0017	0.0016	0.0016
80	0.0019	0.0018	0.0017	0.0016	0.0016	0.0015
82	0.0019	0.0017	0.0016	0.0016	0.0015	0.0015
84	0.0018	0.0017	0.0016	0.0015	0.0015	0.0014
86	0.0018	0.0016	0.0015	0.0015	0.0014	0.0014
88	0.0017	0.0016	0.0015	0.0014	0.0014	0.0014
90	0.0017	0.0015	0.0015	0.0014	0.0014	0.0013

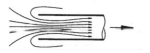

$h_e = 0.93\ VP_d$
PLAIN DUCT END

$h_e = 0.49\ VP_d$
FLANGED DUCT END

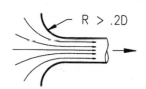

R > .2D

$h_e = 0.04\ VP_d$
BELLMOUTH ENTRY

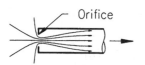

Orifice

$h_e = 1.78\ VP_{Orifice}$
SHARP–EDGED
ORIFICE
* $h_e = F_h\ VP_d$ See 3.5.1

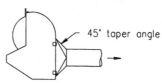

45° taper angle

$h_e = 0.4\ VP_d$ (tapered take–off)
$h_e = 0.65\ VP_d$ (no taper)
STANDARD GRINDER HOOD

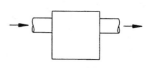

$h_e = 1.5\ VP_d$
TRAP OR SETTLING CHAMBER

TAPERED HOODS

Flanged or unflanged; round, square or rectangular. θ is the major angle on rectangular hoods.

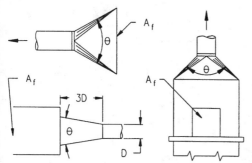

A_f

θ

A_f

3D

θ

D

A_f

θ

Face area (A_f) at least 2 times the duct area.

θ	ENTRY LOSS (h_h) ROUND	RECTANGULAR
15°	0.15 VP	0.25 VP
30°	0.08 VP	0.16 VP
45°	0.06 VP	0.15 VP
60°	0.08 VP	0.17 VP
90°	0.15 VP	0.25 VP
120°	0.26 VP	0.35 VP
150°	0.40 VP	0.48 VP
180°	0.50 VP	0.50 VP

VP = Duct VP = VP_d

Note: 180° values represent round ducts butted into back of booth or hood without a rectangular to round transition.

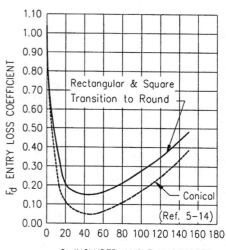

Rectangular & Square Transition to Round

Conical

(Ref. 5–14)

F_d ENTRY LOSS COEFFICIENT

θ, INCLUDED ANGLE IN DEGREES

COMPOUND HOODS

A compound hood, such as the slot/plenum shown to the right, would have 2 losses, one through the slot and the other through the transition into the duct.

The slot entry loss coefficient, F_s, would have a value typically in the range of 1.00 to 1.78 (see Chapters 3 and 10).

The duct entry loss coefficient is given by the above data for tapered hoods.

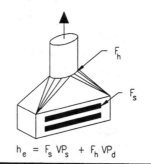

F_h

F_s

$h_e = F_s\ VP_s + F_h\ VP_d$

MISCELLANEOUS VALUES

HOOD	ENTRY LOSS COEFFICIENT F_h
Abrasive blast chamber	1.0
Abrasive blast elevator	2.3
Abrasive separator	2.3
Elevators (enclosures)	0.69
Flanged pipe plus close elbow	0.8
Plain pipe plus close elbow	1.60

AMERICAN CONFERENCE
OF GOVERNMENTAL
INDUSTRIAL HYGIENISTS

*HOOD ENTRY
LOSS COEEFICIENTS*

DATE	*1-95*	FIGURE	*5-15*

Stamped (Smooth)　　5-piece　　4-piece　　3-piece　　Mitered

	R/D					
	0.5	0.75	1.00	1.50	2.00	2.50
Stamped	0.71	0.33	0.22	0.15	0.13	0.12
5-piece	–	0.46	0.33	0.24	0.19	0.17*
4-piece	–	0.50	0.37	0.27	0.24	0.23*
3-piece	0.90	0.54	0.42	0.34	0.33	0.33*

* extrapolated from published data

OTHER ELBOW LOSS COEFFICIENTS
Mitered, no vanes	1.2	
Mitered, turning vanes	0.6	
Flatback (R/D = 2.5)	0.05	(see Figure 5-23)

NOTE: Loss factors are assumed to be for elbows of "zero length." Friction losses should be included to the intersection of centerlines.

ROUND ELBOW LOSS COEFFICIENTS

(Ref. 5.13)

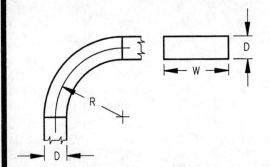

R/D	Aspect Ratio, W/D					
	0.25	0.5	1.0	2.0	3.0	4.0
0.0(Mitred)	1.50	1.32	1.15	1.04	0.92	0.86
0.5	1.36	1.21	1.05	0.95	0.84	0.79
1.0	0.45	0.28	0.21	0.21	0.20	0.19
1.5	0.28	0.18	0.13	0.13	0.12	0.12
2.0	0.24	0.15	0.11	0.11	0.10	0.10
3.0	0.24	0.15	0.11	0.11	0.10	0.10

SQUARE & RECTANGULAR ELBOW LOSS COEFFICIENTS

AMERICAN CONFERENCE OF GOVERNMENTAL INDUSTRIAL HYGIENISTS	*DUCT DESIGN DATA* *ELBOW LOSSES*	
	DATE　*1-95*	FIGURE　*5-16*

TABLE 5-7A. Velocity Pressure to Velocity Conversion—Standard Air

From: $V = 4005\sqrt{VP/\rho}$

V = Velocity, fpm
VP = Velocity Pressure, "wg

VP	V	VP	V	VP	V	VP	V	VP	V	VP	V
0.01	401	0.51	2860	1.01	4025	1.51	4921	2.01	5678	2.60	6458
0.02	566	0.52	2888	1.02	4045	1.52	4938	2.02	5692	2.70	6581
0.03	694	0.53	2916	1.03	4065	1.53	4954	2.03	5706	2.80	6702
0.04	801	0.54	2943	1.04	4084	1.54	4970	2.04	5720	2.90	6820
0.05	896	0.55	2970	1.05	4104	1.55	4986	2.05	5734	3.00	6937
0.06	981	0.56	2997	1.06	4123	1.56	5002	2.06	5748	3.10	7052
0.07	1060	0.57	3024	1.07	4143	1.57	5018	2.07	5762	3.20	7164
0.08	1133	0.58	3050	1.08	4162	1.58	5034	2.08	5776	3.30	7275
0.09	1201	0.59	3076	1.09	4181	1.59	5050	2.09	5790	3.40	7385
0.10	1266	0.60	3102	1.10	4200	1.60	5066	2.10	5804	3.50	7493
0.11	1328	0.61	3128	1.11	4220	1.61	5082	2.11	5818	3.60	7599
0.12	1387	0.62	3154	1.12	4238	1.62	5098	2.12	5831	3.70	7704
0.13	1444	0.63	3179	1.13	4257	1.63	5113	2.13	5845	3.80	7807
0.14	1499	0.64	3204	1.14	4276	1.64	5129	2.14	5859	3.90	7909
0.15	1551	0.65	3229	1.15	4295	1.65	5145	2.15	5872	4.00	8010
0.16	1602	0.66	3254	1.16	4314	1.66	5160	2.16	5886	4.10	8110
0.17	1651	0.67	3278	1.17	4332	1.67	5176	2.17	5900	4.20	8208
0.18	1699	0.68	3303	1.18	4351	1.68	5191	2.18	5913	4.30	8305
0.19	1746	0.69	3327	1.19	4369	1.69	5206	2.19	5927	4.40	8401
0.20	1791	0.70	3351	1.20	4387	1.70	5222	2.20	5940	4.50	8496
0.21	1835	0.71	3375	1.21	4405	1.71	5237	2.21	5954	4.60	8590
0.22	1879	0.72	3398	1.22	4424	1.72	5253	2.22	5967	4.70	8683
0.23	1921	0.73	3422	1.23	4442	1.73	5268	2.23	5981	4.80	8775
0.24	1962	0.74	3445	1.24	4460	1.74	5283	2.24	5994	4.90	8865
0.25	2003	0.75	3468	1.25	4478	1.75	5298	2.25	6007	5.00	8955
0.26	2042	0.76	3491	1.26	4496	1.76	5313	2.26	6021	5.50	9393
0.27	2081	0.77	3514	1.27	4513	1.77	5328	2.27	6034	6.00	9810
0.28	2119	0.78	3537	1.28	4531	1.78	5343	2.28	6047	6.50	10211
0.29	2157	0.79	3560	1.29	4549	1.79	5358	2.29	6061	7.00	10596
0.30	2194	0.80	3582	1.30	4566	1.80	5373	2.30	6074	7.50	10968
0.31	2230	0.81	3604	1.31	4584	1.81	5388	2.31	6087	8.00	11328
0.32	2266	0.82	3627	1.32	4601	1.82	5403	2.32	6100	8.50	11676
0.33	2301	0.83	3649	1.33	4619	1.83	5418	2.33	6113	9.00	12015
0.34	2335	0.84	3671	1.34	4636	1.84	5433	2.34	6126	9.50	12344
0.35	2369	0.85	3692	1.35	4653	1.85	5447	2.35	6140	10.00	12655
0.36	2403	0.86	3714	1.36	4671	1.86	5462	2.36	6153	10.50	12978
0.37	2436	0.87	3736	1.37	4688	1.87	5477	2.37	6166	11.00	13283
0.38	2469	0.88	3757	1.38	4705	1.88	5491	2.38	6179	11.50	13582
0.39	2501	0.89	3778	1.39	4722	1.89	5506	2.39	6192	12.00	13874
0.40	2533	0.90	3799	1.40	4739	1.90	5521	2.40	6205	12.50	14160
0.41	2564	0.91	3821	1.41	4756	1.91	5535	2.41	6217	13.00	14440
0.42	2596	0.92	3841	1.42	4773	1.92	5549	2.42	6230	13.50	14715
0.43	2626	0.93	3862	1.43	4789	1.93	5564	2.43	6243	14.00	14985
0.44	2657	0.94	3883	1.44	4806	1.94	5578	2.44	6256	14.50	15251
0.45	2687	0.95	3904	1.45	4823	1.95	5593	2.45	6269	15.00	15511
0.46	2716	0.96	3924	1.46	4839	1.96	5607	2.46	6282	15.50	1576
0.47	2746	0.97	3944	1.47	4856	1.97	5621	2.47	6294	16.00	16020
0.48	2775	0.98	3965	1.48	4872	1.98	5636	2.48	6307	16.50	16268
0.49	2803	0.99	3985	1.49	4889	1.99	5650	2.49	6320	17.00	16513
0.50	2832	1.00	4005	1.50	4905	2.00	5664	2.50	6332	17.50	16754

TABLE 5-7B. Velocity Pressure to Velocity Conversion—Standard Air

From: $V = 4005\sqrt{VP/\rho}$

V = Velocity, fpm
VP = Velocity Pressure, "wg

VP	V	VP	V	VP	V	VP	V	VP	V	VP	V
400	0.01	2600	0.42	3850	0.92	4880	1.48	5690	2.02	6190	2.39
500	0.02	2625	0.43	3875	0.94	4900	1.50	5700	2.03	6200	2.40
600	0.02	2650	0.44	3900	0.95	4920	1.51	5710	2.03	6210	2.40
700	0.03	2675	0.45	3925	0.96	4940	1.52	5720	2.04	6220	2.41
800	0.04	2700	0.45	3950	0.97	4960	1.53	5730	2.05	6230	2.42
900	0.05	2725	0.46	3975	0.99	4980	1.55	5740	2.05	6240	2.43
1000	0.06	2750	0.47	4000	1.00	5000	1.56	5750	2.06	6250	2.44
1100	0.08	2775	0.48	4020	1.01	5020	1.57	5760	2.07	6260	2.44
1200	0.09	2800	0.49	4040	1.02	5040	1.58	5770	2.08	6270	2.45
1300	0.11	2825	0.50	4060	1.03	5060	1.60	5780	2.08	6280	2.46
1400	0.12	2850	0.51	4080	1.04	5080	1.61	5790	2.09	6290	2.47
1450	0.13	2875	0.52	4100	1.05	5100	1.62	5800	2.10	6300	2.47
1500	0.14	2900	0.52	4120	1.06	5120	1.63	5810	2.10	6310	2.48
1550	0.15	2925	0.53	4140	1.07	5140	1.65	5820	2.11	6320	2.49
1600	0.16	2950	0.54	4160	1.08	5160	1.66	5830	2.12	6330	2.50
1650	0.17	2975	0.55	4180	1.09	5180	1.67	5840	2.13	6340	2.51
1700	0.18	3000	0.56	4200	1.10	5200	1.69	5850	2.13	6350	2.51
1750	0.19	3025	0.57	4220	1.11	5220	1.70	5860	2.14	6360	2.52
1800	0.20	3050	0.58	4240	1.12	5240	1.71	5870	2.15	6370	2.53
1825	0.21	3075	0.59	4260	1.13	5260	1.72	5880	2.16	6380	2.54
1850	0.21	3100	0.60	4280	1.14	5280	1.74	5890	2.16	6390	2.55
1875	0.22	3125	0.61	4300	1.15	5300	1.75	5900	2.17	6400	2.55
1900	0.23	3150	0.62	4320	1.16	5320	1.76	5910	2.18	6410	2.56
1925	0.23	3175	0.63	4340	1.17	5340	1.78	5920	2.18	6420	2.57
1950	0.24	3200	0.64	4360	1.19	5360	1.79	5930	2.19	6430	2.58
1975	0.24	3225	0.65	4380	1.20	5380	1.80	5940	2.20	6440	2.59
2000	0.25	3250	0.66	4400	1.21	5400	1.82	5950	2.21	6450	2.59
2025	0.26	3275	0.67	4420	1.22	5420	1.83	5960	2.21	6460	2.60
2050	0.26	3300	0.68	4440	1.23	5440	1.84	5970	2.22	6470	2.61
2075	0.27	3325	0.69	4460	1.24	5460	1.86	5980	2.23	6480	2.62
2100	0.27	3350	0.70	4480	1.25	5480	1.87	5990	2.24	6490	2.63
2125	0.28	3375	0.71	4500	1.26	5500	1.89	6000	2.24	6500	2.63
2150	0.29	3400	0.72	4520	1.27	5510	1.89	6010	2.25	6550	2.67
2175	0.29	3425	0.73	4540	1.29	5520	1.90	6020	2.26	6600	2.72
2200	0.30	3450	0.74	4560	1.30	5530	1.91	6030	2.27	6650	2.76
2225	0.31	3475	0.75	4580	1.31	5540	1.91	6040	2.27	6700	2.80
2250	0.32	3500	0.76	4600	1.32	5550	1.92	6050	2.28	6750	2.84
2275	0.32	3525	0.77	4620	1.33	5560	1.93	6060	2.29	6800	2.88
2300	0.33	3550	0.79	4640	1.34	5570	1.93	6070	2.30	6900	2.97
2325	0.34	3575	0.80	4660	1.35	5580	1.94	6080	2.30	7000	3.05
2350	0.34	3600	0.81	4680	1.37	5590	1.95	6090	2.31	7100	3.14
2375	0.35	3625	0.82	4700	1.38	5600	1.96	6100	2.32	7200	3.23
2400	0.36	3650	0.83	4720	1.39	5610	1.96	6110	2.33	7300	3.32
2425	0.37	3675	0.84	4740	1.40	5620	1.97	6120	2.34	7400	3.41
2450	0.37	3700	0.85	4760	1.41	5630	1.98	6130	2.34	7500	3.51
2475	0.38	3725	0.87	4780	1.42	5640	1.98	6140	2.35	7600	3.60
2500	0.39	3750	0.88	4800	1.44	5650	1.99	6150	2.36	7700	3.70
2525	0.40	3775	0.89	4820	1.45	5660	2.00	6160	2.37	7800	3.79
2550	0.41	3800	0.90	4840	1.46	5670	2.00	6170	2.37	7900	3.89
2575	0.41	3825	0.91	4860	1.47	5680	2.01	6180	2.38	8000	3.99

TABLE 5-8. Area and Circumference of Circles

Diam. In Inches	AREA		CIRCUMFERENCE		Diam. In Inches	AREA		CIRCUMFERENCE	
	Square Inches	Square Feet	Inches	Feet		Square Inches	Square Feet	Inches	Feet
1	0.79	0.0055	3.14	0.2618	30	706.9	4.909	94.2	7.854
1.5	1.77	0.0123	4.71	0.3927	31	754.8	5.241	97.4	8.116
2	3.14	0.0218	6.28	0.5236	32	804.2	5.585	100.5	8.378
2.5	4.91	0.0341	7.85	0.6545	33	855.3	5.940	103.7	8.639
3	7.07	0.0491	9.42	0.7854	34	907.9	6.305	106.8	8.901
3.5	9.62	0.0668	11.00	0.9163	35	962.1	6.681	110.0	9.163
4	12.57	0.0873	12.57	1.0472	36	1017.9	7.069	113.1	9.425
4.5	15.90	0.1104	14.14	1.1781	37	1075.2	7.467	116.2	9.687
5	19.63	0.1364	15.71	1.3090	38	1134.1	7.876	119.4	9.948
5.5	23.76	0.1650	17.28	1.4399	39	1194.6	8.296	122.5	10.210
6	28.27	0.1963	18.85	1.5708	40	1256.6	8.727	125.7	10.472
6.5	33.18	0.2304	20.42	1.7017	41	1320.3	9.168	128.8	10.734
7	38.48	0.2673	21.99	1.8326	42	1385.4	9.621	131.9	10.996
7.5	44.18	0.3068	23.56	1.9635	43	1452.2	10.085	135.1	11.257
8	50.27	0.3491	25.13	2.0944	44	1520.5	10.559	138.2	11.519
8.5	56.75	0.3941	26.70	2.2253	45	1590.4	11.045	141.4	11.781
9	63.62	0.4418	28.27	2.3562	46	1661.9	11.541	144.5	12.043
9.5	70.80	0.4922	29.85	2.4871	47	1734.9	12.048	147.7	12.305
10	78.54	0.5454	31.42	2.6180	48	1809.6	12.566	150.8	12.566
10.5	86.59	0.6013	32.99	2.7489	49	1885.7	13.095	153.9	12.828
11	95.03	0.6600	34.56	2.8798	50	1963.5	13.635	157.1	13.090
11.5	103.87	0.7213	36.13	3.0107	52	2123.7	14.748	163.4	13.614
12	113.10	0.7854	37.70	3.1416	54	2290.2	15.904	169.6	14.137
13	132.73	0.9218	40.84	3.4034	56	2463.0	17.104	175.9	14.661
14	153.94	1.0690	43.98	3.6652	58	2642.1	18.348	182.2	15.184
15	176.71	1.2272	47.12	3.9270	60	2827.4	19.635	188.5	15.708
16	201.06	1.3963	50.27	4.1888	62	3019.1	20.966	194.8	16.232
17	226.98	1.5763	53.41	4.4506	64	3217.0	22.340	201.1	16.755
18	254.47	1.7671	56.55	4.7124	66	3421.2	23.758	207.3	17.279
19	283.53	1.9689	59.69	4.9742	68	3631.7	25.220	213.6	17.802
20	314.16	2.1817	62.83	5.2360	70	3848.5	26.725	219.9	18.326
21	346.36	2.4053	65.97	5.4978	72	4071.5	28.274	226.2	18.850
22	380.13	2.6398	69.12	5.7596	74	4300.8	29.867	232.5	19.373
23	415.48	2.8852	72.26	6.0214	76	4536.5	31.503	238.8	19.897
24	452.39	3.1416	75.40	6.2832	78	4778.4	33.183	245.0	20.420
25	490.87	3.4088	78.54	6.5450	80	5026.5	34.907	251.3	20.944
26	530.93	3.6870	81.68	6.8068	82	5281.0	36.674	257.6	21.468
27	572.56	3.9761	84.82	7.0686	84	5541.8	38.485	263.9	21.991
28	615.75	4.2761	87.96	7.3304	86	5808.8	40.339	270.2	22.515
29	660.52	4.5869	91.11	7.5922	88	6082.1	42.237	276.5	23.038

The usual sheet metal fabricator will have patterns for ducts in 0.5-inch steps through 5.5-inch diameter; 1 inch steps 6 inches through 20 inches and 2-inch steps 22 inches and larger diameters.

TABLE 5-9A. Circular Equilavents of Rectangular Duct Sizes

A\B	4.0	4.5	5.0	5.5	6.0	6.5	7.0	7.5	8.0	8.5	9.0	9.5	10.0	10.5	11.0	11.5	12.0	12.5	13.0	13.5	14.0	14.5	15.0	15.5	16.0
3.0	3.8	4.0	4.2	4.4	4.6	4.7	4.9	5.1	5.2	5.3	5.5	5.6	5.7	5.9	6.0	6.1	6.2	6.3	6.4	6.5	6.6	6.7	6.8	6.9	7.0
3.5	4.1	4.3	4.6	4.8	5.0	5.2	5.3	5.5	5.7	5.8	6.0	6.1	6.3	6.4	6.5	6.7	6.8	6.9	7.0	7.1	7.2	7.3	7.5	7.6	7.7
4.0	4.4	4.6	4.9	5.1	5.3	5.5	5.7	5.9	6.1	6.3	6.4	6.6	6.7	6.9	7.0	7.2	7.3	7.4	7.6	7.7	7.8	7.9	8.0	8.2	8.3
4.5	4.6	4.9	5.2	5.4	5.7	5.9	6.1	6.3	6.5	6.7	6.9	7.0	7.2	7.4	7.5	7.7	7.8	7.9	8.1	8.2	8.4	8.5	8.6	8.7	8.8
5.0	4.9	5.2	5.5	5.7	6.0	6.2	6.4	6.7	6.9	7.1	7.3	7.4	7.6	7.8	8.0	8.1	8.3	8.4	8.6	8.7	8.9	9.0	9.1	9.3	9.4
5.5	5.1	5.4	5.7	6.0	6.3	6.5	6.8	7.0	7.2	7.4	7.6	7.8	8.0	8.2	8.4	8.6	8.7	8.9	9.0	9.2	9.3	9.5	9.6	9.8	9.9

A\B	6.0	7.0	8.0	9.0	10.0	11.0	12.0	13.0	14.0	15.0	16.0	17.0	18.0	19.0	20.0	22.0	24.0	26.0	28.0	30.0	32.0	34.0	36.0	38.0	40.0
6.0	6.6																								
7.0	7.1	7.7																							
8.0	7.6	8.2	8.7																						
9.0	8.0	8.7	9.3	9.8																					
10.0	8.4	9.1	9.8	10.4	10.9																				
11.0	8.8	9.5	10.2	10.9	11.5	12.0																			
12.0	9.1	9.9	10.7	11.3	12.0	12.6	13.1																		
13.0	9.5	10.3	11.1	11.8	12.4	13.1	13.7	14.2																	
14.0	9.8	10.7	11.5	12.2	12.9	13.5	14.2	14.7	15.3																
15.0	10.1	11.0	11.8	12.6	13.3	14.0	14.6	15.3	15.8	16.4															
16.0	10.4	11.3	12.2	13.0	13.7	14.4	15.1	15.7	16.4	16.9	17.5														
17.0	10.7	11.6	12.5	13.4	14.1	14.9	15.6	16.2	16.8	17.4	18.0	18.6													
18.0	11.0	11.9	12.9	13.7	14.5	15.3	16.0	16.7	17.3	17.9	18.5	19.1	19.7												
19.0	11.2	12.2	13.2	14.1	14.9	15.7	16.4	17.1	17.8	18.4	19.0	19.6	20.2	20.8											
20.0	11.5	12.5	13.5	14.4	15.2	16.0	16.8	17.5	18.2	18.9	19.5	20.1	20.7	21.3	21.9										
22.0	12.0	13.0	14.1	15.0	15.9	16.8	17.6	18.3	19.1	19.8	20.4	21.1	21.7	22.3	22.9	24.0									
24.0	12.4	13.5	14.6	15.6	16.5	17.4	18.3	19.1	19.9	20.6	21.3	22.0	22.7	23.3	23.9	25.1	26.2								
26.0	12.8	14.0	15.1	16.2	17.1	18.1	19.0	19.8	20.6	21.4	22.1	22.9	23.5	24.2	24.9	26.1	27.3	28.4							
28.0	13.2	14.5	15.6	16.7	17.7	18.7	19.6	20.5	21.3	22.1	22.9	23.7	24.4	25.1	25.8	27.1	28.3	29.5	30.6						
30.0	13.6	14.9	16.1	17.2	18.3	19.3	20.2	21.1	22.0	22.9	23.7	24.4	25.2	25.9	26.6	28.0	29.3	30.5	31.7	32.8					
32.0	14.0	15.3	16.5	17.7	18.8	19.8	20.8	21.8	22.7	23.5	24.4	25.2	26.0	26.7	27.5	28.9	30.2	31.5	32.7	33.9	35.0				
34.0	14.4	15.7	17.0	18.2	19.3	20.4	21.4	22.4	23.3	24.2	25.1	25.9	26.7	27.5	28.3	29.7	31.1	32.4	33.7	34.9	36.1	37.2			
36.0	14.7	16.1	17.4	18.6	19.8	20.9	21.9	22.9	23.9	24.8	25.7	26.6	27.4	28.2	29.0	30.5	32.0	33.3	34.6	35.9	37.1	38.2	39.4		
38.0	15.0	16.5	17.8	19.0	20.2	21.4	22.4	23.5	24.5	25.4	26.4	27.2	28.1	28.9	29.8	31.3	32.8	34.2	35.6	36.8	38.1	39.3	40.4	41.5	
40.0	15.3	16.8	18.2	19.5	20.7	21.8	22.9	24.0	25.0	26.0	27.0	27.9	28.8	29.6	30.5	32.1	33.6	35.1	36.4	37.8	39.0	40.3	41.5	42.6	43.7
42.0	15.6	17.1	18.5	19.9	21.1	22.3	23.4	24.5	25.6	26.6	27.6	28.5	29.4	30.3	31.2	32.8	34.4	35.9	37.3	38.7	40.0	41.3	42.5	43.7	44.8
44.0	15.9	17.5	18.9	20.3	21.5	22.7	23.9	25.0	26.1	27.1	28.1	29.1	30.0	30.9	31.8	33.5	35.1	36.7	38.1	39.5	40.9	42.2	43.5	44.7	45.8
46.0	16.2	17.8	19.3	20.6	21.9	23.2	24.4	25.5	26.6	27.7	28.7	29.7	30.6	31.6	32.5	34.2	35.9	37.4	38.9	40.4	41.8	43.1	44.4	45.7	46.9
48.0	16.5	18.1	19.6	21.0	22.3	23.6	24.8	26.0	27.1	28.2	29.2	30.2	31.2	32.2	33.1	34.9	36.6	38.2	39.7	41.2	42.6	44.0	45.3	46.6	47.9
50.0	16.8	18.4	19.9	21.4	22.7	24.0	25.2	26.4	27.6	28.7	29.8	30.8	31.8	32.8	33.7	35.5	37.2	38.9	40.5	42.0	43.5	44.9	46.2	47.5	48.8
54.0	17.3	19.0	20.6	22.0	23.5	24.8	26.1	27.3	28.5	29.7	30.8	31.8	32.9	33.9	34.9	36.8	38.6	40.3	41.9	43.5	45.1	46.5	48.0	49.3	50.7
58.0	17.8	19.5	21.2	22.7	24.2	25.5	26.9	28.2	29.4	30.6	31.7	32.8	33.9	35.0	36.0	38.0	39.8	41.6	43.3	45.0	46.6	48.1	49.6	51.0	52.4
62.0	18.3	20.1	21.7	23.3	24.8	26.3	27.6	28.9	30.2	31.5	32.6	33.8	34.9	36.0	37.1	39.1	41.0	42.9	44.7	46.4	48.0	49.6	51.2	52.7	54.1
66.0	18.8	20.6	22.3	23.9	25.5	26.9	28.4	29.7	31.0	32.3	33.5	34.7	35.9	37.0	38.1	40.2	42.2	44.1	46.0	47.7	49.4	51.1	52.7	54.2	55.7
70.0	19.2	21.1	22.8	24.5	26.1	27.6	29.1	30.4	31.8	33.1	34.4	35.6	36.8	37.9	39.1	41.2	43.3	45.3	47.2	49.0	50.8	52.5	54.1	55.7	57.3
74.0	19.6	21.5	23.3	25.1	26.7	28.2	29.7	31.2	32.5	33.9	35.2	36.4	37.7	38.8	40.0	42.2	44.4	46.4	48.4	50.3	52.1	53.8	55.5	57.2	58.8
78.0	20.0	22.0	23.8	25.6	27.3	28.2	30.4	31.8	33.3	34.6	36.0	37.2	38.5	39.7	40.9	43.2	45.4	47.5	49.5	51.4	53.3	55.1	56.9	58.6	60.2
82.0	20.4	22.4	24.3	26.1	27.8	29.4	31.0	32.5	33.9	35.4	36.7	38.0	39.3	40.6	41.8	44.1	46.4	48.5	50.6	52.6	54.5	56.4	58.2	59.9	61.6
86.0	20.8	22.9	24.8	26.6	28.3	30.0	31.6	33.1	34.6	36.1	37.4	38.8	40.1	41.4	42.6	45.0	47.3	49.6	51.7	53.7	55.7	57.6	59.4	61.2	63.0
90.0	21.2	23.3	25.2	27.1	28.9	30.6	32.2	33.8	35.3	36.7	38.2	39.5	40.9	42.2	43.5	45.9	48.3	50.5	52.7	54.8	56.8	58.8	60.7	62.5	64.3

TABLE 5-9B. Circular Equivalents of Rectangular Duct Sizes (cont'd)

A\B	42.0	44.0	46.0	48.0	50.0	54.0	58.0	62.0	66.0	70.0	74.0	78.0	82.0	86.0	90.0
6.0															
7.0															
8.0															
9.0															
10.0															
11.0															
12.0															
13.0															
14.0															
15.0															
16.0															
17.0															
18.0															
19.0															
20.0															
22.0															
24.0															
26.0															
28.0															
30.0															
32.0															
34.0															
36.0															
38.0															
40.0															
42.0	45.9														
44.0	47.0	48.1													
46.0	48.0	49.2	50.3												
48.0	49.1	50.2	51.4	52.5											
50.0	50.0	51.2	52.4	53.6	54.7										
54.0	52.0	53.2	54.4	55.6	56.8	59.0									
58.0	53.8	55.1	56.4	57.6	58.8	61.2	63.4								
62.0	55.5	56.9	58.2	59.5	60.8	63.2	65.5	67.8							
66.0	57.2	58.6	60.0	61.3	62.6	65.2	67.6	69.9	72.1						
70.0	58.8	60.3	61.7	63.1	64.4	67.1	69.6	72.0	74.3	76.5					
74.0	60.3	61.9	63.3	64.8	66.2	68.9	71.5	74.0	76.4	78.7	80.9				
78.0	61.8	63.4	64.9	66.4	67.9	70.6	73.3	75.9	78.4	80.7	83.0	85.3			
82.0	63.3	64.9	66.5	68.0	69.5	72.3	75.1	77.8	80.3	82.8	85.1	87.4	89.6		
86.0	64.7	66.3	67.9	69.5	71.0	74.0	76.8	79.6	82.2	84.7	87.1	89.5	91.8	94.0	
90.0	66.0	67.7	69.4	71.0	72.6	75.6	78.5	81.3	84.0	86.6	89.1	91.5	93.9	96.2	98.4

$$D_{equiv} = 1.3 \; \frac{(A \times B)^{0.625}}{(A+B)^{0.25}}$$

where:

D_{equiv} = equivalent round duct size of rectangular duct, in.

A = one side of rectangular duct, in.

B = adjacent side of rectangular duct, in.

TABLE 5-10. Air Density Correction Factor, df

					ALTITUDE RELATIVE TO SEA LEVEL, ft											
	−5000	−4000	−3000	−2000	−1000	0	1000	2000	3000	4000	5000	6000	7000	8000	9000	10000
						BAROMETRIC PRESSURE										
"Hg"	35.74	34.51	33.31	32.15	31.02	29.92	28.86	27.82	26.82	25.84	24.89	23.98	23.09	22.22	21.39	20.57
"w"	486.74	469.97	453.67	437.84	422.45	407.50	392.98	378.89	365.21	351.93	339.04	326.54	314.42	302.66	291.26	280.21
Temp. (Deg. F)						DENSITY FACTOR, df										
-40	1.51	1.46	1.40	1.36	1.31	1.26	1.22	1.17	1.13	1.09	1.05	1.01	0.97	0.94	0.90	0.87
0	1.38	1.33	1.28	1.24	1.19	1.15	1.11	1.07	1.03	1.00	0.96	0.92	0.89	0.86	0.82	0.79
40	1.27	1.22	1.18	1.14	1.10	1.06	1.02	0.99	0.95	0.92	0.88	0.85	0.82	0.79	0.76	0.73
70	1.19	1.15	1.11	1.07	1.04	1.00	0.96	0.93	0.90	0.86	0.83	0.80	0.77	0.74	0.71	0.69
100	1.13	1.09	1.05	1.02	0.98	0.95	0.91	0.88	0.85	0.82	0.79	0.76	0.73	0.70	0.68	0.65
150	1.04	1.00	0.97	0.93	0.90	0.87	0.84	0.81	0.78	0.75	0.72	0.70	0.67	0.65	0.62	0.60
200	0.96	0.93	0.89	0.86	0.83	0.80	0.77	0.75	0.72	0.69	0.67	0.64	0.62	0.60	0.57	0.55
250	0.89	0.86	0.83	0.80	0.77	0.75	0.72	0.69	0.67	0.64	0.62	0.60	0.58	0.55	0.53	0.51
300	0.83	0.80	0.78	0.75	0.72	0.70	0.67	0.65	0.62	0.60	0.58	0.56	0.54	0.52	0.50	0.48
350	0.78	0.75	0.73	0.70	0.68	0.65	0.63	0.61	0.59	0.57	0.54	0.52	0.50	0.49	0.47	0.45
400	0.74	0.71	0.69	0.66	0.64	0.62	0.59	0.57	0.55	0.53	0.51	0.49	0.48	0.46	0.44	0.42
450	0.70	0.67	0.65	0.63	0.60	0.58	0.56	0.54	0.52	0.50	0.48	0.47	0.45	0.43	0.42	0.40
500	0.66	0.64	0.61	0.59	0.57	0.55	0.53	0.51	0.49	0.48	0.46	0.44	0.43	0.41	0.39	0.38
550	0.63	0.61	0.58	0.56	0.54	0.52	0.51	0.49	0.47	0.45	0.44	0.42	0.40	0.39	0.38	0.36
600	0.60	0.58	0.56	0.54	0.52	0.50	0.48	0.46	0.45	0.43	0.42	0.40	0.39	0.37	0.36	0.34
700	0.55	0.53	0.51	0.49	0.47	0.46	0.44	0.42	0.41	0.39	0.38	0.37	0.35	0.34	0.33	0.31
800	0.50	0.49	0.47	0.45	0.44	0.42	0.41	0.39	0.38	0.36	0.35	0.34	0.32	0.31	0.30	0.29
900	0.47	0.45	0.43	0.42	0.40	0.39	0.38	0.36	0.35	0.34	0.32	0.31	0.30	0.29	0.28	0.27
1000	0.43	0.42	0.40	0.39	0.38	0.36	0.35	0.34	0.33	0.31	0.30	0.29	0.28	0.27	0.26	0.25

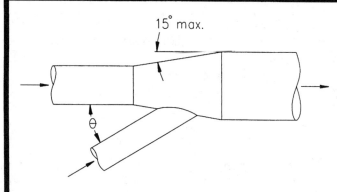

Angle θ Degrees	Loss Fraction of VP in Branch
10	0.06
15	0.09
20	0.12
25	0.15
30	0.18
35	0.21
40	0.25
45	0.28
50	0.32
60	0.44
90	1.00

Note: Branch entry loss assumed to occur in branch and is so calculated.

Do not include an enlargement regain calculation for branch entry enlargements.

BRANCH ENTRY LOSSES

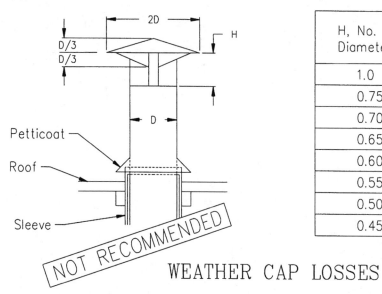

H, No. of Diameters	Loss Fraction of VP
1.0 D	0.10
0.75 D	0.18
0.70 D	0.22
0.65 D	0.30
0.60 D	0.41
0.55 D	0.56
0.50 D	0.73
0.45 D	1.0

WEATHER CAP LOSSES

See Fig. 5-30

AMERICAN CONFERENCE OF GOVERNMENTAL INDUSTRIAL HYGIENISTS	*DUCT DESIGN DATA*	
	DATE *1–95*	FIGURE *5–17*

STATIC PRESSURE REGAINS FOR EXPANSIONS

Within duct

Regain (R), fraction of VP difference					
Taper angle degrees	Diameter ratios D_2/D_1				
	1.25:1	1.5:1	1.75:1	2:1	2.5:1
3 1/2	0.92	0.88	0.84	0.81	0.75
5	0.88	0.84	0.80	0.76	0.68
10	0.85	0.76	0.70	0.63	0.53
15	0.83	0.70	0.62	0.55	0.43
20	0.81	0.67	0.57	0.48	0.43
25	0.80	0.65	0.53	0.44	0.28
30	0.79	0.63	0.51	0.41	0.25
Abrupt 90	0.77	0.62	0.50	0.40	0.25
Where: $SP_2 = SP_1 + R(VP_1 - VP_2)$					

At end of duct

Regain (R), fraction of inlet VP						
Taper length to inlet diam L/D	Diameter ratios D_2/D_1					
	1.2:1	1.3:1	1.4:1	1.5:1	1.6:1	1.7:1
1.0:1	0.37	0.39	0.38	0.35	0.31	0.27
1.5:1	0.39	0.46	0.47	0.46	0.44	0.41
2.0:1	0.42	0.49	0.52	0.52	0.51	0.49
3.0:1	0.44	0.52	0.57	0.59	0.60	0.59
4.0:1	0.45	0.55	0.60	0.63	0.63	0.64
5.0:1	0.47	0.56	0.62	0.65	0.66	0.68
7.5:1	0.48	0.58	0.64	0.68	0.70	0.72
Where: $SP_1 = SP_2 - R(VP_1)$ *						

*When $SP_2 = 0$ (atmosphere) SP_1 will be (−)

The regain (R) will only be 70% of value shown above when expansion follows a disturbance or elbow (including a fan) by less than 5 duct diameters.

STATIC PRESSURE LOSSES FOR CONTRACTIONS

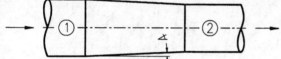

Tapered contraction
$SP_2 = SP_1 - (VP_2 - VP_1) - L(VP_2 - VP_1)$

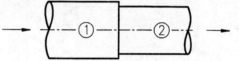

Abrupt contraction
$SP_2 = SP_1 - (VP_2 - VP_1) - K(VP_2)$

Taper angle degrees	L(loss)
5	0.05
10	0.06
15	0.08
20	0.10
25	0.11
30	0.13
45	0.20
60	0.30
over 60	Abrupt contraction

Ratio A_2/A_1	K
0.1	0.48
0.2	0.46
0.3	0.42
0.4	0.37
0.4	0.32
0.6	0.26
0.7	0.20

A = duct area, ft^2

Note:
In calculating SP for expansion or contraction use algebraic signs: VP is (+), and usually SP is (+) in discharge duct from fan, and SP is (−) in inlet duct to fan.

AMERICAN CONFERENCE OF GOVERNMENTAL INDUSTRIAL HYGIENISTS	*DUCT DESIGN DATA*	
	DATE *1-95*	FIGURE *5-18*

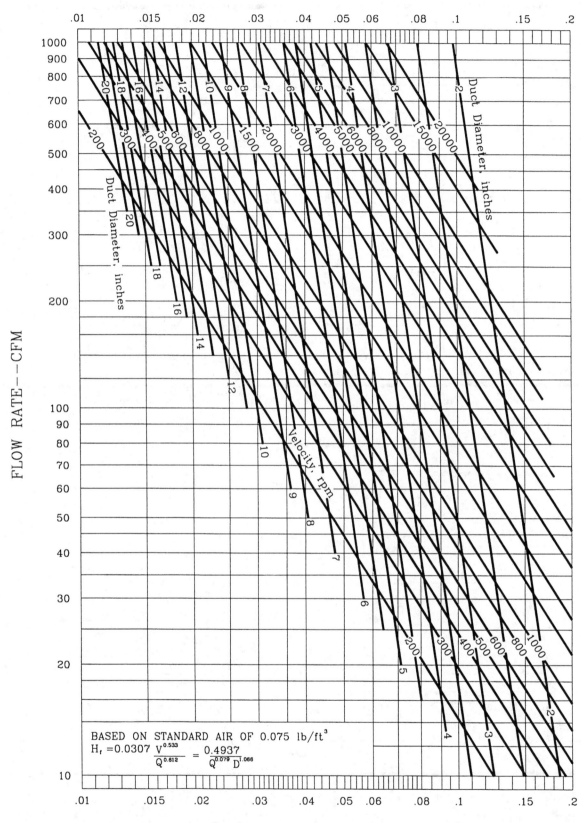

Figure 5-19a

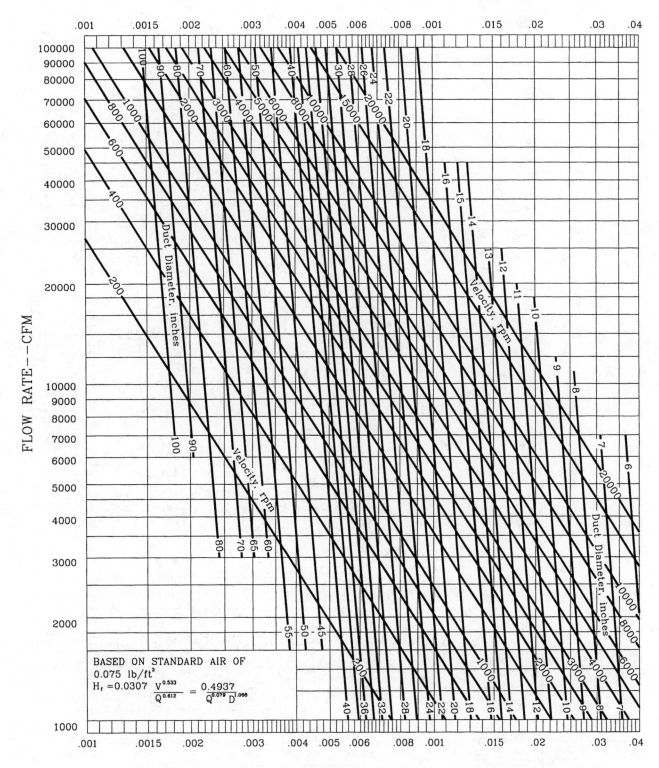

FRICTION LOSS (H_f) -- NUMBER OF VP PER FOOT OF DUCT

Figure 5-19b

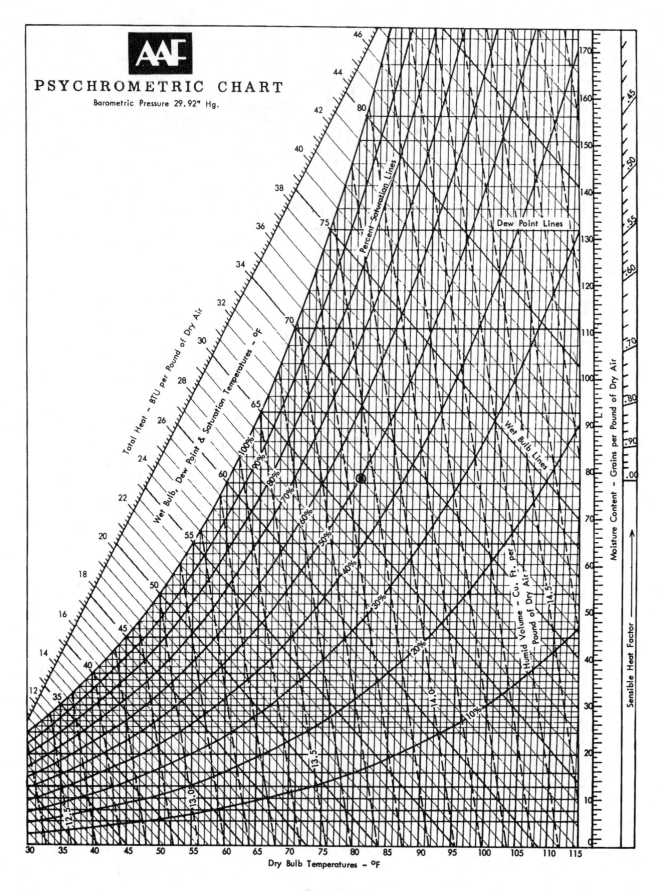

Figure 5-20

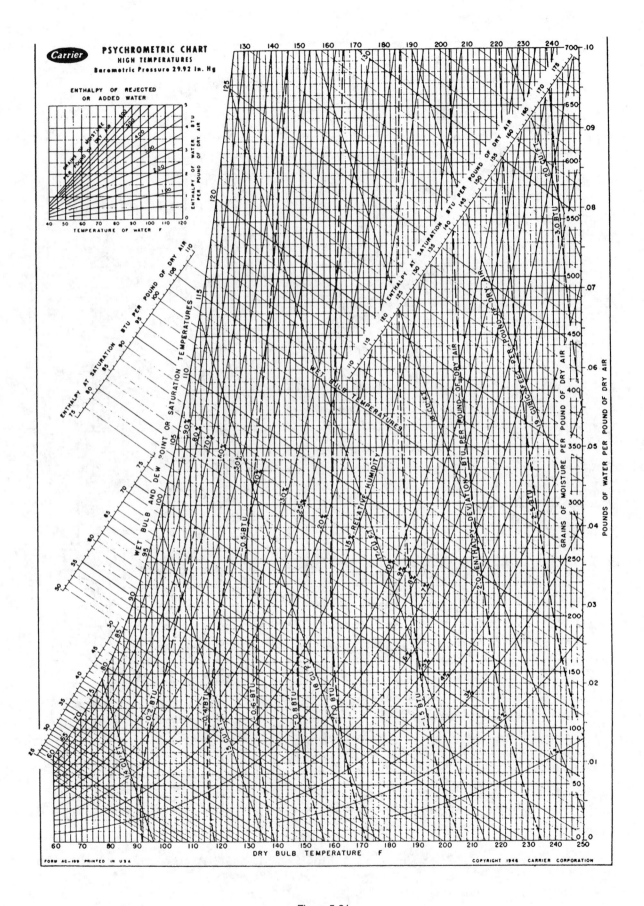

Figure 5-21

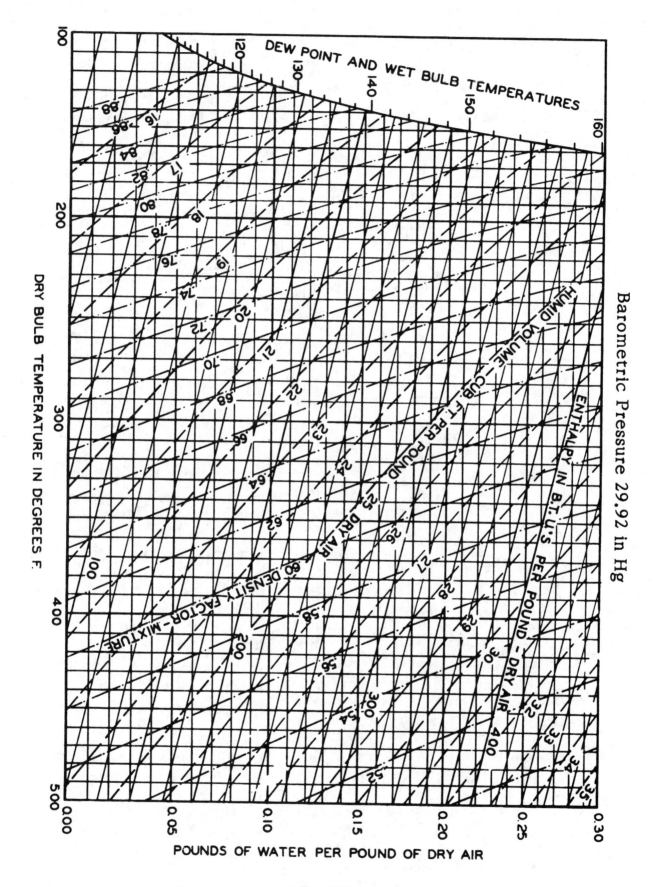

Figure 5-22

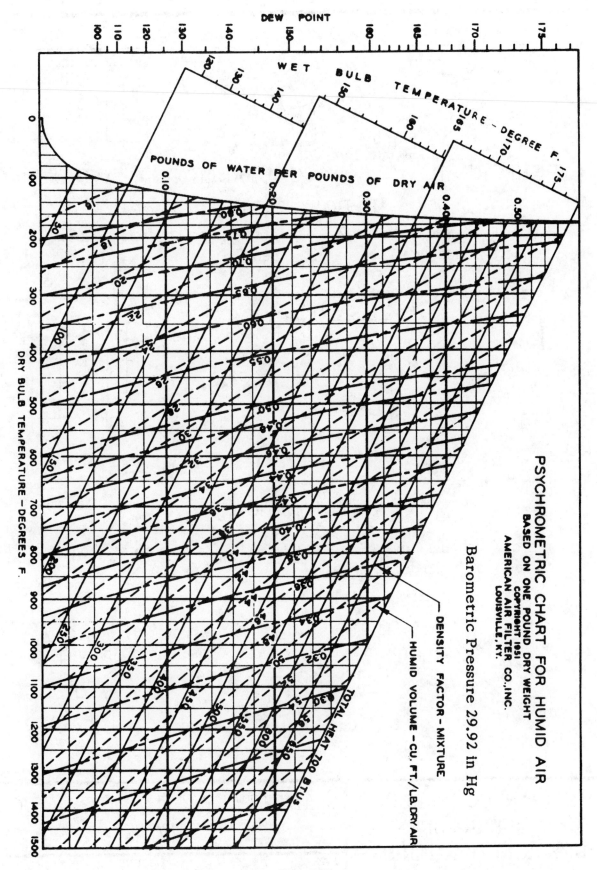

Figure 5-23

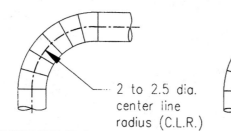 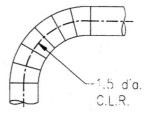 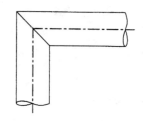

2 to 2.5 dia. center line radius (C.L.R.)

1.5 dia. C.L.R.

PREFERRED   ACCEPTABLE   AVOID

ELBOW RADIUS

Elbows should be 2 to 2.5 diameter centerline radius except where space does not permit. See Fig. 5-13 for loss factor.

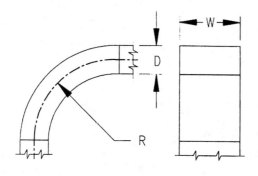 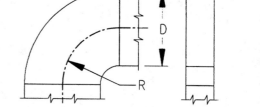

PREFERRED   AVOID

ASPECT RATIO $\left(\frac{W}{D}\right)$

Elbows should have $\left(\frac{W}{D}\right)$ and $\left(\frac{R}{D}\right)$ equal to or greater than (1). See Fig. 5-13 for loss factor.

Note: Avoid mitered elbows. If necessary, use only with clean air and provide turning vanes. Consult mfg. for turning vane loss factor.

AMERICAN CONFERENCE OF GOVERNMENTAL INDUSTRIAL HYGIENISTS	*PRINCIPLES OF DUCT DESIGN* *ELBOWS*	
	DATE *1-95*	FIGURE *5-24*

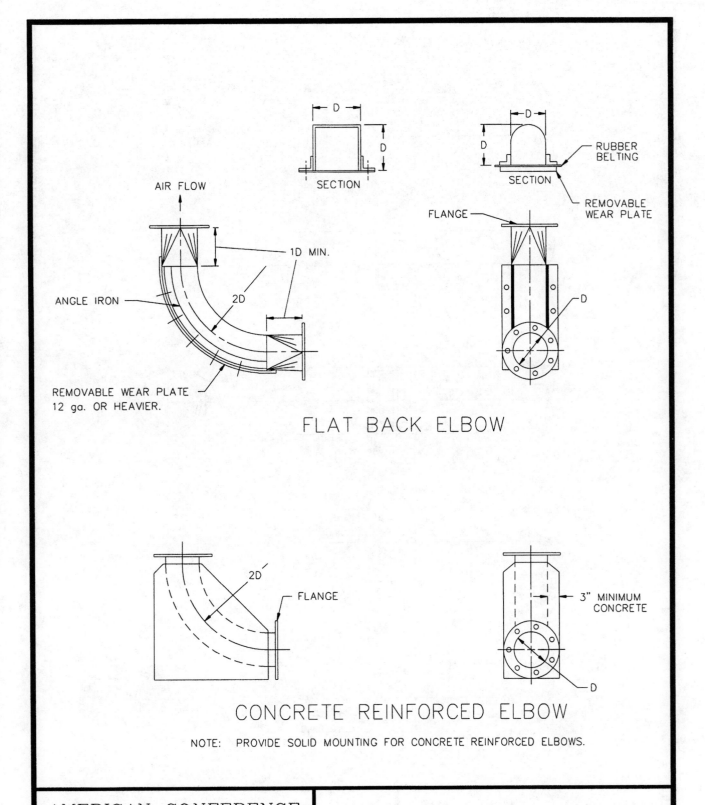

AIR FLOW

1D MIN.

ANGLE IRON

2D

REMOVABLE WEAR PLATE
12 ga. OR HEAVIER.

D

SECTION

D

D

SECTION

RUBBER
BELTING

REMOVABLE
WEAR PLATE

FLANGE

D

FLAT BACK ELBOW

2D

FLANGE

3" MINIMUM
CONCRETE

D

CONCRETE REINFORCED ELBOW

NOTE: PROVIDE SOLID MOUNTING FOR CONCRETE REINFORCED ELBOWS.

AMERICAN CONFERENCE
OF GOVERNMENTAL
INDUSTRIAL HYGIENISTS

HEAVY DUTY ELBOWS

DATE   1-95

FIGURE   5-25

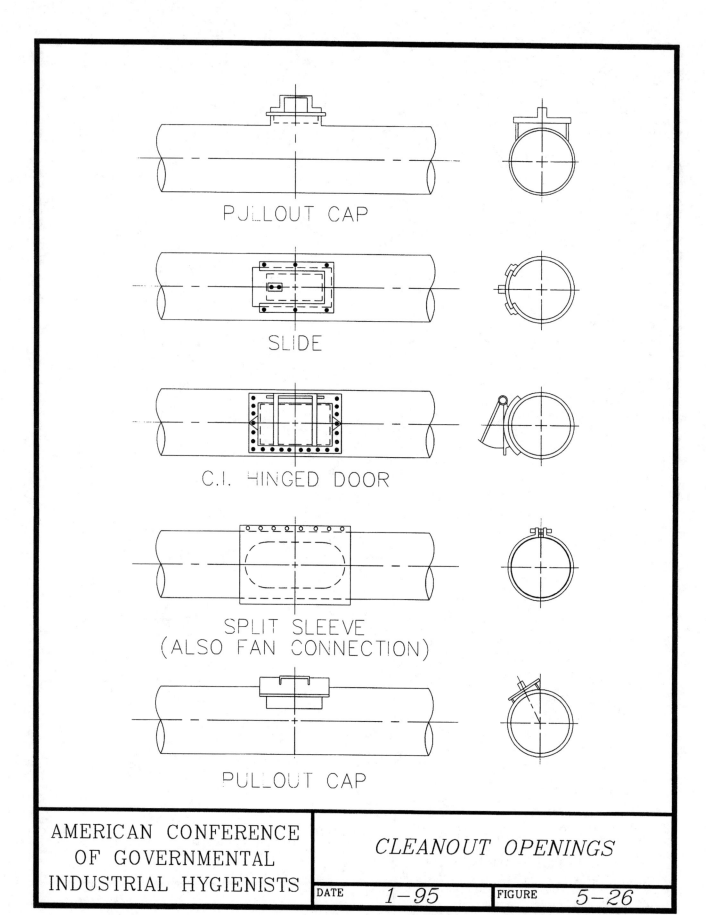

PULLOUT CAP

SLIDE

C.I. HINGED DOOR

SPLIT SLEEVE
(ALSO FAN CONNECTION)

PULLOUT CAP

AMERICAN CONFERENCE OF GOVERNMENTAL INDUSTRIAL HYGIENISTS	CLEANOUT OPENINGS	
	DATE 1—95	FIGURE 5—26

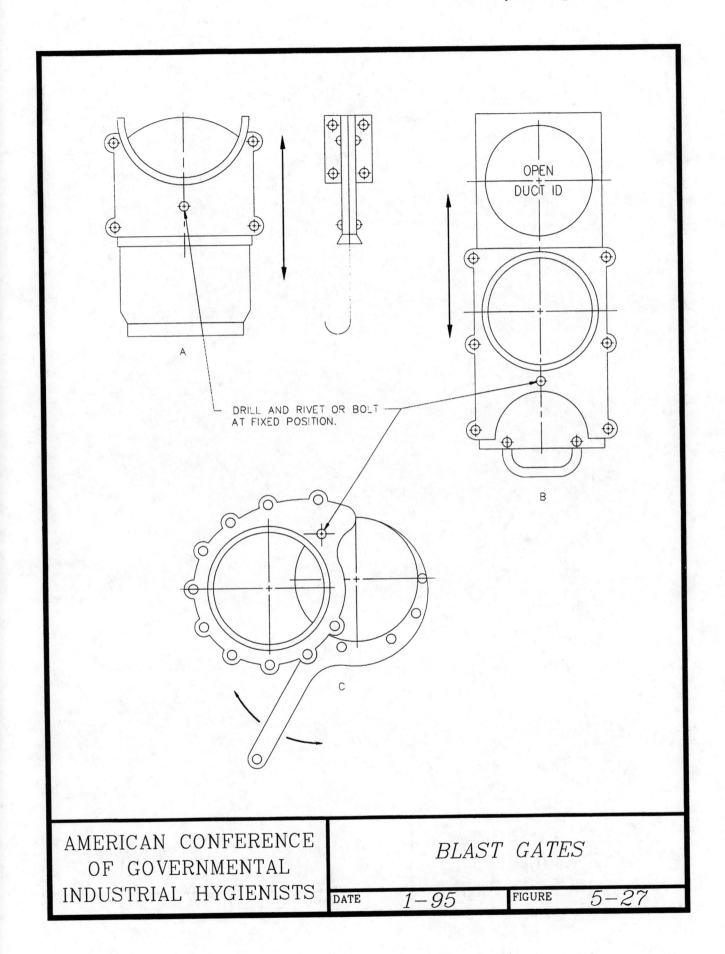

DRILL AND RIVET OR BOLT
AT FIXED POSITION.

OPEN
+
DUCT ID

A

B

C

AMERICAN CONFERENCE OF GOVERNMENTAL INDUSTRIAL HYGIENISTS	*BLAST GATES*	
	DATE *1-95*	FIGURE *5-27*

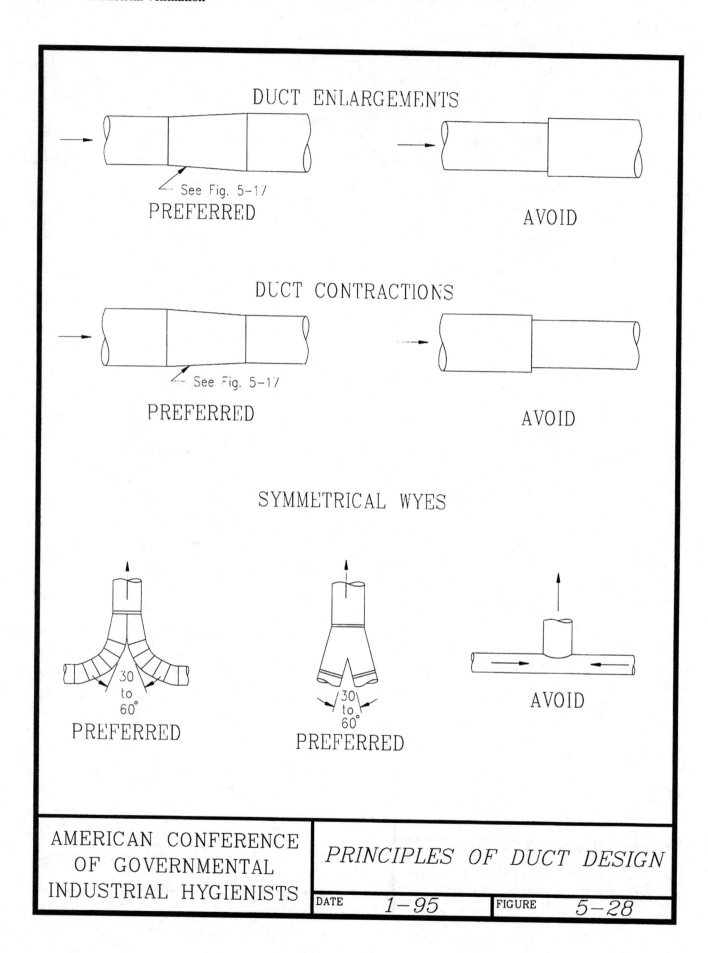

DUCT ENLARGEMENTS

See Fig. 5-17

PREFERRED

AVOID

DUCT CONTRACTIONS

See Fig. 5-17

PREFERRED

AVOID

SYMMETRICAL WYES

30 to 60°

PREFERRED

30 to 60°

PREFERRED

AVOID

AMERICAN CONFERENCE
OF GOVERNMENTAL
INDUSTRIAL HYGIENISTS

PRINCIPLES OF DUCT DESIGN

DATE   *1-95*   FIGURE   *5-28*

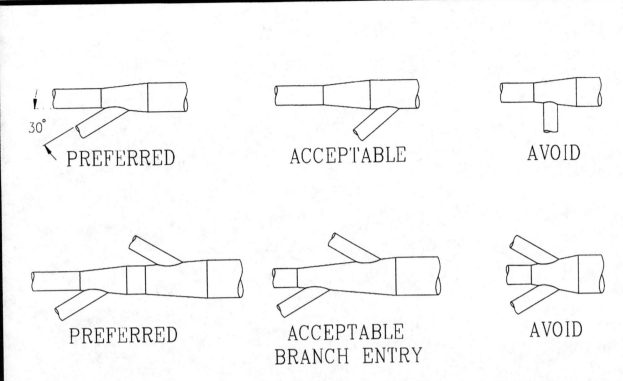

30°   PREFERRED   ACCEPTABLE   AVOID

PREFERRED   ACCEPTABLE   AVOID
                   BRANCH ENTRY

Branches should enter at gradual expansions and at an angle
of 30° or less (preferred) to 45° if necessary. Expansion should
be 15° maximum. See Fig. 5-15 for loss coefficients.

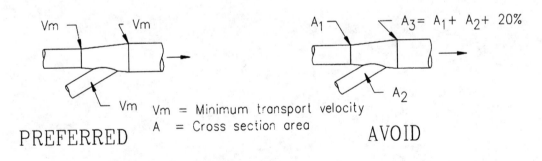

Vm   Vm A_1 $A_3 = A_1 + A_2 + 20\%$

                                                         A_2
              Vm   Vm = Minimum transport velocity
                    A = Cross section area
PREFERRED   AVOID

PROPER DUCT SIZE
Size the duct to maintain the selected or higher
transport velocity.

AMERICAN CONFERENCE OF GOVERNMENTAL INDUSTRIAL HYGIENISTS	*PRINCIPLES OF DUCT DESIGN BRANCH ENTRY*	
	DATE *1-95*	FIGURE *5-29*

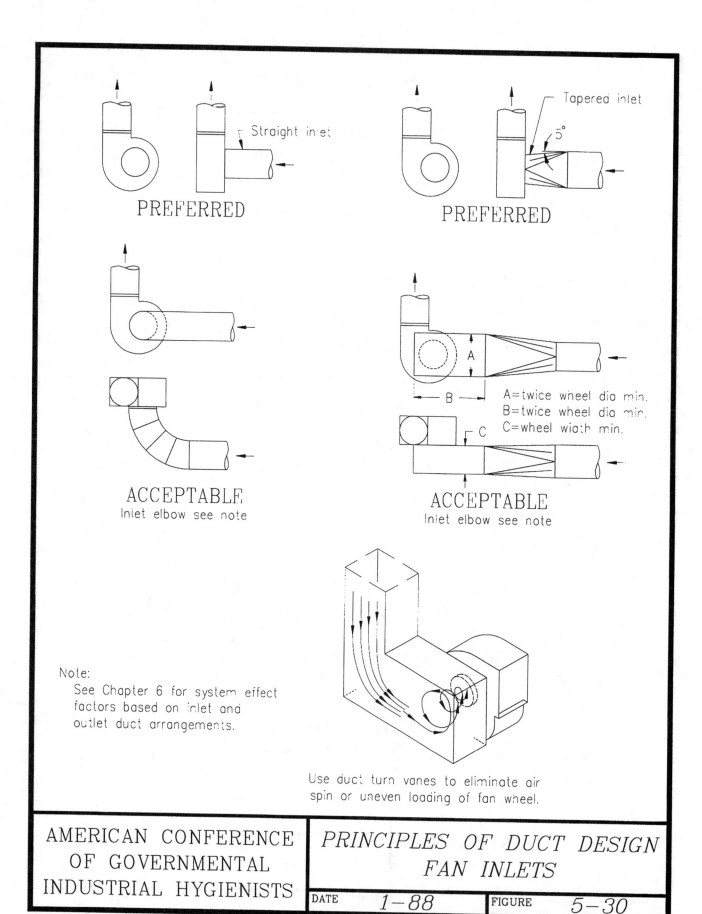

PREFERRED

Straight inlet

PREFERRED

Tapered inlet

5°

ACCEPTABLE
Inlet elbow see note

ACCEPTABLE
Inlet elbow see note

A
B

A=twice wheel dia min.
B=twice wheel dia min.
C=wheel width min.

C

Note:
   See Chapter 6 for system effect
   factors based on inlet and
   outlet duct arrangements.

Use duct turn vanes to eliminate air
spin or uneven loading of fan wheel.

AMERICAN CONFERENCE OF GOVERNMENTAL INDUSTRIAL HYGIENISTS	PRINCIPLES OF DUCT DESIGN FAN INLETS	
	DATE 1-88	FIGURE 5-30

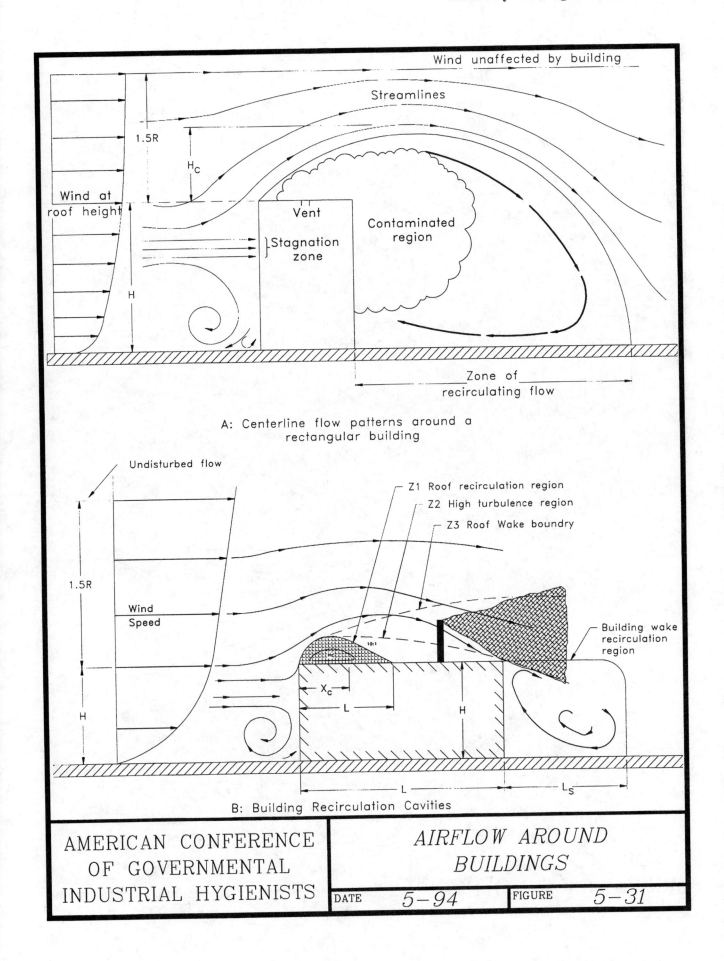

Wind unaffected by building

Streamlines

1.5R

H_C

Wind at roof height

Vent

Stagnation zone

Contaminated region

H

Zone of recirculating flow

A: Centerline flow patterns around a rectangular building

Undisturbed flow

Z1 Roof recirculation region

Z2 High turbulence region

Z3 Roof Wake boundry

1.5R

Wind Speed

Building wake recirculation region

10:1

X_c

L

H

H

L

L_S

B: Building Recirculation Cavities

AMERICAN CONFERENCE OF GOVERNMENTAL INDUSTRIAL HYGIENISTS	*AIRFLOW AROUND BUILDINGS*	
	DATE *5-94*	FIGURE *5-31*

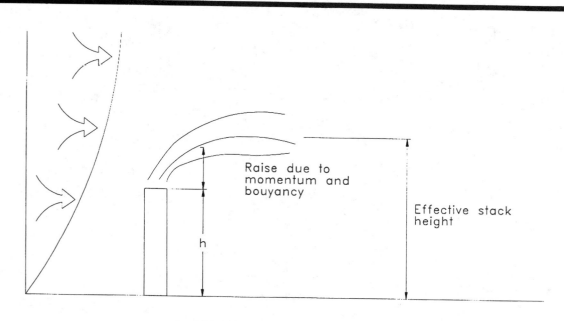

A: Effective stack height

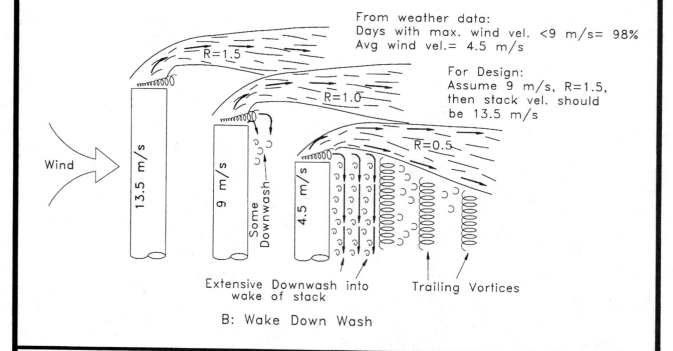

From weather data:
Days with max. wind vel. <9 m/s= 98%
Avg wind vel.= 4.5 m/s

For Design:
Assume 9 m/s, R=1.5,
then stack vel. should
be 13.5 m/s

B: Wake Down Wash

AMERICAN CONFERENCE OF GOVERNMENTAL INDUSTRIAL HYGIENISTS	*EFFECTIVE STACK HEIGHT AND WAKE DOWNWASH*	
	DATE 4-94	FIGURE 5-32

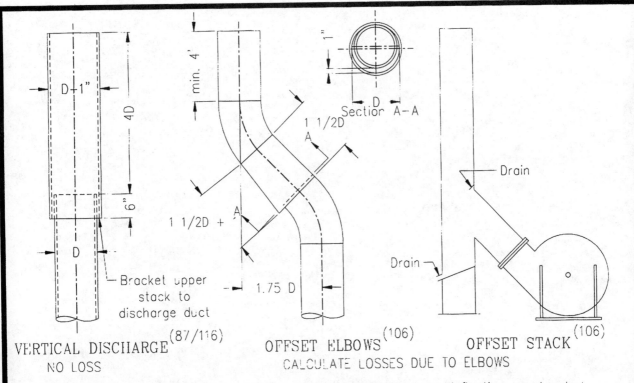

VERTICAL DISCHARGE $^{(87/116)}$
NO LOSS

OFFSET ELBOWS $^{(106)}$
CALCULATE LOSSES DUE TO ELBOWS

OFFSET STACK $^{(106)}$

1. Rain protection characteristics of these caps are superior to a deflecting cap located 0.75D from top of a stack.

2. The length of upper stack is related to rain protection. Excessive additional distance may "blowout" of effluent at the gap between upper and lower sections. (86)

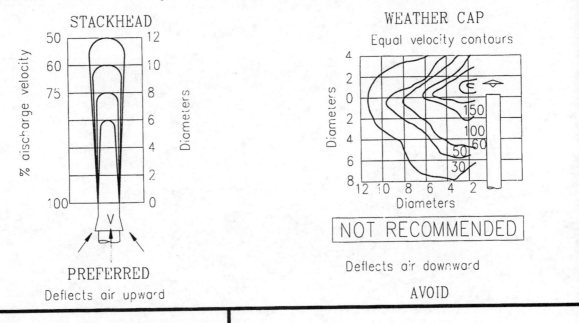

STACKHEAD

PREFERRED
Deflects air upward

WEATHER CAP
Equal velocity contours

NOT RECOMMENDED

Deflects air downward

AVOID

AMERICAN CONFERENCE OF GOVERNMENTAL INDUSTRIAL HYGIENISTS	*STACKHEAD DESIGNS*	
	DATE 1-95	FIGURE 5-33

Chapter 6
FANS

6.1 INTRODUCTION

To move air in a ventilation or exhaust system, energy is required to overcome the system losses. This energy can be in the form of natural convection or buoyancy. Most systems, however, require some powered air moving device such as a fan or an ejector.

This chapter will describe the various air moving devices that are used in industrial applications, provide guidelines for the selection of the air moving device for a given situation, and discuss the proper installation of the air moving device in the system to achieve desired performance.

Selection of an air moving device can be a complex task and the specifier is encouraged to take advantage of all available information from applicable trade associations as well as from individual manufacturers.

6.2 BASIC DEFINITIONS

Air moving devices can be divided into two basic classifications: ejectors and fans. Ejectors have low operating efficiencies and are used only for special material handling applications. Fans are the primary air moving devices used in industrial applications.

Fans can be divided into three basic groups: axial, centrifugal, and special types. As a general rule, axial fans are used for higher flow rates at lower resistances and centrifugal fans are used for lower flow rates at higher resistances.

6.2.1 Ejectors: (see Figure 6-1) These are sometimes used when it is not desirable to have contaminated air pass directly through the air moving device. Ejectors are utilized for air streams containing corrosive, flammable, explosive, hot, or sticky materials that might damage a fan, present a dangerous operating situation, or quickly degrade fan performance. Ejectors also are used in pneumatic conveying systems.

6.2.2 Axial Fans: There are three basic types of axial fans: propeller, tubeaxial, and vaneaxial (see Figures 6-2 and 6-3).

Propeller Fans are used for moving air against low static pressures and are used commonly for general ventilation. Two types of blades are available: disc blade types when there is no duct present; narrow or propeller blade types for moving air against low resistances (less than 1 "wg). Performance is very sensitive to added resistance and a small increase will cause a marked reduction in flow rate.

Tubeaxial Fans (Duct Fans) contain narrow or propeller type blades in a short, cylindrical housing normally without any type of straightening vanes. Tubeaxial fans will move air against moderate pressures (less than 2 "wg).

Vaneaxial Fans have propeller configurations with a hub and airfoil blades mounted in cylindrical housings which normally incorporate straightening vanes on the discharge side of the impeller. Compared to other axial flow fans, vaneaxial fans are more efficient and generally will develop higher pressures (up to 8 "wg). They are limited usually to clean air applications.

6.2.3 Centrifugal Fans: (see Figures 6-4 and 6-7): These fans have three basic impeller designs: forward curved, radial, and backward inclined/backward curved.

Forward curved (commonly called "squirrel cages") impellers have blades which curve toward the direction of rotation. These fans have low space requirements, low tip speeds, and are quiet in operation. They usually are used against low to moderate static pressures such as those encountered in heating and air conditioning work and replacement air systems. This type of fan is not recommended for dusts or particulate that could adhere to the short curved blades, cause unbalance, or reduced performance.

Radial Impellers have blades which are straight or radial from the hub. The housings are designed with their inlets and outlets sized to produce material conveying velocities. There are a variety of impeller types available ranging from "high efficiency minimum material" to "heavy impact resistance" designs. The radial blade shape will resist material buildup. This fan design is used for most exhaust system applications when particulate will pass through the fan. These fans usually have medium tip speeds and are used for a variety of exhaust systems which handle either clean or dirty air.

Backward Inclined/Backward Curved impeller blades are inclined opposite to the direction of fan rotation. This type usually has higher tip speeds and provides high fan efficiency and relatively low noise levels with "non-overloading" horsepower characteristics. In a non-overloading fan, the maximum horsepower occurs near the optimum operating point so any variation from that point due to a change in system resistance will result in a reduction in operating horsepower. The blade shape is conducive to material buildup so fans in this group should be limited as follows:

- *Single Thickness Blade:* Solid blades allow the unit to handle light dust loading or moisture. It should not be used with particulate that would build up on the underside of the blade surfaces.

- *Airfoil Blade:* Airfoil blades offer higher efficiencies and lower noise characteristics. Hollow blades erode more quickly with material and can fill with liquid in high humidity applications. These should be limited to clean air service.

6.2.4 Special Type Fans: (see Figure 6-4): *In-line Centrifugal fans* have backward inclined blades with special housings which permit a straight line duct installation. Pressure versus flow rate versus horsepower performance curves are similar to a scroll type centrifugal fan of the same blade type. Space requirements are similar to vaneaxial fans.

Power Exhausters, Power Roof Ventilators are packaged units that can be either axial flow or centrifugal type. The centrifugal type does not use a scroll housing but discharges around the periphery of the ventilator to the atmosphere. These units can be obtained with either downward deflecting or upblast discharges.

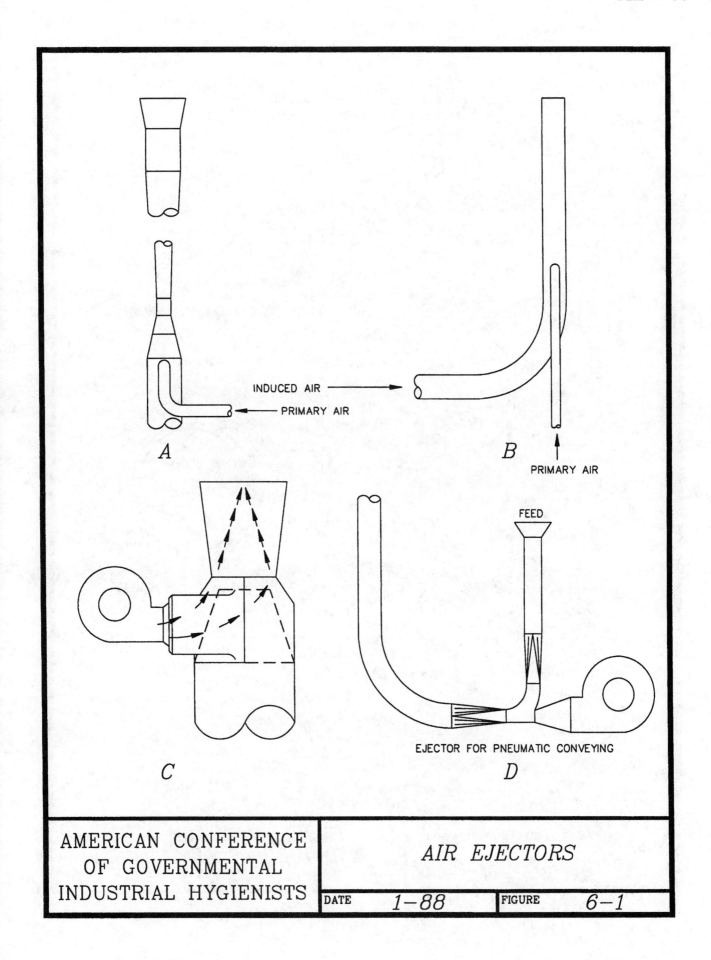

INDUCED AIR →

← PRIMARY AIR

A

B

PRIMARY AIR

FEED

C

EJECTOR FOR PNEUMATIC CONVEYING

D

AMERICAN CONFERENCE OF GOVERNMENTAL INDUSTRIAL HYGIENISTS	*AIR EJECTORS*	
	DATE *1-88*	FIGURE *6-1*

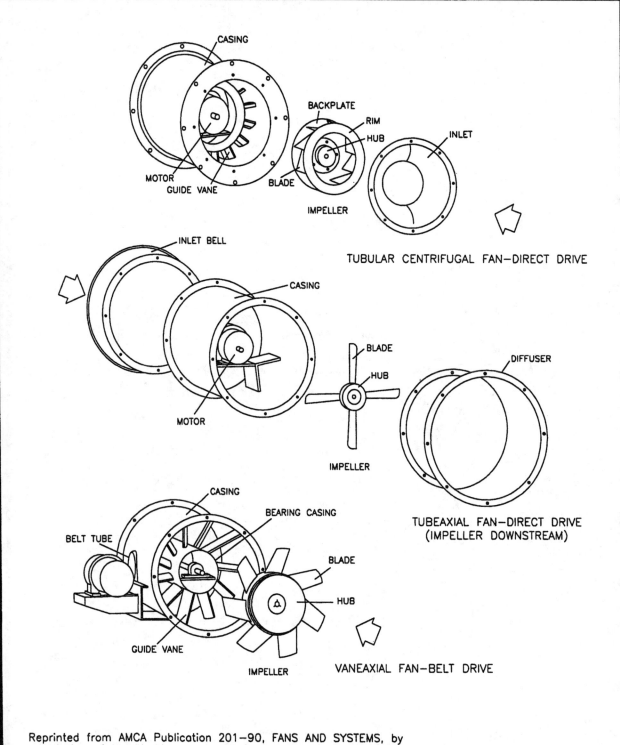

TUBULAR CENTRIFUGAL FAN—DIRECT DRIVE

TUBEAXIAL FAN—DIRECT DRIVE
(IMPELLER DOWNSTREAM)

VANEAXIAL FAN—BELT DRIVE

Reprinted from AMCA Publication 201—90, FANS AND SYSTEMS, by permission of the Air Movement and Control Association, Inc.[6.1]

AMERICAN CONFERENCE OF GOVERNMENTAL INDUSTRIAL HYGIENISTS	TERMINOLOGY FOR AXIAL AND TUBULAR CENTRIFUGAL FANS	
	DATE 5-92	FIGURE 6-2

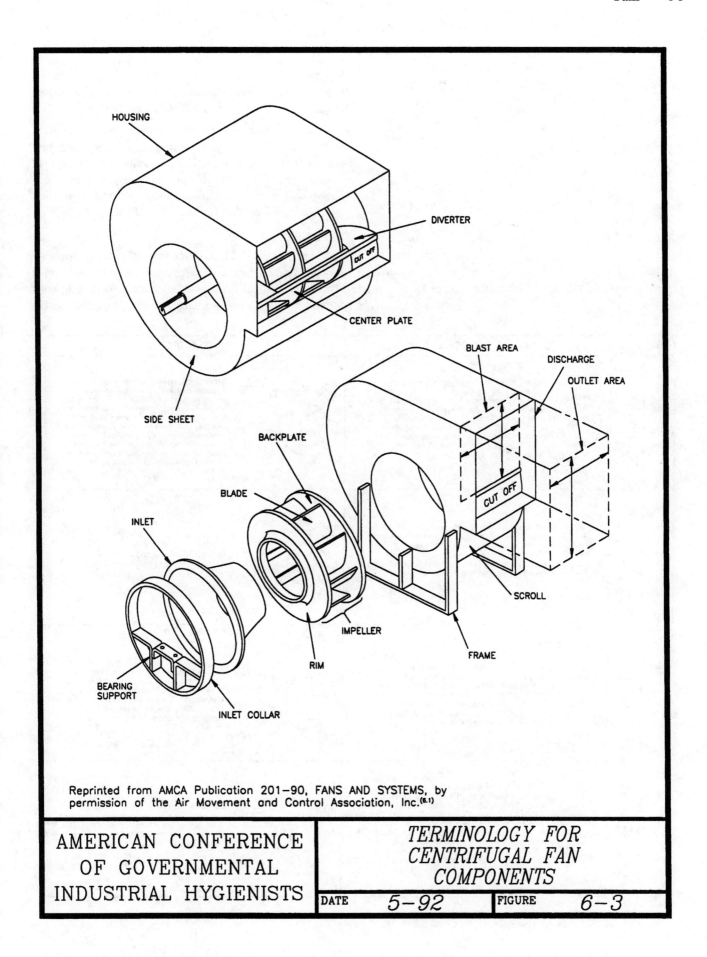

AMERICAN CONFERENCE OF GOVERNMENTAL INDUSTRIAL HYGIENISTS	TERMINOLOGY FOR CENTRIFUGAL FAN COMPONENTS	
	DATE 5-92	FIGURE 6-3

Fan and Dust Collector Combination: There are several designs in which fans and dust collectors are packaged in a unit. If use of such equipment is contemplated, the manufacturer should be consulted for proper application and performance characteristics.

6.3 FAN SELECTION

Fan selection involves not only finding a fan to match the required flow and pressure considerations but all aspects of an installation including the air stream characteristics, operating temperature, drive arrangement, and mounting. Section 6.2 discussed the various fan types and why they might be selected. This section offers guidelines to fan selection; however, the exact performance and operating limitations of a particular fan should be obtained from the original equipment manufacturer.

6.3.1 Considerations for Fan Selection:

CAPACITY

Flow Rate (Q): Based on system requirements and expressed as actual cubic feet per minute (acfm) at the fan inlet.

Pressure Requirements: Based on system pressure requirements which normally are expressed as Fan Static Pressure (FSP) or Fan Total Pressure (FTP) in inches of water gauge at standard conditions (0.075 lbm/ft^3). If the required pressure is known only at non-standard conditions, a density correction (see Section 6.3.8) must be made.

AIRSTREAM

Material Handled Through the Fan: When the exhaust air contains a small amount of smoke or dust, a backward inclined centrifugal or axial fan should be selected. With light dust, fume or moisture, a backward inclined or radial centrifugal fan

TYPE		IMPELLER DESIGN	HOUSING DESIGN
CENTRIFUGAL FANS	AIRFOIL	Highest efficiency of all centrifugal fan designs. 9 to 16 blades of airfoil of airfoil contour curved away from the direction of rotation. Air leaves the impeller at a velocity less than it?s tip speed and relatively deep blades provide for efficient expansion within the blade passages. For given duty, this will be the highest speed of the centrifugal fan designs.	Scroll-type, usually designed to permit efficient conversion of velocity pressure to static pressure, thus permitting a high static efficiency; essential that clearance and alignment between wheel and inlet bell be very close in order to reach the maximum efficiency capability. Concentric housings can also be used as in power roof ventilators, since there is efficient pressure conversion in the wheel.
	BACKWARD-INCLINED BACKWARD-CURVED	Efficiency is only slightly less than that of airfoil fans. Backward-inclined or backward-curved blades are single thickness. 9 to 16 blades curved or inclined away from the direction of rotation. Efficient for the same reasons given for the airfoil fan above.	Utilizes the same housing configuration as the airfoil design.
	RADIAL	Simplest of all centrifugal fans and least efficient. Has high mechanical strength and the wheel is easily repaired. For a given point of rating, this fan requires medium speed. This classification includes radial blades (R) and modified radial blades (M), usually 6 to 10 in number.	Scroll-type, usually the narrowest design of all centrifugal fan designs described here because of required high velocity discharge. Dimensional requirements of this housing are more critical than for airfoil and backward-inclined blades.
	FORWARD-CURVED	Efficiency is less than airfoil and backward-curved bladed fans. Usually fabricated of lightweight and low cost construction. Has 24 to 64 shallow blades with both the heel and tip curved forward. Air leaves wheel at velocity greater than wheel. Tip speed and primary energy transferred to the air is by use of high velocity in the wheel. For given duty, wheel is smallest of all centrifugal types and operates at lowest speed.	Scroll is similar to other centrifugal-fan designs. The fit between the wheel and inlet is not as critical as on airfoil and backward-inclined bladed fans. Uses large cut-off sheet in housing.

FIGURE 6–4. Types of fans: impeller and housing designs (see facing page)

would be the preferred selection. If the particulate loading is high, or when material is handled, the normal selection would be a radial centrifugal fan.

Explosive or Flammable Material: Use spark resistant construction (explosion proof motor if the motor is in the airstream). Conform to the standards of the National Board of Fire Underwriters, the National Fire Protection Association and governmental regulations (see Section 6.3.9).

Corrosive Applications: May require a protective coating or special materials of construction (stainless, fiberglass, etc.)

Elevated Airstream Temperatures: Maximum operating temperature affects strength of materials and therefore must be known for selection of correct materials of construction, arrangement, and bearing types.

PHYSICAL LIMITATIONS

Fan size should be determined by performance requirements. Inlet size and location, fan weight, and ease of maintenance also must be considered. The most efficient fan size may not fit the physical space available.

DRIVE ARRANGEMENTS

All fans must have some type of power source—usually an electric motor. On packaged fans, the motor is furnished and mounted by the manufacturer. On larger units, the motor is mounted separately and coupled directly to the fan or indirectly by a belt drive. A number of standard drive arrangements are shown in Figures 6-5a, 6-5b and 6-5c.

PERFORMANCE CURVES	PERFORMANCE CHARACTERISTICS*	APPLICATIONS
	Highest efficiencies occur 50 to 60% of wide-open volume. This is also the area of good pressure characteristics; the horsepower curve reaches a maximum near the peak efficiency area and becomes lower toward free delivery, a self-limiting power characteristics as shown.	General heating, ventilating and air-conditioning systems. Used in large sizes for clean air industrial applications where power savings are significant.
	Operating characteristics of this fan are similar to the airfoil fan mentioned above. Peak efficiency for this fan is slightly lower than the airfoil fan. Normally unstable left of peak pressure.	Some heating, ventilating, and air-conditioning applications as the airfoil fan. Also used in some industrial applications where the airfoil blade is not acceptable because of corrosive and/or erosion environment.
	Higher pressure characteristics than the above mentioned fans. Power rises continually to free delivery.	Used primarily for material handling applications in industrial plants. Wheel can be of rugged construction and is simple to repair in the field. Wheel is sometimes coated with special material. This design also used for high-pressure industrial requirements. Not commonly found in HVAC applications.
	Pressure curve is less steep than that of backward-curved bladed fans. There is a dip in the pressure curve left of the peak pressure point and highest efficiency occurs to the right of peak pressure, 40 to 50% of wide-open volume. Fan should be rated to the right of peak pressure. Power curve rises continually toward free delivery and this must be taken into account when motor is selected.	Used primarily in low-pressure heating ventilating and air-conditioning applications such as domestic furnaces, central station units, and packaged air-conditioning equipment from room air-conditioning units to roof top units.

Types of fans: performance characteristics and applications. (*These performance curves reflect the general characteristics of various fans as commonly employed. They are not intended to provide complete selection criteria for application purpose. since other parameters, such as diameter and speed, are not defined.)

TYPE		IMPELLER DESIGN	HOUSING DESIGN
AXIAL FANS	PROPELLER	 Efficiency is low. Impellers are usually of inexpensive construction and limited to low pressure applications. Impeller is of 2 or more blades, usually of single thickness attached to relatively small hub. Energy transfer is primarily in form of velocity pressure.	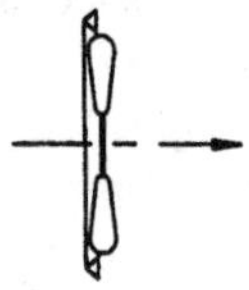 Simple circular ring, orifice place, or venturi design. Design can substantially influence performance and optimum design is reasonably close to the blade tips and forms a smooth inlet flow contour to the wheel.
AXIAL FANS	TUBEAXIAL	 Somewhat more efficient than propeller fan design and is capable of developing a more useful static pressure range. Number of blades usually from 4 to 8 and hub is usually less than 50% of fan tip diameter. Blades can be of airfoil or single thickness cross section.	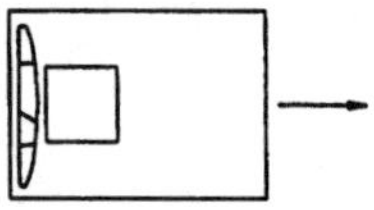 Cylindrical tube formed so that the running clearance between the wheel tip and tube is close. This results insignificant improvement over propeller fans.
AXIAL FANS	VANEAXIAL	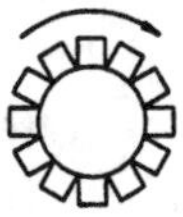 Good design of blades permits medium-to high-pressure capability at good efficiency. The most efficient fans of this type have airfoil blades. Blades are fixed or adjustable pitch types and hub is usually greater than 50% of fan tip diameter.	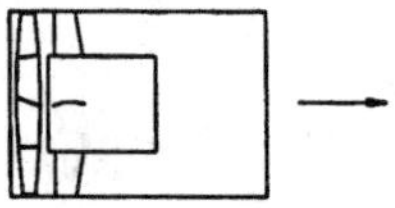 Cylindrical tube closely fitted to the outer diameter of blade tips and fitted with a set of guide vanes. Upstream or downstream from the impeller, guide vanes convert the rotary energy imparted to the air and increase pressure and efficiency of fan.
SPECIAL DESIGNS	TUBULAR CENTRIFUGAL	 This fan usually has a wheel similar to the airfoil backward-inclined or backward-curved blade as described above. (However, this fan wheel type is of lower efficiency when used in fan of type.) Mixed flow impellers are sometimes used.	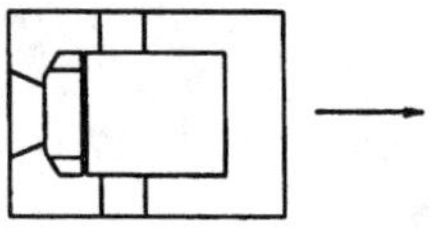 Cylindrical shell similar to vaneaxial fan housing, except the outer diameter of the wheel does not run close to the housing. Air is discharged radially from the wheel and must change direction by 90 degrees to flow through the guide vane section.
SPECIAL DESIGNS	POWER ROOF VENTILATORS CENTRIFUGAL	 Many models use airfoil or backward-inclined impeller designs. These have been modified from those mentioned above to produce a low-pressure, high-volume flow rate characteristic. In addition, many special centrifugal impeller designs are used, including mixed-flow design.	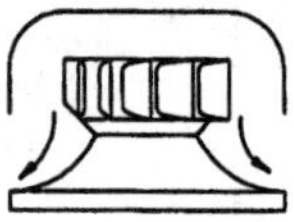 Does not utilize a housing in a normal sense since the air is imply discharged from the impeller in a 360 degree pattern and usually does not include a configuration to recover the velocity pressure component.
SPECIAL DESIGNS	POWER ROOF VENTILATORS AXIAL	 A great variety of propeller designs are employed with the objective of high-volume flow rate at low pressure.	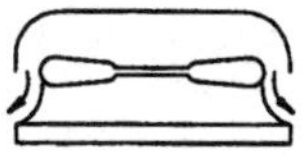 Essentially a propeller fan mounted in a supporting structure with a cover for weather protection and safety considerations. The air is discharged through the annular space around the bottom of the weather hood.

FIGURE 6–4 (continued). Types of fans: impeller and housing designs

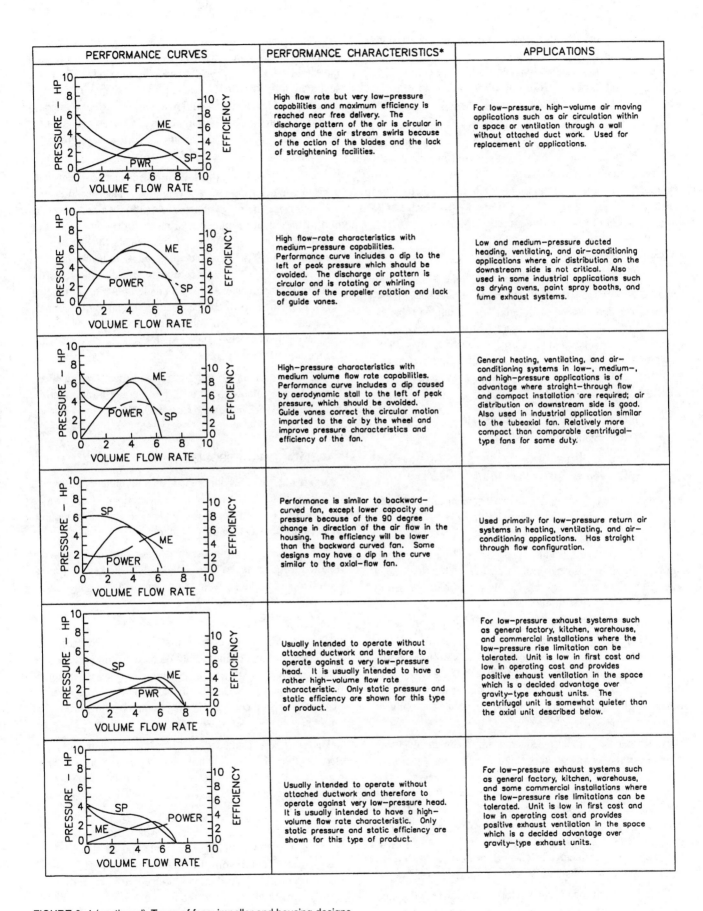

PERFORMANCE CURVES	PERFORMANCE CHARACTERISTICS*	APPLICATIONS
	High flow rate but very low-pressure capabilities and maximum efficiency is reached near free delivery. The discharge pattern of the air is circular in shape and the air stream swirls because of the action of the blades and the lack of straightening facilities.	For low-pressure, high-volume air moving applications such as air circulation within a space or ventilation through a wall without attached duct work. Used for replacement air applications.
	High flow-rate characteristics with medium-pressure capabilities. Performance curve includes a dip to the left of peak pressure which should be avoided. The discharge air pattern is circular and is rotating or whirling because of the propeller rotation and lack of guide vanes.	Low and medium-pressure ducted heating, ventilating, and air-conditioning applications where air distribution on the downstream side is not critical. Also used in some industrial applications such as drying ovens, paint spray booths, and fume exhaust systems.
	High-pressure characteristics with medium volume flow rate capabilities. Performance curve includes a dip caused by aerodynamic stall to the left of peak pressure, which should be avoided. Guide vanes correct the circular motion imparted to the air by the wheel and improve pressure characteristics and efficiency of the fan.	General heating, ventilating, and air-conditioning systems in low-, medium-, and high-pressure applications is of advantage where straight-through flow and compact installation are required; air distribution on downstream side is good. Also used in industrial application similar to the tubeaxial fan. Relatively more compact than comparable centrifugal-type fans for same duty.
	Performance is similar to backward-curved fan, except lower capacity and pressure because of the 90 degree change in direction of the air flow in the housing. The efficiency will be lower than the backward curved fan. Some designs may have a dip in the curve similar to the axial-flow fan.	Used primarily for low-pressure return air systems in heating, ventilating, and air-conditioning applications. Has straight through flow configuration.
	Usually intended to operate without attached ductwork and therefore to operate against a very low-pressure head. It is usually intended to have a rather high-volume flow rate characteristic. Only static pressure and static efficiency are shown for this type of product.	For low-pressure exhaust systems such as general factory, kitchen, warehouse, and commercial installations where the low-pressure rise limitation can be tolerated. Unit is low in first cost and low in operating cost and provides positive exhaust ventilation in the space which is a decided advantage over gravity-type exhaust units. The centrifugal unit is somewhat quieter than the axial unit described below.
	Usually intended to operate without attached ductwork and therefore to operate against very low-pressure head. It is usually intended to have a high-volume flow rate characteristic. Only static pressure and static efficiency are shown for this type of product.	For low-pressure exhaust systems such as general factory, kitchen, warehouse, and some commercial installations where the low-pressure rise limitations can be tolerated. Unit is low in first cost and low in operating cost and provides positive exhaust ventilation in the space which is a decided advantage over gravity-type exhaust units.

FIGURE 6–4 (continued). Types of fans: impeller and housing designs

Direct Drive offers a more compact assembly and assures constant fan speed. Fan speeds are limited to available motor speeds (except in the case of variable frequency controllers). Capacity is set during construction by variations in impeller geometry and motor speed.

Belt Drive offers flexibility in that fan speed can be changed by altering the drive ratio. This may be important in some applications to provide for changes in system capacity or pressure requirements due to changes in process, hood design, equipment location, or air cleaning equipment. V-belt drives must be maintained and have some power losses which can be estimated from the chart in Figure 6-6.

NOISE

Fan noise is generated by turbulence within the fan housing and will vary by fan type, flow rate, pressure, and fan efficiency. Because each design is different, noise ratings must be obtained from the fan manufacturer. Most fans produce a "white" noise which is a mixture of all frequencies. In addition to white noise, radial blade fans also produce a pure tone at a frequency equal to the blade passage frequency (BPF):

$$BPF = RPM \times N \times CF \qquad [6.1]$$

where: BPF = blade passage frequency, Hz

RPM = rotational rate, rpm

N = number of blades

CF = conversion coefficient, 1/60

This tone can be very noticeable in some installations and should be considered in the system design.

Because of its higher efficiency, the backward inclined type of impeller design is generally the quietest. However, for all fan types, non-uniform airflow at the fan inlet or outlet can increase the fan noise level. This is another problem related to "system effect" (see Section 6.4.1).

Most fan manufacturers publish sound ratings for their products. There are a variety of ways to present the ratings. One popular way is to list sound power levels for eight ANSI standard octave bands. The sound power levels are typically in units called "decibels" (dB). The sound **power** level is a characteristic of a fan that varies with the fan speed and point of operation.

For an installed fan, the surrounding environment affects the sound level that is measured or heard. Walls, floors, and other equipment reflect and absorb sound to varying degrees. The sound that reaches the listener will be different than the fan's rated sound power level. Typical sound measuring devices detect sound with a microphone and display sound pressure level in decibels. This sound **pressure** is an environment-dependent measurement that changes with listener location and/or environment changes.

While the decibel unit is used for sound power and sound pressure, the two measures are not interchangeable. Seventy dB sound power is not seventy dB sound pressure. The decibel is not an absolute unit of measure. It is a ratio between a measured quantity and an agreed reference level. Both dB scales are logarithmic. The sound **power** is the log of the ratio of two power levels. The sound **pressure** is the log of the ratio of two pressure levels. The sound power scale uses a reference of 10^{-12} watts. The sound pressure scale uses a reference of 20×10^{-6} N/M^2.

For an installed fan, the sound pressure levels are usually measured in dB using the "A" weighting scale. Measurements obtained using the A-weighting scale provide a better estimation of the threat to human hearing than do other weighting scales. As a result, most criteria for worker's exposure to noise are expressed in "A" weighted sound pressure levels. A sound level meter set on the "A" scale automatically integrates the noise of all frequencies to give a single dBA noise measurement. Expanded detail can be obtained by taking noise measurements with a meter capable of measuring the sound pressure level in each octave band. Such detail can help indicate the predominant source of a noise.

The topic of sound is quite broad and there are many reference texts available to cover it. For a concise introduction, the *ASHRAE Fundamentals Handbook*[6.1] is a good starting point.

SAFETY AND ACCESSORIES

Safety Guards are required. Consider all danger points such as inlet, outlet, shaft, drive, and cleanout doors. Construction should comply with applicable governmental safety requirements and attachment must be secure.

Accessories can help in the installation and in future maintenance requirements. Examples might include drains, cleanout doors, split housings, and shaft seals.

FLOW CONTROL

There are various accessories that can be used to change fan performance. Such changes may be required on systems that vary throughout the day or for reduction in flow rate in anticipation of some future requirement. Dampers, variable pitch blades, and speed control are three common accessories used with fans.

Dampers are installed directly on the fan inlet or outlet. Because they are in the air stream, dampers can build up with material and may not be acceptable on material handling fans. Two types of dampers are available:

- *Outlet Dampers* mount on the fan outlet to add resistance to the system when partially closed. These are available with both parallel and opposed blades. Selection depends on the degree of control required (opposed blade dampers will control the flow more evenly throughout the entire range from wide open to closed).

SW —Single Width   DW —Double Width
SI —Single Inlet   DI —Double Inlet

Arrangements 1,3,7 and 8 are also available with bearings mounted on pedestals or base set independent of the fan housing.

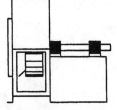

ARR. 1 SWSI For belt drive or direct connection. Impeller overhung. Two bearings on base.

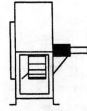

ARR. 2 SWSI For belt drive or direct connection. Impeller overhung. Bearing in bracket supported by fan housing.

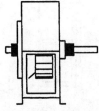

ARR. 3 SWSI For belt drive or direct connection. One bearing on each side and supported by fan housing.

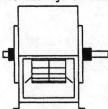

ARR. 3 DWDI For belt drive or direct connection. One bearing on each side and supported by fan housing.

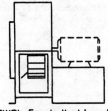

ARR. 4 SWSI For belt drive. Impeller overhung on prime mover shaft. No bearing on fan. Prime mover base mounted or integrally directly connected.

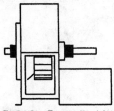

ARR. 7 SWSI For belt drive or direct connection. One bearing on each side and supported by fan housing.

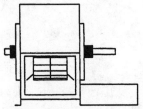

ARR. 7 DWDI For belt drive or direct connection. Arrangemnet 3 plus base for prime mover.

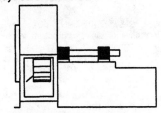

ARR. 8 SWSI For belt drive or direct connection. Arrangement 1 plus extended base for prime mover.

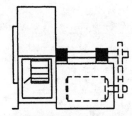

ARR. 9 SWSI For belt drive. Impeller overhung, two bearings, with prime mover outside base.

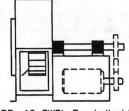

ARR. 10 SWSI For belt drive. Impeller overhung, two bearings, with prime mover inside base.

Reprinted from AMCA Publication 99—86, *STANDARDS HAND-BOOK,* by permission of the Air Movement and Control Association, Inc.[8.1]

AMERICAN CONFERENCE OF GOVERNMENTAL INDUSTRIAL HYGIENISTS	DRIVE ARRANGEMENTS FOR FOR CENTRIFUGAL FANS	
	DATE 5-92	FIGURE 6-5a

SW —Single Width   DW—Double Width
SI —Single Inlet   DI —Double Inlet

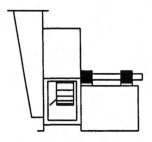

ARR. 1 SWSI WITH INLET BOX   For belt drive or direct connection. Impeller overhung, two bearings on base. inlet box may be self—supporting.

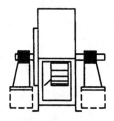

ARR. 3 SWSI WITH INDEPENDENT PEDESTAL   For belt drive or direct, connection fan. Housing is self—supporting. One bearing on each side supported by independent pedestals.

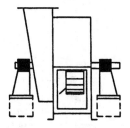

ARR. 3 SWSI WITH INLET BOX AND INDEPENDENT PEDESTALS   For belt drive or direct connection fan. Housing is self—supporting. One bearing on each side supported by in-independent pedestals with shaft extending through inlet box.

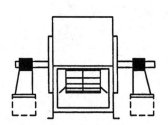

ARR. 3DWDI WITH INDEPENDENT PEDESTAL   For belt drive or direct connection fan. Housing is self—supporting. One bearing on each side supported by independent pedestals.

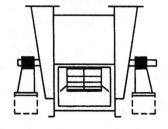

ARR. 3 DWDI WITH INLET BOX AND INDEPENDENT PEDESTALS   For belt drive or direct connection fan. Housing is self—supporting. One bearing on each side supported by in-independent pedestals with shaft extending through inlet box.

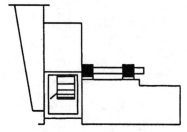

ARR. 8 SWSI WITH INLET BOX   For belt drive or direct connection. Impeller overhung, two bearings on base plus extended base for prime mover. Inlet box may be self—supporting.

Reprinted from AMCA Publication 99—86, *STANDARDS HAND-BOOK*, by permission of the Air Movement and Control Association, Inc.[6.1]

AMERICAN CONFERENCE OF GOVERNMENTAL INDUSTRIAL HYGIENISTS	DRIVE ARRANGEMENTS FOR CENTRIFUGAL FANS	
	DATE 5-92	FIGURE 6-5b

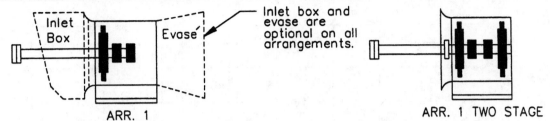

ARR. 1   ARR. 1 TWO STAGE

For belt drive or direct connection. Impeller overhung. Two bearings
located either upstream or downstream of impeller.

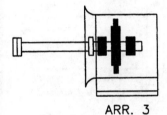

ARR. 3

ARR. 4

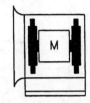

ARR. 4 TWO STAGE

For belt drive or direct
connection. Impeller between
bearings that are on internal
supports. Drive through inlet.

For direct connection. Impeller
overhung on motor shaft. No
bearings on fan. Motor on
internal supports.

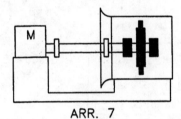

ARR. 7

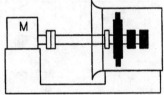

ARR. 8 (1 or 2 stage)

For belt drive or direct connection.
Arr. 3 plus common base for prime
mover.

For belt drive or direct
connection. Arr. 1 plus
common base for prime mover.

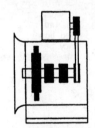

ARR. 9 Motor on Casing

ARR. 9 Motor on Integral Base

For belt drive. Impeller overhung. Two bearings on internal supports.
Motor on casing or on integral base. Drive through belt fairing.

NOTE: All fan orientations may be horizontal or vertical.

Reprinted from AMCA Publication 99–86 Standards Handbook,
by permission of the Air Movement and Control Association Inc. (6.1)

AMERICAN CONFERENCE OF GOVERNMENTAL INDUSTRIAL HYGIENISTS	DRIVE ARRANGEMENTS FOR AXIAL FANS WITH OR WITHOUT EVASÉ AND INLET BOX	
	DATE 11–96	FIGURE 6–5c

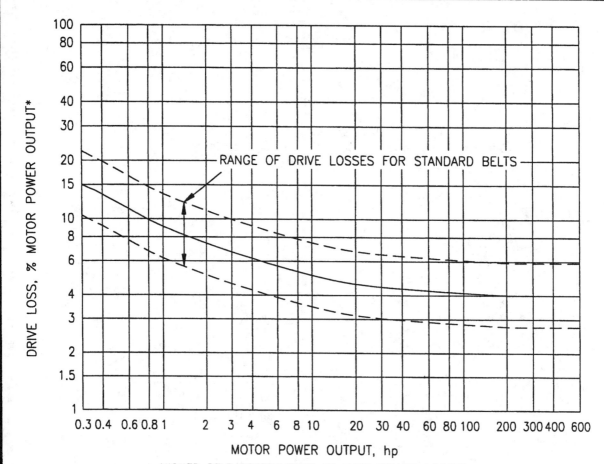

HIGHER BELT SPEEDS TEND TO HAVE HIGHER LOSSES
THAN LOWER BELT SPEEDS AT THE SAME HORSEPOWER

Drive losses are based on the conventional V-belt which has been the "work horse" of the drive industry for several decades.

EXAMPLE
- Motor power output, H_{MO}, is determined to be 13.3 hp
- The belts are the standard type and just warm to the touch immediately after shutdown
- From chart, drive loss   = 5.1%
- Drive loss H_L = 0.051 x 13.3
                             = 0.7 hp
- Fan power input, H   = 13.3 − 0.7
                             = 12.6 hp

Reprinted from AMCA Publication 203-90, *FIELD PERFORMANCE MEASUREMENT OF FAN SYSTEMS*, by permission of the Air Movement and Control Association, Inc.[6.1]

AMERICAN CONFERENCE OF GOVERNMENTAL INDUSTRIAL HYGIENISTS	ESTIMATED BELT DRIVE LOSS	
	DATE 5-92	FIGURE 6-6

- *Inlet Dampers* mount on the fan inlet to pre-spin air into the impeller. This reduces fan output and lowers operating horsepower. Because of the power savings, inlet dampers should be considered when the fan will operate for long periods at reduced capacities.

Variable pitch blades are available with some axial type fans. The fan impellers are designed to allow manual or automatic changes to the blade pitch. "Adjustable" impellers have a blade pitch that can be manually changed when the fan is not running. "Variable" impellers include devices to allow the blade pitch to be changed pneumatically or hydraulically while the fan is operating.

A *Variable Frequency Drive* (VFD) may also be used to control flow. A VFD will control the fan speed, rather than varying the fan inlet flow conditions or the outlet area to change the fan's point of operation. This type of control varies both the flow rate and the fan static pressure.

The VFD control unit is connected in-line between the electric power source and the fan motor. It is used to vary the voltage and frequency of the power input to the motor. The motor speed will vary linearly with the line frequency. Most VFD applications use a direct drive arrangement; however, belt drives are occasionally used.

For a typical system with fixed physical characteristics, the attainable points of operation will fall on the system curve. For example, Figure 6-10 shows points A1 and A2 on a system curve. These two points of operation can be attained with a VFD by adjusting it for speeds of RPM_1 or RPM_2. This will result in fan curve PQ_1 or PQ_2, respectively.

Variable Frequency Drives do have disadvantages. They may have a low speed limitation. Most AC motors are designed to operate at their nameplate speeds. If a VFD is used to run a motor well below its nominal speed, the motor's efficiency will be reduced, and losses will increase. This can increase motor heating and may cause damage.

The VFD can cause harmonic distortion in the electrical input lines from the power source. This may affect other electrical equipment on the same power system. Such distortion can be reduced with the addition of isolation transformers or line inductors.

To properly apply a VFD, the equipment supplier needs to know about its intended usage, about the building's power supply, and about other electrical equipment in use. In general, for applications where the minimum system airflow is 80% or more of the maximum system airflow, the VFD's losses and higher initial cost may make use of the inlet damper a better choice for flow control.

An advantage of the VFD or the Variable Pitch Blade over the dampers is often a dramatic power and noise reduction. However, these accessories usually require additional controlling equipment. An advantage of dampers is their relatively simple installation and use and their lower initial costs.

6.3.2 Rating Tables:
Fan size and operating RPM and Power usually are obtained from a rating table based on required airflow and pressure. Tables are based on Fan Total Pressure or Fan Static Pressure:

$$FTP = (SP_{outlet} + VP_{outlet}) - (SP_{inlet} + VP_{inlet}) \qquad [6.2]$$

$$FSP = SP_{outlet} - SP_{inlet} - VP_{inlet} \qquad [6.3]$$

Fan Rating Tables are based on requirements for air at standard conditions (0.075 lbm/ft^3). If other than standard conditions exist, the actual pressure must be converted to standard conditions. See Section 6.3.8, "Selection at Air Densities Other Than Standard."

The most common form of fan rating table is a "multi-rating table" (see Table 6-1) which shows a range of capacities for a particular fan size. For a given pressure, the highest mechanical efficiency usually will be in the middle third of the "CFM" column. Some manufacturers show the rating of maximum efficiency for each pressure by underscoring or similar indicator. In the absence of such a guide, the design engineer must calculate the efficiency from the efficiency equation

$$\eta = \frac{Q \times FTP}{CF \times PWR} = \frac{Q \times FSP \times VP}{CF \times PWR} \qquad [6.4]$$

where: η = Mechanical efficiency
Q = Volumetric flow rate, cfm
FTP = Fan total pressure, "wg
FSP = Fan Static Pressure, "wg
PWR = Power requirement, hp
CF = Conversion Coefficient, 6362

Even with a multi-rating table it is usually necessary to interpolate in order to select fan RPM and BHP for the exact conditions desired. In many cases a double interpolation will be necessary. Straight line interpolations throughout the multi-rating table will introduce negligible errors.

Certain types of fans may be offered in various Air Movement and Control Association[6.2] performance classes identified as I through IV. A fan designated as meeting the requirements of a particular class must be physically capable of operating at any point within the performance limits for that class. Performance limits for each class are established in terms of outlet velocity and static pressure. Multi-rating tables usually will be shaded to indicate the selection zones for various classes or will state the maximum operating RPM. This can be useful in selecting equipment but class definition is only based on performance and will not indicate quality of construction.

Capacity tables which attempt to show the ratings for a whole series of homologous fans on one sheet cannot be used accurately unless the desired rating happens to be listed on the chart. Interpolation is practically impossible since usually only one point of the fan curve for a given speed is defined in such a table.

TABLE 6-1. Example of Mutli-Rating Table

| | | | | | | | | | | | | | | | | | | | | | | | Inlet diameter: 13" O.D. | | Wheel diameter: 225/8" | |
| | | | | | | | | | | | | | | | | | | | | | | | Outlet area: .930 sq. ft. inside | | Wheel circumference: 5.92 ft. | |

CFM	OV	2" SP		4" SP		6" SP		8" SP		10" SP		12" SP		14" SP		16" SP		18" SP		20" SP		22" SP	
		RPM	BHP	RPM	BHP	RPM	BHP	RPM	BHP	RPM	BHP	RPM	BHP	RPM	BHP	RPM	BHP	RPM	BHP	RPM	BHP	RPM	BHP
930	1000	843	0.57	1176	1.21	1434	1.93	1653	2.75	1846	3.64	2021	4.59	2184	5.62	2333	6.68	2475	7.81	2610	9.01	2738	10.2
1116	1200	853	0.67	1183	1.35	1439	2.12	1656	2.98	1848	3.90	2022	4.89	2182	5.95	2333	7.07	2473	8.23	2606	9.45	2733	10.7
1302	1400	866	0.77	1191	1.51	1445	2.33	1660	3.22	1852	4.20	2025	5.23	2183	6.31	2333	7.47	2474	8.68	2606	9.95	2731	11.2
1488	1600	882	0.89	1201	1.69	1453	2.56	1668	3.50	1857	4.51	2030	5.59	2188	6.72	2337	7.92	2474	9.13	2606	10.4	2734	11.8
1674	1800	899	1.01	1213	1.88	1463	2.81	1676	3.81	1863	4.86	2035	5.98	2194	7.16	2340	8.38	2479	9.67	2610	11.0	2735	12.4
1860	2000	917	1.14	1227	2.09	1474	3.09	1685	4.13	1872	5.24	2040	6.39	2199	7.62	2344	8.89	2484	10.2	2613	11.6	2735	13.0
2046	2200	937	1.29	1242	2.32	1484	3.37	1694	4.48	1879	5.63	2048	6.84	2206	8.13	2351	9.43	2487	10.8	2618	12.2	2741	13.6
2232	2400	961	1.45	1257	2.56	1497	3.68	1704	4.85	1889	6.07	2056	7.33	2212	8.64	2357	10.0	2493	11.4	2622	12.8	2745	14.3
2418	2600	984	1.62	1275	2.81	1513	4.02	1717	5.25	1900	6.53	2065	7.84	2222	9.22	2364	10.6	2501	12.1	2631	13.6	2750	15.1
2790	3000	1038	2.02	1313	3.36	1543	4.73	1744	6.11	1924	7.52	2088	8.96	2241	10.4	2383	12.0	2517	13.5	2644	15.1	2766	16.7
3162	3400	1099	2.50	1358	3.99	1580	5.52	1775	7.05	1952	8.60	2115	10.2	2265	11.8	2405	13.4	2538	15.1	2665	16.8	2783	18.5
3534	3800	1164	3.07	1407	4.69	1620	6.37	1812	8.09	1984	9.79	2144	11.5	2290	13.3	2428	15.0	2562	16.8	2684	18.6	2803	20.5
3906	4200	1232	3.75	1462	5.48	1665	7.31	1851	9.19	2018	11.0	2174	12.9	2320	14.8	2458	16.8	2587	18.7	2708	20.6	2825	22.5
4278	4600	1306	4.56	1520	6.39	1717	8.38	1894	10.4	2058	12.4	2209	14.5	2355	16.5	2489	18.6	2614	20.6	2736	22.7	2852	24.8
4650	5000	1380	5.49	1582	7.41	1770	9.53	1941	11.7	2100	13.9	2247	16.1	2390	18.3	2521	20.5	2645	22.7	2766	25.0	2883	27.3
5022	5400	1457	6.56	1647	8.57	1827	10.8	1990	13.1	2146	15.5	2291	17.8	2428	20.2	2558	22.6	2681	25.0	2798	27.3		
5394	5800	1535	7.79	1719	9.93	1885	12.2	2045	14.7	2194	17.2	2334	19.7	2469	22.2	2594	24.7	2717	27.3	2830	29.8		

Today, most fan manufacturers have "electronic catalogs" available. These catalogs are computer programs which can be used to calculate the correct fan speed and horsepower based on input data such as desired flow rate and fan static pressure or fan total pressure. Some electronic catalogs include estimates of the affects of various fan accessories such as dampers and inlet boxes.

6.3.3 Point of Operation: Fans are usually selected for operation at some fixed condition or single "Point of Opera-

tion." Both the fan and the system have variable performance characteristics which can be represented graphically as curves depicting an array of operating points. The actual "point of operation" will be the one single point at the intersection of the fan curve and the system curve.

Fan Performance Curves: Certain fan performance variables are usually related to volumetric flow rate in graphic form to represent a fan performance curve. Figure 6-7 is a typical representation where Pressure (P) and power requirement (PWR) are plotted against flow rate (Q). Other variables also may be included and more detailed curves representing various fan designs are provided in Figure 6-4. Pressure can be either fan static pressure (FSP) or fan total pressure (FTP). This depends on the manufacturer's method of rating.

It should be noted that a fan performance curve is always specific to a fan of given size operating at a single rotation rate (RPM). Even with size and rotation rate fixed, it should be obvious that pressure and power requirements vary over a range of flow rates.

System Requirement Curves: The duct system pressure also varies with volumetric flow rate. Figure 6-8 illustrates the variation of pressure (P) with flow rate (Q) for three different situations. The turbulent flow condition is representative of duct losses and is most common. In this case the pressure loss varies as the square of the flow rate. The laminar flow condition is representative of the flow through low velocity filter media. Some wet collector designs operate at or close to a constant loss situation.

The overall system curve results from the combined effects of the individual components.

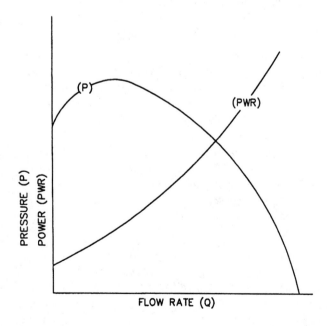

FIGURE 6-7. Typical fan performance curve

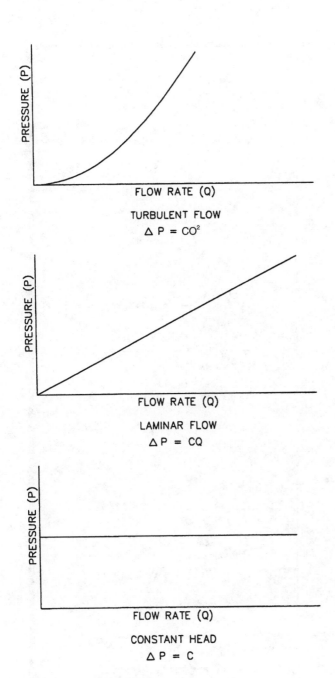

FIGURE 6-8. System requirement curves

6.3.4 Matching Fan Performance and System Requirement: A desired point of operation results from the process of designing a duct system and selecting a fan. Considering the system requirement or fan performance curves individually, this desired point of operation has no special status relative to any other point of operation on the individual curve. Figure 6-9 depicts the four general conditions which can result from the system design fan selection process.

There are a number of reasons why the system design, fan selection, fabrication, and installation process can result in operation at some point other than design. When this occurs, it may become necessary to alter the system physically which will change the system requirement curve and/or cause a

change in the fan performance curve. Because the fan performance curve is not only peculiar to a given fan but specific to a given rotation rate (RPM), a change of rotation rate can be relatively simple if a belt drive arrangement has been used. The "Fan Laws" are useful when changes of fan performance are required.

6.3.5 Fan Laws: Fan laws relate the performance variables for any homologous series of fans. A homologous series represents a range of sizes where all dimensional variables between sizes are proportional. The performance variables involved are fan size (SIZE), rotation rate (RPM), gas density (ρ), flow rate (Q), pressure (P), power requirement (PWR), and efficiency (η). Pressure (P) may be represented by total pressure (TP), static pressure (SP), velocity pressure (VP) fan static pressure (FSP), or fan total pressure (FTP).

At the same relative point of operation on any two performance curves in this homologous series, the efficiencies will be equal. The fan laws are mathematical expressions of these facts and establish the inter-relationship of the other variables. They predict the effect of changing size, speed, or gas density on capacity, pressure, and power requirement as follows:

$$Q_2 = Q_1 \left(\frac{SIZE_2}{SIZE_1} \right)^3 \left(\frac{RPM_2}{RPM_1} \right) \qquad [6.5]$$

$$P_2 = P_1 \left(\frac{SIZE_2}{SIZE_1} \right)^2 \left(\frac{RPM_2}{RPM_1} \right)^2 \left(\frac{\rho_2}{\rho_1} \right) \qquad [6.6]$$

$$PWR_2 = PWR_1 \left(\frac{SIZE_2}{SIZE_1} \right)^5 \left(\frac{RPM_2}{RPM_1} \right)^3 \left(\frac{\rho_2}{\rho_1} \right) \qquad [6.7]$$

As these expressions involve ratios of the variables, any convenient units may be employed so long as they are consistent. Size may be represented by any linear dimension since all must be proportional in homologous series. However, impeller diameter is the most commonly used dimension.

6.3.6 The Effect of Changing Rotation Rate or Gas Density: In practice, these principles are normally applied to determine the effect of changing only one variable. Most often the fan laws are applied to a given fan size and may be expressed in the simplified versions which follow:

- For changes of rotation rate:

    Flow varies directly with rotation rate; pressure varies as the square of the rotation rate; and power varies as the cube of the rotation rate:

$$Q_2 = Q_1 \left(\frac{RPM_2}{RPM_1} \right) \qquad [6.8]$$

$$P_2 = P_1 \left(\frac{RPM_2}{RPM_1} \right)^2 \qquad [6.9]$$

$$PWR_2 = PWR_1 \left(\frac{RPM_2}{RPM_1} \right)^3 \qquad [6.10]$$

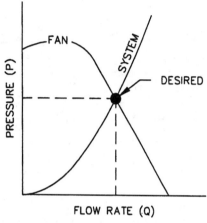

A. FAN AND SYSTEM MATCHED

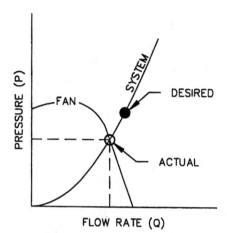

B. WRONG FAN.

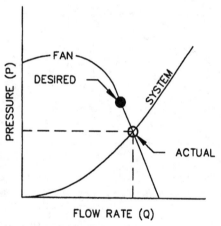

C. WRONG SYSTEM.

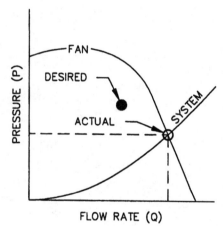

D. BOTH FAN AND SYSTEM WRONG

AMERICAN CONFERENCE OF GOVERNMENTAL INDUSTRIAL HYGIENISTS	*ACTUAL VERSUS DESIRED POINT OF OPERATION*	
	DATE 1-88	FIGURE 6-9

- For changes of gas density:

  Flow is not affected by a change in density; pressure and power vary directly with density:

  $$Q_2 = Q_1 \qquad \text{[6.11]}$$

  $$P_2 = P_1 \left(\frac{\rho_2}{\rho_1} \right) \qquad \text{[6.12]}$$

  $$PWR_2 = PWR_1 \left(\frac{\rho_2}{\rho_1} \right) \qquad \text{[6.13]}$$

6.3.7 Limitations on the Use of Fan Laws: These expressions are equations which rely on the fact that the performance curves are homologous and that the ratios are for the *same relative points of rating* on each curve. Care must be exercised to apply the laws between the same relative points of rating.

Figure 6-10 contains a typical representation of two homologous fan performance curves, PQ_1 and PQ_2. These could be the performances resulting from two different rotation rates, RPM_1 and RPM_2. Assuming a point of rating indicated as A_1 on PQ_1 there is only one location on PQ_2 with the same relative point of rating and that is at A_2. The A_1 and A_2 points of rating are related by the expression

$$P_{A_2} = P_{A_1} \left(\frac{Q_{A_2}}{Q_{A_1}} \right)^2 \qquad \text{[6.14]}$$

The equation can be used to identify every other point that would have the same relative point of rating as A_1 and A_2. The dashed line passing through "A_2, A_1" and the origin locates all conditions with the same relative points of rating. These lines are more often called "system lines" or "system curves." As discussed in Section 6.3.3, there are a number of exceptions to

the condition where system pressure varies as the square of flow rate. These lines representing the same relative points of rating are "system lines" or "system curves" for turbulent flow conditions only.

Where turbulent flow conditions apply, it must be understood that the system curves or lines of relative points of rating represent a system having fixed physical characteristics. For example the, "B_2-B_1" line defines another system which has lower resistance to flow than the "A_2-A_1" system.

Special care must be exercised when applying the fan laws in the following cases:

1. Where any component of the system does not follow the "pressure varies as the square of the flow rate" rule.

2. Where the system has been physically altered or for any other reason operates on a different system line.

6.3.8 Fan Selection at Air Density Other Than Standard: As discussed in Section 6.3.6, fan performance is affected by changes in gas density. Variations in density due to normal fluctuations of ambient pressure, temperature, and humidity are small and need not be considered. Where temperature, humidity, elevation, pressure, gas composition, or a combination of two or more cause density to vary by more than 5 percent from the standard 0.075 lbm/ft^3, corrections should be employed.

Rating tables and performance curves as published by fan manufacturers are based on standard air. Performance variables are always related to conditions at the fan inlet. Fan characteristics are such that volumetric flow rate (Q) is unaffected but pressure (P) and power (PWR) vary directly with changes in gas density. Therefore, the selection process requires that rating tables are entered with *actual* volumetric flow rate but with a corrected or equivalent pressure.

The equivalent pressure is that pressure corresponding to standard density and is determined from Equation 6.12 as follows:

$$P_e = P_2 \left(\frac{0.075}{\rho_a} \right)$$

where: P_e = Equivalent Pressure

P_a = Actual Pressure

ρ_a = Actual density, lbm/ft^3

The pressures (P_e and P_a) can be either Fan Static Pressure or Fan Total Pressure in order to conform with the manufacturer's rating method.

The fan selected in this manner is to be operated at the rotation rate indicated in the rating table and actual volumetric flow rate is that indicated by the table. However, the pressure developed is not that indicated in the table but is the actual value. Likewise, the power requirement is not that of the table as it also varies directly with density. The actual power requirement can be determined from Equation 6.13 as follows:

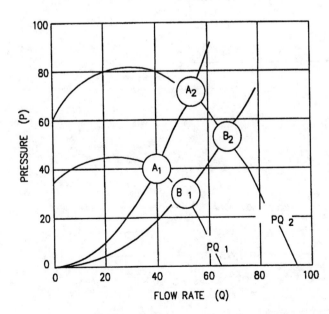

FIGURE 6-10. Homologous performance curves

$$PWR_a = PWR_t \left(\frac{\rho_a}{0.075} \right)$$

where: PWR_a = Actual Power Requirement

PWR_t = Power Requirement in Rating Table

ρ_a = Actual Density, lbm/ft^3

Fan selection at non-standard density requires knowledge of the actual volumetric flow rate at the fan inlet, the actual pressure requirement (either FSP or FTP, depending on the rating table used), and the density of the gas at the fan inlet. The determination of these variables requires that the system design procedure consider the effect of density as discussed in Chapter 5.

EXAMPLE

Consider the system illustrated in Figure 6-11 where the heater causes a change in volumetric flow rate and density. For simplicity, assume the heater has no resistance to flow and that the sum of friction losses will equal FSP. Using the Multi-Rating Table, Table 6-1, select the rotation rate and determine power requirements for the optional fan locations ahead of or behind the heater.

Location 1: *Fan ahead of the heater* (side "A" to "B" in Figure 6-11).

Step 1.   Determine actual FSP

FSP = 1 "wg + 3 "wg = 4 "wg at 0.075 lbm/ft^3.

$$Q = 1000 \left(\frac{0.075}{0.073} \right) = 2000 \text{acfm}$$

Step 2a.   Density at fan inlet is standard. Therefore, enter rating table with actual volumetric flow rate at fan inlet, 1000 acfm, and FSP of 4 "wg.

   b. Interpolation from Table 6-1 results in:

RPM = 1182 rpm

PWR = 1.32 bhp

Step 3.   The fan should be operated at 1182 rpm and actual power requirement will be 1.32 bhp.

Location 2: *Fan behind the heater*.

Step 1.   Determine actual FSP

FSP = 1 "wg + 3 "wg (as in explanation) = 4 "wg at 0.0375 lbm/ft^3

Step 2a.   Density at fan inlet is not standard and a pressure correction must be made (using Equation 6.12) to determine equivalent FSP.

$$FSP_e = FSP_a \left(\frac{0.075}{\rho_a} \right) = 4 \text{ "wg} \left(\frac{0.075}{0.0375} \right) = 8 \text{ "wg}$$

Now, enter rating table with actual volumetric flow rate at fan inlet, 2000 acfm, and equivalent FSP, 8 "wg.

   b. Interpolation from Table 6-1 results in:

RPM = 1692 rpm

PWR = 4.39 bhp

Step 3a.   The fan should be operated at 1692 rpm, but actual power requirements will be affected by the density and can be determined by using Equation 6.13.

$$PWR_2 = PWR_t \left(\frac{\rho_a}{0.075} \right) = 4.39 \left(\frac{0.0375}{0.075} \right) = 2.2 \text{ bhp}$$

Remember that this is the horsepower required when the air is hot. If it is necessary to start the fan with the heater off, when the air is cold, the fan motor should be sized for the cold horsepower calculated in Step 2b.

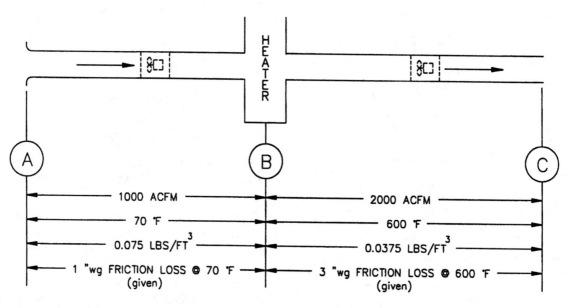

FIGURE 6–11. In-duct heater

b. It should also be noted that a measurement of FSP will result in the value of 4 "wg (actual) and not the equivalent value of 8 "wg.

It will be noted that, regardless of location, the fan will handle the same mass flow rate. Also, the actual resistance to flow is not affected by fan location. It may appear then that there is an error responsible for the differing power requirements of 1.32 bhp versus 2.2 bhp. In fact, the fan must work harder at the lower density to move the same mass flow rate. This additional work results in a higher temperature rise in the air from fan inlet to outlet. A fan located ahead of the heater will require less power and may be quieter due to the lower rotational speed.

6.3.9 Explosive or Flammable Materials: When conveying explosive or flammable materials, it is important to recognize the potential for ignition of the gas stream. This may be from airborne material striking the impeller or by the physical movement of the impeller into the fan casing. AMCA[6.3] and other associations offer guidelines for both the manufacturer and the user on ways to minimize this danger. These involve more permanent attachment of the impeller to the shaft and bearings and the use of buffer plates or spark resistant alloy construction. Because no single type of construction fits all applications, it is imperative that both the manufacturer and the user are aware of the dangers involved and agree on the type of construction and degree of protection that is being proposed.

NOTE: For many years aluminum alloy impellers have been specified to minimize sparking if the impeller were to contact other steel parts. This is still accepted but tests by the U. S. Bureau of Mines[6.4] and others have demonstrated that impact of aluminum with rusty steel creates a "Thermite" reaction and thus possible ignition hazards. Special care must be taken when aluminum alloys are used in the presence of steel.

6.4 FAN MOTORS

Most fans are driven by electric motors. There are many types of motors available on the market. Selecting the right motor for a given installation requires information on the electrical power available, the fan power requirement, the desired fan speed, how the fan is to be driven (belt or direct drive), and the environmental conditions where the fan and motor are to be located. Most motors conform to standards established by the National Electric Manufacturers Association (NEMA). These standards apply to motor design parameters such as dimensions, enclosures, power requirements, and insulation. In addition, the Energy Policy Act (EPACT) of 1999 mandates energy efficiency standards for most types of motors used in the United States.

6.4.1 Considerations for Motor Selection:

POWER SUPPLY

Current: By far the most common form of supply power has alternating current (AC). Traditionally, direct current (DC) has

been used in special-purpose cases where variable speed was needed, but this has been changing due to the availability and cost of variable frequency AC drives.

Voltage: The supply voltage must be known to properly select motors and motor controls. In the United States, three phase power is generally either 230 or 460 volts, although some very high horsepower systems use 575 or 2300 volts. Single phase power is usually either 115 or 230 volts.

Phase: Power is supplied by either a three wire, three phase system or a two wire, single phase system. Three phase is commonly used on motors one horsepower and larger. It is economical because it requires smaller lead wires. Single phase is most commonly used for fractional horsepower motors.

Frequency: The standard frequency for AC current in the United States is 60 cycles per second (Hz). Some foreign countries use 50 cycles.

MOTOR CONSTRUCTION

Power Rating: The power capacity of the motor must be greater than the power requirement of the fan it drives. In the United States, motors are rated in horsepower (hp); in much of the rest of the world they are rated in kilowatts (kW).

Speed: Another important consideration is the motor speed, especially with direct driven fans. The speed of AC motors is a function of the frequency and the number of poles in the motor.

$$N_2 = \frac{120 \times f}{P} \qquad [6.15]$$

where: N_x = synchronous speed (rpm)
f = frequency (Hz)
P = number of poles

Motors run at speeds slightly below the synchronous speed. For example, a four pole, 60 Hz motor has a synchronous speed of 1800 fpm. Most of these motors run between 1725 and 1780 rpm.

Frame: NEMA sets industry standards for motor dimensions, and designates them as frame sizes. Motors with common frame sizes have the same shaft diameter, centerline height, and feet mounting dimensions.

Enclosure: The type of enclosure indicates how much protection there is for the internal motor components from the surrounding environment, and the method of motor cooling.

Open Drip-Proof (ODP) motors allow a free exchange of air through the motor. Air is drawn into the motor and across the windings for cooling. ODP motors should be used for clean, indoor applications.

Totally Enclosed Fan Cooled (TEFC) motors do not have openings in the motor enclosure, but are not necessarily airtight. An integral fan blows air over the enclosure to cool the motor. TEFC motors are used in outdoor, damp, and dirty applications.

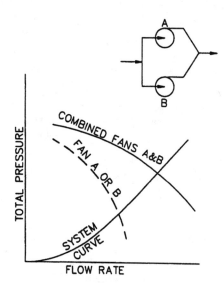

TWO IDENTICAL FANS
RECOMMENDED

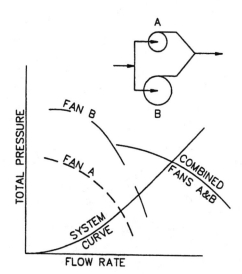

TWO DIFFERENT FANS
SATISFACTORY

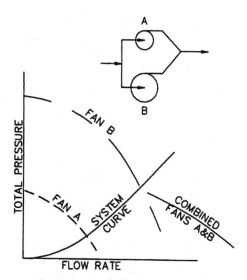

TWO DIFFERENT FANS
UNSATISFACTORY

WHEN SYSTEM CURVE DOES NOT CROSS COMBINED FAN
CURVE, OR CROSSES PROJECTED COMBINED CURVE
BEFORE FAN B, FAN B WILL HANDLE MORE AIR THAN
FANS A AND B IN PARALLEL.

NOTES:

1. TO ESTABLISH COMBINED FAN CURVE, THE
    COMBINED AIR FLOW RATE, Q, IS THE SUM
    OF INDIVIDUAL FAN AIR FLOW RATES AT
    POINTS OF EQUAL PRESSURE

2. TO ESTABLISH SYSTEM CURVE, INCLUDE
    LOSSES IN INDIVIDUAL FAN CONNECTIONS.

3. SYSTEM CURVE MUST INTERSECT COMBINED
    FAN CURVE OR HIGHER PRESSURE FAN
    MAY HANDLE MORE AIR ALONE.

AMERICAN CONFERENCE OF GOVERNMENTAL INDUSTRIAL HYGIENISTS	*FANS PARALLEL OPERATION*	
	DATE *10—96*	FIGURE *6—12*

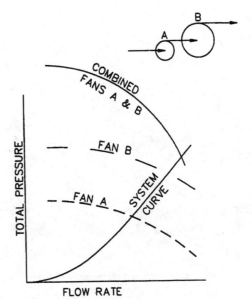

TWO IDENTICAL FANS
RECOMMENDED FOR BEST EFFICIENCY

TWO DIFFERENT FANS
SATISFACTORY

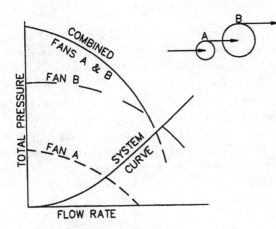

TWO DIFFERENT FANS
UNSATISFACTORY

WHEN SYSTEM CURVE DOES NOT INTERSECT
COMBINED FAN CURVE, OR CROSSES PROJECTED
COMBINED CURVE BEFORE FAN B CURVE, FAN B
WILL MOVE MORE AIR THAN FAN A AND B IN
SERIES.

NOTES:
1. TO ESTABLISH COMBINED FAN CURVE, THE
   COMBINED TOTAL PRESSURE IS THE SUM
   OF INDIVIDUAL FAN PRESSURES AT EQUAL
   AIR FLOW RATES, LESS THE PRESSURE LOSS IN
   THE FAN CONNECTIONS.

2. AIR FLOW RATE THROUGH EACH FAN WILL BE
   THE SAME, SINCE AIR IS CONSIDERED
   INCOMPRESSIBLE.

3. SYSTEM CURVE MUST INTERSECT
   COMBINED FAN CURVE OR LARGE FLOW RATE
   FAN MAY HANDLE MORE AIR ALONE.

AMERICAN CONFERENCE OF GOVERNMENTAL INDUSTRIAL HYGIENISTS	FANS SERIES OPERATION	
	DATE 5-96	FIGURE 6-13

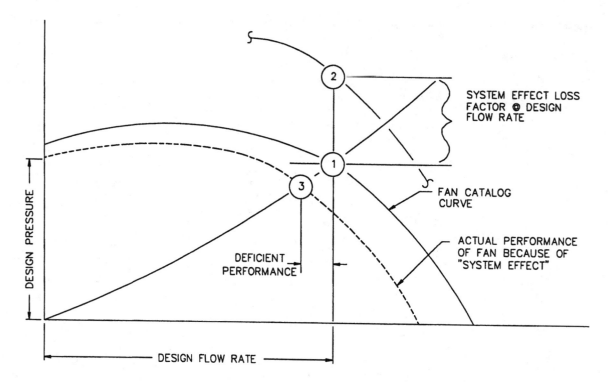

FIGURE 6–14. System effect factor

Total Enclosed Air Over (TEAO) motors are similar to TEFC motors except that there is no integral cooling fan. These motors are frequently used on fans, where the fan provides the cooling airflow over the motor.

Explosion Proof motors are special versions of TEFC motors, with design features to make them suitable for applications where explosive dust or gases are present. The enclosure is designed to withstand an explosion inside the motor, and contain the flame and sparks within the motor. There are different classifications of explosion proof construction, depending on the characteristics of the explosive gas or dust.

Severe Duty Motors are another variation of TEFC motors which have features which make them durable in hostile environments. They have better shaft seals, corrosion resistant paint, and some are available with stainless steel shafts.

Inertia Load Capacity: In some cases it is not the horsepower requirements that determines the size of motor needed but the motor's ability to accelerate the fan to full speed. This is particularly true when using low horsepower motors on large, heavy fans. Motors must have an inertia load capability greater than the inertia of the fan corrected for the drive ratio, as shown in the equation below:

$$WR^2_{motor} \geq WR^2_{fan} \times \left(\frac{RPM_{fan}}{RPM_{motor}} \right)^2 \times 1.1 \qquad \text{[6.16]}$$

where: WR^2_{motor} = inertia load at motor shaft

WR^2_{fan} = inertia of the fan

RPM_{motor} = motor speed

RPM_{fan} = fan speed

The 1.1 factor is an allowance for belts and sheaves. If the motor does not have enough inertia load capacity, either it will not be able to start the fan, or it will take an excessive amount of time (20 seconds or more) to bring the fan up to speed.

6.4.2 Motor Installation: The National Electric Code calls out the special requirements of motor installation and wiring. The sizing of motor lead wires and overload protection must take into account the higher than normal amp draw that occurs when a motor is started and brought up to full speed. As a result, motor branch circuits are sized differently than other types of branch circuits. There are also requirements that specify how close to the motor disconnects should be located. These are very important since they provide protection for workers who must service the fan and motor. Some fans can be provided with integral motor disconnects.

If a fan is belt driven, the motor must be mounted on an adjustable base. This base allows the motor to move with respect to the fan and allows for the adjustment and replacement of the belts.

6.5 FAN INSTALLATION AND MAINTENANCE

Fan rating tests for flow rate, static pressure, and power requirements are conducted under ideal conditions which include uniform straight airflow at the fan inlet and outlet. However, if in practice duct connections to the fan cause non-uniform airflow, fan performance and operating efficiency will be affected. Location and installation of the fan must consider the location of these duct components to minimize losses. If adverse connections must be used, appropriate compensation

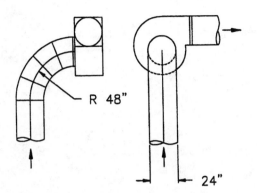

FIGURE 6–16. Inlet elbow

must be made in the system calculations. Once the system is installed and operating, routine inspection and maintenance will be required if the system is to continue to operate at original design levels.

6.5.1 Fan Installation: It is important to install a fan on a structure strong enough to support the loads produced by the fan. The support structure must be designed to carry not only the weight of the fan, but also the dynamic loads produced while the fan is operating. A well-designed support is rigid enough to keep vibration levels low. A wood stud wall may be adequate for a small lightweight wall propeller fan, but a large industrial exhaust fan requires more consideration. The ideal mounting for large fans is a concrete pad mounted on grade with a weight of at least three times the fan. Often this is not possible, and structural steel supports are used. To avoid problems with vibration, it is important that the dynamic loads are considered in the design of the support.

Consider maintenance when deciding how and where to mount the fan. Provide ample room around the fan to gain access to the motor, drives, and bearings. Include safety features such as guards, electrical disconnects, and safety railings where necessary.

6.5.2 System Effect: System effect is defined as the estimated loss in fan performance from this non-uniform airflow. Figure 6-14 illustrates deficient fan system performance. The system pressure losses have been determined accurately and a suitable fan selected for operation at Point 1. However, no allowance has been made for the effect of the system connections on fan performance. The point of intersection between the resulting fan performance curve and the actual system curve is Point 3. The resulting flow rate will, therefore, be deficient by the difference from 1 to 3. To compensate for this system effect, it will be necessary to add a "system effect loss" to the calculated system pressure. This will be equal to the pressure difference between Points 1 and 2 and will have to be added to the calculated system pressure losses. The fan then will be selected for this higher pressure (Point 2) but will operate at Point 1 due to loss in performance from system effects.

One commonly neglected system effect is a duct elbow at the fan inlet. For example, consider the fan shown in Figure 6-16.

This fan has a four-piece 90° round duct elbow immediately in front of the inlet. There are no turning vanes inside the duct. The required flow rate is 5000 cfm and the system pressure losses are 8 "wg at standard conditions (0.075 lb/ft^3). Selecting a fan without the system effect, using Table 6-1, would result in a fan speed of 1987 rpm and power consumption of 13.02 hp.

With the elbow at the inlet, the airflow into the fan inlet will be degraded. Such a change in the airflow requires use of a system effect factor (SEF) to select a fan that overcomes the degradation in performance. The system effect factor is used to determine a correction value, in inches water gauge, to be added to the system pressure losses.

In this example, the duct diameter is 24" with a turning radius of 48". This is a radius-to-diameter (r/d) ratio of 2.0. In Figure 6-20, Item C, we find the system effect curve to use is "R". To find the system effect correction value in inches water

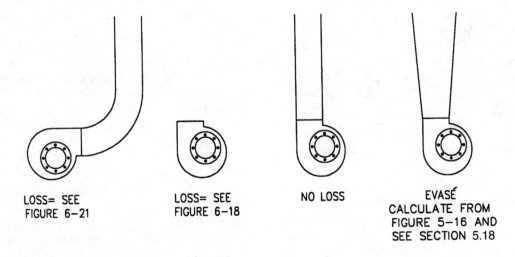

LOSS= SEE   LOSS= SEE   NO LOSS   EVASÉ
FIGURE 6–21   FIGURE 6–18   CALCULATE FROM
                                             FIGURE 5–16 AND
                                           SEE SECTION 5.18

FIGURE 6–15. System effect factor

TABLE 6-2. Fan Balancing and Vibration Categories

Application	Examples	Driver Power Limits kW (hp)	Fan Application Category
Residential	Ceiling fans, attic fans, window air conditioners	≤ 0.15 (0.2) > 0.15 (0.2)	BV-1 BV-2
HVAC & Agricultural	Building ventilation and air conditioning; commercial systems	≤ 3.7 (5.0) > 3.7 (5.0)	BV-2 BV-3
Industrial Process & Power Generation, etc.	Baghouse scrubber, mine, conveying, boilers, combustion air, pollution control, wind tunnels	≤ 300 (400) > 300 (400)	BV-3 BV-4
Transportation & Marine	Locomotives, trucks, automobile	≤ 15 (20) > 15 (20)	BV-3 BV-4
Transit/Tunnel	Subway emergency ventilation, tunnel fans, garage ventilation, tunnel jet fans	≤ 75 (100) > 75 (100) ANY	BV-3 BV-4 BV-4
Petrochemical Process	Hazardous gases, process fans	≤ 37 (50) > 37 (50)	BV-3 BV-4
Computer Chip Mfg.	Clean room fans	ANY	BV-5

gauge, we use the fan inlet velocity with Figure 6-26. Since the duct area is 3.142 ft^2, the velocity is 1592 fpm (5000 cfm ÷ 3.142 ft^2 = 1592 fpm). From Figure 6-26 we get a correction value of 0.19 "wg This 0.19" value is added to the fan static pressure when selecting the fan from the multi-rating table. Select the fan for a static pressure of 8.19 "wg. Interpolating in Table 6-1, we find a selection for 5000 cfm and 8.19 "wg at 2002 rpm and 13.25 hp. This selection for a fan with an elbow at the inlet will result in operation at 5000 cfm and 8 "wg drawing 13.25 hp.

NOTE: The system effect factor compensates for the affect on the fan of an irregular air stream. This system effect factor is taken in addition to the friction loss used to calculate the system loss (Figure 5-13.)

Figure 6-15 illustrates typical discharge conditions and the losses which may be anticipated. The magnitude of the change in system performance caused by elbows and other obstructions placed too close to a fan inlet or outlet can be estimated for the conditions shown on Figures 6-17 through 6-24.

An alternate way of determining the additional static pressure, in "wg, is by obtaining the appropriate system effect factor from Figure 6-25 and multiplying it by the fan inlet or discharge velocity pressure.

A vortex or spin of the air stream entering the fan inlet may be created by non-uniform flow conditions as illustrated in Figure 6-23. These conditions may be caused by a poor inlet box, multiple elbows or entries near the inlet, or by other spin producing conditions. Since the variations resulting in inlet spin are many, no System Effect Factors are tabulated. Where

a vortex or inlet spin cannot be avoided or is discovered at an existing fan inlet, the use of turning vanes, splitter sheets, or egg crate straighteners will reduce the effect.

6.5.3 Inspection and Maintenance: Material accumulation or abrasive wear on an impeller can cause a fan to "go out of balance." This unbalance will cause vibration of the fan. This may result in damage to or failure of the fan impeller, housing, bearings, or pedestal. Periodic cleaning and rebalancing of fans operating in air streams handling abrasive, sticky, or wet materials is recommended.

Regular observation of fan vibration levels can detect problems before they increase in amplitude to the point where fan components become damaged. Different types of fans and fan installations can tolerate higher levels of vibration than others. Table 6-2 shows fan application categories for determining acceptable levels of vibration. Most fans used in industrial ventilation systems fall in category BV-3. Once the fan application category is determined, use Table 6-3 to determine acceptable levels of vibration. The levels shown are for filter-out readings, which takes into account vibrations at all frequencies. The rigidly mounted column is for fans mounted directly to structural steel or concrete. The flexibly mounted column applies to fans mounted on spring or rubber-in-shear isolators. The start-up row gives acceptable levels of vibration for new or recently repaired fans. As the fan operates over time, parts wear, material builds up on the impeller, and vibration levels increase. When the vibration levels reach the level shown in the alarm row, corrective action should be taken at the next available shut down. If corrective action is not taken, and the vibration levels increase to the shutdown levels, the fan should be shut down immediately and the

TABLE 6-3. Vibration Limits for Tests Conducted In-Situ (Values show are peak velocity, mm/s (inches/s), Filter-Out)

Condition	Fan Application Category	Rigidly Mounted mm/s (inches/s)	Flexibly Mounted mm/s (inches/s)
Start-Up	BV-1	14.0 (0.55)	15.2 (0.60)
	BV-2	7.6 (0.30)	12.7 (0.50)
	BV-3	6.4 (0.25)	8.8 (0.35)
	BV-4	4.1 (0.16)	6.4 (0.25)
	BV-5	2.5 (0.10)	4.1 (0.16)
Alarm	BV-1	15.2 (0.60)	19.1 (0.75)
	BV-2	12.7 (0.50)	19.1 (0.75)
	BV-3	10.2 (0.40)	16.5 (0.65)
	BV-4	6.4 (0.25)	10.2 (0.40)
	BV-5	5.7 (0.20)	7.6 (0.30)
Shut Down	BV-1	NOTE 1	NOTE 1
	BV-2	NOTE 1	NOTE 1
	BV-3	12.7 (0.50)	17.8 (0.70)
	BV-4	10.2 (0.40)	15.2 (0.60)
	BV-5	7.6 (0.30)	10.2 (0.40)

NOTE 1: Shutdown levels for Fan Applications categories BV-1 and BV-2 must be established based on historical data.

problem must be found and corrected. Failure to do so could lead to catastrophic failure of fan components. Refer to AMCA Standard 204[6.5] for more information on fan balancing and vibration levels.

Modern maintenance equipment permits the inspector to record vibration spectra. Review of changes in these spectra taken over time can indicate specific areas of developing problems with bearings, balance, belts, or motors. Electronic or computerized vibration monitors are available to mount on fans used in critical operations. These devices can be set up with automatic alarm functions and/or to provide continuous information about a unit's vibration level.

It is not uncommon, during fan installation or motor/starter maintenance, for the fan impeller rotation direction to be inadvertently reversed. Since fans do move a fraction of their rated capacity when running backward, incorrect rotation often goes unnoticed in spite of less effective performance of the exhaust system.

Scheduled inspection of fans is recommended. Items checked should include:

1. Bearings for proper operating temperature (lubricate them on the manufacturer's recommended schedule).
2. Excessive vibration of bearings or housing.
3. Belt drives for proper tension and minimum wear.
4. Correct coupling or belt alignment.
5. Fan impeller for proper alignment and rotation.
6. Impeller free from excess wear or material accumulation.
7. Tight fan hold-down bolts.
8. Tight fan impeller set screws or bushings.
9. Proper installation of safety guards.

Standard lockout/tagout procedures should be observed when servicing fan equipment or its associated duct. The electrical supply must be shut off and locked out at a disconnect near the fan. When opening access doors or reaching into the fan inlet or outlet, the fan must be mechanically locked out by blocking the impeller from rotating. A warning tag should be used when blocking a fan. Do not open an access door while the fan is operating or coasting down.

BE SURE to remove any inserted obstructions used to block impeller rotation when servicing is complete.

REFERENCES

6.1   American Society of Heating, Refrigeration, and Air-Conditioning Engineers, Inc.: Fundamentals Handbook 1993; 1791 Tullie Circle, NE, Atlanta, GA 30329.

6.2.   Air Movement and Control Association, Inc.: Standards Handbook, Publication 99-86, 30 W. University Dr., Arlington Heights, IL 60004-1893.

6.3.   Air Movement and Control Association, Inc.: AMCA Publication 201-90, Fans and Systems, 30 W. University Dr., Arlington Heights, IL 60004-1893; (847)394-0150; FAX: (847)394-0088; Publications: (847)394-0404.

6.4.   Gibson, N.; Lloyd, F. C.; and Perry, G. R.: Fire Hazards in Chemical Plants from Friction Sparks Involving the Thermite Reaction. Symposium Series No. 25. Insn. Chem. Engrs., London (1968).

6.5.   Air Movement and Control Association, Inc.: ANSI/AMCA Standard 204-96, Balance Quality and Vibration Levels for Fans, 30 W. University Dr., Arlington Heights, IL 60004-1893, (847)394-0150, FAX: (847)253-0099, Publications (847)253-0088.

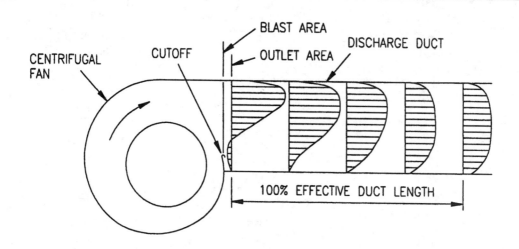

TO CALCULATE 100% EFFECTIVE DUCT LENGTH, ASSUME A MINIMUM OF 2-1/2 DUCT DIAMETERS FOR 2500 FPM OR LESS. ADD 1 DUCT DIAMETER FOR EACH ADDITIONAL 1000 FPM.

EXAMPLE: 5000 FPM = 5 EQUIVALENT DUCT DIAMETERS. IF THE DUCT IS RECTANGULAR WITH SIDE DIMENSIONS a AND b, THE EQUIVALENT DUCT DIAMETER IS EQUAL TO $(4ab/\pi)^{0.5}$

	No Duct	12% Effective Duct	25% Effective Duct	50% Effective Duct	100% Effective Duct
Pressure Recovery	0%	50%	80%	90%	100%
<u>Blast Area</u> Outlet Area	System Effect Curve				
0.4	P	R–S	U	W	–
0.5	P	R–S	U	W	–
0.6	R–S	S–T	U–V	W–X	–
0.7	S	U	W–X	–	–
0.8	T–U	V–W	X	–	–
0.9	V–W	W–X	–	–	–
1.0	–	–	–	–	–

DETERMINE SEF BY USING FIGURE 6–25 OR 6–26

Reprinted from AMCA Publication 201–90, *FAN AND SYSTEMS,* by permission of the Air Movement and Control Association, Inc.[6.1]

AMERICAN CONFERENCE OF GOVERNMENTAL INDUSTRIAL HYGIENISTS	SYSTEM EFFECT CURVES FOR OUTLET DUCTS– CENTRIFUGAL FANS	
	DATE *1–88*	FIGURE *6–17*

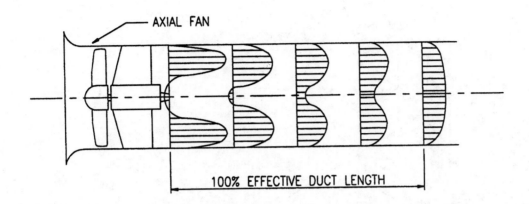

TO CALCULATE 100% EFFECTIVE DUCT LENGTH, ASSUME A MINIMUM OF 2-1/2 DUCT DIAMETERS FOR 2500 FPM OR LESS. ADD 1 DUCT DIAMETER FOR EACH ADDITIONAL 1000 FPM.

EXAMPLE: 5000 FPM = 5 EQUIVALENT DUCT DIAMETERS

	No Duct	12% Effective Duct	25% Effective Duct	50% Effective Duct	100% Effective Duct
Tubeaxial Fan	–	–	–	–	–
Tubeaxial Fan	U	V	W	–	–

DETERMINE SEF BY USING FIGURE 6-25 OR 6-26

Reprinted from AMCA Publication 201-90, *FANS AND SYSTEMS,* by by permission of the Air Movement and Control Association, Inc.[6.1]

AMERICAN CONFERENCE OF GOVERNMENTAL INDUSTRIAL HYGIENISTS	*SYSTEM EFFECT CURVES FOR OUTLET DUCTS- AXIAL FANS*	
	DATE *5-92*	FIGURE *6-18*

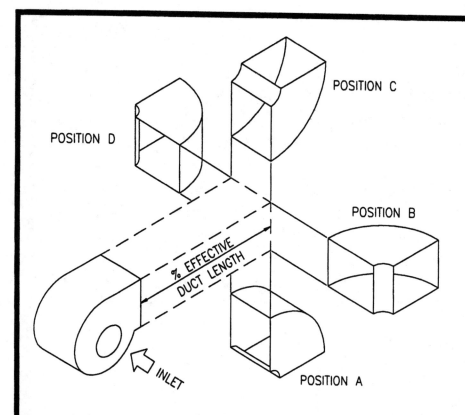

POSITION C

POSITION D

POSITION B

% EFFECTIVE DUCT LENGTH

INLET

POSITION A

DETERMINE SEF BY USING FIGURES 6-25 AND 6-26

For DWDI fans determine SEF using the curve for SWSI fans. Then apply the appropriate multiplier from the tabulation below

MULTIPLIERS FOR DWDI FANS

ELBOW POSITION A = ΔP X 1.00
ELBOW POSITION B = ΔP X 1.25
ELBOW POSITION C = ΔP X 1.00
ELBOW POSITION D = ΔP X 0.85

Blast Area / Outlet Area	Outlet Elbow Position	No Outlet Duct	12% Effective Duct	25% Effective Duct	50% Effective Duct	100% Effective Duct
0.4	A	N	O	P–Q	S	
	B	M–N	N	O–P	R–S	
	C	L–M	M	N	Q	
	D	L–M	M	N	Q	
0.5	A	O–P	P–Q	R	T	
	B	N–O	O–P	Q	S–T	
	C	M–N	N	O–P	R–S	
	D	M–N	N	O–P	R–S	
0.6	A	Q	Q–R	S	U	
	B	P	Q	R	T	
	C	N–O	O	Q	S	
	D	N–O	O	Q	S	
0.7	A		S	T	V	
	B	Q–R	R–S	S–T	U–V	
	C	P	Q	R–S	T	
	D	P	Q	R–S	T	
0.8	A	S	S–T	T–U	W	
	B	R–S	S	T	V	
	C	Q–R	R	S	U–V	
	D	Q–R	R	S	U–V	
0.9	A	T	T–U	U–V	W	
	B	S	S–T	T–U	W	
	C	R	S	S–T	W–V	
	D	R	S	S–T	V	
1.0	A	T	T–U	U–V	W	
	B	S–T	T	U	W	
	C	R–S	S	T	W–V	
	D	R–S	S	T	V	

NO SYSTEM EFFECT FACTOR

Reprinted from AMCA Publication 201–90, *FANS AND SYSTEMS*, by permission of the Air Movement and Control Association, Inc.[6.1]

AMERICAN CONFERENCE OF GOVERNMENTAL INDUSTRIAL HYGIENISTS

SYSTEM EFFECT CURVES FOR OUTLET ELBOWS ON CENTRIFUGAL FANS

| DATE | 5-92 | FIGURE | 6-19 |

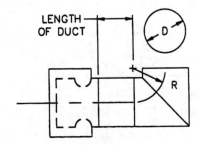

A. TWO—PIECE MITERED 90° ROUND SECTION ELBOW —— NOT VANED.

SYSTEM EFFECT FACTORS

R/D	NO DUCT	2D DUCT	5D DUCT
—	3.2	2.0	1.0

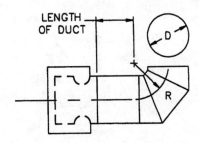

B. THREE—PIECE MITERED 90° ROUND SECTION ELBOW —— NOT VANED.

SYSTEM EFFECT FACTORS

R/D	NO DUCT	2D DUCT	5D DUCT
0.5	2.5	1.6	0.8
0.75	1.6	1.0	0.47
1.0	1.2	0.66	0.33
2.0	1.0	0.53	0.33
3.0	0.8	0.47	0.26

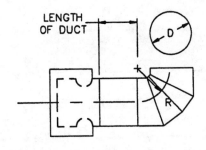

C. FOUR OR MORE PIECE MITERED 90° ROUND SECTION ELBOW —— NOT VANED.

SYSTEM EFFECT FACTORS

R/D	NO DUCT	2D DUCT	5D DUCT
0.5	1.8	1.0	0.53
0.75	1.4	0.8	0.40
1.0	1.2	0.66	0.33
2.0	1.0	0.53	0.33
3.0	0.66	0.40	0.22

D= Diameter of the inlet collar.
The inside area of the square duct (H x H) should be equal to the inside area of the fan inlet collar.
+ The maximum permissible angle of any converging element of the transition is 15°, and for a diverging element 7°.

Reprinted from AMCA Publication 201—90, *FANS AND SYSTEMS*, by permission of the Air Movement and Control Association, Inc.[6.1]

AMERICAN CONFERENCE OF GOVERNMENTAL INDUSTRIAL HYGIENISTS	SYSTEM EFFECT CURVES FOR FOR VARIOUS MITERED ELBOWS WITHOUT TURNING VANES	
	DATE 1-88	FIGURE 6-20

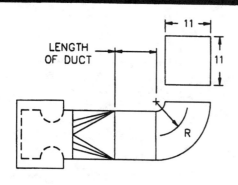

A. SQUARE ELBOW WITH INLET TRANSITION -- NO TURNING VANES.

SYSTEM EFFECT FACTORS			
R/D	NO DUCT	2D DUCT	5D DUCT
0.5	2.5	1.6	0.8
0.75	2.0	1.2	0.66
1.0	1.2	0.66	0.33
2.0	0.8	0.47	0.26

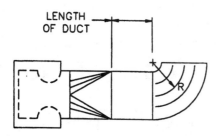

B. SQUARE ELBOW WITH INLET TRANSITION -- 3 LONG TURNING VANES.

SYSTEM EFFECT FACTORS			
R/D	NO DUCT	2D DUCT	5D DUCT
0.5	0.8	0.47	0.26
1.0	0.53	0.33	0.18
2.0	0.26	0.22	0.14

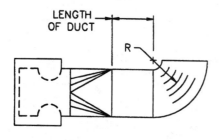

C. SQUARE ELBOW WITH INLET TRANSITION -- SHORT TURNING VANES.

SYSTEM EFFECT FACTORS			
R/D	NO DUCT	2D DUCT	5D DUCT
0.5	0.8	0.47	0.26
1.0	0.53	0.33	0.18
2.0	0.26	0.22	0.14

$$D = \frac{2H}{\sqrt{\pi}}$$

THE INSIDE AREA OF THE SQUARE DUCT (H X H) IS EQUAL TO THE INSIDE AREA CIRCUMSCRIBED BY THE FAN INLET COLLAR. THE MAXIMUM PERMISSIBLE ANGLE OF ANY CONVERGING ELEMENT OF THE TRANSITION IS 15°, AND FOR A DIVERGING ELEMENT 7.5°.

Reprinted from AMCA Publication 201-90, *FANS AND SYSTEMS*, by permission of the Air Movement and Control Association, Inc. [6.1]

AMERICAN CONFERENCE OF GOVERNMENTAL INDUSTRIAL HYGIENISTS	*SYSTEM EFFECT CURVES FOR OUTLET DUCTS- AXIAL FANS*	
	DATE *5-92*	FIGURE *6-21*

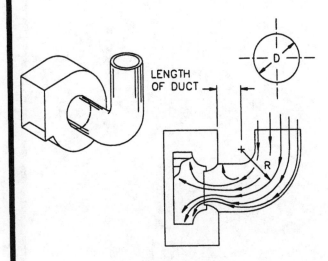

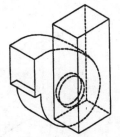
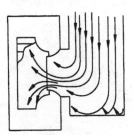

SYSTEM EFFECT FACTORS*

R/D	NO DUCT	2D DUCT	5D DUCT
0.75	Q–R	S	U
1.0	R	S–T	U–V
2.0	R–S	T	U–V
3.0	S–T	U	V–W

A. NON–UNIFORM FLOW INTO A FAN INLET BY A 90° <u>ROUND</u> SECTION ELBOW – NO TURNING VANES.

*Values shown are in modification of the original chart.

THE REDUCTION IN FLOW RATE AND PRESSURE FOR THIS TYPE OF INLET CONDITION IS IMPOSSIBLE TO TABULATE. THE MANY POSSIBLE VARIATIONS IN WIDTH AND DEPTH OF THE DUCT INFLUENCE THE REDUCTION IN PERFORMANCE TO VARYING DEGREES AND THEREFORE THIS INLET SHOULD BE AVOIDED. FLOW RATE LOSSES AS HIGH AS 45% HAVE BEEN OBSERVED. EXISTING INSTALLATIONS CAN BE IMPROVED WITH GUIDE VANES OR THE CONVERSION TO SQUARE OR MITERED ELBOWS WITH GUIDE VANES.

B. NON–UNIFORM FLOW INDUCED INTO FAN INLET BY A <u>RECTANGULAR</u> INLET DUCT.

Reprinted from AMCA Publication 201–90. *FANS AND SYSTEMS*, by permission of the Air movement and Control Association, Inc.

AMERICAN CONFERENCE OF GOVERNMENTAL INDUSTRIAL HYGIENISTS

NON–UNIFORM INLET FLOWS

DATE 5-92   FIGURE 6-22

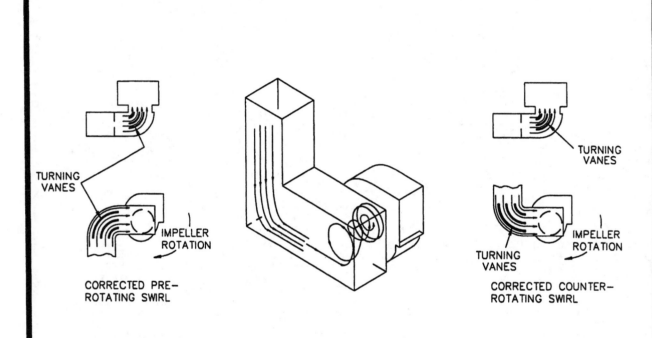

TURNING VANES

IMPELLER ROTATION

CORRECTED PRE-ROTATING SWIRL

TURNING VANES

TURNING VANES

IMPELLER ROTATION

CORRECTED COUNTER-ROTATING SWIRL

C. NON—UNIFORM FLOW INTO A FAN INLET BY AN INDUCED VORTEX, SPIN OR SWIRL.

Reprinted from AMCA Publication 201—90 FANS AND SYSTEMS by permission of the Air Movement and Control Association Inc. (6.1)

AMERICAN CONFERENCE OF GOVERNMENTAL INDUSTRIAL HYGIENISTS	*NON—UNIFORM INLET CORRECTIONS*	
	DATE *5—92*	FIGURE *6—23*

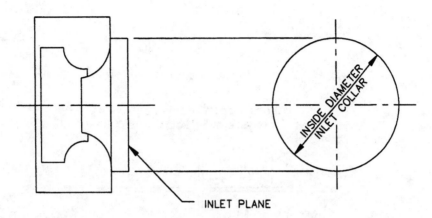

A. FREE INLET AREA PLANE -- FAN WITH INLET COLLAR.

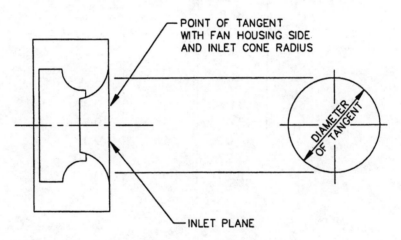

B. FREE INLET AREA PLANE -- FAN WITHOUT INLET COLLAR.

PERCENTAGE OF UNOBSTRUCTED INLET AREA	SYSTEM EFFECT FACTORS
100	NO LOSS
95	V
90	U
85	T
75	S
50	Q
25	P

DETERMINE SEF BY CALCULATING INLET VELOCITY AND USING FIGURE 6-25 OR 6-26

Reprinted from AMCA Publication 210-90, FANS AND SYSTEMS, by permission of the Air and Control Association Inc. (6.1)

AMERICAN CONFERENCE OF GOVERNMENTAL INDUSTRIAL HYGIENISTS	SYSTEM EFFECT CURVES FOR INLET OBSTRUCTIONS	
	DATE 5-92	FIGURE 6-24

Loss Factor Equivalents
for System Effect Curves*

Curve	F_{sys}	Curve	F_{sys}
F	16.0	P	1.98
G	14.3	Q	1.60
H	12.8	R	1.20
I	11.3	S	0.80
J	9.62	T	0.53
K	8.02	U	0.40
L	6.42	V	0.26
M	4.63	W	0.18
N	3.20	X	0.10
O	2.51		

To use this table:

1) Obtain the curve letter from Figures 6—17 through 6—22 or Figure 6—24.
2) For inlet system effects, multiply the equivalent loss coefficient from the above table by the fan inlet velocity pressure.
3) For outlet system effects, multiply the equivalent loss coefficient from the above table by the fan outlet velocity pressure.

*F_{sys} values are in number of velocity pressures. For loss directly in "Wg, refer to Figure 6—27.

AMERICAN CONFERENCE OF GOVERNMENTAL INDUSTRIAL HYGIENISTS	*SYSTEM EFFECT CURVES*	
	DATE *10—96*	FIGURE *6—25*

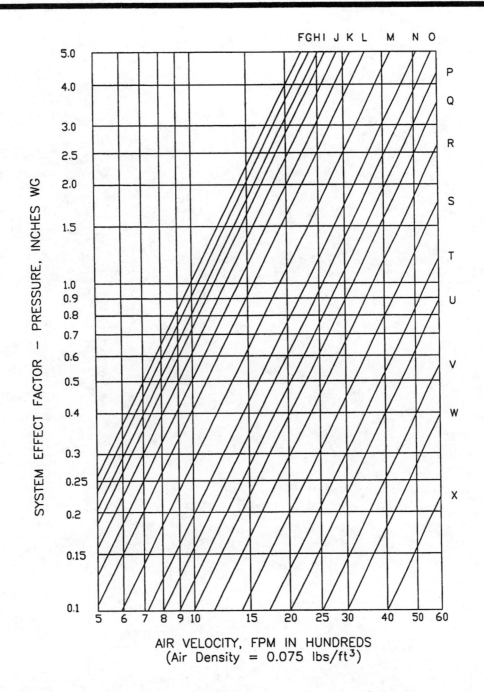

AIR VELOCITY, FPM IN HUNDREDS
(Air Density = 0.075 lbs/ft^3)

*Enter the chart at the appropriate air velocity (on the abcissa) read up to the applicable curve, then across from the curve (to the ordinate) to find the SEF at standard air density.
**Adapted for metric from AMCA Publication 201—90, FANS AND SYSTEMS, by permission of the Air Movement and Control Association, Inc. (6.1)

AMERICAN CONFERENCE OF GOVERNMENTAL INDUSTRIAL HYGIENISTS	SYSTEM EFFECT CURVES	
	DATE 6—92	FIGURE 6—26

Chapter 7
SUPPLY AIR SYSTEMS

7.1 INTRODUCTION

Supply air systems are critical to the success of industrial ventilation systems. They allow exhaust systems to breathe and provide dilution of contaminants that escape into the general workspace. The supply air system may also control the heating, cooling, and humidity in the workspace. The supply air duct design is less critical to its system's performance and thus the design procedures are less rigorous and usually simpler to accomplish.

Manufacturing facilities have evolved to widespread use of automation/computers and the production of parts made to tight tolerances. Facility occupants and/or equipment often require some degree of temperature control. Air cleanliness requirements have been raised to improve worker health, reduce housekeeping/maintenance costs, and increase product quality. The supply air ventilation system plays a significant role in balancing these collective needs and maintaining the proper work space environment.

In some industrial plants, ventilation systems have become key elements of a process. A few have become critical to the success of that process; this is the case in automotive painting. A number of years ago, automobiles were painted in an open booth by people who sprayed paint onto the vehicle body. Air was exhausted to remove solvent vapors so the workers would not be exposed to hazardous concentrations. The replacement make-up air entering the booth had a minimum degree of filtration and no significant temperature or humidity control. Supply air was distributed to provide good air exchange throughout the booth so the concentration of paint solvent vapors would be low. Over time, the quality of the paint coating became more important and the performance of ventilation systems began to improve.

Currently supply air humidity and temperature are controlled to improve paint curing time. The air is well filtered to eliminate defects in the painted surface. Painting operations are conducted in a clean-room type space that is pressurized to maintain high levels of cleanliness.

In other plants, the distribution of supply air may not be as critical for product quality but will always be important for the

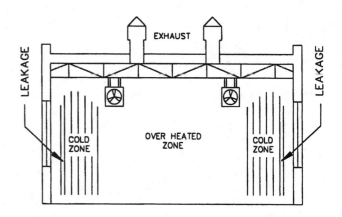

FIGURE 7-1. Under negative pressure conditions, workers in the cold zones turned up thermostats in an attempt to get heat. Because this did nothing to stop leakage of cold air, they remained cold while the center of plant was overheated.

proper operation of exhaust systems and plant comfort control. Poorly distributed supply air sometimes overwhelms a well-designed exhaust hood and destroys the hood's ability to capture contaminants. Therefore, the designer should pay equal attention to both the quantity and distribution of the supply air system.

7.2 PURPOSE OF SUPPLY AIR SYSTEMS

A proper supply air ventilation system can serve several proposes in an industrial facility: (1) plant ventilation, (2) exhaust air replacement, (3) building pressurization, (4) building heating, cooling, and humidification, and (5) space air cleanliness. The purposes of the supply air system are discussed in the following paragraphs. The total amount of supply air should be the amount that satisfies all the requirements of the supply air system. For example, a small amount of air may be required for replacing the exhaust air, but a much larger amount may be required to deliver enough tempered air for heating or cooling.

7.2.1 Plant Ventilation: Outside air brought into an industrial plant is utilized to replace air that is exhausted and may

TABLE 7-1. Negative Pressures which May Cause Unsatisfactory Conditions within Buildings

Negative Pressure, "wg	Adverse Conditions
0.01 to 0.02	Worker Draft Complaints—High velocity drafts through doors and windows
0.01 to 0.05	Natural Draft Stacks Ineffective—Ventilation through roof exhaust ventilators, flow through stacks with natural draft greatly reduced
0.02 to 0.05	Carbon Monoxide Hazard—Back drafting will take place in hot water heaters, unit heaters, furnaces, and other combustion equipment not provided with induced draft.
0.03 to 0.10	General Mechanical Ventilation Reduced—Air flows reduced in propeller fans and low pressure supply and exhaust systems.
0.05 to 0.10	Doors Difficult to Open—Serious injury may result from non-checked, slamming doors.
0.10 to 0.25	Local Exhaust Ventilation Impaired—Centrifugal fan exhaust flow reduced.

TABLE 7-2. Negative Pressures and Corresponding Velocities Through Crack Openings (Calculated with air at room temperature, standard atmospheric pressure, $C_e = 0.6$.)

Negative Pressure, "wg	Velocity, fpm
0.004	150
0.008	215
0.010	240
0.014	285
0.016	300
0.018	320
0.020	340
0.025	380
0.030	415
0.040	480
0.050	540
0.060	590
0.080	680
0.100	760
0.150	930
0.200	1080
0.250	1200
0.300	1310
0.400	1520
0.500	1700
0.600	1860

help dilute airborne contaminants present in the workspace. As discussed in Chapters 1,3, 4, and 5, exhaust air systems are used to remove unwanted airborne contaminants, heat, odors, and gases by placement as close to the source of generation as possible. The supply air system can aid in contaminant control by diluting remaining contaminants with outdoor air. Chapter 2 discusses the design approach for sizing the supply air rate for this purpose. Outdoor air can also be used to reduce the temperature by blending the warmer plant air with cooler outside air. The air can be blown across a person to achieve a greater cooling effect than still air. Chapter 2 also discusses heat relief and measurements of the air relating to the ability to cool a person.

Ventilation air is also needed to deliver oxygen for breathing. This is a concern with buildings having weather tight enclosures, but most industrial plants have porous building shells and infiltration of outside air is normally more than adequate to provide fresh air for breathing. Air can easily flow through cracks around doors, operable windows, utility entrances, conveyor openings, and through roof mounted equipment components. Infiltration of air in this manner may cause drafts or cold/hot spots within the plant and should be avoided.

7.2.2 Exhaust Air Replacement: Air will enter a building in an amount equal to the flow rate of exhaust air whether or not provision is made for replacement. However, the actual exhaust flow rate will be less than the design value if the plant is under negative pressure. If the building perimeter is tightly sealed, thus blocking effective infiltration of outdoor air, a severe decrease of the exhaust flow rate will result. If, on the other hand, the building is relatively old with large sash areas, air infiltration may be quite pronounced and the exhaust system performance will decrease only slightly. However, other problems may occur as identified in Table 7-1. When the building is relatively open, the resultant in-plant environmental condition is often undesirable since the influx of cold outdoor air in the northern climates chills the perimeter of the building. Exposed workers are subjected to drafts, space temperatures are not uniform, and the building heating system is usually overtaxed (see Figure 7-1). Although the air may eventually be tempered to acceptable conditions by mixing as it moves to the building interior, this is an ineffective way of transferring heat to the air and usually results in fuel waste. For an estimated value of the amount of air that enters a building through cracks that occur around doors or windows or other small openings in a building exterior, refer to Table 7-2. Figure 7-2 presents the force necessary to open a door against a building's negative pressure. The performance of a fan operation can also suffer as shown in Figure 7-3.

In most cases, replacement airflow rate should approximate the total airflow rate removed from the building by exhaust ventilation systems, process systems, and combustion processes. Determination of the actual flow rate of air removed usually requires an inventory of air exhaust locations with airflow testing of these sources. When conducting the exhaust inventory, it is necessary not only to determine the quantity of air removed, but also identify the need to upgrade any part of the ventilation system. At the same time, reasonable projections should be made of the total plant exhaust requirements for the next one to two years, particularly if process changes or plant expansions are contemplated. In such cases it can be practical to purchase a replacement air unit slightly larger than immediately necessary with the knowledge that the increased capacity will be required within a short time. The additional cost of a larger unit is relatively small and in most cases the fan drive can be adjusted to supply the desired quantity of air at the time of installation.

Having established the minimum air supply quantity necessary for replacement air purposes, many plants have found that it is wise to provide additional supply airflow to overcome natural ventilation leakage and further minimize drafts at the perimeter of the building. Conversely, some facilities deliberately design for a higher exhaust flow rate to prevent fugitive emissions from migrating into "clean" areas of the building or to the outdoors. In this case the control of the building pressure is quite important.

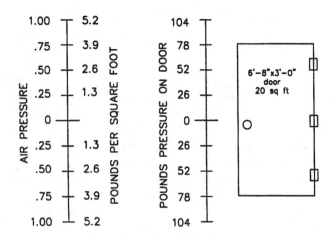

FIGURE 7–2. Relationship between air pressure and amount of force needed to open or close an average-sized door.

7.2.3 Pressurize Building: While negative pressure can cause adverse conditions, there are situations where negative pressures are desired. An example is a room or area where a contaminant must be prevented from escaping into the surrounding area. It also may be desirable to maintain a room or area under positive pressure to maintain a clean environment. Either of these conditions can be achieved by setting and maintaining the proper exhaust/supply flow differential. Negative pressure can be achieved by setting the exhaust volumetric flow rate (Q) from the area to a level higher than the supply rate. A good performance standard for industrial processes is to set a negative pressure differential of 0.04 ± 0.02 "wg. Conversely, positive pressure is achieved by setting the supply airflow rate higher than the exhaust rate. The proper flow differential will depend on the physical conditions of the area, but a general guide is to set a 5% flow difference but no less than 50 cfm. If the volume flows vary during either a negatively or positively pressurized process, it is easier to maintain the desired room pressure by adjusting the supply air.

Some designers use transfer grilles and a pressure sensor in the room to maintain a desired room pressure. Air is allowed to seep from adjacent hallways, offices, and other non-industrial areas. Transfer grilles should not be used between areas where contaminant migration is possible.

7.2.4 Building or Process Temperature Control, Heating, and Cooling: In addition to toxic contaminants, which are most effectively controlled by hoods, industrial processes may create an undesirable heat load in the workspace. Modern automated machining, conveying, and transferring equipment requires considerable horsepower. It is not uncommon for the process to have an electrical use of 10 to 20 watts per square foot of floor space. Precision manufacturing and assembling demand increasingly higher light levels in the plant with correspondingly greater heat release. The resulting in-plant heat burden raises indoor temperatures, often beyond the limits of efficient and healthful working conditions and, in some cases, beyond the tolerance limits for the product.

Environmental control of these factors can be accommodated through the careful planning and use of the supply system. Industrial air conditioning may be required to maintain process specifications and reduce hot working conditions.

For a large industrial plant whose size is several hundred thousand square feet, the internal process heat more than equals the heat loss through the building's walls and roof on the coldest of days. Therefore, this plant needs to be cooled throughout the year. The supply air must be heated to the degree that cold drafts are avoided. Heated air should also be utilized at door openings to reduce the cold drafts occurring with an open door. With these large facilities, the issue is how best to accomplish plant cooling.

Cooling the workspace in the summer is often more difficult than heating this space. In the heating season, the outdoor air temperatures are cool and it is relatively easy to obtain a 60 F to 70 F degree supply air temperature with normal process heat release to the space. In the summer when the outside temperature is in the 80s and 90s, reasonable space temperatures can be obtained by bringing in additional outside air or using evaporative coolers or refrigeration equipment to cool the supply air.

When applying a cooling system to industrial operations, the objective is often to obtain a plant temperature of approximately 80 F. The intent is not to try to provide a high level of comfort or control humidity; it is only to control heat. ASHRAE[7.1] gives basic criteria for industrial air conditioning in HVAC applications. Sensible and latent heat released by people and processes can be controlled to desired limits by proper use of air conditioning equipment. Radiant heat cannot be controlled by cooler air or increased ventilation and methods such as shielding, described in Chapter 2, are required.

To obtain the most cost-effective cooling system, a comparison should be performed between the use of extra air and refrigeration. The extra air approach often uses twice the wintertime airflow of outside air to dilute the increase in workspace temperature due to process heat. This results in the operation of an oversized fan and air distribution year round. Compare this to a system with cooling capability that is used only when needed. Air distribution is not as important in this system since cool air is denser than the warm inside air allowing it to displace air in the lower occupied zones.

For industrial plants larger than 400,000 square feet in size the supply inlet air temperature is typically five to ten degrees warmer in the summer than the actual outside temperature. The combination of the building process heat and solar radiation heat on the roof results in the situation that the air for approximately two feet above the roof at the supply unit intake is warmer than the surrounding ambient air. The fan and motor also increase the air temperature by approximately three degrees. If the motor is located outside the air stream, the temperature rise can be reduced by two degrees.

7.2.5 Product Protection and Space Air Cleanliness: If a space requires a higher level of cleanliness than adjacent

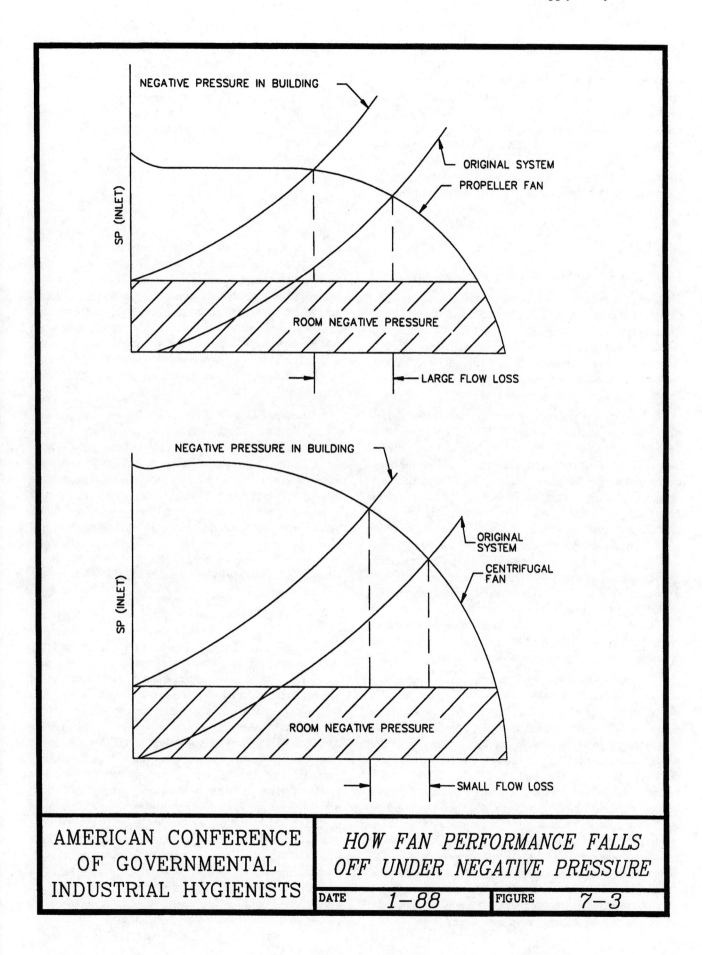

NEGATIVE PRESSURE IN BUILDING

ORIGINAL SYSTEM

PROPELLER FAN

SP (INLET)

ROOM NEGATIVE PRESSURE

LARGE FLOW LOSS

NEGATIVE PRESSURE IN BUILDING

ORIGINAL SYSTEM

CENTRIFUGAL FAN

SP (INLET)

ROOM NEGATIVE PRESSURE

SMALL FLOW LOSS

AMERICAN CONFERENCE OF GOVERNMENTAL INDUSTRIAL HYGIENISTS	HOW FAN PERFORMANCE FALLS OFF UNDER NEGATIVE PRESSURE	
	DATE 1-88	FIGURE 7-3

spaces, there should be an excess flow of clean air into the clean space, resulting in space pressurization and an outward airflow from the clean space to the less clean spaces. The clean air displaces the air in the space and the amount of airborne contaminants is reduced. To achieve a high degree of air cleanliness, special filters provide the final filtration. Refer to Chapter 4 for air cleaning characteristics of HEPA and other filter systems. The air exchange rate of cleanrooms must increase to achieve higher degrees of special air cleanliness depending upon the process and work practices involved. In most situations the supply air enters the room from ceiling panels or diffusers and is exhausted near the floor. Room velocities in the range of 50 to 100 feet per minute are typically used in the cleanest spaces.

7.3 SUPPLY AIR EQUIPMENT

A supply ventilation system consists of the supply air handling unit, the air distribution duct, and the supply air outlet. The supply air unit has components to temper, clean, and move the air. A microprocessor normally controls these devices through sensors and actuators. Since there can be significant internal heat generation in many industrial plants, cooling of the space is the objective for most of the year.

There are several grades of air handling units: heavy industrial, light industrial, and commercial. The heavy industrial units are normally custom or modular type and can provide many years of continuous service. If well maintained, they can easily operate for 20 years or more. The components are stronger and there is significantly more space for access to fans, filters, coils, and dampers. This facilitates the ability to maintain and repair the equipment. A light industrial grade unit typically has less space for maintenance of components and uses parts that are less suitable for rough use. They are often mass-produced with some flexibility to make modifications. They offer the same wide choice of heating and cooling media as the heavy industrial unit. In contrast, the commercial unit has less of a choice of heating and cooling types, is mass produced, has a minimum amount of space for maintenance, and is structurally designed for non-industrial buildings.

7.3.1 Heating Systems: With the availability of piped natural gas, many new heating systems are of the direct gas-fired type instead of heated water flowing through a coil. Figure 7-6 illustrates the layout of this type of unit. The direct gas-fired approach offers more than 90% heating efficiency since the gas is burned in the supply air stream. The burner must use outside air to prevent the build-up of carbon dioxide in the building. An alternative heating approach is indirect gas-fired heating, but it has a higher first cost and the heating efficiency is less. The related disadvantage of the direct gas-fired system is the requirement to use outside air. Since outside air is brought into the building it also must be exhausted. In the situation where there is enough process exhaust to remove the outside air, which is heated by the burner, no energy loss occurs. If there is an excessive amount of supply air, the excess air must be heated, which represents an energy loss.

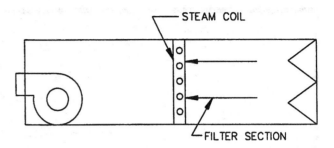

FIGURE 7–4. Single steam coil unit

Air handling units (AHUs) are usually categorized according to the source of heat: steam and hot water units, indirect gas and oil-fired units, and direct gas-fired units. Each type is capable of constant operation. Variations occur within each type in their capability of delivering a wide range of air temperatures. Each type of air heater has specific advantages and limitations which must be understood by the designer when making a selection. Hot water and steam coil types are better able to achieve a narrow temperature range of desired room conditions due to superior modulation ability and low heat control.

7.3.2 Steam Coil Heating: Steam heating was probably used in the earliest air heaters applied to general industry as well as commercial and institutional buildings (see Figure 7-4.) When properly designed, selected, and installed, they are reliable and safe. They require a reliable source of clean steam at a dependable pressure. For this reason they are applied most widely in large installations since smaller industrial plants often do not have sufficient boiler or steam capacity. Principal disadvantages of steam units are potential damage from freezing or water hammer in the coils, the complexity of controls when close temperature limits must be maintained, high cost, and excessive piping.

Freezing and water hammer are the result of poor equipment selection and installation. Both can be minimized through careful design. The coil must be sized to provide the desired heat output at the available steam pressure and flow. The coil preferably should be of the steam distributing type with vertical tubes. The traps and return piping must be sized for the maximum condensate flow at minimum steam pressure plus a safety factor. Atmospheric vents must be provided to minimize the danger of a vacuum in the coil which would keep condensate from draining. Finally, the condensate must never be lifted by steam pressure. The majority of freeze-up and water hammer problems relate to the steam modulating type of unit which relies on throttling of the steam supply to achieve temperature control. When throttling occurs, a vacuum can be created in the coil; unless adequate venting is provided, condensate will not drain and can freeze rapidly under the influence of cold outdoor air. Most freeze-ups occur when outdoor air is in the range of 20-30 F and the steam control valve is partially closed, rather than when the outdoor air is a minimum temperature and full steam supply is occurring (see Figure 7-5.)

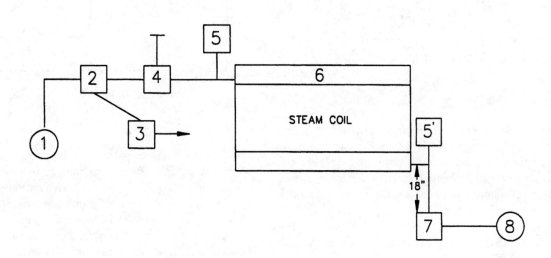

1. STEAM SUPPLY
       PROVIDE STEAM FROM A CLEAN SOURCE
       MAINTAIN CONSTANT PRESSURE WITH REDUCING VALVES IF REQUIRED
       PROVIDE TRAPPED DRIPS FOR SUPPLY LINES
       SIZE SUPPLY PIPING FOR FULL LOAD AT AVAILABLE PRESSURE
2. STRAINER
       1/32" DIAMETER MINIMUM PERFORATIONS
3. DRIP TRAP
       INVERTED BUCKET TRAP PREFERRED
4. CONTROL VALVE
       SIZE FOR MAXIMUM STEAM FLOW
       MAXIMUM PRESSURE DROP EQUAL TO 50% INLET STEAM PRESSURE
5. VACUUM BREAKER
       1/2" CHECK VALVE TO ATMOSPHERE
5'. ALTERNATE VACUUM BREAKER
6. STEAM COIL
       A.   SIZE FOR DESIGN CAPACITY AT INLET STEAM PRESSURE (SUPPLY-VALVE DROP)
       B.   VERTICAL COILS PREFFERED
       C.   HORIZONTAL COILS MUST BE PITCHED 1/4" PER FOOT TOWARD DRAIN.
            6' MAXIMUM LENGTH RECOMMEMDED
7. CONDENSATE TRAP
       A.   INVERTED BUCKET PREFERRED
       B.   SIZE TRAP FOR THREE TIMES MAXIMUM CONDENSATE LOAD AT PRESSURE
            DROP EQUAL TO 50% INLET PRESSURE
       C.   INDIVIDUAL TRAP FOR EACH COIL
8. CONDENSATE RETURN
       ATMOSPHERIC DRAIN ONLY

AMERICAN CONFERENCE OF GOVERNMENTAL INDUSTRIAL HYGIENISTS	*STEAM COIL PIPING*	
	DATE *1-74*	FIGURE *7-5*

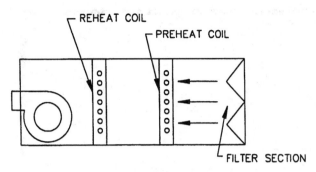

FIGURE 7–6. Multiple coil steam unit

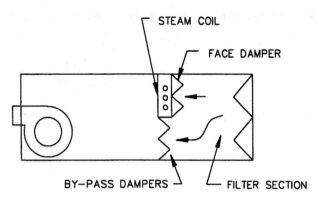

FIGURE 7–7. By-pass steam system

"Safety" controls are often used to detect imminent danger from freeze-up. A thermostat in the condensate line or an extended bulb thermostat on the downstream side of the coil can be connected into the control circuit to shut the unit down when the temperature falls below a safe condition. An obvious disadvantage is that the plant air supply is reduced; if the building should be subjected to an appreciable negative pressure, unit freeze-up still may occur due to cold air leakage through the fresh air dampers.

Temperature control with steam coils is accomplished by operating a valve that allows steam to flow into the coil. The steam condenses and the water drains away through a steam trap. Control is often an on/off modulation of the steam coil, which does not provide good close temperature control. Improved temperature control can be accomplished by using two control valves instead of one. One valve is usually sized for about two-thirds the capacity and the other valve one-third. Through suitable control arrangements, both valves will provide 100% steam flow when fully opened and various combinations will provide a wide range of temperature control. Controls are complex in this type of unit and care must be taken to insure that pressure drop through the two valve circuits is essentially equal.

Multiple coil steam units (Figure 7-6) and bypass designs (Figure 7-7) are available to improve the temperature control range and help minimize freeze-up. With multiple coil units, the first coil (preheat) is usually sized to raise the air temperature from the design outdoor temperature to at least 40 F. The coil is controlled with an on-off valve which will be fully open whenever the outdoor temperature is below 40 F. The second (reheat) coil is designed to raise the air temperature from 40 F to the desired discharge condition. Temperature control will be satisfactory for most outdoor conditions, but overheating can occur when the outdoor air temperature approaches 40 F (39 F + the rise through the preheat coil can give temperatures of 79-89 F entering the reheat.) Refined temperature control can be accomplished by using a second preheat coil to split the preheat load.

Bypass units incorporate dampers to direct the airflow. When maximum temperature rise is required, all air is directed through the coil. As the outdoor temperature rises, more and more air is diverted through the bypass section until finally all air is bypassed. Controls are relatively simple. The principal disadvantage is that the bypass is not always sized for full air-

flow at the same pressure drop as through the coil, thus (depending on the damper position) the unit may deliver differing airflow rates. Damper airflow characteristics are also a factor. An additional concern is that in some units the air coming through the bypass and entering the fan compartment may have a nonuniform temperature characteristic which might affect the ability to deliver air within a close temperature range.

Another type of bypass design, called integral face and bypass (Figure 7-8),[7.2] features alternating sections of coil and bypass. This design promotes more uniform mixing of the air stream, minimizes any nonuniform flow effect, and, through carefully engineered damper design, permits minimum temperature pickup of about 3 F, even at full steam flow and full bypass.

7.3.3 Hot Water Coil Heating:
Hot water is an excellent heating medium for air heaters. As with steam, there must be a dependable source of water at predetermined temperatures for accurate sizing of the coil. Hot water units are less susceptible to freezing than steam because the pumped water flow ensures that the cooler water can be positively removed from the coil. Practical difficulties and pumping requirements thus far have limited the application of hot water to relatively small systems. For a 100 F air temperature rise and an allowable 100 F water temperature drop, 1 gpm of water will provide heat for only 450 cfm of air. This range can be extended with high temperature hot water systems.

Temperature control for all applications is excellent with hot water coils. Temperatures are easily maintained in a narrow range since the temperature of the hot water can be varied. The operation of the coil control valve to reduce or increase flow for temperature changes does not need to be as precise as with a steam coil.

Hybrid systems using an intermediate heat exchange fluid, such as ethylene glycol water mixtures, also have been installed by industries with critical air supply problems and a desire to eliminate all freeze-up dangers. A primary steam system provides the necessary heat to a converter which supplies a secondary closed loop of the selected heat exchange fluid. The added equipment cost is at least partially offset by the less complex control system.

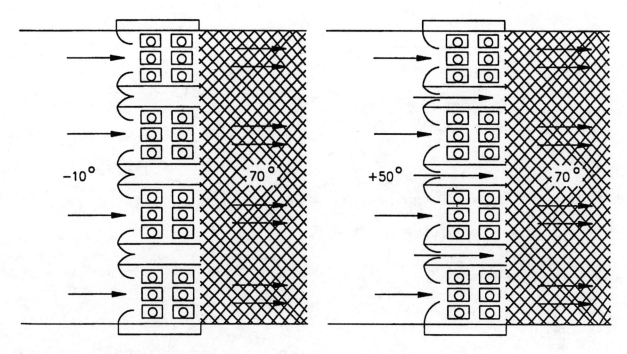

FIGURE 7–8. Integral face and by-pass coil (ref. 7–4)

7.3.4 Indirect Gas/Oil-fired Units: Indirect gas/oil-fired units (Figure 7-9) are widely applied in small industrial and commercial applications. Economics appear to favor their use up to approximately 10,000 cfm; above this size the capital cost of direct-fired air heaters is normally lower. Indirect-fired heaters incorporate a heat exchanger, commonly stainless steel, which effectively separates the incoming air stream from the products of combustion. Positive venting of combustion products is usually accomplished with induced draft fans. Venting is required to minimize interior corrosion damage from condensation in the heat exchanger due to the chilling effect of the incoming cold air stream. The indirect-fired air heater permits the use of room air recirculation since the air stream is separated from the products of combustion. This separation also allows oil to be used as a heat source. Since the supply air is not exposed to an open flame, this type of heater is well suited to ventilate areas such as paint mix rooms and storage areas that have potentially explosive fumes released in the workspace.

Temperature control, "turn-down ratio," is limited to about 3:1 or 5:1 due to burner design limitations and the necessity to maintain minimum temperatures in the heat exchanger and flues. Temperature control can be extended through the use of a bypass system similar to that described for single coil steam air heaters. Bypass units of this design offer the same advantages and disadvantages as the steam bypass units.

Another type of indirect-fired unit incorporates a rotating heat exchanger. Temperature control turn down with these units can be as high as 20:1.

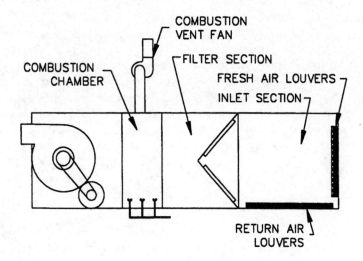

FIGURE 7–9. Indirect-fired unit

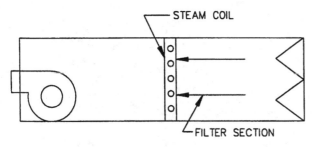

FIGURE 7–10. Direct-fired unit

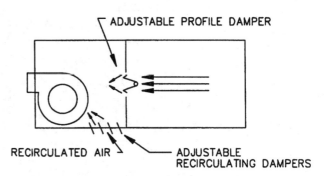

FIGURE 7–11. Direct-fired by-pass unit

7.3.5 Direct Gas-Fired Heaters: Direct-fired heaters, where natural or LPG gas is burned directly in the air stream and the products of combustion are released in the air supply, have been commercially available for some years (Figure 7-10). These units are economical to operate since all of the heating value of the fuel is available to raise the temperature of the air. This results in a net heating efficiency over 90+%. Commercially available burner designs provide turndown ratios from approximately 25:1 to as high as 45:1 permitting good temperature control.

In sizes above 10,000 cfm, the units are relatively inexpensive on a cost per cfm basis; below this capacity, the costs of the additional combustion and safety controls weigh heavily against this design. A further disadvantage is that governmental codes often prohibit the recirculation of room air across the burner. Controls and sensors in these units are designed to provide (1) a positive proof of airflow before the burner can ignite, (2) a timed pre-ignition purge to insure that any leakage gases will be removed from the housing, and (3) a constantly supervised flame operation which includes both flame controls and high temperature limits. For safety purposes the flame controls have a number of pressure sensors and valves in the gas piping to stop flow if significant changes in gas pressure are experienced.

Concerns are often expressed with respect to potentially toxic concentrations of carbon monoxide, oxides of nitrogen, aldehydes, and other contaminants produced by combustion and the resulting gases released into the supply air stream. Practical field evaluations and detailed studies show that with a properly operated, adequately maintained unit, carbon monoxide concentrations should not exceed 5 ppm, and oxides of nitrogen and aldehydes should be well within acceptable limits.[7.3] Before specifying direct-fired equipment, evaluate all the expected contaminants to determine if direct-fired heating is appropriate in the space. For example, direct-fired heating should not be used in heating/ventilating paint mix rooms or fiberglass lay-up operations.

A variation of this unit, known as a bypass design, has gained acceptance in larger plants where there is a desire to circulate large airflows at all times (see Figure 7-11). The large airflow is needed for summer ventilation with outdoor air to reduce hot plant temperatures. In the heating season the outdoor air amount is reduced by recirculating plant air in the air-handling unit. In the bypass design, controls are arranged to reduce the flow of outdoor air with a certain percentage flowing across the burner and the balance of the airflow provided by the permit entry of room air into the fan compartment. In this way the fan airflow rate remains constant and circulation in the space is maintained. It is important to note that the bypass air does not cross the burner; only 100% outdoor air is allowed to pass through the combustion zone. Controls are arranged to regulate outdoor airflow to insure that burner profile velocity (the rate of airflow through the burner plates) remains within the limits specified by the burner manufacturer—usually in the range of 2,000 to 3,000 fpm. This is accomplished by providing a variable profile which changes area as the damper positions changes. A similar type unit has a fixed amount of outside air passing over the burner. This is mixed with return or unheated outside air. The total amount of outside air is varied to provide adequate replacement air and to achieve a building positive pressure. The air passing over the burner is heated to higher temperatures for mixing with the unheated air. A minimum of 20 percent of the total air must pass over the burner to maintain suitable carbon dioxide levels. Direct-fired heaters are not well suited for heating areas at outside doors unless they operate continuously since it takes two to three minutes before it can deliver warm air. This time period is required to purge the unit, have the safety devices in the natural gas line check themselves, and open the gas valve.

With the availability of piped natural gas, many new heating systems are of the direct gas-fired type. The direct gas-fired approach offers a high heating efficiency since the gas is burned in the supply air stream. The related disadvantage of the direct gas-fired system is the requirement to use outside air. Since outside air is brought into the building, it must also be exhausted. In the situation where there is enough process exhaust to remove the outside air, which is heated by the burner, no energy loss occurs. If there is an excessive amount of supply air over the process exhaust, the excess air must be heated and then exhausted. This represents an energy loss.

Inasmuch as there are advantages and disadvantages to both direct-fired and indirect-fired replacement air heaters, a careful consideration of characteristics of each heater should be made. A comparison of the heaters is given in Table 7-3.

TABLE 7-3. Comparison of Heater Advantages and Disadvantages

Advantages	Disadvantages
Direct-fired Unvented:	1. Products of combustion in heater air stream (some CO_2, CO, oxides of nitrogen, and water vapor present.)
1. Good turndown ratio—8:1 in small sizes; 25:1 in large sizes. Better control; lower operating costs.	2. First cost higher in small size units.
2. No vent stack, flue or chimney necessary. Can be located in sidewalls of the building.	3. May be limited in application by governmental regulations. Consult local ordinances.
3. Higher efficiency (90+%). Lower operating costs. (Efficiency based on available sensible heat.)	4. Extreme care must be exercised to prevent minute quantities of chlorinated or other hydrocarbons from entering air intake or toxic products may be produced in heated air.
4. Can heat air over a wide temperature range.	5. Can be used only with natural gas or LPG.
5. First cost lower in large size units.	6. Burner must be tested to assure low CO and oxides of nitrogen content in air stream.
	7. Outside air brought into building may be significantly more than process exhaust causing an excessive amount of heating energy use.
Indirect Exchanger:	
1. No products of combustion are discharged into building.	1. First cost higher in large size units.
2. Allowable in all types of applications and buildings if provided with proper safety controls.	2. Turn down ratio is limited — 3:1 usual, maximum 5:1.
3. Small quantities of chlorinated hydrocarbons will not normally break down on exchanger to form toxic products in heated air.	3. Flue or chimney required. Can be located only where flue or chimney is available.
4. Can be used with oil, LPG, and natural gas as fuel.	4. Low efficiency (80%). Higher operating cost.
5. First cost lower in small size units.	5. Can heat air over a limited range of temperatures.
6. Can be used in air recirculation mode as well as for make-up air.	6. Heat exchanger may be subject to severe corrosion condition. Needs to be checked periodically for leaks after a period of use.
	7. Difficult to provide combustion air from outdoors unless roof or outdoor mounted.

7.3.6 Air Cooling Equipment: Since most industrial facilities have a process heat release, the supply air system is required to reduce the effect of this heat for summer temperature control. The ability to use untempered outside air to obtain space cooling depends upon the amount of heat release from equipment in the space and the outside air temperature. If the supply air temperature needs to be lowered, air-cooling is accomplished by means of a cooling coil (mechanical cooling) or an evaporative cooling unit. A detailed discussion regarding air-cooling can be found in Chapters 19 and 21 of the ASHRAE Handbook of HVAC Systems and Equipment.[7.4] Cooling is utilized for process requirements and to provide summer heat relief.

To provide summer relief of hot space temperatures, a greater amount of outside supply air may be needed than that required for replacement air purposes. In this situation, the use of cooling may be justified since a lower airflow is required compared to using untempered outdoor air ventilation to achieve reasonable space temperatures. When using outside air for cooling the supply air temperature rise is limited to 15 to 20 F when trying to maintain space temperatures less than 100 F. If a cooling unit is used, the entering temperature is lower, allowing a supply air temperature rise of 30 to 40 F. Thus with cooling less air flow is needed.

7.3.7 Mechanical Cooling: With mechanical cooling, the cooling coil has a chilled fluid flowing through it to remove the heat from the air stream. This heat exchange reduces the temperature of the air stream and warms the chilled fluid. The fluid typically is a refrigerant or water. Air handling units that use a refrigerant have a compressor and condenser nearby to change the refrigerant gas back into a liquid and reduce its temperature. The act of quickly reducing the pressure on the liquid allows it to change into a gas and become cold, thus chilling the coil. In a chilled water unit, water of approximately 45 F flows through the cooling coil. The water is chilled by a central chiller and pumped through a pipe distribution system to each air-handling unit. Commercial and light industrial type AHUs most often use the refrigerant type system commonly called direct expansion (DX) cooling equipment. The first cost of the chilled water system is higher than the DX system, but it offers longer component life, reduced maintenance, and lower energy costs.

The use of a cooling coil often can reduce both air temperature and humidity. The humidity reduction is caused by dropping the air temperature below its dew point. The objective is to get the air temperature cold enough so the the concentration of water vapor in the air can no longer be maintained. The air begins to fog and water droplets called condensate begin to form on the cooling coil. The condensing of the water vapor to reduce humidity requires additional cooling over and above that for reducing the air temperature.

7.3.8 Evaporative Cooling: Evaporative cooling systems rely upon the evaporation of water vapor to lower the air temperature. The air also becomes more humid since the water vapor evaporates into the air stream. In the evaporative cooling unit, air absorbs water vapor as it passes through a wetted pad or through a water spray zone. Energy is given up by the air to evaporate the water and the air temperature is reduced. Since evaporative coolers raise the relative humidity in the space, the impact on the industrial processes should be evaluated. Some evaporative cooling systems have their own pumps and water circulating systems. Others rely on the pressure in the water line to generate a water spray. Evaporative coolers are commonly used in dry areas of the world, but can be applied to almost all areas of the United States. They are also used in industrial applications that have high replacement airflow or large internal heat releases. For an evaporative cooling unit to operate at peak efficiency the pads must be well wetted and reasonably clean. Spray nozzles must be kept free of clogging deposits. The following formulae can be used to identify the temperature leaving an evaporative cooler:

Dry-Bulb Temperature Leaving = Dry-Bulb
Temperature Entering − Efficiency Factor (Dry-Bulb
Temperature Entering − Wet-Bulb Temperature Entering)

The Wet-Bulb temperature is the value measured using a psychrometer as discussed in Chapter 2. The efficiency is normally 80%.

7.3.9 Air Filtration: Supply air filtration for workspaces is not a major concern for most industrial processes; however, seasonal factors such as insects, pollen, organic debris, etc., may require removal before the air is supplied. The filters are typically selected on the basis of keeping the supply air unit clean. However, in some cases, filters are selected for employee health considerations or process concerns. When outside air sources are contaminated, air cleaning is required to remove those contaminants. Filters for normal service typically have a 30% contaminant removal rate based on the ASHRAE Atmospheric Dust Spot Efficiency Test (Standard 52.1-92).[7.5] When a process requires a high level of cleanliness, such as food processing, painting, or assembly of parts where a fine dust is a detriment, a more efficient filtration system is required. Refer to Chapter 4 for more discussion regarding air cleaning equipment.

7.3.10 System Temperature Control: Some processes require a space that has close control of temperature and humidity. This often requires both heating and cooling of the supply air to achieve the desired thermal conditions. Often these spaces also require humidification if the air is too dry; a condition that is most likely in the winter. An example could be a powder painting operation that requires air entering the paint spray booth to be 70 F and 50% relative humidity (RH).

This temperature condition is necessary to achieve proper drying of the paint and to prevent arcing and sparks inside the booth (a fire prevention concern).

In summer the supply air would need to be cooled below 51 F to condense enough water vapor from the air to achieve the 50 % RH. This air would then need to be reheated to raise the temperature to the 70 F goal. The layout of the air handling unit would have the cooling coil followed by the reheat coil.

In winter the air must be heated and water vapor added to the air to achieve the desired 70 F, 50% RH. A heating coil or gas-fired device can be utilized. Either a humidifier or an evaporative cooler is used to add humidity. If a humidifier is used, the heat in the vapor must be identified and the energy of the heater reduced accordingly. Refer to Figure 7- 12 for a representation of the performance of this equipment during the cooling and heating seasons. As can be seen, on a cold day the air must be heated to a temperature of 99 F to achieve a condition of 70 F and 50% RH. The proper air handling arrangement would have the humidifier behind the heating device.

The closeness of control desired will dictate the component type to be utilized in the system. Heating and cooling water coils provide the best control with gas-fired equipment providing the least level of control.

7.3.11 Unit Location: Air supply units are normally located in the upper level of the plant or on the roof. In some recent designs these units have been placed just below the roof (in the truss space) and have a catwalk system for ease of access. Rooftop units create the need for people to walk on the roofs. It is good practice to provide a walkway to minimize excessive wear on the single-ply roofs in common use today. Some systems have the unit placed along an outer wall inside the building. Outside air is mixed with room air to satisfy general building heating and replacement air requirements. This type of system has little distribution duct and its ventilation effectiveness is low except in small buildings.

7.3.12 Size and Cost Considerations: There are several cost considerations to a supply air system installed in an industrial facility. First, the relative cost for the supply air unit decreases as the size increases. Some cost elements of the unit increase with unit size: the unit housing, fan, filters, and coils. The unit's control cost depends on the control functions being performed and is approximately the same for all size units. Anther major cost element is the air distribution system; i.e. the duct work and diffusers/grilles. The duct work and diffuser costs increase as the system gets larger. The final cost consideration is installation which includes lifting the unit; structural steel supports, electrical, natural gas, and other piping system hook-ups; unit start-up; and warranty. Installation cost is somewhat independent of unit size and increases at a rate slower than the unit size.

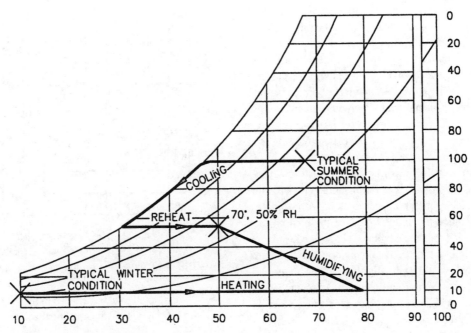

FIGURE 7–12. Air heating and cooling requirements

7.4 SUPPLY AIR DISTRIBUTION

In an industrial facility, the supply air distribution plays an important role in the success of controlling airborne contaminants. If contaminants are controlled by local exhaust ventilation, the supply/replacement air should be introduced into the space in a way that does not interfere with the capture effectiveness of the exhaust hoods. Such interferences are created when supply/replacement air is introduced at an excessive velocity into the vicinity of an exhaust hood, thus interrupting the protective flow path of the hood's exhaust air volume.

There are additional supply air design considerations when dilution ventilation is used rather than local exhaust ventilation to control contaminants. These include the location of the supply air outlets, the rate of airflow, and the placement of the exhaust air intakes. Refer to Chapter 2 for more discussion and system sizing considerations. The choice of dilution ventilation vs. local exhaust ventilation depends on the nature and quantity of the contaminants and the workspace. Several supply air design approaches are discussed in the following sections. Regardless of the selected supply air design, emphasis should be given to avoid creation of a working environment undesirable for space inhabitants.

7.4.1 Unidirectional or Plug Airflow:
The use of non-turbulent or laminar supply airflow is required in situations where high cleanliness or extreme contaminant control is desired. This approach has clean supply air moving across the space area in a uniform direction and the air is removed from the space at a location opposite the supply air entry point. This design scheme is often referred to as unidirectional, laminar, or plug airflow. It is normally employed to protect workers and critical processes. In addition to careful consideration of the supply air distribu-

tion design, physical obstructions such as partitions or furniture should be minimized to avoid any turbulent airflow. Examples of this type of supply air design can be can be found in industries or activities associated with firing ranges, pharmaceutical manufacturing, semiconductor manufacturing, healthcare treatment, aerospace, and painting operations.

For areas that require non-turbulent air for proper exhaust system operation, one approach is to pass air through a supply air plenum built as part of a perforated ceiling and/or through perforated duct. The ceiling plenum or duct runs should cover as large an area as possible to diffuse the airflow. A plenum wall providing cross-flow ventilation should be used when the workers are positioned between the supply air system and the contaminant source or exhaust hood. This approach should not be used for design velocities at the worker over 100 fpm since a low pressure zone can be created causing contaminants to be carried into the worker's breathing zone.

Perforated drop-type ceilings work best in spaces with ceiling heights of less than 15 feet. Hoist tracks, lighting, and fire protection systems can be built into the ceiling. In some cases, fire protection will be required above and below the ceiling. Use the perforated duct approach when ceiling heights are over 15 feet. Perforated duct manufacturers typically have computer programs to assist designers in determining duct sizes, shapes, and types as well as the location of pressure adjusting devices such as orifice plates and reducers. Airflow delivery in large bays may require supplemental air delivered at work stations to provide comfortable conditions for workers.

How the supply air is fed into a plenum is critical to its performance. High velocity flow into the plenum can cause turbulence problems similar to large diffusers. Air that is introduced into a plenum at an excessive velocity will bounce off the floor or an opposite wall causing turbulence inside the plenum. This can cause re-entrainment of contaminants from the room into the clean replacement air via a low-pressure area created near the introduction point. The low-pressure phenomenon also creates uneven replacement air distribution in the room. Providing a wide replacement air plenum and slowly introducing supply air into the plenum will reduce the problem. However, space for a wide plenum is frequently unavailable. One solution is to feed the plenum with a perforated duct to diffuse the air inside the plenum. Ensure that the proper pressure adjusting devices (e.g. orifice plates) are installed per the manufacturer's recommendations. Another approach to distribute air from either a ceiling or wall-mounted plenum is to design the plenum face with two overlapping perforated plates, one fixed and one adjustable, at the time of air flow balancing, located 2 - 6 inches apart. Air flowing through slightly offset holes will encounter more resistance; thus, air quantities passing through the low-flow areas will increase. The holes must be small enough to fine-tune the airflow from the plenum. Openings of 3/8" diameter in the adjustable plates with sufficient numbers to provide a velocity of 2000 fpm seems to work well.

This approach is used in clean room and paint booth designs to achieve a high control on air cleanliness. For these applications, clean supply air flows through a grid of filters in the ceiling and is exhausted at floor level. Flow velocities in the range of 50 to 100 fpm are common.

7.4.2 Mixing Ventilation Systems: The mixing approach to the supply air ventilation system relies on high-velocity air streams leaving supply diffusers/grilles as the means of delivering air to the workspace. These jets of supply air quickly entrain and mix with the space air. As shown in Figure 7 -13, the average temperature of this air stream begins to approach the space temperature as the velocity of the jets slows. This example has air leaving a diffuser at a velocity of 2000 fpm and a temperature of 20 F below room temperature. At a work station twenty-five feet from the diffuser, the average speed of the jet has dropped to 200 fpm and the air temperature will approach the room temperature of 86 F. The actual conditions depend upon the diffuser selected, but velocities of 100 to 200 fpm and temperatures of one to two degrees below the room temperature are likely.

Mixing systems dilute airborne contaminants the same way that the air jets dilute temperature. Care should should be taken to direct the supply air jets so as not to disturb the performance of local exhaust systems. Otherwise the resulting air currents can sweep contaminants away from exhaust hoods rendering them less effective. The local exhaust hoods may then require additional airflow to control the contaminants. Increasing exhaust airflow also increases energy costs due to the need for larger fans and motors. In extreme cases of high room air motion, the hoods remain ineffective even with substantial increases in airflow. Hence, workers could still be overexposed

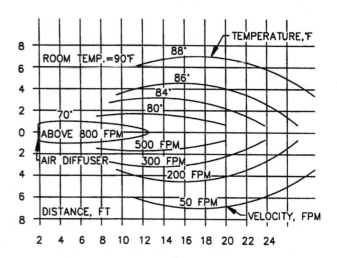

FIGURE 7–13. Air jet temperature and velocity profile

even with a local exhaust system in place. Therefore, locate air supply discharges away from local exhaust hoods.

If the supply air system does not sufficiently cool the employees, pedestal fans are often used for greater air movement. Care must be used in their placement since pedestal fans can degrade contaminant control by causing turbulence near local exhaust hoods.

Mixing systems can have air outlets in the truss space (20 feet or higher) blowing downward or placed at lower levels. For those systems where the air is discharged below the truss, duct routing must be coordinated with the process layout and the needs of the process equipment. Quite often the use of cranes, gantries, conveyors, and other material handling equipment greatly reduces the access to space for routing duct below the truss. A common low-level discharge height is 10 feet above the floor with the air directed horizontally with a slight downward deflection. The lower-height-discharge approach provides a cooler workspace and should be considered. Supply air not removed by process exhaust systems is normally removed from the building through the use of roof-mounted exhaust fans.

7.4.3 Air Displacement Ventilation Systems: Areas that require year-round cooling due to process heat can utilize a nonturbulent approach to adding air into the workspace called air displacement. Air displacement ventilation systems were first applied in the welding industry in 1978, and now are widely used in Scandinavian countries. This type of supply air system relies upon the natural effect of warm air rising. Provision is made to remove the warm air at the top of the space. The supply air is introduced into the space through low-velocity diffusers placed near the floor. The objective of the air displacement system is to achieve air quality conditions in the occupied zone that are similar to those of the supply air.

As illustrated in Figure 7-14, there are two air distribution zones in an air displacement system, the upper and lower strata.

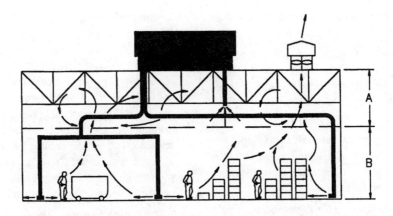

A – STRATIFICATION LEVEL
B – LOWER ZONE OR DISPLACEMENT LEVEL

FIGURE 7–14. Air flow in displacement ventilation system

The upper zone is formed at the elevation where the supply air quantity equals the total air moving upward in the thermal plumes caused by the process heat. As this warm air rises, it entrains adjacent air and the total volume of moving air increases. When this total air volume equals the supply air, there is no more incoming air to feed the plume and recirculation of space air begins. The elevation where the recirculation starts is called the stratification level. Properly designed air displacement systems have the stratification level well above the occupied lower zone. The height of this lower zone is dependent on the amount of supply air, the nature of the heat sources, and the air distribution across the floor.

When designing a displacement ventilation system, the following parameters need to be considered: (1) supply airflow rate and temperature; (2) air temperature at floor level; (3) vertical temperature gradient; (4) maximum air velocity at floor level; and (5) first cost, operating cost, and energy consumption.[7.6]

The supply air temperature can be 4 F to 6 F warmer than that used in a mixing type system to achieve the same occupied space temperature.[7.7] The vertical temperature gradiant or the temperature rise of the supply air compared to the exhaust is greater in the displacement type system. Typical temperature differences compared with increases in building height are:

Building Height, Ft	Temperature Rise. F[7.8]
Less than 10	11 - 13
10 to 20	15 - 18
over 30	18 - 22

This increase in temperature difference will reduce the amount of exhaust air required.

The advantage of not significantly mixing the space air with the supply air is a workspace that is cooler and has less airborne contaminants. The process heat and many of its associated contaminants are carried away as the warm air rises. Spe-

cial provisions must be made for supply air outlets. Since they are on the floor, they must be coordinated with the process equipment layout to allow access to operate, service and maintain the equipment. Air outlets need to be placed a reasonable distance from each other to avoid drafts caused by the high quantity of supply air leaving the diffusers.

7.4.4 Duct Materials: Supply duct materials are generally Sheet Metal and Air Conditioning Contractors National Association (SMACNA) Class I or II medium gauge sheet metal but other materials such as specially coated cloth, may be used. The material does not need to be as strong as exhaust duct for several reasons:

1. It is not exposed to the transport of abrasive process contaminants
2. The system operates at a relative low pressure
3. Much of the duct is on the downstream side of the fan and is under a positive pressure
4. Duct leaks do not pose a health hazard and have little affect on system performance.

The duct needs to be strong enough to last in its environment. Often the abuse of plant operations requires a heavier duct system than one which is hidden above a ceiling. It needs to be able to withstand the rigors of people walking on it and being hit by forklift trucks.

If too light a sheetmetal gauge is selected, fan noise may be more pronounced due to vibration of the duct. Metal stiffeners attached to the outside of the duct help prevent this type of noise. SMACNA standards provide detailed information on duct construction.[7.9, 7.10]

7.4.5 Sheet Metal: Sheet metal materials typically include galvanized steel, uncoated steel, stainless steel and aluminum. In addition to round ducts, oval or rectangular ducts are often used in order to adjust the cross-sectional area to avoid obstructions in the building space. SMACNA standards use pressure ranges to classify duct thickness and construction methods. The allowable duct leakage and acoustical considerations also dictate the construction methods.

7.4.6 Plastic: Thermosetting (glass-fiber reinforced polyester) and thermoplastic (polyvinyl chloride, polyethylene, polypropylene, acrylonitrile butadiene styrene) construction standards are provided by SMACNA's Thermoplastic Duct Construction Manual. [7.11]

7.4.7 Fiberglass: For acoustical reasons, supply duct may be lined for better sound adsorption. The lining used is a fiberglass-based material treated to minimize moisture absorption. The coating also is mold and fungus resistant.

7.4.8 Supply Air System Design Considerations: A properly designed ventilation system must adhere to building codes, requirements established by National Fire Protection Association (NFPA), and standards developed by SMACNA. There are also standards published by ASHRAE, ANSI, and AMCA as well as those developed by specific industrial corporations.

There are several design tools currently available to aid in the design of industrial ventilation systems. Many involve rules of thumb, spreadsheet evaluations, or simple one or two-dimensional models. These design tools are used to evaluate building air balance, heating and cooling loads, special pressures, smoke/contaminant migration, and migration and dilution of gases and/or fumes.

With the recent availability of low-cost, powerful computers, designers have been applying Computational Fluid Dynamics (CFD) to the analysis of ventilation system performance. With CFD, the geometry of a space can be configured and airflow rates, temperatures, contaminant migration, and exhaust capture efficiency can be evaluated. The CFD model divides time and distance into discrete intervals. The modeled space is divided into many smaller volumes that interact with each other based on fundamental conservation equations. An iterative process is used to calculate the results and computation times can take a number of hours. [7.12]

There are numerous computer programs, nomagraphs, and other catalog-type data available from manufacturers for selecting and sizing system components. Air handling unit fans, coils, filters, and humidifiers are selected with this information. Elements in the air distribution system (duct, diffusers, etc.) are also selected with these aids. It should be noted that supply air duct pressure loss calculations are much easier to accomplish than those for exhaust air systems. The air is clean and dampers are used to adjust airflow through the duct system. Duct velocity is typically limited to 2500 to 3000 fpm to avoid excessive noise and minimize horsepower requirements of the fan motor. Diffusers are selected to obtain the desired air throw or air distribution in the space. Dampers in the branch ducts limit the airflow to each branch and are used to balance the system.

7.5 AIRFLOW RATE

The design supply airflow rate depends on several factors, including health and comfort requirements. Sensible heat can be removed through simple air dilution (see Chapter 2, Section 2.14.) "Nuisance" or undesirable contaminants can also be reduced by dilution with outdoor air as described in Chapter 2. For many industrial facilities, experience shows that when the air supply is properly distributed to the working level (i.e., in the lower 8-10 ft of the space), outdoor air supply of 1-2 cfm/ft^2 of floor space will give good results. This flow rate will normally satisfy the process exhaust quantity as well as circulate adequate air for building heating requirements and general ventilation. Specific quantities of minimum outdoor air supply may be obtained from building and health codes or from criteria developed by groups such as ASHRAE.

7.5.1 Air Changes: "Number of air changes per minute or per hour" is the ratio of the airflow ventilation rate (per minute or per hour) to the room volume. "Air changes per hour" or "air changes per minute" is a poor basis for ventilation criteria where environmental control of hazards, heat, and/or odors is required. The required ventilation depends on the generation rate and toxicity of the contaminant not on the size of the room in which it occurs. For example, let us assume a situation where an airflow of 11,650 cfm would be required to control solvent vapors by dilution. The operation may be conducted in either of two rooms, but in either case, 11,650 cfm is the required ventilation. The "air changes," however, would be quite different for the two rooms. As can be seen in Table 7-4, for the same "air change" rate, a high ceiling space will require more ventilation than a low ceiling space of the same floor area. Thus, there is little relationship between "air changes" and the required contaminant control.

TABLE 7-4. Air Exchanges Vs. Room Size

Room Size	Room ft^3	Air changes/ minute	Air changes/ hour
40 x 40 x 12 high	19,200	11,650/19,200 = 0.61	36
40 x 40 x 20 high	32,000	11,650/32,000 = 0.364	22

The "air change" basis for ventilation does have some applicability for relatively standard situations such as office buildings and school rooms where a standard ventilation rate is reasonable. Building codes for the design of certain types of buildings often use a minimum air change per hour for specific spaces. For example, a flammable storage room requires six air changes per hour using OSHA requirements. This approach is easily understood and reduces the engineering effort required to establish a design criteria for ventilation. It is this ease of application, in fact, which often leads to lack of investigation of the real engineering parameters involved with correspondingly poor results.

7.6 HEATING, COOLING AND OTHER OPERATING COSTS

Operating the supply air can be a major expense for a manufacturing plant. In addition to heating the air during the cold weather and possibly cooling in the hotter months, there are other operational concerns. Perhaps the highest energy user is the electric motor that creates the air movement. A rough estimate value for motor size is one horsepower for every 1,000 cfm of airflow. Other operational costs are air cleaning component replacement, control calibration, and component maintenance.

7.6.1 Estimating Heating Energy Use:
Supply air temperature is controlled by the demand for heating and cooling. Factors to consider in maintaining a comfortable work environment for occupants are: setpoint temperature, humidity control, air distribution, and airflow rate. Where high internal heat loads are to be controlled, a low air supply temperature can be obtained by reducing the amount of heat supplied to the air during the winter months and by deliberately cooling the air in the summer. When a large airflow rate is delivered at approximately space temperatures or below, the distribution of the air becomes vitally important in order to maintain satisfactory environmental conditions for the persons in the space.

Maximum utilization of the supply air is achieved when the air is distributed in the "living zone" of the space—below the 10 foot level (see Figure 7-15).[7.4] When delivered in this manner, where the majority of the people and processes are located, maximum ventilation results with minimum air handling. During the warm months of the year, large airflow in the working space at relatively high velocities is welcomed by the workers. During the winter months, however, care must be taken to insure that air velocities over the person, except when extremely high heat loads are involved, are kept within acceptable values (see Table 2-3). To accomplish this, the air can be distributed uniformly in the space or where required for worker comfort. Heavy-duty, adjustable, directional grilles and louvers have proven to be very successful in allowing individual workers to direct the air as needed.[7.1] Light gauge, stamped grilles intended for commercial use are not satisfactory. Suitable control must be provided to accommodate seasonal and even daily requirements with a minimum of attention by supervision or maintenance forces. *Warning: when the work process generates a hazardous contaminant, worker adjustable supply grilles may be incompatible with the contaminant control scheme.*

7.6.2 Air Supply vs. Plant Heating Costs:
Even if the supply air were drawn into the building only by the action of the exhaust fans, there will be an added burden on the plant heating system during the winter months and fuel costs will rise. Normally such a system would use unit heaters for building temperature control and numerous openings in the building for outside air supply. Compared to a situation where the same flow rate of outdoor air is introduced through properly designed supply replacement air heaters, experience has shown that the overall fuel cost is less than or equal to that consumed by the unit heater system. A partial explanation of this savings is more efficient heat transfer. The most important factor, however, is that a well-designed air supply system is

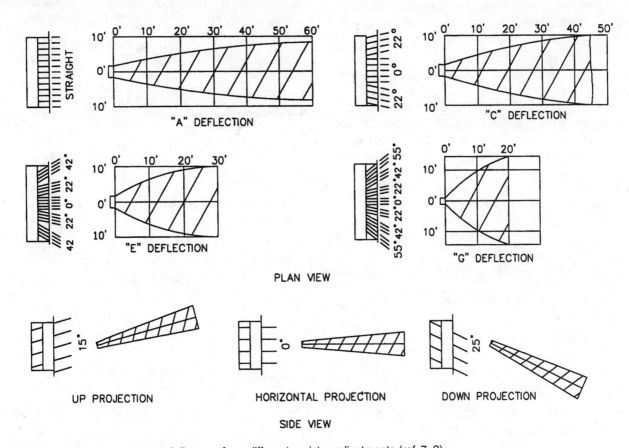

FIGURE 7-15. Throw patterns and distance from different register adjustments (ref. 7-2)

not dependent on the plant space heating system; rather, the two systems operate in an independent fashion. The air supply system and the plant heating system can be understood best by considering the building as a whole. In order for a temperature equilibrium to be established, the heat outflow from the building must balance the heat inflow. To obtain additional energy saving during downtime, one should design the supply system to provide sufficient heating to counter air entering the building through infiltration and to prevent freezing.

7.6.3 Cost of Heating Supply Air: The cost of heating supply air is a significant portion of the annual operating cost of a ventilation system. Processes requiring cooling also need to be evaluated for their energy and operating costs. Occupant comfort is more important than saving a few dollars in energy costs. Recent indoor air quality studies quantify diminished productivity when workers are uncomfortable. In addition to the equipment first cost, local building codes, and environmental regulations, designer experience in utility incentives and operating costs are involved in purchasing decisions.

ASHRAE, the U. S. Department of Energy, and others have developed equations and computer programs to determine the life-cycle costs of various air handling equipment. The equations and programs are not intended to determine the annual utility bill. Instead, they help compare the costs of various options in providing heating and cooling to a variety of industrial and commercial operations. The following two equations may be used to estimate replacement air heating costs on an hourly and yearly basis. They are based on average usage schedules and typical weather conditions rather than worst case conditions and maximum usage.

Since there is an allowance for the efficiency of the supply air unit, these equations will tend to give an incorrect low result if air is allowed to enter by infiltration only. They are also based on normal temperatures, moisture, moisture ratios, and standard atmospheric pressure of 14.7 psi (101.4 kPa). Due to the heavy nature of the work in many industrial facilities, it may be more desirable to have cooler supply air than for an office setting. Table 7-5 gives equation values (N) for supply air delivered at 70 F and 65 F. The moisture content, sometimes called the humidity ratio (W), is assumed to be 0.01 pounds of water per pound of dry air.

$$C_1 = \text{Hourly cost} = 0.001 \frac{QN}{q} c \qquad [7.1]$$

$$C_2 = \text{Yearly cost} = \frac{0.154(Q)(dg)(T)(c)}{q} \qquad [7.2]$$

where: Q = airflow rate, cfm

N = required heat, BTU/hr/1000 cfm (Table 7-5 and Table 7-7)

T = operating time, hours/week

q = available heat per unit of fuel (Table 7-6)

dg = annual degree days (Table 7-7)

c = cost of fuel, $/unit

TABLE 7-5. Required Heat for Outside Air Temperatures

Av. Outside Air Temperature, F	N, Required Heat, BTU/hr/1,000 cfm @ 70 F	N, Required Heat, BTU/hr/1,000 cfm @ 65 F
0	77,000	71,500
5	71,500	66,000
10	66,000	60,500
15	60,500	55,000
20	55,000	49,500
25	49,500	44,000
30	44,000	38.500
35	38,500	33,000
40	33,000	27,500
45	27,500	22,000
50	22,000	16,500
55	16,500	11,000
60	11,000	5,500
65	5,500	—

NOTE: Sensible Heat Equation used: q = 1.1 (cfm) delta t. Moisture content is assumed to be 0.01 pounds of moisture per pound of dry air.

TABLE 7-6. Available Heat per Unit of Fuel

Fuel	Btu Per Unit	Efficiency %	Available Btu Per Unit
Coal	12,000 Btu/lb	50	6,000
Oil	142,000 Btu/gal	75	106,500
Gas			
Heat Exchanger	1,000 Btu/ft	80	800
Direct-Fired	1,000 Btu/ft	90	900

EXAMPLE PROBLEM 1

Find the hourly and yearly cost of tempering 10,000 cfm of supply air to 70 F in St. Louis, Missouri, using oil at $1.35/gallon.

Average winter temperature = 31 F

$$\text{Hourly cost} = 0.001\frac{QN}{q}c$$

$$= 0.001 \times 10^4 \times \frac{42,000}{106,500} \times \$1.35 = \$5.32$$

$$\text{Yearly Cost} = \frac{(0.154)(10^4)(6023)(40)}{106,500} \times \$1.35$$

$$= \$4,700 \text{ (assuming 40 hr/week of operation)}$$

The yearly cost is more representative because both the length and severity of the heating season are taken into account.

7.6.4 Cooling Energy Considerations: The values for heating air presented in Table 7-5 considered only raising the air temperature which is sensible heat energy. If the quantity of water vapor in the air is changed, a latent energy transfer takes place. In most cooling system operations, a latent energy transfer takes place to lower the air humidity level. This latent energy transfer occurs when the air is cooled to a temperature below the dew point of the air. When this occurs, water is condensed from the air stream onto the cooling coil.

In plant operations, the humid air can come from the outside or be created by a process that releases water vapor into the general air.

The cooling system is sized to overcome several energy sources: the heat released to the space by the process, the heat absorbed by the building structure (since the outdoor air is warmer than the inside space temperature), the heat absorbed by the building structure by solar radiation, and the heat caused by the outside supply air being warmer than the desired space temperature. The internal heat released by the process varies with the process rate of production. A good measure of this variance is to observe the changes in the electrical use over a time period. Most other cooling loads are weather dependent.

7.6.5 Filter Replacement: As the filter works to remove airborne material from the air stream, it becomes saturated with

TABLE 7-7. Heating Degree Day Normals and Average Winter Temperatures

City	Albany	Boston	Chicago	Cleveland	Detroit	Minneapolis	NY	Philadelphia	Pittsburgh	St. Louis	Wash., DC
Avg Temp (F) Dec-Feb	24	22.4	25	28	25.9	16	33.2	33.3	29	32.2	33.4
Discharge Air Temp (F)						Heating Degree Days					
80	11782	10409	10613	11343	10959	13176	9284	9652	10797	8943	8422
79	11425	10049	10277	10982	10605	12826	8937	9300	10436	8624	8089
78	11062	9690	9940	10621	10256	12478	8596	8954	10076	8310	7764
77	10709	9242	9610	10265	9914	12135	8265	8619	9726	8003	7446
76	10356	8994	9283	9915	9581	11797	7938	8285	9379	7702	7139
75	10009	8652	8972	9570	9247	11475	7620	7959	9036	7413	6835
74	9669	8317	8656	9229	8920	11142	7308	7641	8702	7121	6538
73	9333	7790	8349	8898	8599	10816	7004	7328	8372	6839	6250
72	9007	7668	8046	8567	8291	10496	6706	7028	8050	6560	5974
71	8682	7354	7750	8248	7981	10180	6421	6728	7740	6289	5703
70	8364	7046	7468	7928	7678	9870	6146	6438	7429	6023	5438
69	8256	6749	7183	7617	7383	9567	5871	6158	7127	5767	5179
68	7750	6458	6905	7313	7100	9269	5606	5886	6833	5523	4929
67	7452	6175	6635	7016	6816	8975	5349	5618	6546	5277	4690
66	7162	5903	6373	6722	6543	8687	5101	5360	6272	5053	4455
65	6881	5633	6122	6445	6278	8410	4858	5109	5997	4822	4229
64	6607	5370	5875	6165	6020	8131	4621	4864	5734	4595	4014
63	6340	5118	5638	5897	5772	7858	4394	4628	5483	4379	3798
62	6081	4873	5399	5636	5533	7590	4176	4397	5234	4168	3588
61	5829	4643	5164	5381	5290	7339	3957	4172	5006	3963	3383
60	5586	4399	4936	5140	5054	7086	3747	3952	4769	3761	3182

that material and the pressure drop for air to pass through the filter increases. As the pressure drop rises, the airflow decreases unless the fan speed is increased or other adjustments are made. Unless a replacement filter is installed, the original filter will become blinded allowing little or no air to pass. Refer to Chapter 4, Section 9 for more information regarding supply air filter efficiency and application by type.

7.6.6 System Maintenance: Maintenance of the supply air system is mainly associated with the supply air unit and its operating controls. In addition to filter replacement, there are fan bearings to grease and belts to replace. Coils and drain pans must be cleaned and dampers lubricated. If the system includes humidifying equipment, there are spray nozzles to clean/replace and there may be a pump to service as well as controls to check and adjust. A major maintenance issue is the recalibration of the systems controls. If the controls are not routinely calibrated, operating set points may drift resulting in energy waste and poor system performance.

7.7 CONSERVATION APPROACHES

The costs of supply and exhaust air are represented by both the capital and the annual operating cost. The costs associated with heating can be quite sizable in northern climates. There are four methods by which the cost of heating and cooling a large flow of outdoor air can be reduced: (1) reduction in the total flow of air handled, (2) delivery of untempered outdoor air to the space, (3) recovery of energy from the exhaust air, and (4) recovery of warm, uncontaminated air from processes.

The successful application of these engineering methods without reduction in health hazard control and without impairing the inplant environment requires careful consideration. Special care must be taken if mixing the air from several spaces where the combination of contaminants may result in a more hazardous condition.

7.7.1 Reduced Flow Rate: A reduction of total airflow should be accomplished only after conducting a careful inventory of all exhaust and supply systems in the plant. Determine which are necessary, which can be replaced with more efficient systems or hood designs, and which systems may have been rendered obsolete by changes.

Numerous hood designs presented in Chapter 10 are intended to provide for adequate contaminant capture without unnecessarily high airflow rates. For instance, the use of a horizontal sliding sash in the laboratory hood can provide a 30% saving in exhaust airflow without impairing capture velocity. The saving is accomplished by having at least a third of the face area covered by sash. (See VS-35-01 for a picture of this hood type.) The use of a tailored hood design, such as the evaporation hood shown in VS-35-40, provides good contaminant capture with far lower exhaust flow rates than would be required for a typical laboratory bench hood. Low Volume-High Velocity hoods and systems such as those illustrated in

VS-40-01 through VS-40-20 are used for many portable hand tool and fixed machining operations and can provide contaminant capture at far lower air handling requirements.

Throughout industry, window exhaust fans and power roof exhausters are often used to remove heat or nuisance contaminants that could be captured more readily at the source with lower airflow rates. Many roof exhausters were installed initially to combat problems caused by a lack of replacement air. When air supply and balanced ventilation conditions are established, their use may no longer be necessary.

7.7.2 Industrial Exhaust Recirculation: Where large amounts of air are exhausted from a room or building in order to remove particulate, gases, fumes, or vapors, an equivalent amount of fresh tempered replacement air must be supplied to the room. If the amount of replacement air is large, the cost of energy to condition the air can be very high. Recirculation of the exhaust air after thorough cleaning is one method of reducing the amount of energy consumed. Acceptance of such recirculating systems will depend on the degree of health hazard associated with the particular contaminant being exhausted as well as other safety, technical, and economic factors. A logic diagram listing the factors that must be evaluated is provided in Figure 7-16.[7.13]

Essentially this diagram states that recirculation may be permitted if the following conditions are met:

1. The chemical, physical, and toxicological characteristics of the chemical agents in the air stream to be recirculated must be identified and evaluated. Exhaust air containing chemical agents whose toxicity is unknown or for which there is no established safe exposure level should not be recirculated. Exhaust air from processes using or generating explosive agents should not be recirculated if another process or system may add additional amounts of that agent to the air stream.

2. All governmental regulations regarding recirculation must be reviewed to determine whether recirculation is restricted or prohibited for the system under review.

3. The effect of a recirculation system malfunction must be considered. Recirculation should not be attempted if a malfunction could result in exposure levels that would cause worker health problems. Substances which can cause permanent damage or significant physiological harm from a short overexposure shall not be recirculated.

4. The availability of a suitable air cleaner must be determined. An air cleaning device capable of providing an effluent air stream contaminant concentration sufficiently low to achieve acceptable workplace concentrations must be available. For example, a scrubber or mist collector may provide suitable cleaning efficiency but adds significant humidity to the air.

5. The effects of minor contaminants should be reviewed. For example, welding fumes can be effectively

I. INITIAL DECISION

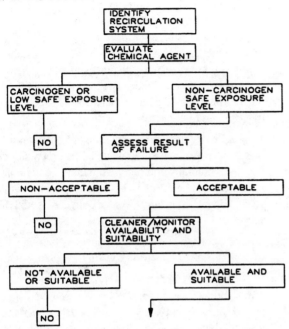

II. DESIGN AND ASSESSMENT

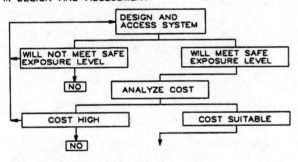

III. SYSTEM EVALUATION

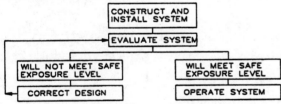

FIGURE 7–16. Recirculation decision logic

removed from an air stream with a fabric filter; however, if the welding process produces oxides of nitrogen, recirculation could cause a concentration of these gases to reach an unacceptable level.

6. Recirculation systems must incorporate a monitoring system that provides an accurate warning or signal capable of initiating corrective action or process shutdown before harmful concentrations of the recirculated agents build up in the workplace. Monitoring may be accomplished by a number of methods and must be

determined by the type and hazard of the substance. Examples include area monitoring for nuisance type substances and secondary high efficiency filter pressure drop indicators or on-line monitors for more hazardous materials. Explosive agent concentration must be monitored to assure the concentration stays well below the Lower Explosive Limit (vapors) or the minimum explosive concentration (particulates).

7.7.3 Evaluation of Employee Exposure Levels: Under equilibrium conditions, the following equations may be used to determine the concentration of a contaminant permitted to be recirculated in the return air stream:

$$C_R = \frac{(1 - \eta)(C_E - K_R C_M)}{1 - [(K_R)(1 - \eta)]} \qquad [7.3]$$

Where: C_R = air cleaner discharge concentration after recirculation, mg/m^3

η = fractional air cleaner efficiency

C_E = local exhaust duct concentration before recirculation, mg/m^3

K_R = coefficient which represents a fraction of the recirculated exhaust stream that is composed of the recirculation return air (range 0 to 1.0)

C_M = replacement air concentration, mg/m^3

$$C_B = \frac{Q_B}{Q_A}(C_G - C_M)(1 - f) + (C_O - C_M) f +$$
$$K_B C_R + (1 - K_B)(C_m) \qquad [7.4]$$

Where: C_B = 8-hr TWA worker breathing zone concentration after recirculation, mg/m^3

Q_B = total ventilation airflow before recirculation

Q_A = total ventilation airflow after recirculation

C_G = general room concentration before recirculation, mg/m^3

f = coefficient which represents the fraction of time the worker spends at the work station

C_O = 8-hr TWA breathing zone concentration at work station before recirculation

K_B = fraction of worker's breathing zone air that is composed of recirculation return air (range 0 to 1.0)

The coefficients K_R, K_B, and f are dependent on the workstation and the worker's position in relation to the source of the recirculation return air and in relation to the exhaust hood. The value of K_R can range from 0 to 1.0 where 0 indicates no recirculation return air entering the hood and 1.0 indicates 100% recirculation air entering the hood. Similarly, the value of K_B can range from 0 to 1.0 where 0 indicates there is no recirculation return air in the breathing zone and 1.0 indicates that the breathing zone air is 100% recirculated return air. The coefficient "f" varies from 0 where the worker does not spend any time at the workstation where the air is being recirculated to

1.0 where the worker spends 100% time at the workstation. In many cases it will be difficult to attempt quantification of the values required for solution of these equations for an operation not yet in existence. Estimates based on various published and other available data for the same or similar operations may be useful. The final system must be tested to demonstrate that it meets design specifications.

An example of use of Equations 7.3 and 7.4 and the effect of the various parameters is as follows. Consider a system consisting of 5,000 cfm of general exhaust and 5,000 cfm of local exhaust. If the local exhaust is recirculated the ventilation system of 10,000 cfm changes to 5,000 cfm recirculated and 5,000 cfm fresh airflow. Assume poor placement of the recirculation return (K_R and $K_B = 1$) and that the worker spends all his time at the work station ($f = 1$); the air cleaner efficiency $\eta = 0.90$; exhaust duct concentration (C_E) = 500 ppm; general room concentration (C_G) = 20 ppm; replacement air concentration (C_M) = 2 ppm; work station (breathing zone) concentration before recirculation (C_O) = 20 ppm; and a contaminant TLV of 50 ppm.

Equation 7.3 gives recirculation air return concentration:

$$C_R = \frac{(1 - 0.90)(500 - 1 \times 2)}{1 - [(1)(1 - .090)]} = 55 \text{ ppm}$$

Equation 7.4 gives the worker breathing zone concentration:

$$C_B = Q_A(C_G - C_M)(1 - f) + (C_O - C_M)f + K_B C_R + (1 - K_B)(C_M)$$

$$Q_A = 10,000(20 - 2)(1 - 1) + (20 - 2)1 + 1 \times 55 + (1 - 1)(2) = 73.0 \text{ ppm}$$

The concentration of 73 ppm is over the TLV of 50 ppm and therefore is not an acceptable value for an engineered ventilation solution to this situation.

In order to achieve lower concentrations (C_B), two modifications in the design are made. First, the efficiency of the air cleaning device is improved to 99%. Second, the system configuration is redesigned so that only 30% of the recirculation return air reaches the workstation. Thus, K_R and K_B are reduced to 0.3. Substituting these new data in Equations 7.3 and 7.4, the concentration in the air stream leaving the air cleaner drops to 5.0 ppm and the breathing zone concentration calculates as 24.4 ppm. This is less than half of the TLV of 50 ppm and, therefore, the design would normally be acceptable.

7.7.4 Design Considerations for Air Recirculation: More requirements associated with the recirculation of exhaust can be found in published standards. The American National Standards Institute (ANSI) issued ANSI 9.7, *Recirculation of Air from Industrial Process Exhaust Systems.*[7.14]

Care must be taken in the design of recirculated air systems. Considerations for good system performance are:

1.   Recirculating systems should, whenever practicable, be designed to bypass to the outdoors, rather than recirculate, when weather conditions permit. If a system is intended to conserve heat in winter months and if adequate window and door openings permit sufficient replacement air when open, the system can discharge outdoors in warm weather. In other situations where the workspace is conditioned or where mechanically supplied supply air is required at all times, continuous bypass operation may not be attractive.

2.   Wet collectors also act as humidifiers. Recirculation of humid air from such equipment can cause uncomfortably high humidity and require auxiliary ventilation or some method to prevent excess humidity. Return of this air should be especially avoided into air conditioned spaces.

3.   The exit concentration of typical collectors can vary with time. Design data and testing programs should consider all operational time periods.

4.   The layout and design of the recirculation duct should provide adequate mixing with other supply air and avoid uncomfortable drafts on workers or air currents which would upset the capture velocity of local exhaust hoods.

5.   Odors or nuisance values of contaminants should be considered as well as official exposure limit values. In some areas, adequately cleaned recirculated air, provided by a system with safeguards, may be of better quality than the ambient outdoor air available for replacement air supply.

6.   Routine testing, maintenance procedures, and records should be developed for recirculating systems.

7.   Periodic testing of the workroom air should be provided.

8.   An appropriate sign should be displayed in a prominent place reading as follows:

CAUTION

AIR CONTAINING HAZARDOUS SUBSTANCES IS BEING CLEANED TO A SAFE LEVEL IN THIS EQUIPMENT AND RETURNED TO THE BUILDING. SIGNALS OR ALARMS INDICATE MALFUNCTIONS AND MUST RECEIVE IMMEDIATE ATTENTION: STOP RECIRCULATION, DISCHARGE THE AIR OUTSIDE, OR STOP THE PROCESS IMMEDIATELY.

7.7.5 Recirculation Air Monitor Selection: While all system components are important, special consideration should be given to the monitor. The prime requisites are that the monitor be capable of sensing a system malfunction or failure and of providing a signal which will initiate an appropriate sequence of actions to assure that overexposure does not occur. The sophistication of the monitoring system can vary widely. The type of monitor selected will depend on various parameters (i.e., location, nature of contaminant—including shape and size—and degree of automation). The safe operation of a

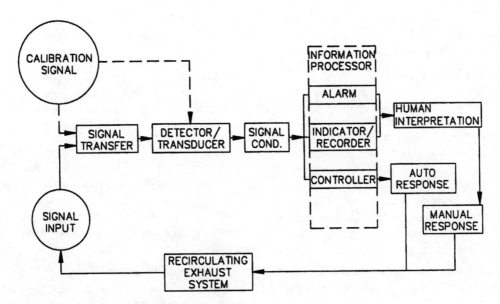

FIGURE 7–17. Schematic diagram of recirculation monitoring system

recirculating system depends on the selection of the best monitor for a given system. Reference 7.4 describes four basic components of a complete monitoring system which includes signal transfer, detector/transducer, signal conditioner, and information processor. Figure 7-17 shows a schematic diagram of the system incorporating these four components. It is quite likely that commercially available monitors may not contain all of the above four components and may have to be custom engineered to the need.

In addition to the four monitoring system components, the contaminant samples must be collected from the air stream either as an extracted sample or in total. If a sample is taken, it must be representative of the average conditions of the air stream. At normal duct velocities, turbulence assures good mixing so gas and vapor samples should be representative. For aerosols, however, the particle size discrimination produced by the probe may bias the estimated concentration unless isokinetic conditions are achieved.

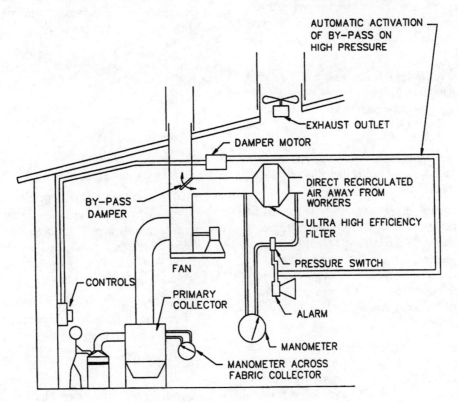

FIGURE 7–18. Schematic of recirculation from air cleaning devices (particulates)

The choice of detection methods depends on the measurable chemical and physical properties of the contaminants in the air stream. Quantifying the collected contaminants is generally much easier for particulate than for gases, vapors, or liquid aerosols.

Particulates: Where the hazardous contaminant constitutes a large fraction of the total dust weights, filter samples may allow adequate estimation of concentration in the recirculated air. If the primary collector (e.g., bag filters, cartridge filters) allows very low penetration rates, it may be more economical to use high efficiency filters as secondary filters. If the primary filter fails, the secondary filter not only will experience an easily measured increase in pressure drop, but will filter the penetrating dust as well—earning this design the sobriquet, "safety monitor" system (see Figure 7-18).

Non-particulates: Continuously detecting and quantifying vapor and gas samples reliably and accurately is a complex subject beyond the scope of this manual.

Air Sampling Instruments for Evaluation of Atmospheric Contaminants, published by ACGIH,[7.16] describes and evaluates different air monitoring devices. The monitor in a recirculating system must be capable of reliably monitoring continuously and unattended for an extended period of time. It must also be able to quickly and accurately sense a change in system performance and provide an appropriate warning if a preselected safety level is reached. In order to function properly, monitors must be extremely reliable and properly maintained. Monitors should be designed so that potential malfunctions are limited in number and can be detected easily by following recommended procedures. Required maintenance/recalibration should be simple, infrequent, and of short duration.

7.7.6 Untempered Air Supply: In many industries utilizing hot processes, cold outdoor air is supplied untempered or moderately tempered to dissipate sensible heat loads on the workers and to provide effective temperature relief for workers exposed to radiant heat loads. The air required for large compressors, as well as for cooling tunnels in foundries, also can come directly from outside the plant and thus eliminate a load of the tempered replaced air.

7.7.7 Energy Recovery: Energy recovery from exhaust air is accomplished through the use of heat exchange equipment to extract heat from the air stream before it is exhausted to the outside. The application of return or recirculated cleaned air from industrial exhaust systems is another method of recovering process heat for use in the building. The application of heat exchangers to industrial exhaust systems has been limited primarily by the ratio of installed cost to annual return.

Heat Exchangers—Air-to-air heat exchangers have been used to reduce energy consumption. This is achieved by transferring waste energy from the exhaust to supply replacement air streams of a building or process. The methods and equipment used will depend on the characteristics of the air streams.

Major categories of equipment include heat wheels, fixed plate exchangers, heat pipes, and run-around coils.

A *heat wheel* is a revolving cylinder filled with an air permeable media. As the exhaust air passes through the media, heat is transferred to the media. Since the media rotates, the warm media transfers heat to the cooler supply replacement air. Special care is required to ensure that this transfer does not cause a transfer of contaminants.

A *fixed plate exchanger* consists of intertwined tunnels of exhaust and supply replacement air separated by plates (or sometimes a combination of plates and fins). The warm exhaust air heats the plates which in turn heats the replacement air on the other side of the plate. This exchanger uses no transfer media other than the plate forming wall of the unit.

A *heat pipe*, or thermo siphon, uses a pipe manifold with one end in the warm exhaust air stream and the other in the cool supply replacement air stream. The pipe contains a fluid which boils in the warm exhaust air stream extracting heat and condenses in the cool supply replacement air stream releasing heat. Thus the heat pipe operates in a closed loop evaporation/condensation cycle.

A *run-around coil exchanger* uses a pair of finned-tube coils. A fluid circulates through the coils extracting heat from the warm exhaust air releasing heat to the cool supply replacement air. An advantage of the run-around coil is that the exhaust and supply duct systems can be separated by a significant distance, which results in a reduced potential for re-entry of unwanted exhaust materials. The system also normally requires less ductwork than other systems and usually occupies less roof area.

Several factors are important in the selection of the appropriate heat exchanger. A partial list is as follows:

1. The nature of the exhaust stream. A corrosive or dust laden stream may need to be precleaned and special construction materials may be required.

2. The need to isolate the contaminated exhaust stream from the clean supply replacement air stream.

3. The temperature of the exhaust stream. Unless the hot air stream is well above the desired delivery temperature of the supply replacement air stream and the exhaust air stream is at elevated temperatures whenever heat is demanded by the supply replacement air stream, additional heating capacity will be required.

4. Space requirements. Space requirements for some heat exchangers can be very extensive, especially when the additional duct runs are considered.

5. The need for a by-pass. During failure mode or summer conditions, a by-pass will be required.

6. Need good distribution of air to prevent ice, etc., in potential dead air spots in the system.

7.8 SYSTEM CONTROL

7.8.1 Building Air Balance: Proper building air balance is needed to control space cleanliness, contaminants, and temperatures. Air that is supplied to a building is also removed by a combination of methods. When there is adequate replacement air, any additional clean plant air can be returned to the supply air unit. Obviously, the contaminant-laden air should be captured by means of a local exhaust hood or ventilation system and removed from the building. Sensors are available to monitor the building pressure to maintain a building positive pressure. Another approach is to use a central control system that tracks which exhaust systems are operating and their associated airflow. The control system also operates the supply system to assure the necessary amount of outside air is brought into the plant to obtain the desired building pressure. The remainder of the airflow is obtained from returning plant air to the air handler units.

In industrial plants where there is no concern for maintaining close temperature control or high air cleanliness levels, the maintenance of the building air balance is only required during the heating season. During other times of the year the building temperature is not controlled and doors are left open to allow as much outside air to enter as possible.

7.8.2 Temperature: Return air temperature and humidity are other characteristics that will cause the discharge of clean return air outdoors. These air qualities can be monitored and used to vary the return airflow to the supply air unit. The HVAC industry uses automated building control and direct digital control (DDC) in many facilities. The technology can be applied to industrial ventilation with careful planning. DDC uses computers and microprocessors tied to sensors and actuators to form a feedback and control system. DDC can be useful in industrial ventilation systems to control temperature, humidity, and relative room pressures. DDC systems can also track the system performance at hoods, fans, heating and cooling, and air pollution control equipment. DDC is especially useful in preventive maintenance. However, DDC systems for industrial ventilation systems are complicated. Many are "one-of-a-kind" systems designed by a controls manufacturer and require trained personnel to install, calibrate, and operate.

7.8.3 Indoor Air Quality: Many industrial processes release minor amounts of "nuisance" contaminants which, at low concentrations, have no known health effects but are unpleasant or disagreeable to the workers or harmful to the product. The desire to provide a clean working environment for both the people and the product often dictates controlled airflow between rooms or entire departments. The air streams recirculated into the facility must be evaluated to determine if the air pollution control devices (e.g., filters, cyclones) are providing sufficient cleaning to prevent employee exposure to "nuisance" contaminants. In addition, systems with known contaminants require the controls listed in Section 7.7.2 under "Industrial Exhaust Recirculation". The facility must employ trained

mechanics and support a preventive maintenance program to sufficiently protect the workers.

7.9 SYSTEM NOISE

Supply air systems have several sources for objectionable noise. Care must be taken in selecting the fan and avoiding high air velocities in the duct system. The fan may develop unwanted noise if it operates at high speeds or if it is not properly isolated from the rest of the system. Using a larger fan at a lower speed will usually avoid high frequency noise. Duct silencers and other acoustical treatment can be applied to noisy systems to achieve sound reduction. Isolation by springs or other vibration absorbing devices is needed to limit the transmission of fan noise into the building structure. Additional information regarding sound and vibration control can be found in the ASHRAE Handbook of Fundamentals.

There are several places in a duct system where noise can occur. Diffusers/grilles that are providing long throws can create excessive noise due to the high air velocities required. Sound data is provided in the manufacturer's catalog to aid in the selection of the most appropriate diffuser. Care should be taken to specify devices that can operate under the static pressures found in industrial supply air systems. Commercial grade devices may become stressed or their components may loosen causing unwanted vibration and noise.

REFERENCES

7.1.   American Society of Heating, Ventilating and Air Conditioning Engineers: HVAC Application. ASHRAE, Atlanta, GA (1999).

7.2   National Fire Protection Association, 1 Batterymarch Park, P. O. Box 9101, Quincy, MA 02269-9101.

7.3.   Hama, G.: How Safe Are Direct-Fired Makeup Units? Air Engineering, p. 22 (September 1962).

7.4.   American Society of Heating, Refrigeration and Air Conditioning Engineers: HVAC Systems and Equipment. ASHRAE, Atlanta, GA (1996).

7.5.   American Society of Heating, Refrigerating, and Air Conditioning Engineers: Method of Testing General Ventilation Air Cleaning Devices for Removal Efficiency by Particle Size, ASHRAE Publication No. 52.1-92, ASHRAE, Atlanta, GA (1992).

7.6.   Yuan, X.; Chen, Q.; Glicksman, L.R.: A Critical Review of Displacement Ventilation, ASHRAE Transactions, (January 1998).

7.7.   Skistad, H.: Displacement Ventilation. Taunton, Somerset, England: Research Studies. Press, Ltd. (1994).

7.8.   Kristensson, J.A.; Lindqvist, O.A.: Displacement Ventilation Systems in Industrial Buildings, ASHRAE Transactions, 99/1 (1993).

7.9.   Sheet Metal and Air Conditioning Contractors National Association, Inc: Rectangular Industrial Duct Construction Standards, SMACNA, Vienna, VA (1980).

7.10.   Sheet Metal and Air Conditioning Contractors National Association, Inc: Round Industrial Duct Construction Standards, SMACNA, Vienna, VA (1999).

7.11.   Sheet Metal and Air Conditioning Contractors National Association, Inc: Thermoplastic Duct (PVC) Construction Manual, SMACNA, Vienna, VA (1994).

7.12.   Thomson, M.; Goodfellow, H.: Computational Fluid Dynamics as a Design Tool for Industrial Ventilation, Ventilation (1997).

7.13.   Hughes, R.T.; Amendola, A.A.: Recirculating Exhaust Air: Guides, Design Parameters and Mathematical Modeling. Plant Engineering (March 18, 1982).

7.14.   ANSI/AIHA; Recirculation of Air from Industrial Process Exhaust Systems. ANSI/AIHA Z9.7 - 1988, American National Standards Institute, Apr., 1998.

7.15.   National Institute for Occupational Safety and Health: The Recirculation of Industrial Exhaust Air - Symposium Proceedings. Pub. No. 78-141 Department of Health, Education and Welfare (NIOSH), Cincinnati, OH (1978).

7.16.   American Conference of Governmental Industrial Hygienists: Air Sampling Instruments for Evaluation of Atmospheric Contaminants, 9th Edition. ACGIH, Cincinnati, OH (in press).

Chapter 8
VENTILATION ASPECTS OF INDOOR AIR QUALITY

8.1 INTRODUCTION

There are two ventilation aspects which are major causes of the complaints noted in the vast majority of reported problems from all parts of this and other countries. They are complaints of unsatisfactory indoor air quality (which may be due to the lack of sufficient outdoor air for dilution of "normal" indoor airborne contaminants) and the failure to deliver supply air properly to the occupied zones.

Indoor air quality is defined as the overall quality of the indoor air and includes biological, chemical, and comfort factors. This chapter is designed to familiarize the reader with heating, ventilation, and air conditioning (HVAC) systems used in office and similar spaces. The individual components of a typical HVAC system are defined and the operation of the more common types of HVAC systems found are discussed.

8.2 DILUTION VENTILATION FOR INDOOR AIR QUALITY

The oil shortage and the resulting energy crisis of the late 1960's and early 1970's is considered by some as the most significant cause of the current indoor air quality concern. In the past, when energy costs were relatively low, the design of heating, ventilation, and air conditioning (HVAC) systems for buildings included the infiltration of outdoor air through doors, windows, and other sources. Also, up to 25%[8.1] outdoor air was supplied by the system, in addition to the infiltration, for general ventilation purposes. The outdoor air had the effect of diluting the "normal" indoor contaminants to a very low level of concentration, which had little effect on the occupants.

Since the energy crisis resulted in major increases in energy costs, an extensive effort was made to reduce the infiltration of outdoor air by constructing the building as airtight as possible. Outdoor air supplied by the HVAC system was reduced to a minimum and in some instances eliminated entirely. Airborne contaminants found in indoor environments were present in extremely small quantities and had not been a health problem in the past due to the dilution effect of the outdoor air. New concepts of office design that utilize fabric partitions, particle board furniture, increased use of carpets, office copy machines, etc., have increased the potential for indoor contaminants. As buildings became more energy efficient, there was an increase in complaints of stuffiness, drowsiness, tiredness, eye irritation, throat irritation, and stale air.

Existing health standards are not usually violated by the low-level concentrations and the only current legal requirement for outdoor air is found in the building codes. The Uniform Building Code[8.2] is the most widely accepted standard for providing outdoor air. Section 605 states that 5 cfm of outdoor air per occupant shall be mechanically supplied to all parts of the building during occupancy. Carbon dioxide concentrations from occupant respiration within a space are often used as an indicator of the quantity of outdoor air being supplied to that space. When the indoor air concentration reaches approximately 800-1000 ppm (excluding external combustion

sources), complaints may escalate. As the carbon dioxide levels increase, the number of complaints will increase more rapidly.

In 1989 the American Society of Heating, Refrigeration and Air Conditioning Engineers (ASHRAE) developed and adopted ASHRAE 62-1989, "Ventilation for Acceptable Indoor Air Quality.[8.3] The standard recognized the health problems resulting from the changes in construction and HVAC methods. It is based on occupancy of spaces and provides the outdoor air requirement for that space. Requirements for outdoor air for offices based on an occupancy of seven people per 1000 square feet is currently 20 cfm per person. This is based on a total occupancy, including transients, and is in addition to the usual HVAC requirements. The standard is expected to satisfy the requirements for 80% or more of the occupants.

Provision for delivery of the outdoor air for dilution of the normal indoor airborne contaminants in the occupied space is a major factor of indoor air quality considerations. It is obvious that if the outdoor air included as part of the total supply air is not delivered to the occupied zone, the potential for unsatisfactory indoor air quality increases. Another important factor in the delivery of the air to the occupied zone is the location of the supply and return air grilles to avoid short-circuiting. Ideally, the supply air diffusers and the air grilles are so located that a uniform flow of air through the space occurs to avoid both stagnant air and drafts.

Temperature and humidity can play a role in how people perceive indoor environment. ASHRAE 55-1992[8.4] provides guidance in design and maintenance of indoor thermal environments. ASHRAE recommends temperature ranges of 67 to 76 F in winter (heating season) and 72 to 81 F in summer (cooling season). However, complaints may increase when temperatures rise above 74 F. Similarly, it is preferable to keep relative humidities above 20-30% during the heating season and below 60% during the cooling season. ASHRAE also suggests limits on air movement. The average air movement in an occupied space should not exceed 30 fpm in winter or 50 fpm in summer.

8.3 HVAC COMPONENTS AND SYSTEM TYPES

When considering the ventilation aspects of HVAC systems, the type of system and its components should be reviewed for potential sources or causes of complaints regarding indoor air quality. Detailed descriptions of the systems and components can be found in the **Systems and Equipment** volume of the ASHRAE Handbook.[8.5]

8.3.1 Components: The components that make up HVAC systems generally include the following:

A. **HVAC System:** HVAC system refers to the equipment and distribution system used for heating, ventilating, cooling, humidifying, dehumidifying, and cleansing air for a building or building zone for the purpose of comfort, safety, and health of the occupants.

B. **Dampers:** Dampers are devices of various types used to vary the volume of air passing through an outlet, inlet, or duct.

C. **Outdoor Air (Fresh Air; Replacement Air; Compensating Air):** Outdoor air used to replace all or part of the air in a building or building space.

D. **Return Air:** Return air is air that has been in the building for a period of time and is returned to the HVAC system. Varying percentages of return air are exhausted outdoor with the remaining air (recirculated air) mixed with outdoor air for conditioning and distribution.

E. **Mixing Plenum:** A mixing plenum is a chamber within an HVAC system where outdoor air is mixed with returned air. The mixed air, after cleaning and conditioning, comprises the supply air for the building.

F. **Air Cleaners:** Air cleaners are devices designed for the purpose of removing atmospheric airborne impurities such as dusts, gases, vapors, fumes, and smoke. (Air cleaners include air washers, air filters, electrostatic precipitators, and charcoal filters.)

G. **Heating Coils:** Heating coils are heat transfer devices which utilize hot water, steam, or electricity to heat the supply air.

H. **Cooling Coils:** Cooling coils are heat transfer devices which utilize chilled water or a refrigerant to cool the supply air.

I. **Condensate Pan (Drip Tray; Defrost Pan):** A vessel or tray under the cooling coil to receive water extracted from the supply air by condensation from the cooling coil.

J. **Humidifier/Dehumidifier:** Humidifier/dehumidifiers are devices to add/remove moisture to/from the supply air.

K. **Fans (Supply and Return):** Fans are devices for moving ventilation air through the HVAC system.

L. **Supply Air:** Supply air is conditioned ventilation air delivered to zones within a building.

M. **Control Zone:** Control zone is a space or group of spaces within a building served by an HVAC system. Depending on the space requirements, the control zone may be designated as core or interior zone and/or perimeter zone.

N. **Occupied Zone:** The occupied zone is the region within an occupied space between 3 and 72 inches above the floor.

O. **Control Box (Variable Air Volume, Bypass, Dual Duct):** Control boxes are devices to which the supply air may be delivered by the HVAC system prior to delivery to the supply diffuser. These boxes may include means of controlling supply air temperature and volume to the diffuser or multiple diffusers within a HVAC zone.

P. **Supply Air Diffusers:** Supply air diffusers are devices whose function is to deliver the supply air to the occupied zone and to provide a desired distribution pattern. The diffusers may be circular, square, rectangular, linear slots, louvered, fixed, adjustable, or a combination.

Q. **Return Air Grilles:** Return air grilles may be louvered or perforated coverings for openings located in the sidewall, ceiling, or floor of a zone through which the return air enters. The return air grilles may be directly connected to an open return air plenum or to a ducted return air system.

R. **Return Air Plenum:** A return air plenum is the space usually located above the ceiling where the return air is collected from a zone prior to entering the return air system.

S. **Economizer:** An economizer is a control system which reduces the heating and cooling load through the use of outdoor air for free cooling when the total heat of the return air exceeds the total heat of the outdoor air.

8.3.2 Types of Systems: There are different types of HVAC systems: single-duct systems, dual-duct systems, multi-zone systems, and special systems. These systems may be considered basic and subject to variations that are necessary to meet specific requirements. The following descriptions of the basic systems are intended as a guide and the referenced ASHRAE Handbook should be reviewed for system details and variations.

Single-Duct Systems may be either a constant or a variable air volume system. The constant volume system maintains constant airflow with the temperature of the supply air controlled in response to the space load. See Figures 8-1 and 8-2. The system may be a single zone, a zoned reheat, multiple-zone modification, or a by-pass variation using a by-pass box in lieu of reheat constant volume primary system with a variable air volume secondary system. A variable air volume (VAV) system controls the temperature within a zone by varying the supply air volume. See Figures 8-3, 8-4, and 8-5. This type of system may include reheat at the terminals, induction unit, fan-powered distribution box, dual conduit, and variable diffusers.

Dual-Duct Systems condition all the air in a central apparatus and distributes it to the conditioned zones through two parallel mains, one carrying cold air and the other warm air. The system may be a constant volume type single fan with or without reheat capability. See Figure 8-6. Also, the system may be VAV which mixes the cold and warm air in various volume combinations depending on the zone load. In both system types, cold and warm air are delivered to a dual duct box which mixes the air prior to delivery to the supply air diffuser.

Multizone Systems supply several zones from a centrally located HVAC unit. Supply air for the different zones consists of mixed cold and warm air through zone dampers in the central HVAC unit in response to zone thermostat control. From there the supply air is distributed through the building by single zone ducts which, in turn, supply the air to the zone diffusers. See Figure 8-7.

Fan Coil Units are usually located along the outdoor wall of a building for heating and cooling the perimeter up to 15 feet from the outdoor wall. These units may have a through-wall duct for outdoor air and can be totally self contained or have the heating and cooling media supplied from a central mechanical room. See Figure 8-8. Controls for temperature and operation will vary although control of the outdoor air is usually at the unit and by the nearest occupant.

Zone Heat Pumps are packaged HVAC units that may provide the heating and cooling for individual zones within a building. These units vary in how the heating and cooling media is provided, but the function is generally constant (see Figure 8-9). Also, these units may be located within the individual zone above the ceiling in the return air space or remotely such as on the building roof. The supply air is delivered to the entire zone through a duct distribution and diffuser system. Return air for a pump located in the building enters the return air plenum above the ceiling due to zone pressure and migrates to the unit for reconditioning. For the remote unit, the return air is ducted from the ceiling plenum or from return air grilles to the unit. Outdoor air for interior units may be provided by a separate system and delivered to the return air plenum above the ceiling. Some building codes require that the outdoor air be directly supplied to the interior units. For the remote unit located on the roof, the outdoor air may be provided by the unit on the return air side through a damper that usually is set manually.

8.4 HVAC COMPONENTS, FUNCTIONS AND MALFUNCTIONS

8.4.1 Outdoor Air: The outdoor air requirement for a space or an entire building must satisfy the need for acceptable indoor air quality and to replace air removed from the space or building by process or other exhaust. For indoor environment, ASHRAE Standard 62-1989, "Ventilation for Acceptable Indoor Air Quality",[8.3] is the accepted design criteria. Replacement air, however, will depend on factors such as total exhaust volume and pressure differential requirements of the space or building plus the evaluation of potential airborne contaminants that may be generated inside or outside the building. For example, in the "open concept" type of office layout where partitions approximately five feet high enclose office spaces, the supply air has a tendency to ventilate only the space between the partitions and the ceiling. Very little, if any, of the supply air enters the actual occupied space directly to provide the necessary dilution. This allows contaminants in the occupied space to increase in concentration resulting in the potential for unsatisfactory air quality complaints.

ASHRAE Standard 62-1989 recommends the measurement and documentation of the outdoor air intake volumetric flow rate on all configurations of HVAC systems. The primary purpose of this requirement is to control the level of carbon dioxide, human odors and the normal airborne contaminants generated within the space. The published ventilation rates are based on occupancy or space usage and on an assumed occupant density. If the occupant density increases or the space usage increases, a degradation of the indoor air quality will occur which, in turn, will require an increase in outdoor air.

It is possible to estimate the percentage of outdoor air by equation using the return, outdoor, and mixed air temperatures. The percentage of outdoor air also can be determined by equation using the carbon dioxide concentrations in the same airflow areas. Using these results, the estimated volumetric flow rate of the outdoor can be determined. The equations are as follows:

Temperature Method:

$$\% \text{ outdoor air} = \frac{t_{RA} - t_{MA}}{t_{RA} - t_{OA}} \times 100$$

where: t_{RA} = temperature, return air

t_{MA} = temperature, mixed air

t_{OA} = temperature, outdoor air

Carbon Dioxide Method:

$$\% \text{ outdoor air} = \frac{\text{ppm/RA} - \text{ppm/MA}}{\text{ppm/RA} - \text{ppm/OA}} \times 100$$

where: ppm/RA = CO_2 concentration, return air

ppm/MA = CO_2 concentration, mixed air

ppm/OA = CO_2 concentration, outdoor air

Given the legal implications, the direct measurement and documentation of the outdoor air volumetric flow rate is recommended.

The concentration of carbon dioxide within a space may provide a good indication of the outdoor air being delivered to the space. A study conducted by the Ontario Inter-Ministerial Committee on Indoor Air Quality reported on the relationship between levels of complaints, carbon dioxide concentrations, and the outdoor air ventilation rates. The results are indicated in Table 8-1.

Location of the outdoor air intake may be found on the building roof, sidewall, at ground level, or possibly at all three locations for very large building complexes. Figure 5-31, "Airflow Around Buildings", clearly illustrates the potential for airborne contaminants to enter the building through any of the outdoor air intakes. Sources of potential airborne contaminants from the building and from sources remote or adjacent to the building should be thoroughly investigated. Assistance with this investigation should be requested of industrial hygiene and environmental organizations who have responsibilities for the building. The location of the outdoor air intakes

TABLE 8-1[8.6] Relationships among extent of complaints regarding indoor air quality, CO_2 levels and outdoor air ventilation rates

COMMENTS	CO_2 (ppm)	Outdoor Air Ventilation Rate/Person	
		CFM	L/s
Occasional complaints, particularly if the air temperature rises	600	35	16.5
Complaints are more prevalent	800	21	10
Insufficient replacement air, complaints more general	1000	15	7

will be affected by the atmospheric airflow over the building as will the location and height of any exhaust stacks. Criteria for the atmospheric airflow characteristics and stack heights may be found in Figures 5-31, 5-32, and 5-33 of this manual or in the *1993 ASHRAE Handbook Fundamentals*, Chapter 14, "Airflow Around Buildings".[8.7]

Roof intakes generally are located within a few feet of the roof surface. Standing water on the roof from weather conditions, HVAC equipment drains, or other sources present the potential for biological growth and entry into the intake. Unless discharged vertically above the recirculation region (see Figure 5-31), building exhaust systems from restrooms, processes within the building, and restaurant kitchens have significant potential for re-entry.

Building sidewall intakes have the potential for entry of airborne contaminants from street level automotive traffic, shipping and receiving docks, and adjacent buildings. In the building wake region, see Figure 5-31, the potential for re-entry increases for the outdoor air intakes and open windows or doors since the pressure in the recirculation region is lower than the surrounding area. Airborne debris such as leaves, paper, and atmospheric dirt may tend to collect on the intake bird screens which can reduce the intake area and may reduce the flow rate into the intakes.

Ground level outdoor air intakes are possibly the least desirable location of the three described. This location offers the potential for air quality problems caused by standing water, automotive emissions, and as a collection point for dirt and debris. The security of a building can be compromised through the ground level intakes by the deliberate addition of foreign materials.

8.4.2 Dampers: A typical office building HVAC system will include outdoor and return air dampers. Airflow through these dampers will vary over a wide range depending on the damper opening settings and the space or building requirements. Indoor air quality problems often result if the outdoor air damper is not designed or adjusted to allow introduction of sufficient outdoor air for the current use of the building. Outdoor air requirements for acceptable indoor air quality indicate that the actual volumetric flow rate through the damper sec-

tions be monitored. When the outdoor air and return air dampers are combined in an HVAC system, there may be an imbalance in volumetric flow rates.

It is customary to report the volumetric airflow rate through dampers in terms of damper opening. However, damper opening is not linearly proportionate to volumetric flow rate. Another misconception regarding dampers is that a "closed" damper will leak approximately 10%. Closed dampers may not leak at all.

Dampers are mechanical devices (either parallel or opposed blade, see Figure 8-11) that require routine maintenance and periodic settings checks to assure proper airflow passage. Actuators, connecting arms and damper bearings are components that can affect the airflow if not properly connected or adjusted. This is an area where potential problems affecting the IAQ are not uncommon. In older buildings, the practice of disconnecting the outdoor air dampers to conserve energy is fairly common. This practice has been found by current surveys in some older buildings and also in newer buildings which have been occupied for an extended period. The result, of course, is a significant potential source of unsatisfactory IAQ complaints.

8.4.3 Air Cleaning: The requirements for air cleaning vary according to the space or building requirements. There are, however, some basic factors that should be included in the design of the HVAC filter section. It is considered essential that all ventilation supply air including outdoor and recirculated air, pass through a prefilter and a high efficiency final filter. Depending on requirements, filters such as charcoal, potassium permanganate, HEPA and others may be specified. See Figure 8-12 for various types.

For example, paper dust is one of the contributors to unsatisfactory indoor air quality. The paper dust in itself is an irritant to the eyes and respiratory system. Also, many papers are chemically treated which tends to compound the irritant effect. The dust generated enters the return air section of the HVAC system, and may be reintroduced to the space being served by the system. Studies[8.8-8.10] have indicated that a significant percentage of the paper dust will be removed by high efficiency type filters which, as stated, should be included in the HVAC filter section. Figure 8-10[8.5] shows approximate efficiency versus particle size for typical air filters.

In some older HVAC equipment and also in perimeter fan coil units and self-contained heat pumps, low efficiency filters are noted. It may be possible to replace these filters with medium efficiency filters of the same dimensions. The medium efficiency pleated filter has more than twice the filtering area, thereby increasing the interception of the airborne particulates without a significant increase in the static pressure requirements.

The air cleaning or filter section of the HVAC system requires routine maintenance for replacing dirty filters, or in some instances, cleaning a reusable type of air cleaner. Routine maintenance would also bring attention to damaged filters or filter frames and uneven airflow (by the dirt pattern on the face of the filters). Even though a regular maintenance program may be in force, the filter sections, both pre- and final filters, present a potential source for IAQ complaints.

Some HVAC systems utilize self-contained heat pumps to control conditions in specific zones. These heat pumps can be located above the ceiling in the return air plenum near the zone being served. This location results in a difficult situation in terms of providing service for the unit. The zonal heat pump usually has a low efficiency filter which can be completely blocked or missing due to the difficulty of servicing.

8.4.4 *Heating/Cooling Coils:* Heating and cooling coils must be free of damage, especially the heat transfer fins. Irregularities in the fins will result in unequal heat transfer and will provide an area for dirt and other materials to accumulate. Air cleaning sections are not 100% perfect in removing the airborne contaminants regardless of efficiency ratings. Convenient access to the coil section for inspection, cleaning, and maintenance is essential to the proper functioning of the coil. See Figure 8-13.

Cooling coils require some additional considerations. The supply air will pass through at a relatively low velocity and the heat transfer will condense moisture on the coil fins. This moisture will drain to the condensate pan below the coil. Provision must be made to properly discharge the condensate. Since the air cleaning section is not perfect, some airborne contaminants will reach the cooling coils. The moisture accumulating on the coil fins will collect a significant percentage of these contaminants, which may adhere to the fins or drain to the pan below with the condensate. Accumulations of these contaminants create a source of molds, spores, bacteria, etc., that may enter the supply air stream. The condensate pan drain may allow condensate to accumulate at or near the outdoor air intake and can re-enter the HVAC system. It is essential that the cooling coil condensate pan be properly drained. The pan drain must be directed away from any outdoor air intake. The coil and pan must be inspected and cleaned on a regular basis. Microorganisms may proliferate if this is not done.

8.4.5 *Fans:* HVAC systems vary in size and complexity over a wide range as do the fans as the system prime mover of volumetric flow for both supply, outdoor, and return air. The fans may be the axial or centrifugal type with inlet vanes, outlet dampers, variable speed, direct, or belt drive (see Figure 8-14). Also, the fan or fans may be inside the housing of a self-contained HVAC unit or a separate component in a mechanical room or penthouse. See Figure 8-16 for a typical layout of self-contained and mechanical room system.

Since the fan is the prime mover of the HVAC system, a preventive maintenance program usually will reveal any potential malfunctions before they occur. Failures of the fan are usually noted immediately and corrected by maintenance. There is, however, a maintenance procedure, lubrication of moving components, that may be a source of odor complaints by the building occupants. Over lubrication, which is not an uncommon practice, may place a small quantity of the lubricant in the airflow into the fan. This may cause the blades to become coated and the lubricant odor to be carried into occupied areas.

8.4.6 *Humidifiers/Dehumidifiers:* The incorporation of humidifiers/dehumidifiers is dependent on the space requirements of the building. Humidifiers add moisture to the supply air by direct water or by steam spray. Dehumidifiers remove moisture from the supply air by a desiccant type filter or by cooling coils. Of the two processes, humidification is more widely used in HVAC systems. The equipment used for humidification has a reputation for requiring a high level of maintenance for proper operation (see Figure 8-15). For this reason, it is fairly common to find that the humidifier has been shut off—especially in office buildings.

Both humidifying and dehumidifying are associated with water and dampness. This association presents the potential for the growth of molds, spores, bacteria, etc., that may enter the supply airflow. Proper drainage of any water or moisture generated by either process is essential.

8.4.7 *Supply Air Distribution:* The air supply distribution system should be through sheet metal, steel and aluminum, or some type of non-fibrous duct material. There is increasing concern that fibrous materials such as fiberglass board ducts may produce fibers that may be potentially harmful. The use of interior duct insulation should also be avoided to eliminate the possibility of fibers entering the supply air stream. Supply air duct systems should be designed in accordance with accepted standards as detailed in current publications such as the ASHRAE Handbook series, SMACNA Standards, NFPA Standards and other applicable criteria sources.

The physical condition of the air supply duct system is important in the overall evaluation. Duct systems are usually located above the ceiling in the return air space together with utility lines, sprinkler lines, computer cables, etc. This space is relatively small and when repairs, rearrangements, installations, etc., occur damage to the duct system may not be noticed but may effect the air distribution.

It is common practice to connect the supply air duct to mixing boxes and/or diffusers with flexible duct. The frictional resistance can be up to five times that of sheet metal and the manufacturer's data should be reviewed. Bends and turns using flexible duct will compound the losses and have a tendency to reduce the cross-section, which may in turn reduce the air volume. Improper hangers and supports also have the same tendency and results. The use of flexible ducts should be limited to minimum lengths, properly supported, and securely fastened at each end.

8.4.8 *Supply Air Diffuser:* The function of the supply air diffuser is to deliver and distribute the supply air throughout the occupied zone. Diffusers are available in a wide variety of types, shapes, and sizes—all of which will provide the proper air volume according to the supplier. See Figure 8-17 for illustrations of various types of diffusers. The suppliers or manufacturers usually rate the diffusers in terms of supply air volume, static pressure drop, and the "throw" or pattern of the air delivery. Also, the published data will include illustrations of the airflow pattern created by the diffuser in a totally empty space and rely on the "coanda effect" for mixing the air in the space. However, when the space is occupied by people, equipment, file cabinets, cubicle partitions, library shelves, etc., the supply air pattern changes dramatically. This results in less supply air to the occupied zone. This ventilation aspect can be easily recognized through the use of a simple hand held smoke test.

Some of the more common problems associated with diffusers are as follows:

1. Variable air volume HVAC systems with fixed supply air diffusers vary the airflow rate depending on temperature demand. Even if the minimum outdoor air is provided at all times, the reduced flow rate through the diffusers will reduce the throw and flow pattern. This may result in some areas within the occupied zone receiving little or no supply air. There are diffusers that automatically adjust for reduced airflow rates in order to maintain a constant throw and flow pattern utilizing the "coanda effect". Reports from the field vary over a wide range. Some reports state that technical maintenance is relatively high to assure proper functioning. Others report that the pressure required increases as the slot area decreases which decreases the airflow rate.

2. Variable air volume systems may include constant airflow to the diffusers through terminal boxes serving specific zones. These boxes contain an air supply fan with sensors and controls that draw air from the return air system or the specific zone based on the flow rate from the main system. Even though this will assure a constant airflow rate to the diffuser, it also presents some potential problems by localized recirculation within the specific zone.

3. Supply air diffusers with fixed blades, diffusers covered by a perforated plate, linear fixed diffusers, and fluorescent light troffers direct the supply air across the ceiling depending on the coanda effect for delivery to the occupied zone. In the "open concept" office layout with partitions five feet high enclosing office spaces, the supply air from the diffusers described will have a tendency to provide continuous supply only to the space between the partitions and the ceiling. See Figure 8-18. Very little if any of the supply air enters the occupied zone directly which may result in complaints. This particular ventilation aspect may occur even though the system is providing 100% outdoor air and is often referred to as "short circuiting." The flow pattern above the partitions can usually be observed by using the simple smoke test. Another test that is done which may give a more qualitative result is the measurement of the carbon dioxide

concentrations in the occupied zone and in the space between the partitions and ceiling. A concentration in the occupied zone that is significantly higher than the concentration above the partitions indicates that possibly up to 75% of the supply is above the partitions.

4. Supply air diffusers with adjustable blades are available in the multi-directional ceiling type, linear diffusers with adjustable T-bars, sidewall supply grilles, and other types. The adjustable feature does offer a means of better directing the supply air to the occupied zone. However, locations of the diffusers and the adjustment of the blades is critical to the distribution of the supply air. Improper adjustment may result in complaints by the occupants of excessive drafts.

Location and type of supply air diffusers should be such that a continuous flow of air through the occupied space will occur at all times. Avoid situations that result in localized recirculation or short circuiting to the return air system. In general, the airflow pattern through a space by the supply air should receive critical attention and can be characterized in terms of ventilation efficiency. Two efficiencies should be considered: system efficiency and ventilation efficiency. System efficiency is defined as the ratio of the actual volumetric flow rate to a specific space to the design volumetric flow rate for that specific space. Ventilation efficiency is defined as the ratio of the actual volumetric flow rate to a specific occupied zone to the design volumetric flow rate for that specific occupied space. Location and type of supply air diffusers is critical in the development of good ventilation efficiency. Design criteria in ASHRAE 62-1989 will assist the design engineer in this effort.

8.4.9 Return Air Grilles: The return grilles have the function of receiving or exhausting air from a space through the return air system. Also, it is the function of the return air grilles to enhance the flow of the supply air through the space. The size and number of return grilles must be such that 100% of the supply air can be returned to the return air system. Location of the return air grilles influences the airflow pattern through the space and proper location will minimize localized recirculation zones.

There is little design data available on the placement of the return air grilles but the location should be considered as important as the location of the supply air diffusers. The short-circuiting of the supply air directly to the ceiling return grilles may result in less than 50% of the supply air reaching the occupied zone. Development of an airflow pattern through an occupied zone from the supply diffusers to the return air grilles is a primary consideration.

8.4.10 Return Air: The return air system may be either an open plenum type or a ducted system both of which are typically located above the ceiling. In the return system, a static pressure balance between return air points must be part of the system design. It is obvious that the open ceiling plenum cannot be balanced by design which accounts for difficulty in providing a balanced supply air volume. For ducted return, the approach is similar to an industrial exhaust system. The static pressure in each run at their junction must be balanced by design which also accounts for difficulty in providing a balanced supply air volume.

Pressure differentials at any junction are limited to 20% which is the maximum correction possible by damper. For differentials over this limit, re-design is necessary. Flexible duct is used at times to connect return air grilles to the ducted return. Since the negative pressure will tend to collapse the flexible duct, this practice should be avoided.

8.4.11 Fan Coil Unit: The fan coil units used for HVAC are commonly located around the perimeter of a building and serve up to 15 feet from the outdoor wall. See Figure 8-8 for an illustration of a typical fan coil unit. These units may be totally self-contained with automatic controls; may include a through-wall duct for outdoor air; may have remote heating and cooling media, or may be controlled manually at the unit. Since the fan coil units are rather compact, the filters are relatively small and in the low efficiency range. This will tend to increase the maintenance requirements since the return air is at the floor level—a potential significant source for dirt and possibly other contaminants. A provision for outdoor air may be a feature of the fan coil unit especially for units used to provide the HVAC for the building perimeter. The outdoor air intake is normally screened and may, over time, become blocked by dirt and debris from the outside atmosphere. Also, the intake may be located on an outside ledge of the building, depending on the building design, which may be a roosting area for birds. The outdoor air intake presents a significant source for contaminants and a difficult location to maintain.

8.5 HVAC COMPONENT SURVEY OUTLINE

The responsibility for monitoring the IAQ within a building may be assigned to an office individual, the building maintenance department, an outside environmental firm, or an HVAC maintenance contractor. In order to meet this responsibility, the assignee should conduct periodic walk-through surveys of the HVAC system and its components. The assignee should have a procedure or outline of the system components in order to conduct the survey. Basic information required to develop the procedure would including the following:

1. The mechanical plans and specifications for the HVAC system to be surveyed including modifications or rearrangements which are essential to conducting the survey.

2. A detailed description of the type of HVAC system, its features and functions is necessary especially for those who are not thoroughly acquainted with the system.

3. The current test and balance reports can provide information on air distribution and design vs. performance data. These reports may also indicate a specific component problem such as outdoor air requirements.

4. Reports of complaints regarding the indoor air quality (which should include the nature and location) are essential to conducting this survey. These reports may indicate a component problem such as a disconnected diffuser and the lack of air movement in an occupied zone.

In addition to the basic information, the walk-through survey includes observation or inspection of each of the HVAC system components for potential malfunction. The procedure or survey outline of the components together with specific notes follows.

1. **Outdoor Air** (see Figure 5-31):

   A. Intake location and physical condition

   B. Building exhaust stacks and vent pipes adjacent to intake

   C. Cooling tower, type, and location

   D. Building entryways, doors, and windows as potential entries for airborne contaminants

   E. Areas adjacent to the building as potential sources: shipping/receiving docks, parking lots, high traffic roads, adjacent buildings, and operations, etc.

2. **Dampers** (see Figure 8-11):

   A. Outdoor air; type and physical condition

   B. Return air; type and physical condition

   C. Face and by-pass; type and physical condition

   D. Exhaust/pressure relief; type and physical condition

3. **Air Cleaning** (see Figure 8-12):

   A. Type and general condition

   B. Prefilter; type, efficiency, and condition

   C. Final filter; type, efficiency, and condition

4. **Heating/Cooling Coils** (see Figure 8-13):

   A. Pre-heat; type and condition

   B. Cooling; type and condition

   C. Condensate pan and drain

   D. Re-heat; type and condition

5. **Fans/Blowers** (see Figure 8-14):

   A. Supply air; type and condition

   B. Return air; type and condition

   C. Exhaust/pressure relief; type and condition

6. **Humidifier/Dehumidifier** (see Figure 8-15):

   A. Type and general condition

   B. Condensate pan and drain

7. **Supply Air Distribution:**

   A. Duct system; type and general condition

   B. Control box; type and condition

   C. Control box function

   D. Control box/diffuser connection; type and condition

8. **Supply Air Diffusers** (see Figure 8-17):

   A. Type and general condition

   B. Characteristics of area served

   C. Number of diffusers this area

   D. Occupied zone airflow pattern; smoke test results

   E. Obstructions to flow pattern

9. **Return Air Grilles** (see Figure 8-17):

   A. Type, location, and general condition

   B. Airflow pattern, supply to return; smoke test

   C. Obstructions to flow pattern

10. **Return Air System:**

    A. Open plenum, general condition

    B. Location of return air opening; return air fan/duct

    C. Ducted return, location and general condition

    D. Balancing dampers; type and condition

11. **Miscellaneous Potential Contaminant Sources:**

12. **General Comments and Notes**

REFERENCES

8.1   The Trane Company, Trane Air Conditioning Manual, (February, 1961).

8.2   International Conference of Building Officials, Uniform Building Code, "Light, Ventilation and Sanitation", Section 605 (1988).

8.3   American Society of Heating, Refrigeration and Air Conditioning Engineers, Ventilation for Acceptable Indoor Air Quality, ASHRAE, Atlanta, GA.

8.4   American Society of Heating, Refrigeration and Air Conditioning Engineers, Thermal Environmental Conditions for Human Occupancy, ASHRAE, Atlanta. GA (1992).

8.5   American Society of Heating, Refrigeration and Air Conditioning Engineers, ASHRAE Handbook, 1992 HVAC Systems and Equipment (1992).

8.6   Rajhans, G. S.: "Findings of the Ontario Inter-Ministerial Committee on Indoor Air Quality", Proceedings of the ASHRAE/SOEN Conference, IAQ '89, ASHRAE, Atlanta, GA (1990).

8.7   American Society of Heating, Refrigeration and Air Conditioning Engineers: ASHRAE Handbook, Fundamentals. ASHRAE, Atlanta, GA (1989).

8.8   Bauer, E. J., et al, Use of Particle Counts for Filter Evaluation. ASHRAE Journal (October, 1973).

8.9   Duffy, G: "Filter Upgrades" Engineered Systems (July/August 1993).

8.10   Ottney, T. C.: Particle Management for HVAC Systems. ASHRAE Journal, page 23 (July, 1993).

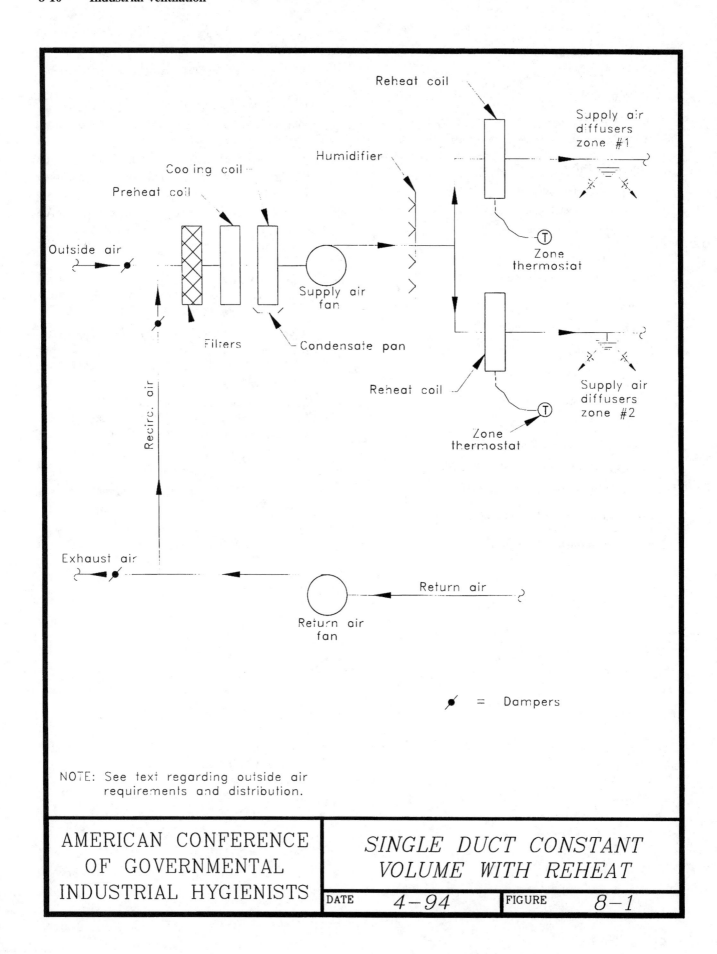

NOTE: See text regarding outside air
requirements and distribution.

AMERICAN CONFERENCE
OF GOVERNMENTAL
INDUSTRIAL HYGIENISTS

*SINGLE DUCT CONSTANT
VOLUME WITH REHEAT*

| DATE | 4—94 | FIGURE | 8—1 |

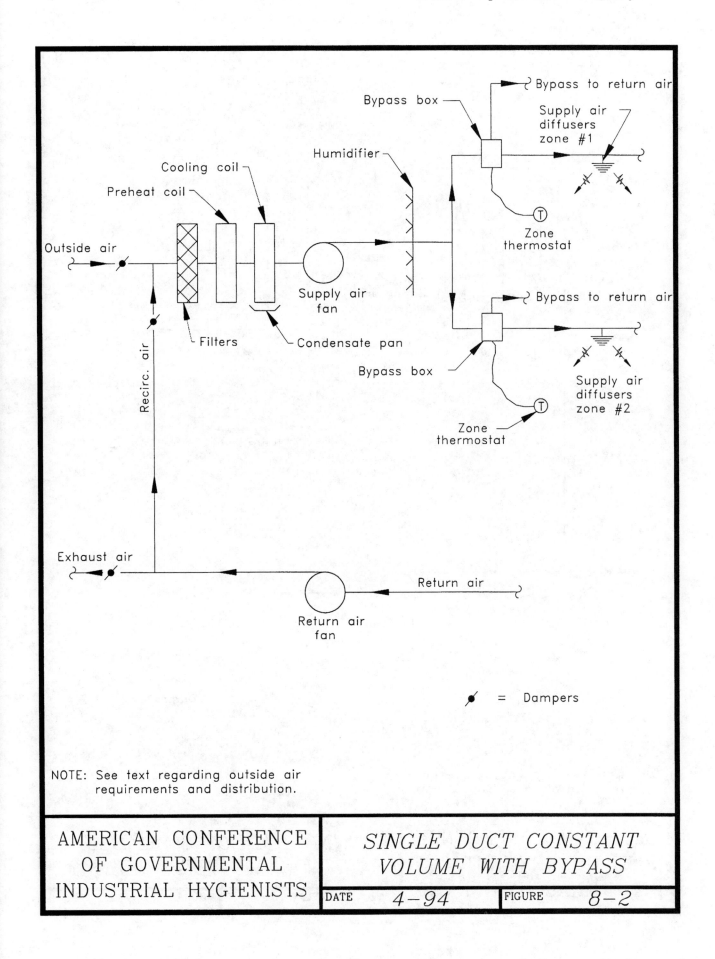

AMERICAN CONFERENCE
OF GOVERNMENTAL
INDUSTRIAL HYGIENISTS

SINGLE DUCT CONSTANT
VOLUME WITH BYPASS

DATE   4-94   FIGURE   8-2

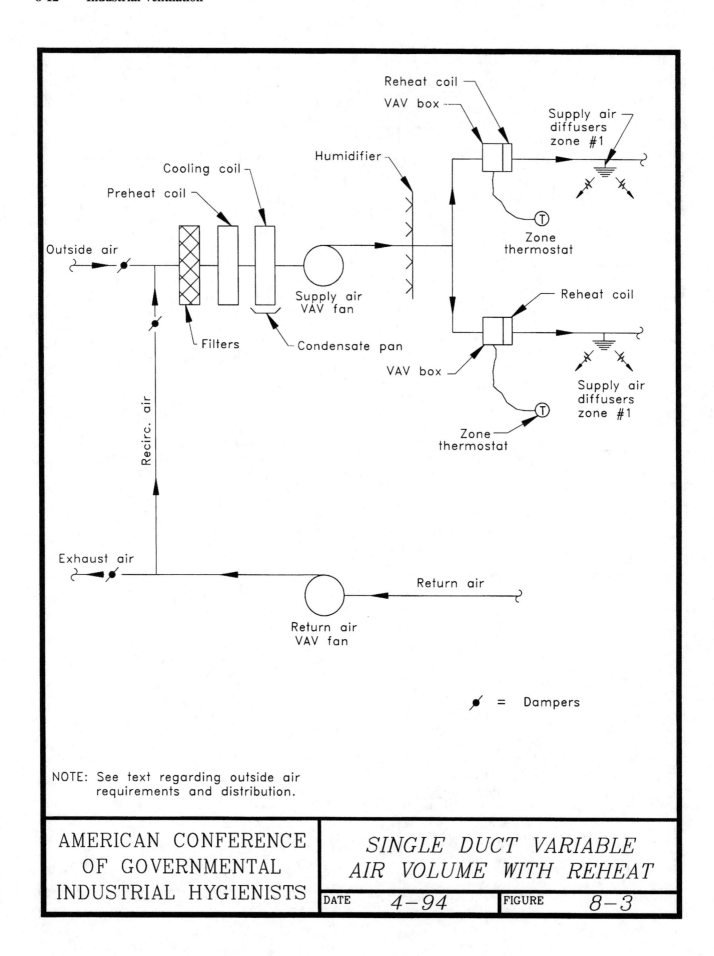

NOTE: See text regarding outside air
requirements and distribution.

AMERICAN CONFERENCE	SINGLE DUCT VARIABLE	
OF GOVERNMENTAL	AIR VOLUME WITH REHEAT	
INDUSTRIAL HYGIENISTS	DATE 4-94	FIGURE 8-3

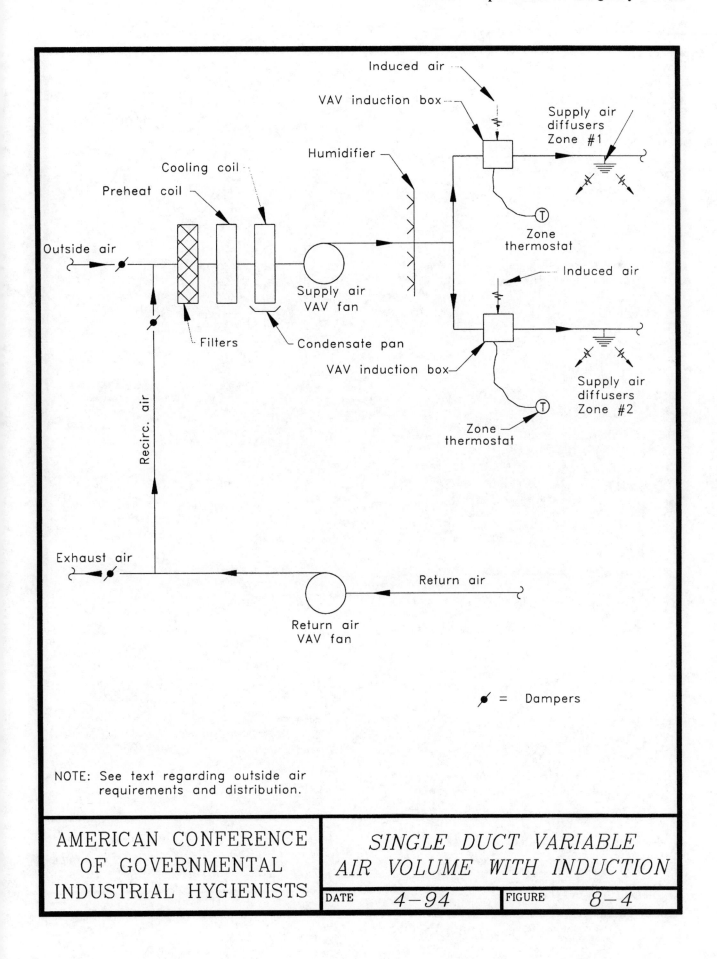

NOTE: See text regarding outside air
requirements and distribution.

AMERICAN CONFERENCE OF GOVERNMENTAL INDUSTRIAL HYGIENISTS	SINGLE DUCT VARIABLE AIR VOLUME WITH INDUCTION	
	DATE 4—94	FIGURE 8—4

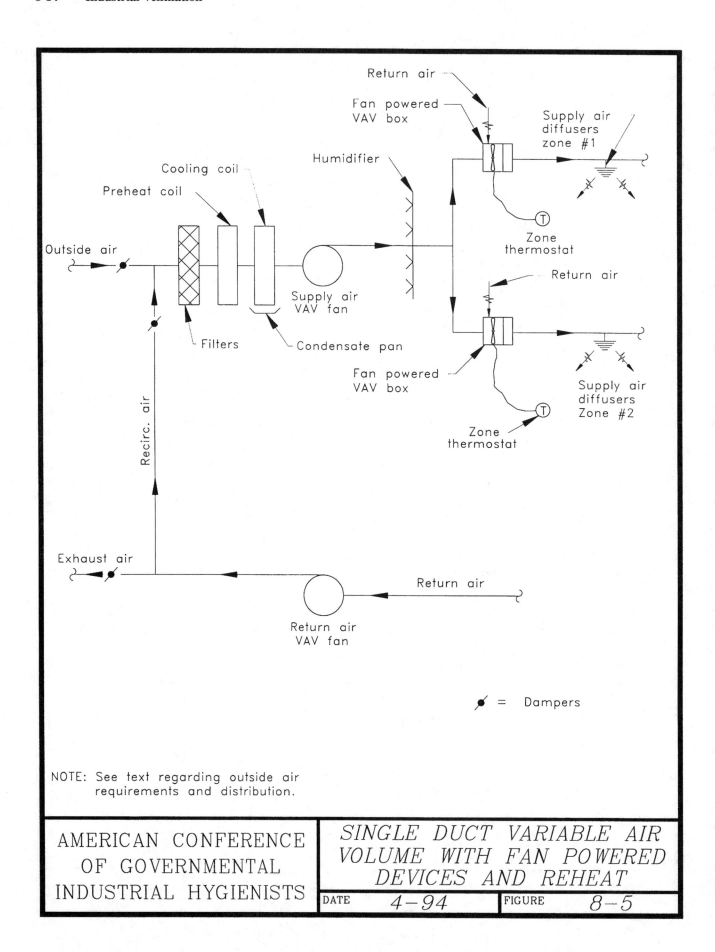

Outside air

Preheat coil

Cooling coil

Filters

Condensate pan

Supply air VAV fan

Humidifier

Recirc. air

Exhaust air

Return air VAV fan

Return air

Return air

Fan powered VAV box

Supply air diffusers zone #1

Zone thermostat

Fan powered VAV box

Zone thermostat

Supply air diffusers Zone #2

⊷ = Dampers

NOTE: See text regarding outside air requirements and distribution.

AMERICAN CONFERENCE OF GOVERNMENTAL INDUSTRIAL HYGIENISTS

SINGLE DUCT VARIABLE AIR VOLUME WITH FAN POWERED DEVICES AND REHEAT

DATE   *4—94*

FIGURE   *8—5*

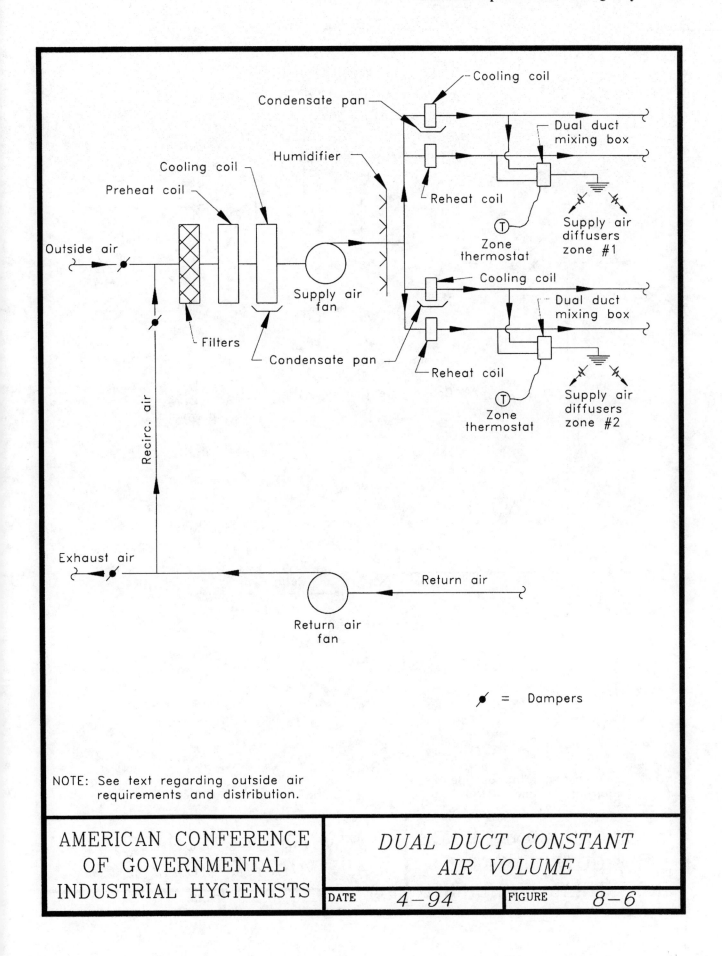

NOTE: See text regarding outside air
requirements and distribution.

AMERICAN CONFERENCE OF GOVERNMENTAL INDUSTRIAL HYGIENISTS	*DUAL DUCT CONSTANT AIR VOLUME*	
	DATE *4—94*	FIGURE *8—6*

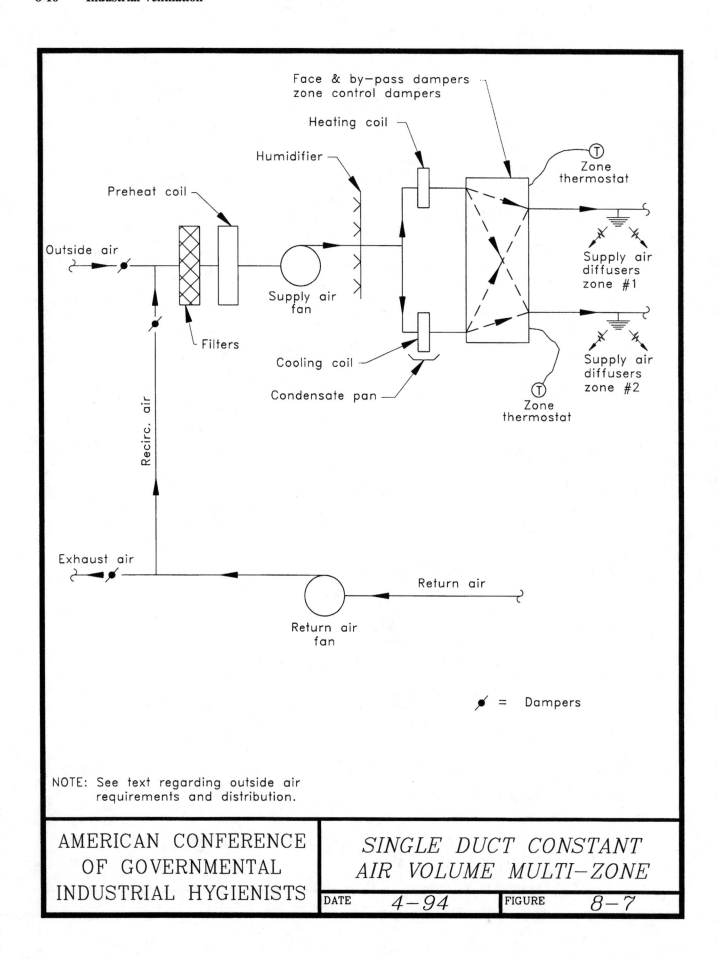

Face & by-pass dampers
zone control dampers

Heating coil

Humidifier

Preheat coil

Outside air

Supply air
fan

Filters

Recirc. air

Cooling coil

Condensate pan

Zone
thermostat

Supply air
diffusers
zone #1

Supply air
diffusers
zone #2

Zone
thermostat

Exhaust air

Return air

Return air
fan

≠ = Dampers

NOTE: See text regarding outside air
requirements and distribution.

AMERICAN CONFERENCE OF GOVERNMENTAL INDUSTRIAL HYGIENISTS	SINGLE DUCT CONSTANT AIR VOLUME MULTI-ZONE	
	DATE 4-94	FIGURE 8-7

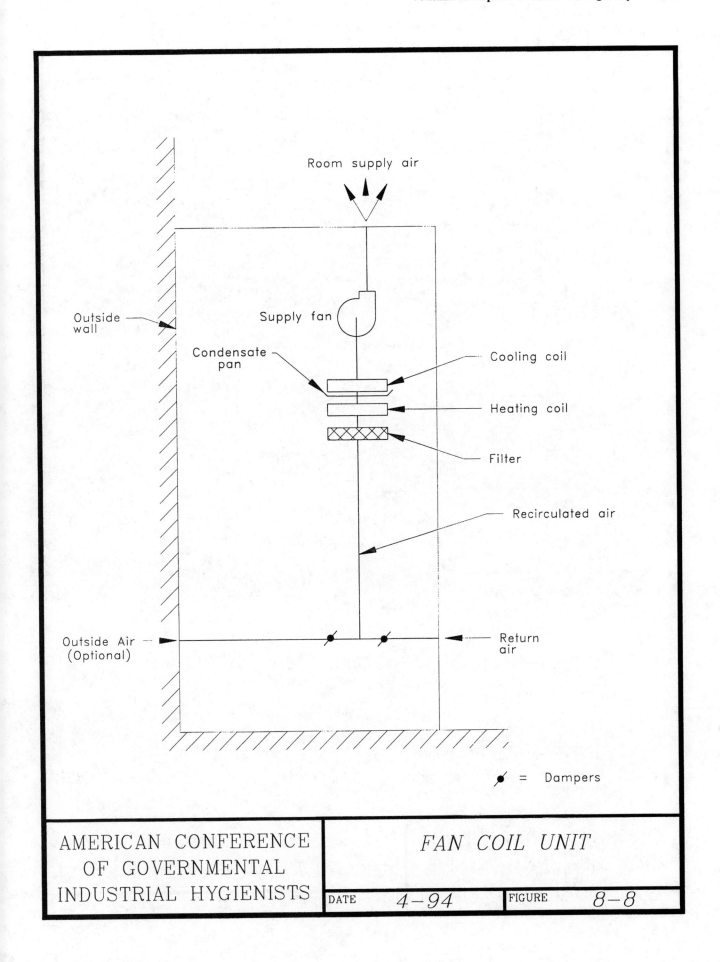

Room supply air

Outside wall

Supply fan

Condensate pan

Cooling coil

Heating coil

Filter

Recirculated air

Return air

Outside Air (Optional)

✦ = Dampers

AMERICAN CONFERENCE
OF GOVERNMENTAL
INDUSTRIAL HYGIENISTS

FAN COIL UNIT

DATE 4-94

FIGURE 8-8

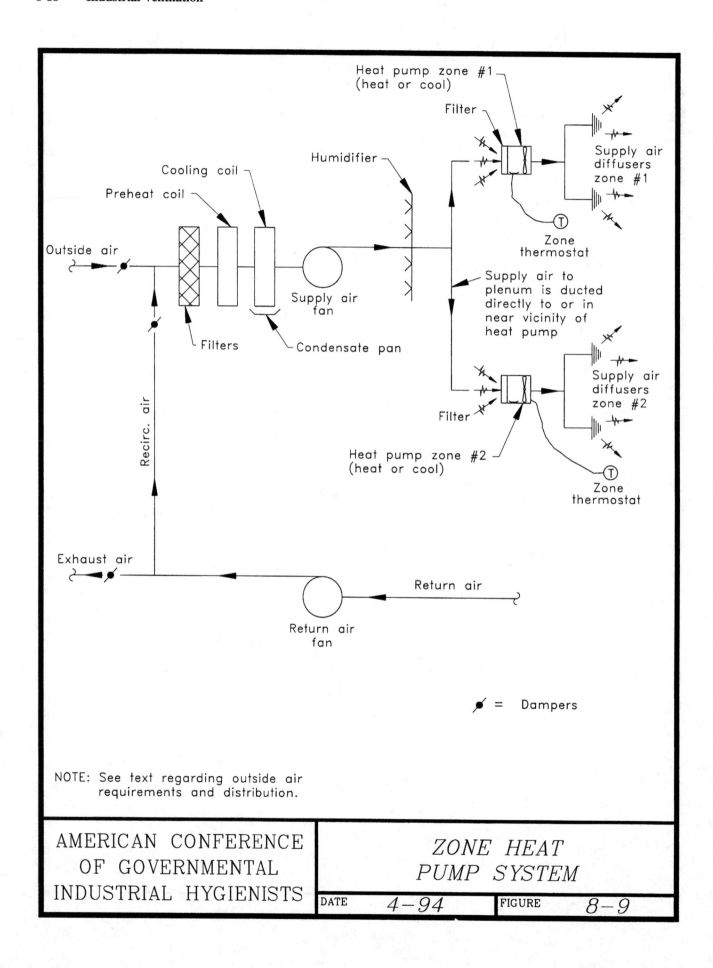

Heat pump zone #1
(heat or cool)

Filter

Supply air
diffusers
zone #1

Humidifier

Cooling coil

Preheat coil

Zone
thermostat

Outside air

Supply air to
plenum is ducted
directly to or in
near vicinity of
heat pump

Supply air
fan

Filters

Condensate pan

Recirc. air

Supply air
diffusers
zone #2

Filter

Heat pump zone #2
(heat or cool)

Zone
thermostat

Exhaust air

Return air

Return air
fan

$\rlap{/}{\bullet}$ = Dampers

NOTE: See text regarding outside air
requirements and distribution.

AMERICAN CONFERENCE OF GOVERNMENTAL INDUSTRIAL HYGIENISTS	*ZONE HEAT PUMP SYSTEM*	
	DATE *4—94*	FIGURE *8—9*

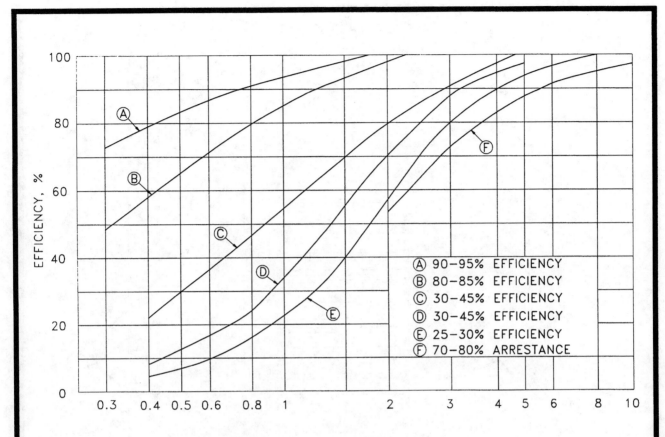

PARTICLE SIZE, MICROMETERS

Approximate Efficiency Versus Particle Size
for Typical Air Filters (See notes 1 & 2)

NOTE: 1. Compiled and averaged from manufacturer data
Efficiency and arrestance per ASHRAE Standard
52 – 76 Test Methods.
2. Caution: Curves are approximations only for general guidance.
Values from them must not be used to specify air filters,
since a generally recognized test standard does not exist.

From: ASHRAE Equipment

AMERICAN CONFERENCE OF GOVERNMENTAL INDUSTRIAL HYGIENISTS	FILTER EFFICIENCY VS PARTICLE SIZE	
	DATE *8-96*	FIGURE *8-10*

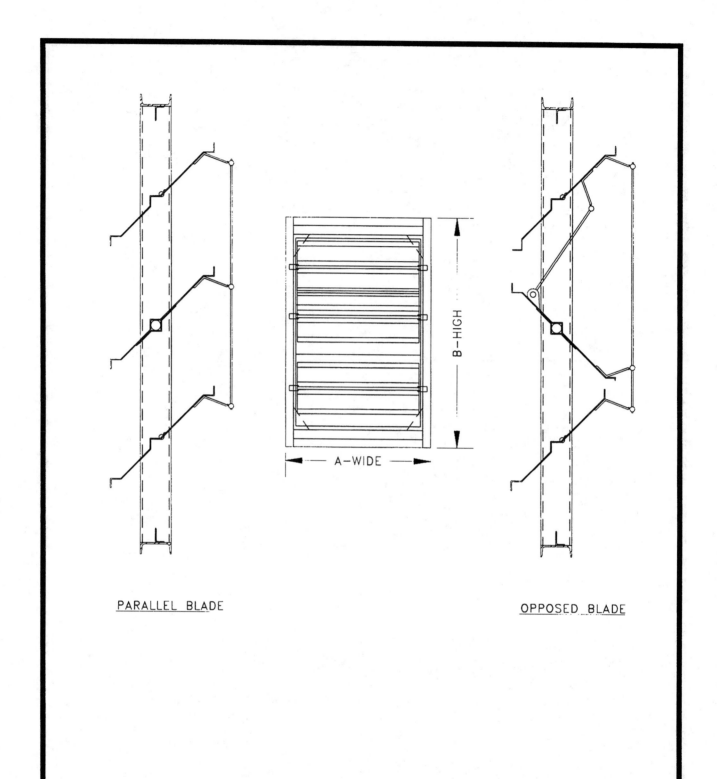

PARALLEL BLADE

OPPOSED BLADE

A—WIDE

B—HIGH

AMERICAN CONFERENCE OF GOVERNMENTAL INDUSTRIAL HYGIENISTS	DAMPERS: PARALLEL AND OPPOSED BLADE	
	DATE 02-97	FIGURE 8-11

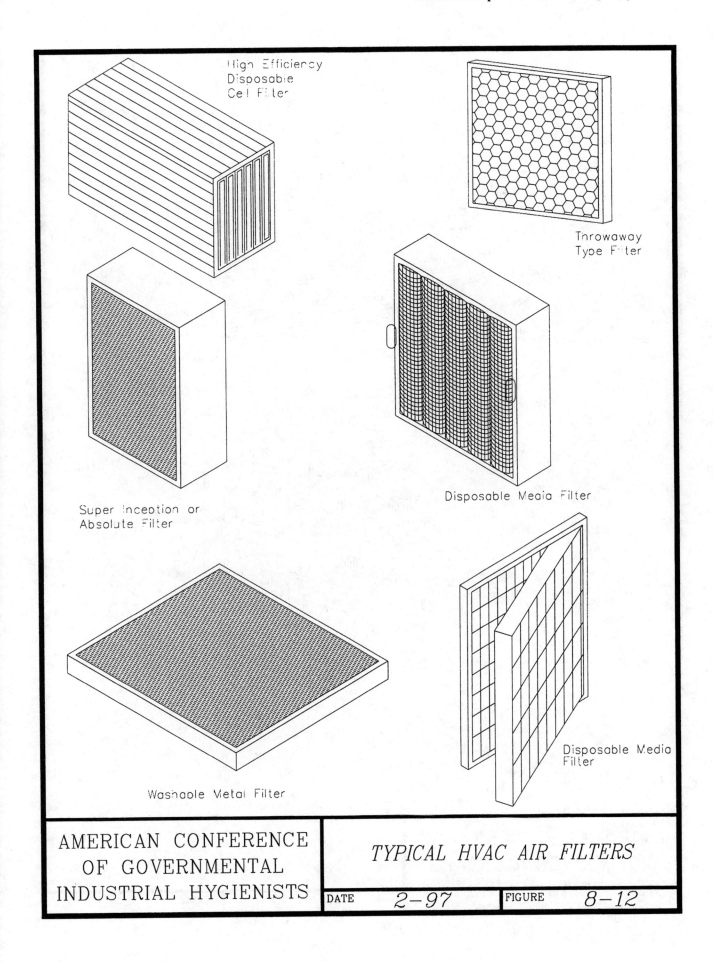

High Efficiency
Disposable
Cell Filter

Throwaway
Type Filter

Super Inception or
Absolute Filter

Disposable Media Filter

Washable Metal Filter

Disposable Media
Filter

AMERICAN CONFERENCE OF GOVERNMENTAL INDUSTRIAL HYGIENISTS	*TYPICAL HVAC AIR FILTERS*	
	DATE *2-97*	FIGURE *8-12*

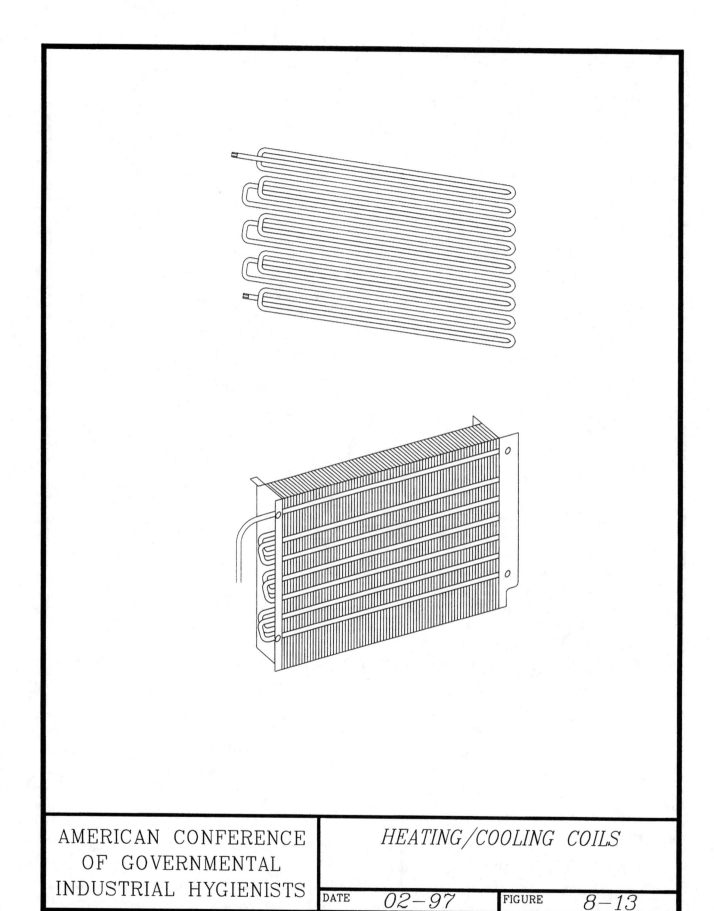

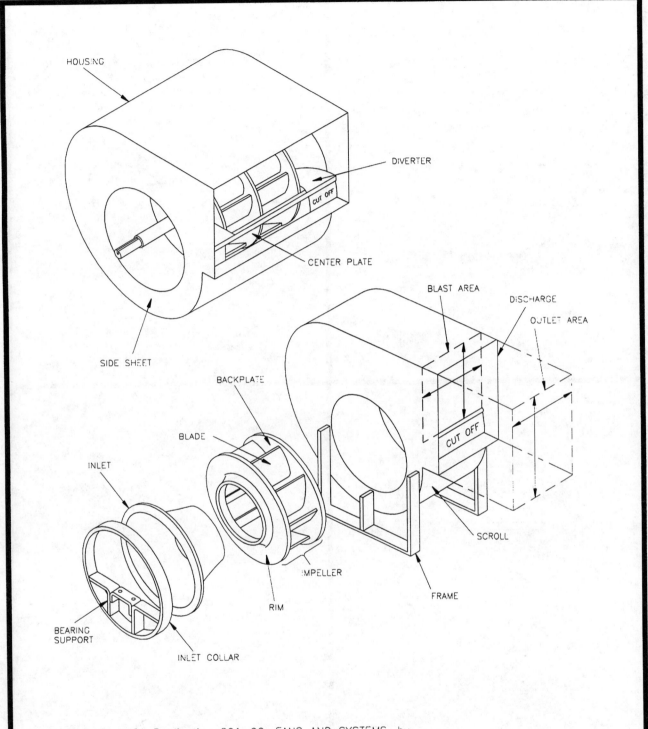

HOUSING

DIVERTER

CUT OFF

CENTER PLATE

SIDE SHEET

BLAST AREA

DISCHARGE

OUTLET AREA

BACKPLATE

BLADE

CUT OFF

INLET

SCROLL

IMPELLER

RIM

FRAME

BEARING
SUPPORT

INLET COLLAR

Reprinted from AMCA Publication 201-90, FANS AND SYSTEMS, by
permission of the Air Movement and Control Association, Inc.[6.1]

AMERICAN CONFERENCE OF GOVERNMENTAL INDUSTRIAL HYGIENISTS	*TERMINOLOGY FOR CENTRIFUGAL FAN COMPONENTS*	
	DATE *5-92*	FIGURE *8-14*

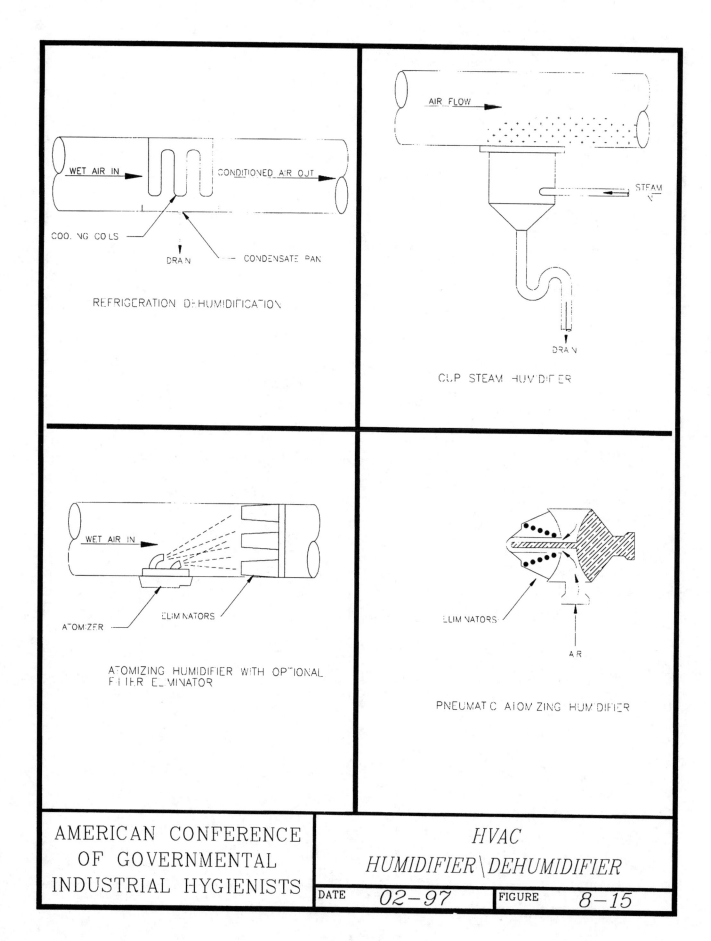

REFRIGERATION DEHUMIDIFICATION

CUP STEAM HUMIDIFIER

ATOMIZING HUMIDIFIER WITH OPTIONAL
FILTER ELIMINATOR

PNEUMATIC ATOMIZING HUMIDIFIER

AMERICAN CONFERENCE OF GOVERNMENTAL INDUSTRIAL HYGIENISTS	*HVAC HUMIDIFIER\DEHUMIDIFIER*	
	DATE *02-97*	FIGURE *8-15*

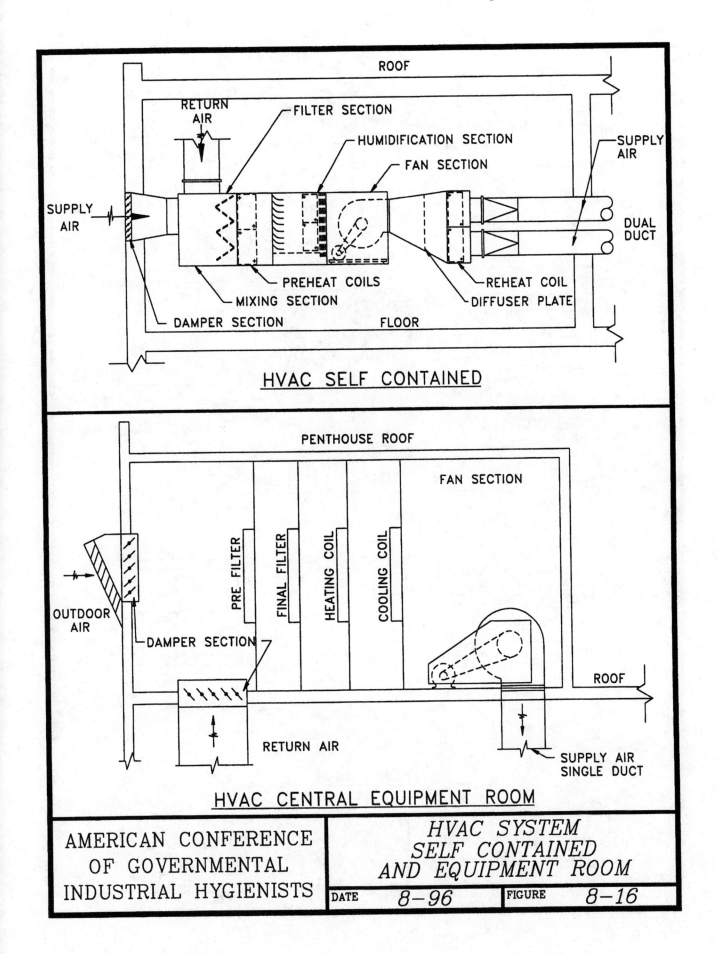

ROOF

RETURN AIR — FILTER SECTION

— HUMIDIFICATION SECTION

— FAN SECTION

SUPPLY AIR

SUPPLY AIR

DUAL DUCT

PREHEAT COILS

MIXING SECTION

DAMPER SECTION

FLOOR

REHEAT COIL

DIFFUSER PLATE

HVAC SELF CONTAINED

PENTHOUSE ROOF

FAN SECTION

PRE FILTER

FINAL FILTER

HEATING COIL

COOLING COIL

OUTDOOR AIR

— DAMPER SECTION

ROOF

RETURN AIR

SUPPLY AIR SINGLE DUCT

HVAC CENTRAL EQUIPMENT ROOM

AMERICAN CONFERENCE OF GOVERNMENTAL INDUSTRIAL HYGIENISTS	HVAC SYSTEM SELF CONTAINED AND EQUIPMENT ROOM	
	DATE 8-96	FIGURE 8-16

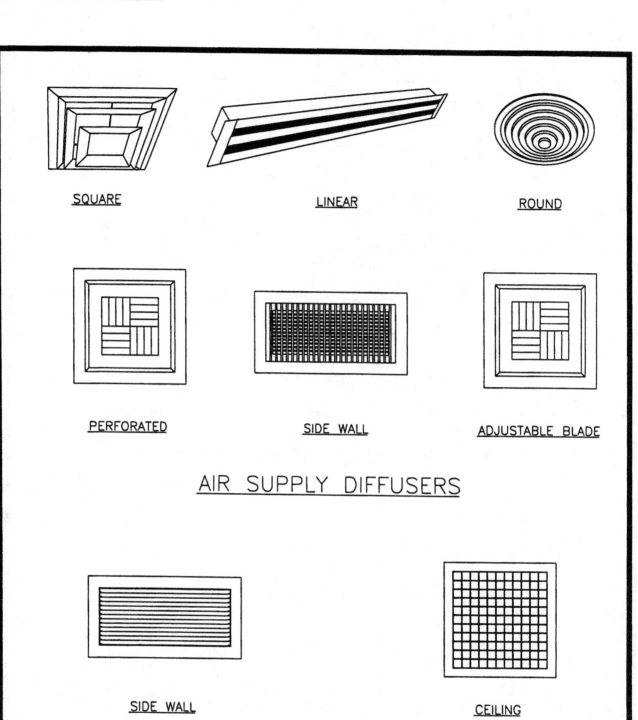

SQUARE

LINEAR

ROUND

PERFORATED

SIDE WALL

ADJUSTABLE BLADE

AIR SUPPLY DIFFUSERS

SIDE WALL

CEILING

RETURN AIR GRILLES

AMERICAN CONFERENCE OF GOVERNMENTAL INDUSTRIAL HYGIENISTS	AIR SUPPLY DIFFUSERS & RETURN AIR GRILLES	
	DATE 8-96	FIGURE 8-17

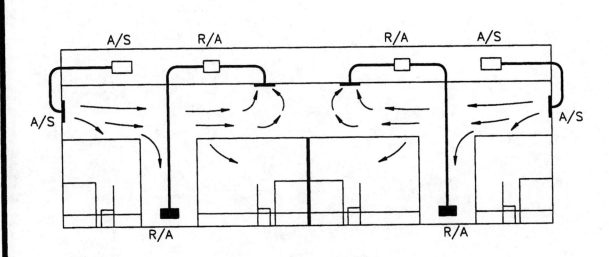

SIDE WALL SUPPLY
GRILLES

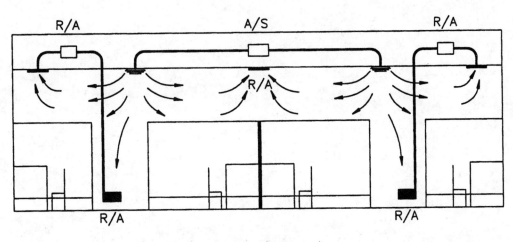

CEILING SUPPLY
GRILLES

AMERICAN CONFERENCE OF GOVERNMENTAL INDUSTRIAL HYGIENISTS	*TYPICAL PARTITIONED OFFICE AIR PATTERN*	
	DATE *8-96*	FIGURE *8-18*

Chapter 9
MONITORING AND TESTING OF VENTILATION SYSTEMS

9.1 INTRODUCTION

The effectiveness of ventilation systems in controlling contaminant exposures can be assured only by appropriate installation, operation, and maintenance of the system. For that reason, every system should be carefully inspected during and immediately after installation to insure that the system is installed as specified. Once the system is installed, it should be thoroughly tested before acceptance to determine if it functions as designed. Finally, to insure continuing performance, tests also should be made periodically throughout the life of the system and whenever there are complaints or other evidence of poor performance. Step-by-step procedures for such inspections and tests are listed at the end of this chapter.

If airflow levels decline, it is important to determine the cause. Until it is possible to see inside of ducts conveniently, practitioners must rely on indirect indicators of plugging, settling, and other problems within ducts. As will be discussed, the most convenient indicator is often changes in relationships between static pressures.

Early sections of this chapter discuss a variety of commonly used measurement devices and describe methods and techniques to insure that: (1) the measurements are as accurate as the device allows, (2) the measurements are representative of actual conditions, and (3) measurements are taken frequently enough to avoid long episodes of poor performance. Later sections list procedures and discuss techniques for inspecting and evaluating both new and long-installed systems.

9.1.1 Reasons for Monitoring System Performance Using Measured Airflows and Pressures: It is important to measure system pressures and airflows for many reasons, including:

1. Recording the initial performance of the system and determining if it is functioning in accordance with specifications.
2. Determining the degree of compliance with applicable codes or trade association standards.
3. Providing data upon which to base any necessary alterations to the system.
4. Obtaining data to assist in the design of future systems.
5. Determining whether the system has sufficient capacity for additional exhaust points or other alterations.

6. Obtaining data through periodic checks to determine when maintenance or repairs are necessary.

9.1.2 Measurements Necessary for Routine Monitoring:

Until hood effectiveness is evaluated routinely in the field using tracer gases or other direct measures of performance, practitioners must rely on indirect measures of hood (and thus system) effectiveness. An important indicator is level of airflow. Although very little is known about the sensitivity of hood effectiveness to changes in airflow levels, it is prudent to insure that hood airflow levels do not fall below recommended levels. In addition, a decline in hood airflow produces a corresponding decline in downstream duct velocities, increasing the risk of settling and plugging in particulate control systems. For that reason, a decline from specified (or previous) airflow levels should be considered a cause for concern unless extensive exposure sampling and lack of settling demonstrates otherwise.

It is important to measure airflow directly from time to time, but, as will be discussed more in succeeding sections, airflow measurement is time-consuming and is of limited value in diagnosing causes of changes. Measuring pressures often is faster and easier. Since changes in pressures can correlate to changes in airflow and to changes in resistance to flow, pressure measurements can be convenient indicators of potential problems.

The most important indirect indicators of system functioning are hood static pressure (SP_h) and airflow (Q) for each branch duct (see Figure 9-1), and the static pressure (SP_{end}) at the terminus of each run of duct (e.g., branch, submain, or main.) For example, for the portion of a system shown in Figure 9-1, the important measurements would be SP_{hA}, SP_{hB}, SP_{hC}, SP_{endA}, SP_{endB}, SP_{endC}, Q_A, Q_B, and Q_C. The recommended minimal schedule for those parameters is shown in Table 9-1.

It is recommended that levels of airflow be determined for each branch duct at least annually and whenever there has been a major alteration to the system (e.g., adding or removing a branch duct). Values of SP_h and SP_{end} should be measured at the same time (see Figure 9-1). For hoods that prevent high exposures to particularly hazardous airborne contaminants, values of SP_h should be measured at least monthly. For very high hazard hoods, values of SP_h should be displayed constantly and monitored on a daily basis. Any significant change should prompt an immediate investigation (see Section 9.10).

TABLE 9-1. Recommended Minimal Monitoring Schedule

Time since last measurement	Expect to find Alterations?	SP_h	Temp.*	SP_{end}	Fan Inlet	Across Air Cleaning Device	Traverse
< Month	No	Yes				Yes	
< Month	Yes	Yes		Yes		Yes	
< 2 Years	No	Yes		Yes	Yes	Yes	Yes
< 2 Years	Yes	Yes	Yes	Yes	Yes	Yes	Yes
> 2 Years	Of Course	Yes	Yes	Yes	Yes	Yes	Yes

*Temperature of the air through a branch duct. In many cases the duct temperature is about the same as the room temperature.

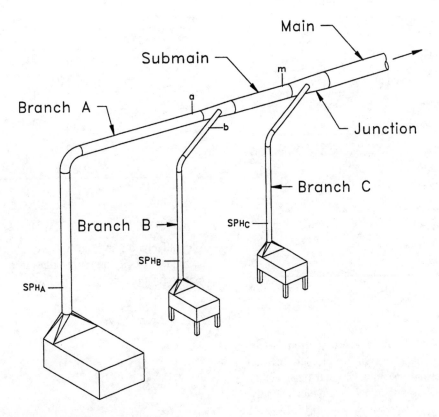

FIGURE 9–1. Example portion of system

9.1.3 Limitations of Monitoring: The monitoring and tests described in this guide pertain to measures of airflow, temperatures, and pressures. These tests are useful indicators of consistent behavior by systems in moving air through hoods, but they do not directly predict hood effectiveness in controlling exposures. For that reason, environmental and exposure sampling should be conducted prior to and after installation to verify system performance in reducing exposures and ambient contamination. The services of a qualified industrial hygienist may be required for sampling contaminant exposures.

9.2 COMPUTING AIR VELOCITY AND AIRFLOW RATE

There are no instruments suitable for measuring airflow rate (Q) directly. However, there are many instruments whose sensor output can be used to measure air velocity at a point. As is discussed in following sections, Q can be estimated from a representative sampling of point velocities and from knowledge of the cross-section area normal to flow.

9.2.1 Computing Airflow from Estimated Average Velocity: The estimated airflow can be computed from the average velocity multiplied by the cross-sectional area normal to the flow:

$$Q = VA \qquad [9.1]$$

where: Q = volumetric flow rate

A = average velocity normal to the cross-section

V = cross-sectional area of duct or hood at the measurement location

For example, if the average velocity in a 6-inch diameter duct (area = 0.196 ft^2) is 3000 fpm, the estimated airflow would be:

$$Q = (3000 \text{ fpm})(0.196 \text{ ft}^2) = 588 \text{ cfm}$$

For another example, if the average velocity at the face of a 3 ft by 4 ft enclosing hood is 100 fpm, the estimated airflow into the hood can be determined from:

$$Q = (100 \text{ fpm})(3 \text{ ft})(4 \text{ ft}) = 1200 \text{ cfm}$$

For this estimate of airflow to be accurate, the estimate of average velocity must be accurate. As discussed in the following section, it is unlikely that a single reading can provide an accurate estimate of the true average velocity.

9.2.2 Computation of Average Velocity from Multiple Velocity Readings: For the estimated velocity and airflow to be good estimates of the true values, the samples taken must be representative of the values at the cross-section and each individual reading must be accurate. The velocities of a hood face or duct cross-section are seldom uniform. For that reason, a single reading is seldom representative of the average. It is important to measure the velocities at several locations chosen to be representative, then compute the average of those values to estimate the true average. Stated mathematically:

$$V = \frac{1}{n} \sum_{i=1}^{n} V_i \qquad [9.2]$$

where: n = number of samples taken across area

$\quad\quad$ V_i = point velocity at i

$\quad\quad$ ΣV_i = sum of velocities

This computation is illustrated in the example table given below.

Example of Computing Average Velocity

First 5 V_i Values		Second V_i Values	
Point i	V_i fpm	Point i	V_i fpm
1	2000	6	2770
2	2510	7	2690
3	2613	8	2620
4	2700	9	2413
5	2780	10	2235

V_i = 2553

V = 2553

9.2.3 Computation of Average Velocity from Velocity Pressure:

It is much simpler to calibrate pressure measurement devices than thermal anemometers and other velocity measurement devices. Hence, if velocities are high enough to produce significant velocity pressures (e.g., 0.15 "wg), one should measure velocity pressures and compute the associated velocities rather than measuring the velocities with a thermal anemometer or other velocity meter. For standard density air, a velocity of 1500 fpm would produce a velocity pressure of 0.15 "wg. Velocity can be computed from observed velocity pressures if the air density is known or can be determined. For the velocity at a single point, i:

$$V_i = 1096 \sqrt{\frac{VP_i}{\rho}} \quad\quad\quad [9.3a]$$

$$V_i = 4005 \sqrt{\frac{VP_i}{df}} \quad\quad\quad [9.3b]$$

where: V_i = Velocity, fpm, at a single location, i

$\quad\quad$ VP_i = Velocity pressure, "wg, measured at a single location, i

$\quad\quad$ ρ = Density of the air in lb/ft^3

$\quad\quad$ df = Ratio of actual density to standard density

For conditions where the density factor is unity (standard density), velocities may be taken from Table 5-7A in Chapter 5.

Note that although a point velocity can be computed from a point velocity pressure, the average velocity cannot be computed from the average velocity pressure. Instead, when determining the average velocity from VP measurements, the average velocity must be computed by calculating the velocity from each individual velocity pressure (see examples in the following sections), then computing the average velocity from Equation 9.2.

Example Problem: Computing V from 10 VP_i Values

First 5 VP_i Values			Second 5 VP_i Values		
Point i	VP_i "wg	V_i fpm	Point i	VP_i "wg	V_i fpm
1	0.22	2003	6	0.35	2526
2	0.28	2259	7	0.33	2453
3	0.32	2415	8	0.32	2415
4	0.33	2453	9	0.30	2338
5	0.34	2489	10	0.24	2092

V = 4688 fpm

Note: computed using df = 0.88 and Equation 9.3b

Alternatively, the average velocity may be determined from individual velocity pressure values using either of the following two relationships:

$$V_1 = \frac{1096}{n\sqrt{\rho}} \sum_{i=1}^{n} \sqrt{VP_i} \quad\quad\quad [9.4a]$$

$$V_1 = \frac{4005}{n\sqrt{df}} \sum_{i=1}^{n} \sqrt{VP_i} \quad\quad\quad [9.4b]$$

Where: $\sum_{i=1}^{n} \sqrt{VP_i}$ = sum of square roots of all point velocity pressures

Note that the average velocity pressure (VP) is not computed as the mean of individual VP_i values but is instead estimated as:

$$VP = \rho \left(\frac{V}{1096} \right)^2 \qu\quad\quad [9.5a]$$

$$VP = df \left(\frac{V}{4005} \right)^2 \quad\quad\quad [9.5b]$$

9.2.4 Use of Pipe Factors:

The pipe factor (PF) is the ratio of the average velocity to the centerline velocity. There is a rule of thumb that the pipe factor is typically 0.90. Thus the average velocity can be estimated as 90% or some other fixed percentage of the centerline velocity (V_{cl}):

$$V = 0.90 V_{cl} \times A \quad\quad\quad [9.6]$$

However, the error from such estimates can exceed 20%, particularly when it is applied to measurements taken immediately downstream from an elbow or other disturbance to airflow. Indeed, Wang[9.19] found errors as high as 25% in a field study in which the best available locations were always employed. For this reason, pipe factors should not be used except to provide rough estimates of airflows.

9.2.5: Estimating Airflow from Hood Static Pressure:

Since hood static pressures are proportional to VP (see Chapter 5), it is possible to compute the value of VP from an observed value of SP_h if the value of the hood loss coefficient

(F_h) relating SP_h to VP is also known. Airflow can be estimated from (see Chapter 5 for F_h values):

$$Q = 1096A \sqrt{\frac{SP_h}{\rho(1 + F_h)}} \qquad \text{[9.7a]}$$

$$Q = 4005A \sqrt{\frac{SP_h}{df(1 + F_h)}} \qquad \text{[9.7b]}$$

Where: A = area of duct where SP_h is measured

F_h = hood entry loss coefficient

SP_h = magnitude of the hood static pressure (i.e., stated as a positive value)

The accuracy of this relationship depends on the accuracy of the observed value of SP_h, the density, and the F_h coefficient. Each can contribute substantial errors. For the latter, the values of F_h for flanged and tapered duct to hood transitions are well-established and can be used with confidence. Some others (especially for slot/plenum losses) are not as well documented and may vary considerably. In addition, there may be hidden obstructions and manufacturing defects that would invalidate the published value of F_h. Finally, slot/plenum hoods have two losses (i.e., entering the slot and entering the duct), so no single published value of F_h can be reliably applied for all slot/plenum hoods. However, if the air density in the room and the duct are the same, one could determine an equivalent total loss coefficient for a specific slot/plenum hood using the expected duct entry coefficient, F_h, and the expected coefficient for the slot, F_s:

$$\text{Equivalent } F = F_h + F_s(A_d/A_s)^2 \qquad \text{[9.7c]}$$

Where: A_d = cross-sectional area of the duct where SP_h will be measured

A_s = cross-sectional area of the slot openings

One could then substitute that F value for F_h in Equations 9.7a or 9.7b. For example, suppose a slot/plenum hood has an observed hood static pressure of 1.4 "wg, a df of 0.9, a slot area of 1.5 ft^2, a duct area of 0.79 ft^2, and a 45 degree rectangular to round taper from the plenum to the duct (i.e., $F_h = 0.25$) and a value of F_s of 1.78. Then the equivalent value to use in place of F_h in Equations 9.7a or 9.7b is:

$$\text{Equivalent } F = 0.25 + 1.78(0.90/1.5)^2 = 0.695$$

and,

$$Q = 4005A \,(0.79) \sqrt{\frac{1.4}{0.09(1 + 0.74)}} = 3031 \text{ cfm}$$

If the conditions for measurement are unacceptable immediately downstream of the duct connection to the hood, there may be no good alternative to measuring well downstream of the disturbing condition. However, that means that the hood transition will not be the only source of resistance to the flow. In that case, one could substitute the sum of coefficients for all intervening components along with F_h (including friction for that length of the duct) when computing Equations 9.7a, 9.7b, and 9.7c.

As a final alternative, if air density is not expected to change over time, one could use the value of SP_h and airflow observed above and estimate the new airflow from values of SP_h and a previous determination of air flow (Q_1):

$$Q_2 = Q_1 \sqrt{\frac{SP_{h_2}}{SP_{h_1}}} \qquad \text{[9.7d]}$$

Where: 1 = Time 1

2 = Time 2

For example, if the airflow were 2150 cfm when the hood static pressure was 1.32 "wg and now the pressure is 1.01 "wg, then if the hood has not been obstructed or altered, the airflow now can be computed as:

$$Q_2 = 2150 \text{ cfm} \sqrt{\frac{1.01}{1.32}}$$

In applying Equation 9.7d, no published loss coefficients are employed so it does not matter if the hood is compound (i.e., slot/plenum) or if the measurement was taken downstream of an elbow or other disturbance. However, the estimate will be inaccurate if the resistance to flow upstream of H has changed from Time 1 to Time 2.

9.2.6 Using Tracer Gases to Estimate Airflow: The principle of dilution sometimes is used to determine rate of airflow in a duct or hood.[9.2] A tracer gas of known concentration (C_{feed}) is metered (Q_{feed}) continuously as it is released into the hood or into the duct downstream of the hood. The diluted tracer gas concentration in the duct (C_{duct}) is measured 10 diameters distance further downstream. Since the mass flow rate of the tracer gas in the duct downstream must equal the rate the tracer gas was released upstream, then:

$$Q_{feed}C_{feed} = Q_{duct}C_{duct}$$

$$Q_{duct} = Q_{feed}C_{feed} / C_{duct} \qquad \text{[9.8]}$$

The tracer gas usually should be selected for the following characteristics: (1) ease of feeding into the airstream (i.e., a gas at room temperature); (2) convenience and accuracy of measurement at both the feed concentration and the diluted concentration; (3) not otherwise present in the process being studied; (4) not absorbed chemically or physically in the duct system; (5) non-reactive with other constituents of the gas stream; and (6) measurable at safe concentrations, non-explosive, and does not interfere with the process. Sulfur hexafluoride, nitrous oxide, and carbon dioxide are used frequently as tracer gases. Note that Equation 9.8 must be modified to subtract background concentrations when carbon dioxide is used as a tracer gas.

9.2.7 Correcting Meter Velocity Readings for Density: The scales for nearly all velocity meters are calibrated for standard density of air. If air density is non-standard, then that scale can be significantly in error. Note that it is the instrument readings—not the velocity—that should be "corrected" for density effects.

A Pressure Device That Displays Velocity Pressure: Manometers sense static and velocity pressures directly, so manometer readings for velocity pressure and static pressure require no correction for density. However, the velocity conversion scales often printed on manometers would be incorrect for non-standard air. This would apply to the velocity displays for digital manometers, inclined and vertical manometers, velometers, aneroid gauges, and most other gauges that respond directly to pressure changes.

If the instrument can display velocity pressure (VP), the actual velocity should be calculated from the velocity pressure measurement and the density (see discussion in Chapter 5 on density computations using Equation 9.3 or 9.4).

Pressure Devices That Display Only Velocity: Some instruments do not measure or display velocity pressure, yet have sensing mechanisms that report velocity values incorrectly if the air density is different from the density that existed during calibration. That is true for almost all mechanical devices (e.g., velometers). The practitioner can compute the correct velocity (V) from the meter reading (V_{meter}) of such a device by:

$$V = \frac{V_{meter}}{\sqrt{df}}$$ [9.9a]

Where: V = Actual velocity

V_{meter} = Velocity reading of instrument

df = Actual density/standard density

On the other hand, for devices that measure transfer of heat (e.g., thermal anemometers) compute the correct velocities from meter readings from:

$$V = \frac{V_{meter}}{df}$$ [9.9b]

Computing Estimated Density Factor: For the relatively low temperatures and humidities found in most ventilation systems, the density factor can be estimated from:

$$\omega = \frac{\text{mass of moisture}}{\text{mass of dry air}}$$ [9.10]

$$P_{bar} + P_{std}\left[1 - \left(C_o \times 10^{-6}\right) \times \text{Altitude}\right]^{5.258}$$ [9.11]

Where: C_o = 6.73 for altitude in feet

C_o = 20.5 for altitude in meters

Values of df can be determined from the psychrometric charts shown in Chapter 5 and P_{bar} can be determined from Table 5-10 in Chapter 5. The combined effects of altitude, duct pressure, temperature, and humidity on air density can be estimated from:

$$df = \left(\frac{P_{bar} + SP_{duct}}{P_{std}}\right)\left(\frac{T_{std}}{T_{act}}\right)\left(\frac{1 + \omega}{1 + 1.607\omega}\right)$$ [9.12a]

Where: P_{std} = 407 "wg or 760 mmHg or 101 kPa

T_{std} = 530 R or 294.3 K

T_{act} = (460 R + T_F) or (273 K + T_C)

It can be useful to state Equation 9.12 in terms of component density factors for the effects of pressure, temperature, and humidity on air density:

$$df = df_p \times df_t \times df_\omega$$ [9.12b]

Where: $df_p = \dfrac{P_{bar} + SP_{duct}}{P_{std}}$

$df_t = \dfrac{T_{std}}{T_{act}}$

$df_\omega = \dfrac{1 + \omega}{1 + 1.607\omega}$

The error associated with the use of Equations 9.12a and 9.12b increases as moisture levels and temperature increase, especially when coupled with elevations well above sea level. For those cases, the density factor should be determined from psychrometric charts drawn for that altitude (see Chapter 5, Figures 5-20 to 5-23). Note that Equations 9.12a and 9.12b do not consider density effects due to combustion products or very high contamination levels (e.g., >2% by ratio of contaminant mass to dry air mass).

Computing the effects of static pressure in the duct on density can be tedious to employ when doing pressure calculations for system design since the static pressure depends on the density and the density depends on the static pressure, forcing iterative solutions. Furthermore, the effects of static pressure on density are typically much less than 3% for conditions upstream of an air cleaning device. For those reasons, it is common practice to ignore effects of static pressure (not barometric pressure!) on density except at air cleaning devices and fan inlets:

$$df = df_p^1 \times df_p \times df_\omega$$ [9.12c]

Where: $df_p^1 = \left(\dfrac{P_{bar}}{P_{std}}\right)$

For systems expected to have relatively high duct pressures (e.g., >5 "wg upstream of the fan and air cleaning device), a slightly more accurate alternative would be to use half of the expected average pressure (e.g., 2.5 "wg) upstream of the fan and air cleaning device.

Density is important in interpreting the output of most pressure and velocity measuring devices. In general, any device that attempts to convert velocity pressures to velocities without computing the effects of density will display incorrect values. Some electronic instruments can sense the temperature in the duct and automatically account for temperature effects with internal computations. However, there are none to date that measure barometric pressure or humidity and automatically account for it in determining the actual velocity.

9.2.8 When Is It Safe to Ignore Density Effects? It is sometimes asserted that small deviations from standard conditions produce small errors which may be safely ignored. It is true that a 5% error due to density will occur for a deviation of 30 F in temperature, a change of 1,000 ft in altitude, or a deviation of 20 "wg in static pressure. Furthermore, a 5% deviation due solely to moisture is not possible at 70 F.

However, a combination of deviations from standard conditions can produce errors much higher than that due to a single factor. For example, conditions of 100 F, +1,000 ft altitude, and -20 "wg pressure, and 50% relative humidity would produce a combined error in density of roughly 20% and an error in velocity of 10%. Thus, one could be well within the "safe" range for each parameter yet produce more than a 5% total error. For another example, ignoring simultaneous deviations of +17 F, + 800 ft and -12 "wg would produce a combined error greater than 5%.

These combined effects are not uncommon since such deviations from standard all generally tend to decrease the density of air. Ventilated air is seldom cooled to substantially below 70 F, altitudes are seldom substantially less than sea level, and humidity cannot be less than zero (i.e., dry air). On the contrary, altitudes frequently exceed 500 ft, air usually has some moisture, many systems have duct temperatures somewhat above 70 F, and every exhaust system necessarily has some ducts with negative pressures.

The practitioner should evaluate all density parameters before concluding that the density factor is close enough to unity to ignore computing the actual value. As was discussed earlier, accounting for the effects of duct pressure on density is difficult to do using calculators and spreadsheet computer programs. Since the effects are rarely large upstream of the air cleaner or fan, one can ignore that contribution for most systems except when selecting the air cleaning device and fan.

EXAMPLE 1: Computation of Velocity from Velocity Pressure for "Non-Standard Conditions"

Consider a system with a velocity pressure reading of 1.0 "wg taken with a Pitot tube in a duct where the dry-bulb temperature is 300 F, the moisture content is negligible and the static pressure is -23.5 "wg. The system is installed at an elevation of 5,000 ft. What would the density and actual velocity be at that point?

Since the moisture content is low, Equations 9.10, 9.11, and 9.12a can be used directly to determine the density factor.

From Equation 9.10: $\omega = \dfrac{0}{\text{mass of dry air}} = 0$

From Equation 9.11: $P_{bar} = 407\text{"wg}[1 - (6.73 \times 10^{-6}) \times 5000\ \text{ft}]^{5.285} = 340\text{"wg}$

From Equation 9-12a:

$$df = \left(\frac{340 - 23.5}{407}\right)\left(\frac{530}{460 + 300}\right)\left(\frac{1 + 0}{1 + 1.607 \times 0}\right)$$

From Equation 9.9b: $V = 4005 \times \sqrt{\dfrac{1.01}{1.32}} = 5440\ \text{fpm}$

Note that the value of velocity would have been 4005 fpm—an error of 26%—if density effects had been ignored.

EXAMPLE 2: Swinging Vane Corrected for Density

A swinging vane anemometer is used to determine the velocity in a duct at sea level where the dry-bulb temperature is 250 F, the SP = -10 "wg and moisture is negligible. What is the actual duct velocity if the anemometer reading is 3150?

From Equation 9-10: $\omega = \dfrac{0}{\text{mass of dry air}} = 0$

From Equation 9.11: $P_{bar} = 407\text{"wg}[1 - (6.73 \times 10^{-6}) \times 0\text{ft}]^{5.285} = 407\text{"wg}$

From Equation 9-12a: $df_p = \left(\dfrac{407 - 10}{407}\right) = 0.975$

$$df_t = \left(\frac{530}{460 - 250}\right) = 0.746$$

$$df_\omega = \left(\frac{1 + 0}{1 + 1.607 \times 0}\right) = 1.000$$

From Equation 9-12.b: $df = df_p \times df_t \times df_\omega =$ (0.975)(0.746)(1.000) = 0.727

From Equation 9.9b:

$$V = 3150\ \text{fpm} \times \sqrt{\frac{1}{0.727}} = 3694\ \text{fpm}$$

EXAMPLE 3: VP Traverse for Nearly Dry Air

Measurement of air velocity at non-standard conditions requires calculation of the true air velocity, accounting for difference in air density due to air temperature, humidity, and barometric pressure. The following calculations illustrate the method of calculation and the effect of varying air density.

Conditions: SP = +2 "wg; Air Temp. = 79 F;
Wet-Bulb Temp. = 50 F

True Barometer = 720 mm Hg;
Duct diameter = 24"

From Figure 5-17: = 3 grains moisture/lb dry air = 3 grains $\times$ (1.43 $\times$ 10^{-4} lbs/grain)

From Equation 9-11: P_{bar} = 407 "wg 720 mm HG/760 mm HG = 385.4 "wg

Note: Even in high altitude cities, local weather stations usually report barometric pressure as if the normal value were 760 mm Hg. The computation here must use the true value, not the so-called "corrected value."

From Equation 9-12a:

$$df = \left(\frac{385.4 + 2}{407}\right)\left(\frac{530}{460 + 79}\right)\left(\frac{1 + 0}{1 + (1.607 \times 0)}\right) = 0.936$$

Solution Using Equation 9.12a

Vertical Traverse			Horizontal Traverse		
Traverse Pt	VP, "wg	V, fpm	Traverse Pt	VP	V, fpm
1	0.22	1941	1	0.23	1985
2	0.28	2190	2	0.27	2151
3	0.32	2341	3	0.33	2378
4	0.33	2378	4	0.34	2413
5	0.34	2413	5	0.34	2413
6	0.35	2449	6	0.35	2449
7	0.33	2378	7	0.34	2413
8	0.32	2341	8	0.32	2341
9	0.30	2267	9	0.32	2341
10	0.24	2028	10	0.25	2069
V = 2273			V = 2295		

Note: Computed using df = 0.936 and Equation 9.3a or 9.3b.
Note that the centerline value is not included in the computations.

Airflow: $Q = V\, A_{duct}$

$$A = \pi\left(\frac{D}{2}\right)^2 = \pi\left(\frac{24/12}{2}\right)^2 = (24"/24)^2\ \text{ft}^2 = 3.142\ \text{ft}^2$$

$$Q = \left(\frac{2273 + 2295}{2}\right)\ \text{fpm} \times 3.142\ \text{sq ft} = 7176\ \text{cfm} = 7176\ \text{acfm}$$

EXAMPLE 4: VP Traverse for Moist Air

Elevated Temperature: Air Temp. = 150 F;
Wet-Bulb Temp. = 87.5 F

SP = −2 "wg; Barometer = P_{std};
12" Inside Diameter Duct

From Figure 5-18: ω = 0.15 lbs of moisture/lb of dry air

From Equation 9-11: P_{bar} = 407 "wg

From Equation 9-12a:

$$df = \left(\frac{407 - 2}{407}\right)\left(\frac{530}{460 + 150}\right)\left(\frac{1 + 0.15}{1 + (1.607 \times 0.15)}\right) = 0.801$$

Note: If the effect of static pressure (SP) in the duct on density were ignored, then df = 0.805, a difference of only 0.5%. The computations below use the slightly less accurate value.

Solution Using Equation 9.12a for Density Factors

Vertical Traverse			Horizontal Traverse		
Traverse Pt	VP, "wg	V, fpm	Traverse Pt	VP	V, fpm
1	0.22	2094	1	0.23	2141
2	0.28	2362	2	0.27	2319
3	0.32	2525	3	0.33	2564
4	0.33	2564	4	0.34	2603
5	0.34	2603	5	0.34	2603
6	0.35	2641	6	0.35	2641
7	0.33	2564	7	0.34	2603
8	0.32	2525	8	0.32	2525
9	0.30	2445	9	0.32	2525
10	0.24	2187	10	0.25	2232
V = 2451			V = 2476		

Note: Computed using df = 0.805 and Equation 9.3a or 9.3b.
Note that the centerline value is not included in the computations.

TABLE 9-2A. Recommended Traverse Insertion Depths for Rectangular Ducts

No. of Insertions	Traverse Position									
	1	2	3	4	5	6	7	8	9	10
5	0.074	0.288	0.500	0.712	0.926					
6	0.061	0.235	0.437	0.563	0.765	0.939				
7	0.053	0.203	0.366	0.500	0.634	0.797	0.947			

Distance from wall in fractions of a duct dimension, Log-Tchebycheff rule. Minimum of 25 points.

TABLE 9-2B. Recommended Traverse Insertion Depths for Round Ducts

No. of Insertions	Traverse Position									
	1	2	3	4	5	6	7	8	9	10
4	0.043	0.290	0.710	0.957						
6	0.032	0.135	0.321	0.679	0.865	0.968				
8	0.021	0.117	0.184	0.345	0.655	0.816	0.883	0.979		
10	0.019	0.077	0.153	0.217	0.361	0.639	0.783	0.847	0.923	0.981

Distance from wall in fractions of a duct diameter, log-linear rule.

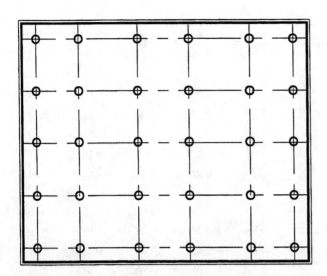

FIGURE 9–2. Insertion depths for rectangular ducts

Airflow: $Q = V \times A_{duct}$

$$A = \pi \left(\frac{D}{2}\right)^2 = \pi \left(\frac{12/12}{2}\right)^2 \text{ft}^2 = \pi \ (12 \text{ in}/24)^2 \text{ft}^2 = 0.786 \text{ ft}^2$$

$$Q = \left(\frac{2451 + 2476}{2}\right) \text{fpm} \times 0.786 \text{ ft}^2 = 1936 \text{ cfm} = 1936 \text{ acfm}$$

9.3 REPRESENTATIVE SAMPLING FOR VELOCITIES

As stated earlier, air flowing through a duct is not uniform (see Section 9.3.2), particularly if there are obstructions upstream. The velocity generally will be lowest at the skin of the duct and it usually will increase with distance from the skin to a maximum value at the center of the duct. Thus a center-line velocity will tend to over estimate the average velocity.

9.3.1 Traverse Insertion Depths: To accurately estimate mean velocity, one should take measurements at representative points across the entire cross-section of the duct (a "traverse"). For sampling locations to be representative, every packet of airflow should have an equal chance of being sampled. The measurement locations listed in Tables 9-2A and 9-2B (also see Figures 9-2 and 9-3) provide the greatest accuracy for the least number of measurement locations for rectangular and round ducts respectively.[9.1]

Note that the insertion depths recommended in Tables 9-2A and 9-2B are different from those shown in earlier editions of *Industrial Ventilation*. The values also differ from those required by the Environmental Protection Agency for stack sampling.

Note, also, that centerline values are not used to compute average velocities. However, the centerline value can be useful for quick comparisons and should be taken along with the traverse values (see following sections).

The more sampling points that are measured and the more they are spread across the cross-section, the less deviation there will be between the true average velocity and the average of the measurements taken. For a round duct, use of two or more diameters is more efficient than taking the same number of measurements along a single diameter. For example, it is much better to take two 10-point traverses, one perpendicular to the other (see Figure 9-3) than to take 20 measurements along the same diameter. Furthermore, for diameters less than 10 inches the insertion depths are too closely packed to take more than 10 points along a given traverse. The optimum for accuracy for round ducts is 8 insertion points along each of 3 equally separated traverse diameters. However, 10-point traverses along two perpendicular diameters is nearly as accurate and is more convenient.

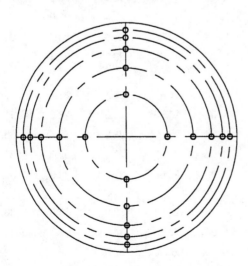

Insertion depths for
two 10-pt. traverses

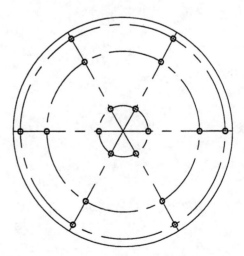

Insertion depths for
three 6-pt. traverses

FIGURE 9–3. Insertion depths for round ducts

TABLE 9-2C. 10-Point Log-linear Traverse Points

Dia.	No. 1	No. 2	No. 3	No. 4	No.5	Mid	No. 6	No. 7	No. 8	No. 9	No. 10
1.0	0.019	0.077	0.153	0.217	0.361	0.50	0.639	0.783	0.847	0.923	0.981
3.0	0.06	0.23	0.46	0.65	1.08	1.50	1.92	2.35	2.54	2.77	2.94
3.5	0.07	0.27	0.54	0.76	1.26	1.75	2.24	2.74	2.96	3.23	3.43
4.0	0.08	0.31	0.61	0.87	1.44	2.00	2.56	3.13	3.39	3.69	3.92
4.5	0.09	0.35	0.69	0.98	1.62	2.25	2.88	3.52	3.81	4.15	4.41
5.0	0.10	0.39	0.00	1.09	1.81	2.50	3.20	3.92	4.24	4.62	4.91
5.5	0.10	0.42	0.84	1.19	1.99	2.75	3.51	4.31	4.66	5.08	5.40
6.0	0.11	0.46	0.92	1.30	2.17	3.00	3.83	4.70	5.08	5.54	5.89
7.0	0.13	0.54	1.07	1.52	2.53	3.50	4.47	5.48	5.93	6.46	6.87
8.0	0.15	0.62	1.22	1.74	2.89	4.00	5.11	6.26	6.78	7.38	7.85
9.0	0.17	0.69	1.38	1.95	3.25	4.50	5.75	7.05	7.62	8.31	8.83
10	0.19	0.77	1.53	2.17	3.61	5.00	6.39	7.83	8.47	9.23	9.81
11	0.21	0.85	1.68	2.39	3.97	5.50	7.03	8.61	9.32	10.15	10.8
12	0.23	0.92	1.84	2.60	4.33	6.00	7.67	9.40	10.16	11.1	11.8
13	0.25	1.00	1.99	2.82	4.69	6.50	8.31	10.18	11.0	12.0	12.8
14	0.27	1.08	2.14	3.04	5.05	7.00	8.95	10.96	11.9	12.9	13.7
15	0.29	1.16	2.30	3.26	5.42	7.50	9.59	11.75	12.7	13.8	14.7
16	0.30	1.23	2.45	3.47	5.78	8.00	10.22	12.5	13.6	14.8	15.7
18	0.34	1.39	2.75	3.91	6.50	9.00	11.50	14.1	15.2	16.6	17.7
20	0.38	1.54	3.06	4.34	7.22	10.00	12.78	15.7	16.9	18.5	19.6
22	0.42	1.69	3.37	4.77	7.94	11.00	14.06	17.2	18.6	20.3	21.6
24	0.46	1.85	3.67	5.21	8.66	12.00	15.34	18.8	20.3	22.2	23.5
26	0.49	2.00	3.98	5.64	9.39	13.00	16.61	20.4	22.0	24.0	25.5
28	0.53	2.16	4.28	6.08	10.11	14.00	17.89	21.9	23.7	25.8	27.5
30	0.57	2.31	4.59	6.5	10.83	15.00	19.17	23.5	25.4	27.7	29.4
32	0.61	2.46	4.90	6.9	11.55	16.00	20.45	25.1	27.1	29.5	31.4
34	0.65	2.62	5.20	7.4	12.27	17.00	21.73	26.6	28.8	31.4	33.4
36	0.68	2.77	5.51	7.8	13.00	18.00	23.00	28.2	30.5	33.2	35.3
38	0.72	2.93	5.81	8.2	13.72	19.00	24.28	29.8	32.2	35.1	37.3
40	0.76	3.08	6.12	8.7	14.44	20.00	25.56	31.3	33.9	36.9	39.2
42	0.80	3.23	6.43	9.1	15.16	21.00	26.84	32.9	35.6	38.8	41.2
44	0.84	3.39	6.73	9.5	15.88	22.00	28.12	34.5	37.3	40.6	43.2
46	0.87	3.54	7.04	10.0	16.61	23.00	29.39	36.0	39.0	42.5	45.1
48	0.91	3.70	7.34	10.4	17.33	24.00	30.67	37.6	40.7	44.3	47.1
50	0.95	3.85	7.65	10.9	18.05	25.00	31.95	39.2	42.4	46.2	49.1

Note: Do not include midpoint in determining average velocity.

TABLE 9-2D. 8-Point Log-linear Traverse Points

Dia.	No. 1	No. 2	No. 3	No. 4	Mid	No. 5	No. 6	No. 7	No. 8
1.0	0.021	0.117	0.184	0.345	0.50	0.655	0.816	0.883	0.979
3.0	0.06	0.35	0.55	1.04	1.50	1.97	2.45	2.65	2.94
3.5	0.07	0.41	0.64	1.21	1.75	2.29	2.86	3.09	3.43
4.0	0.08	0.47	0.74	1.38	2.00	2.62	3.26	3.53	3.92
4.5	0.09	0.53	0.83	1.55	2.25	2.95	3.67	3.97	4.41
5.0	0.11	0.59	0.92	1.73	2.50	3.28	4.08	4.42	4.90
5.5	0.12	0.64	1.01	1.90	2.75	3.60	4.49	4.86	5.38
6.0	0.13	0.70	1.10	2.07	3.00	3.93	4.90	5.30	5.87
7.0	0.15	0.82	1.29	2.42	3.50	4.59	5.71	6.18	6.85
8.0	0.17	0.94	1.47	2.76	4.00	5.24	6.53	7.06	7.83
9.0	0.19	1.05	1.66	3.11	4.50	5.90	7.34	7.95	8.81
10	0.21	1.17	1.84	3.45	5.00	6.55	8.16	8.83	9.79
11	0.23	1.29	2.02	3.80	5.50	7.21	8.98	9.71	10.8
12	0.25	1.40	2.21	4.14	6.00	7.86	9.79	10.6	11.7
13	0.27	1.52	2.39	4.49	6.50	8.52	10.6	11.5	12.7
14	0.29	1.64	2.58	4.83	7.00	9.17	11.4	12.4	13.7
15	0.32	1.76	2.76	5.18	7.50	9.83	12.2	13.2	14.7
16	0.34	1.87	2.94	5.52	8.00	10.5	13.1	14.1	15.7
18	0.38	2.11	3.31	6.21	9.00	11.8	14.7	15.9	17.6
20	0.42	2.34	3.68	6.90	10.0	13.1	16.3	17.7	19.6
22	0.46	2.57	4.05	7.59	11.0	14.4	18.0	19.4	21.5
24	0.50	2.81	4.42	8.28	12.0	15.7	19.6	21.2	23.5
26	0.55	3.04	4.78	8.97	13.0	17.0	21.2	23.0	25.5
28	0.59	3.28	5.15	9.66	14.0	18.3	22.8	24.7	27.4
30	0.63	3.51	5.52	10.4	15.0	19.7	24.5	26.5	29.4
32	0.67	3.74	5.89	11.0	16.0	21.0	26.1	28.3	31.3
34	0.71	3.98	6.26	11.7	17.0	22.3	27.7	30.0	33.3
36	0.76	4.21	6.62	12.4	18.0	23.6	29.4	31.8	35.2
38	0.80	4.45	6.99	13.1	19.0	24.9	31.0	33.6	37.2
40	0.84	4.68	7.36	13.8	20.0	26.2	32.6	35.3	39.2
42	0.88	4.91	7.73	14.5	21.0	27.5	34.3	37.1	41.1
44	0.92	5.15	8.10	15.2	22.0	28.8	35.9	38.9	43.1
46	0.97	5.38	8.46	15.9	23.0	30.1	37.5	40.6	45.0
48	1.01	5.62	8.83	16.6	24.0	31.4	39.2	42.4	47.0
50	1.05	5.85	9.20	17.3	25.0	32.8	40.8	44.2	49.0

Note: Do not include midpoint in determining average velocity.

TABLE 9-2E. 6-Point Log-linear Traverse Points

Dia.	No. 1	No. 2	No. 3	Mid	No. 4	No. 5	No. 6
1.0	0.032	0.135	0.321	0.5	0.679	0.865	0.968
3.0	0.10	0.41	0.96	1.50	2.04	2.60	2.90
3.5	0.11	0.47	1.12	1.75	2.38	3.03	3.39
4.0	0.13	0.54	1.28	2.00	2.72	3.46	3.87
4.5	0.14	0.61	1.44	2.25	3.06	3.89	4.36
5.0	0.16	0.68	1.61	2.50	3.40	4.33	4.84
5.5	0.18	0.74	1.77	2.75	3.73	4.76	5.32
6.0	0.19	0.81	1.93	3.00	4.07	5.19	5.81
7.0	0.22	0.95	2.25	3.50	4.75	6.06	6.78
8.0	0.26	1.08	2.57	4.00	5.43	6.92	7.74

Note: Do not include midpoint in determining average velocity.

Determining the minimum number of measurement points for rectangular ducts is more complicated since the aspect ratio can vary from 1:1 to 5:1 or higher. *ASHRAE FUNDAMENTALS*[9.2] recommends a minimum of 25 points. The maximum distance between any two points should be 8 inches.

If the measurement point is preceded by 7 or more duct diameters of straight duct with no obstructions, fewer traverse points will give acceptable results. For that reason, Table 9-2A shows traverse insertion depths for 5, 6, and 7-point traverses for rectangular ducts and Table 9-2B shows traverse insertion depths for 6, 8, and 10-point traverses for round ducts.[9.2] Tables 9-2C, 9-2D, and 9-2E show 10 insertion depths for a variety of round duct sizes for 10-, 8-, and 6-point traverses.

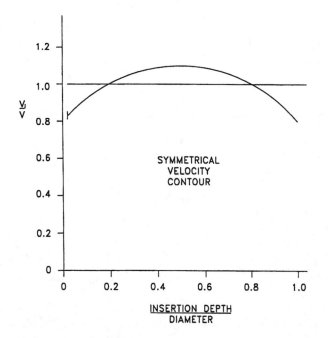

FIGURE 9–4. "Ideal" velocity contour

9.3.2 Probe Alignment and the Effects of Obstructions to Flow in a Duct: For each individual measurement to be accurate, in many instruments it is important that the sensing probe be oriented properly to airflow. That requires, for example, that the visible stem of a Pitot tube be aligned with the duct so that the unseen probe opening is in line with the airflow. If the airflow is aligned with the duct, a plot of the velocities across the duct is typically symmetrical with the highest velocity in the center (see Figure 9-4).

The air stream will not align well with the duct just downstream from a duct entry (i.e., the hood), obstruction, elbow, or junction—making it difficult to position the probe properly. One can learn to recognize effects of upstream disturbances (e.g., elbows) by the shape of the velocity contours (see Figures 9-5 and 9-6[9.12]). As shown in Figure 9-5, the velocity contour just downstream of a plain duct opening is symmetrical but becomes more parabolic in shape the closer the measurements are taken to the duct opening. In Figure 9-6 one can see that the profile perpendicular to the plane of an elbow is quite symmetrical while the profile in the plane can be highly asymmetric. As is discussed in the following sections, symmetry does not insure accuracy and asymmetry does not preclude accurate measurements.

For those reasons, velocity and velocity pressure measurements ideally are taken at least 7 duct diameters downstream from elbows, duct entries, or other major obstructions to straight-line airflow. Measurement should be taken at least one duct diameter *upstream* from the same obstruction. If it is not possible to find or use a location that meets those restrictions, one must make do with the best available location. For such relatively poor conditions, it is crucial that two perpendicular traverses be done instead of relying on a single diameter traverse. A two-diameter traverse can be surprisingly accurate even when velocity contours are highly asymmetric. For example, use of two diameter traverses should produce less than 6%

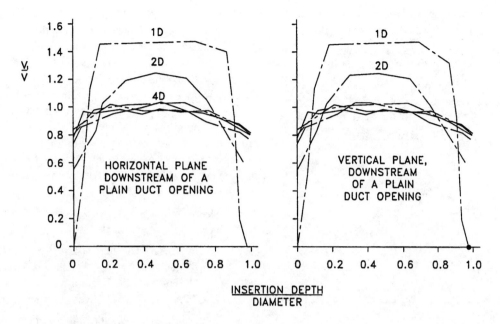

FIGURE 9–5. Velocity contours downstream of a plain duct opening

error when taken only 2 diameters distance downstream from smooth elbows.[9.12] Note in Figures 9-5 and 9-6[9.12] that accuracy may be good even when velocity profiles are highly asymmetrical. Table 9-3 suggests some reasonable distances downstream and upstream from different disturbances.

It is also important that any probe or instrument inserted into the airstream be small compared to the duct cross-section. The larger the obstruction to flow, the greater the error due to the changes in flow direction introduced by the obstruction. As a rule of thumb, the probe or device should have a cross-sectional area normal to flow that is less than

one-twentieth of the cross-section. For Pitot tubes, for example, one should select the thinnest, readily available Pitot tube long enough to traverse the diameter comfortably. Under some conditions, larger diameter stems must be used because thin-stemmed Pitot tubes plug more readily with water and particulates.

9.3.3 Velocity Traverses of Hood Faces: It is likely that airflow that is substantially lower than design values will be associated with degraded performance for a given hood. Therefore, it is prudent to maintain hood velocities at levels that meet or moderately exceed recommended levels.

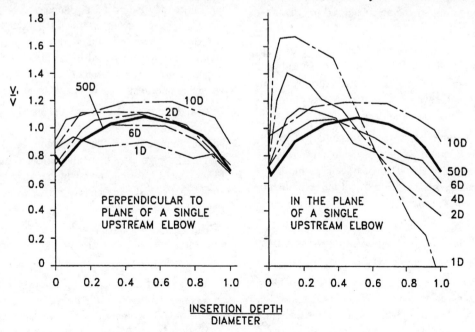

FIGURE 9–6. Velocity contours downstream from a single elbow

TABLE 9-3. Recommended Minimum Distances from Disturbances for SP, VP, and Velocity Measurement Locations

Condition	Location of Measurement Point in Multiples of The Duct Diameter, D		
	Downstream of Condition for VP or V Traverse	Downstream of Condition for SP	Upstream of Condition
45° Tapered Hood Connection	6	2	N/A
Flanged Hood Connection or Takeoff	7	3	N/A
90% Radius Elbow	7	4	1
Junction Fitting	7	6	3
Damper or Fan	12-20	6-20	2-4

In most cases, the most accurate way to determine the average velocity at an open hood face is to determine the airflow using Pitot traverses of the branch duct connected to the hood, then divide the airflow by the open cross-sectional area of the hood face. However, it can be desirable to measure velocities directly at the hood face if:

1. Only a rough check is needed.

2. The duct is difficult to access.

3. The duct velocity is too low for accurate VP measurement in Pitot traverses (e.g., < 1500 fpm).

In addition, a traverse of the hood face provides information on the uniformity and stability of the velocities at the hood face. The following points should be considered in evaluating such data:

1. A mean face velocity that is moderately higher (e.g., < 20%) than recommended values may produce lower exposures and is unlikely to increase exposures compared to those that would have existed at recommended levels for the same conditions.

2. It is generally undesirable for the magnitude of velocities to deviate more than plus or minus 20% from the mean velocity spatially. This is especially true if the lowest velocities are less than 80% of the recommended velocity and the source is near the face of the hood.

3. It is undesirable for the values to vary with time at a given location by more than plus or minus 20% from the mean value.

Excessive spatial and temporal variability are associated with turbulent conditions outside of the hood, replacement air approaching the hood face at a high velocity or perpendicular to the hood face, and with obstructions inside the hood, especially those near the face.

In some cases large eddies at the face of the hood can be energetic enough to push flow out of the hood at specific locations, leading to very poor hood effectiveness. Such reverse flows can be difficult to detect with most low velocity instruments. Some instruments cannot record a negative value and will simply show a zero value. Others (i.e., thermal anemometers) will display positive values even if airflow is moving out of the hood instead of into it. Therefore, if some individual values are far below the mean value, one should employ smoke or other means to visualize the flow; find the cause of the large eddies; and then take action to restore uniformity to the flow.

Measuring face velocities is similar to measuring duct velocities in some respects. It is important to:

1. Divide an enclosing hood face into equal areas and sample the center points of each area. Note that one would NOT use the log-linear traverse values shown in Table 9.2A since the objective is to assess non-uniformity.

2. Measure all velocities in the same plane while orienting the probe properly.

3. At each measurement point, hold the probe in place at least 30 seconds or long enough to collect at least ten measurements—whichever is longer. The mean velocity for a given point is then determined from the average of the values recorded during the sampling period.

Items 2 and 3 are difficult to do unless the probe is held by a camera tripod, microphone stand, or something similar.

For the latter, it should be noted that apparent levels of spatial variability can be exaggerated by temporal variations. In other words, the velocity at a given point will vary with time. Hence, even if the mean value at each individual point were the same, they would falsely appear to be different because some readings were taken when the value at that point happened to be low and others were taken when the value at another location happened to be high. For that reason, it is important to sample repeatedly over 30 seconds or more and use the temporal average of the measured values at each point.

To facilitate taking average samples, many electronic devices sample values several times over some set or adjustable time period (the "time constant") and compute the moving average over that time before refreshing the instrument display. It is important to note that the "hold" function on some electronic devices causes the peak value to be displayed, not the moving average.

The location of the probe is also important. Keeping the probe in the correct plane is important and can be difficult for enclosing hoods:

1. It is not always clear what plane is appropriate. As a practical matter, for unobstructed openings it always should be at least one inch inside the enclosure. For hoods with sashes (e.g., laboratory hoods), the plane should be at the center of the sash depth. For walk-in

booths where workers are completely inside the hood, it should be at the cross-section where workers would stand while exposed to contaminants.

2. Values generally fall rapidly if the probe wanders outside the face of enclosing hoods. It is difficult to hold a probe in one place without allowing it to wander up or down or side to side.

Avoiding distorting the probe readings due to probe movement or obstructions to flow is also important:

1. If the arm is fully extended, arm tremor can introduce enough movement to the probe tip to inflate the instrument reading of air velocity. The solution is to avoid supporting the wand or probe solely by hand. For example, one can press the base of a thermal anemometer wand or the forearm holding the wand against one edge of the hood face. A better solution is to mount the probe on a camera tripod.

2. Some instruments have no detachable probe and cannot be read unless one is standing in the hood or at the face of the hood. The body changes the airflow patterns, making interpretation of readings difficult. These types of instruments should not be used in such cases.

Although any low-velocity anemometer can be used to measure the low velocities typically found at hood faces, thermal anemometers are the most frequently used because of their convenience and quick responses. The wand and probe are thin enough to have little effect on airflow patterns and the wand's length allows one to keep one's body out of the airstream near the probe.

9.3.4 Velocity Measurements Near Capturing Hoods: For capturing hoods one is concerned about the velocity at the source locations, not the average face velocity (which has no direct relevance). Thus, one measures velocities at the boundary of the source at the greatest distance from the hood opening. Many of the issues and problems associated with enclosing hoods apply in measuring velocities near capturing hoods.

1. One should select the measurement locations. However, they may not be in a plane. Instead, they would follow the boundary of the source emissions.

2. The lowest velocity in the region of contaminant release may be of greater interest than the average velocity.

3. As with enclosing hoods, the investigator should avoid distorting the velocity patterns with the instrument or his or her body. Although it seems unrealistic to do so, it may be best to determine velocities without the worker in place. It simply is not clear how to interpret the effects of the worker's body on velocity profiles. To investigate deleterious effects of the worker's body, release a non-irritating smoke at the source while the worker is working normally.

4. As with enclosing hoods, the probe should be held steadily in place, ideally with a camera tripod. At the least, one should take advantage of fixed objects to steady the probe.

9.4 PRESSURE MEASUREMENT

It is possible to measure static pressure accurately using either a wall pressure or a Pitot tube probe. As with velocity measurements, it is important when measuring static pressures that the probe be aligned correctly with airflow and that the measurement location be chosen to avoid conditions that are difficult to measure accurately. There are four conditions that produce error: (1) Venturi effects due to flow disturbances at the opening of the probe; (2) measurement error due to probe not being perpendicular to flow; (3) sampling error, especially when a single reading is taken and is falsely assumed to equal the mean value; and (4) incomplete conversion of energy from kinetic to potential energy.

9.4.1 Wall Pressure Measurements: At the inner wall of a duct, airflows are parallel to the duct (and perpendicular to the hole) unless elbows or other disturbances are immediately upstream. In general, the average of several wall pressures at a perpendicular cross-section should equal the true mean across the duct.

If the static pressure is uniform across the duct then a single reading taken at a small, clean hole in the duct may accurately represent the average value across the duct. However, conditions upstream that would disturb the airflow, (e.g., a nearby elbow, damper, hood duct entry, fan, etc.) can easily render a single reading unrepresentative of the true average. For such conditions or when greater accuracy is desired, measurements should be taken at three holes drilled equally spaced around the perimeter. The average of the three locations is used to estimate the mean static pressure at the cross-section.

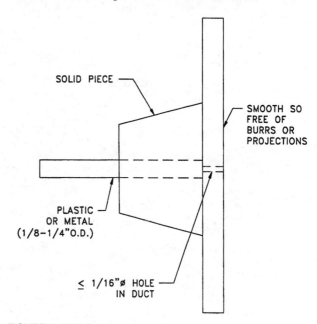

FIGURE 9–7. Wall pressure mount

If wall pressure data is taken, the static pressure opening should be flush with the inner surface of the pipe wall and there should be no burrs or projections on the inner surface. This is extremely difficult to do with a punch and very difficult to do with a drill, especially for holes larger than 1/16 inch (see Figure 9-7). The hole should be as small as possible both to avoid reducing projections inside the duct and to avoid Venturi effects due to air flowing over the hole. Note that the holes can fill quickly with particulate contaminants. Care also should be taken not to widen the hole when cleaning it out.

Wall pressures are sometimes measured through a small clean hole in a duct which is covered by a "suction cup" probe. The suction cup is then connected to a sensor using plastic tubing. Such suction cup probes are often used with thermal anemometers, velometers, and other devices that cannot sense pressure but report it by measuring airflow through a calibrated orifice. It is important that the suction cup cover the hole in the duct completely to prevent leakage. In practice it is difficult to determine whether the suction cup is tightly sealed on the duct.

9.4.2 Pitot Tubes Used for SP Measurements: Given the difficulties in creating and maintaining clean holes in the duct, taking measurements through a probe inserted into the duct is often more convenient unless continuous monitoring is desired. However, simply inserting a hollow tube into the duct can produce substantial errors due to Venturi and stem effects. The error will vary with the velocity pressure, distance from the duct wall, and other factors. A Pitot tube should be used instead (see Figure 9-8).

Note that there are two sources of error if the airflow is not inline with the flow due to upstream conditions or other factors. The first is the error of measurement that occurs if the probe is out of line with the flow by more than 5%. The second is due to the practice of computing mean velocity pressure from the average velocity rather than integrating the square of the velocity over the cross-sectional area. That shortcut introduces an error that varies with the velocity profile of the flow. For the conditions far downstream of disturbances it is roughly 2%. For conditions immediately downstream of a disturbance, the error can be 10% or more. As long as all readings are based on good conditions, their effects cancel when comparing one good condition to another. However, if some measurements are taken under poor conditions, the errors may be neither small nor self-canceling.

9.5 USING PITOT TUBE PROBES WITH PRESSURE SENSORS

Pitot tubes are probes used to conduct pressure to a pressure sensor, such as an inclined, U-tube or digital manometer. The Pitot tube is actually a tube-within-a-tube. As shown in Figure 9-8, the inner tube is a straight conduit for total pressure while the outer tube conducts static pressure only. If the TP "leg" and the SP "leg" are connected to opposite sides of a manometer, the fluid level is affected by SP equally on both sides, leaving only the effects of VP. Hence, VP can be observed simply by connecting both legs of the Pitot tube to a manometer (see Figure 9-9).

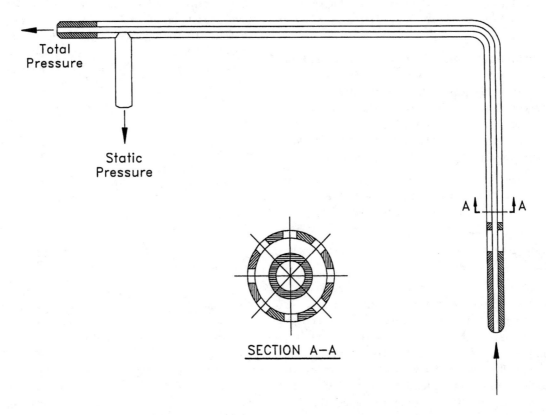

FIGURE 9–8. Pitot tube

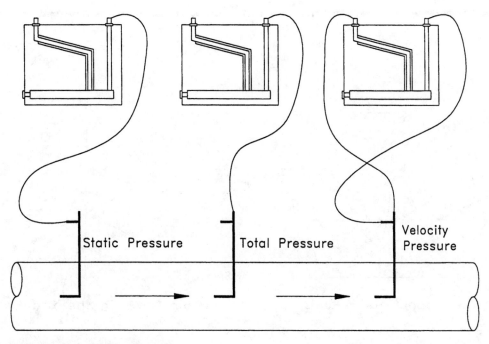

FIGURE 9–9. Pitot tube connection for different pressures

Static pressure and VP measurements should be taken perpendicular to airflow to avoid errors due to the effects of velocity pressures. For that reason, the Pitot tube is inserted with its stem perpendicular to the duct and its probe in line with the airflow. In this orientation, the static pressure openings on the probe are perpendicular to the airflow.

9.5.1 Insertion Depth for Static Pressure Measurements: For static pressure measurements (see Figure 9-9), the Pitot tube should be inserted to the centerline of the duct. If poor uniformity is suspected, one can traverse the ducts for SP. If the values vary significantly, a location farther downstream should be employed, if possible. As with velocity pressure traverses, one should use the smallest Pitot tube that can conveniently reach the desired insertion depths.

9.5.2 Alignment with Airflow: The probe of a Pitot tube must be directly inline with the flow to avoid so-called "yaw" and "pitch" errors. For the probe to be inline to the flow, one must keep the stem perpendicular to the duct and the static pressure leg aligned with the duct (see Figures 9-10, 9-11, and 9-12).

9.5.3 Making Standard Pitot Tubes More Convenient to Use: Holding a Pitot tube at a particular insertion depth while holding the stem perpendicular to the duct with its probe inline with flow certainly sounds tedious, and it can be. However, some practical pointers may reduce the degree of difficulty if readings are frequently taken in the same size ducts:

1. Acquire a Pitot tube for each duct diameter you will frequently encounter. On each Pitot tube, mark the insertion depths for one of the duct diameters using a fine-tip permanent marker and mark the diameter on a tag affixed to the Pitot tube.

2. When the ink is dry, score a mark around the circumference of the shaft at each insertion mark using a straight edge and a sharp-edged file or equivalent (don't score so deeply that you create a leak.)

3. Re-ink each insertion point using "permanent" inks. For example, the odd points could be blue (except for red for the centerline) and even points could be black or green.

4. Attach two feet of 0.25" plastic tubing to each "leg" of each Pitot tube. At the other end of each tube insert a male plastic coupler to the SP leg and a female coupler to the TP leg (see Figure 9-11). Attach similar plastic tubes and couplers to the ports of all pressure measurement devices and never remove them. Use the couplers to connect and disconnect Pitot tubes from sensors.

5. Make a 10 to 20 foot long extension with couplers at both ends matching the Pitot tube couplers. Mark SP leg and "negative" ports with red ink.

NOTE: Avoid removing the plastic tubing from an instrument or Pitot tube and reattaching it because it will have stretched and may leak. If it is necessary to remove the tubing and use it again, cut off about 0.5" from the stretched end before reattaching.

Instead of holding Pitot tubes by hand during measurements, it is also possible to hold the tube in alignment using jigs and holders. As shown in Figure 9-13, one such device maintains alignment using a horizontal and vertical section that holds the Pitot tube, and the desired insertion depth is achieved by sliding the static pressure leg until it clicks into a notch on a scale with such notches cut for each insertion point. Scales can be made for any desired set of insertion depths

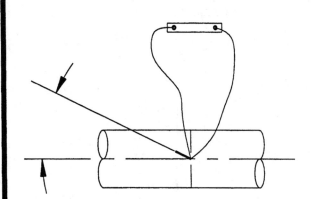

Rotated about the z-axis

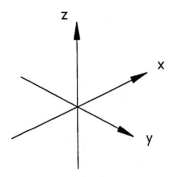

(air flows in the x direction)

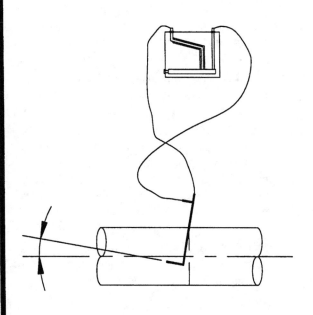

Rotated about the y-axis

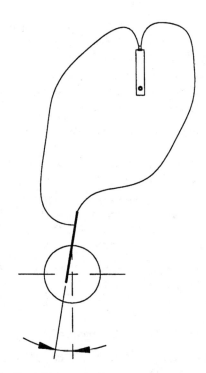

Rotated about the x-axis

AMERICAN CONFERENCE OF GOVERNMENTAL INDUSTRIAL HYGIENISTS	ORIENTING THE PITOT TUBE IN A DUCT	
	DATE 12-99	FIGURE 9-10

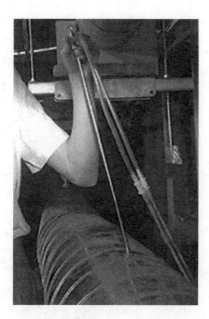

FIGURE 9–11. Pitot tube misaligned

FIGURE 9–12. Pitot tube aligned at insertion depth

within the range of a particular size holder. Note that the holder is not produced commercially at this writing but the construction specifications were published by its developers.[9.5]

9.5.4 Variations in Pitot Tubes: Other types of Pitot tubes have been developed for special needs. Modified Pitot tubes have been made in an effort to reduce plugging in heavy dust streams or to increase manometer differentials for lower air velocity measurements in the field. These "S" type (Staubscheide) tubes usually take the form of two relatively large impact openings, one facing upstream and the other facing downstream. Such tubes are useful when thick walled ducts, such as boiler stacks, make it difficult or impossible to insert a conventional Pitot tube through any reasonably sized port opening.

Measurements made with an "S" type Pitot tube cannot be used directly. First the tube must be calibrated against a standard Pitot tube and the velocity pressure measured and corrected to the actual velocity pressure.

Other modified forms of the Pitot tube include the air foil pitometer, the Pitot Venturi, and the air speed nozzle.

9.6 SELECTION AND USE OF INSTRUMENTS

The selection of pressure or flow sensors should depend on the range of values to be measured, the required accuracy, and the conditions of measurement. Important conditions include: (1) vulnerability to high temperatures, (2) presence of corrosive gases and contaminated atmospheres, (3) required portability and ruggedness, and (4) the size of the measuring probe relative to the available sampling port. A brief summary of the characteristics of a few of the instruments which can be used is given in Table 9-4.

The instruments recommended vary with the intended purpose. Those listed in Table 9-4 are recommended for general practice.

Note that the Photohelic™ versions of Magnehelic™ gauges are useful (1) for alarms, (2) for continuous recording, or (3) if it is desired to relay pressure information to remote locations. Digital manometers can be used for the same purposes but they are much more expensive.

TABLE 9-4. Recommended Usage

Instrument	Parameter	Range	Comment
Pitot tube	SP	All SP	Measure at centerline
Pitot tube	VP	V >1500 fpm	10-point traverses
Digital manometer	SP	Mfg. rec. range	"Wall" port or use with Pitot tube
Digital manometer	VP	V >1500 fpm	Use with Pitot tube
Inclined manometer	SP	0 to 2" wg typically	Use for calibration
U-tube manometer	SP	1 to 20 "wg typically	Use for calibration for SP >2 "wg
Thermal anemometer	Velocity	30 to 1500 fpm	Beware of high temperatures and abrasive, sticky, or flammable contaminants
Magnehelic™ gauges	SP, VP	Range of particular device	Inexpensive: good for continuous monitoring

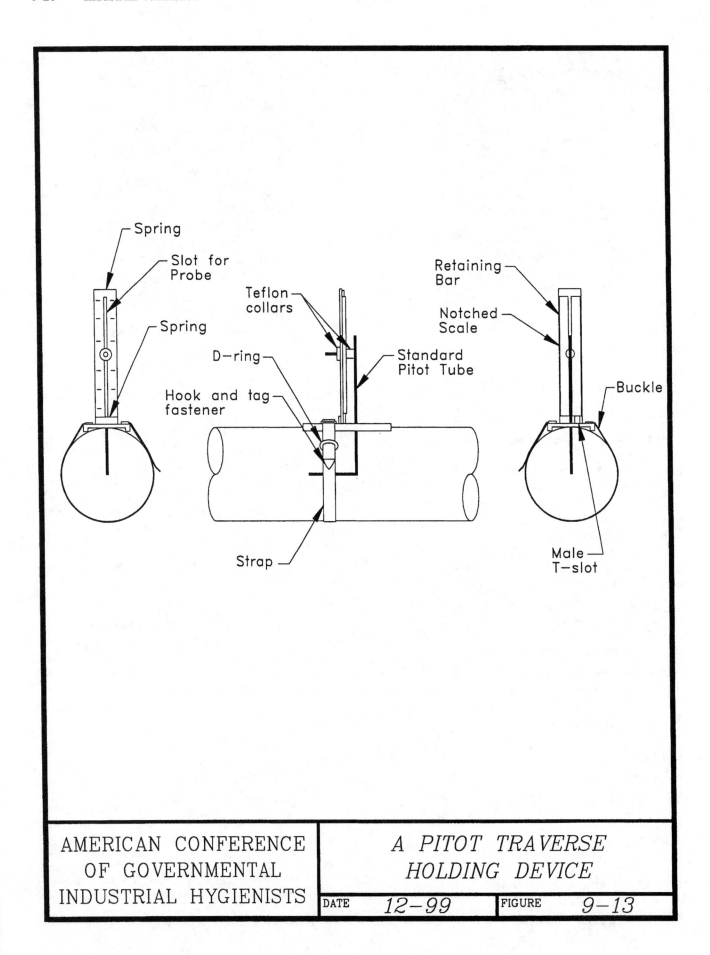

Spring

Slot for
Probe

Spring

Teflon
collars

D—ring

Hook and tag
fastener

Standard
Pitot Tube

Retaining
Bar

Notched
Scale

Buckle

Strap

Male
T—slot

AMERICAN CONFERENCE	A PITOT TRAVERSE
OF GOVERNMENTAL	HOLDING DEVICE
INDUSTRIAL HYGIENISTS	DATE 12—99 FIGURE 9—13

NOTE: Pitot tubes are generally constructed of stainless steel, making them extremely tough and durable. High particulate or mist levels can cause plugging which is easily removed but may form so quickly that measurements are impracticable. No other probe will work under those conditions. The ability of the pressure sensor attached to it to measure low pressures limits the use of Pitot tubes to duct velocities above 1500 fpm.

Inclined manometers are difficult to use accurately under field conditions, especially if they must be moved from location to location to take measurements. For that reason they are best suited to calibrating more convenient devices. Magnehelic™ gauges and digital manometers are both convenient and easily calibrated by the user, but digital manometers are generally more precise. In addition, many digital manometers can be connected to computers for faster data acquisition.

Specific instruments are discussed in more detail in the following sections.

9.6.1 Air Velocity Instruments: There are many instruments that can measure air velocity at a point. The accuracy of the average velocity (Equation 9.2) depends on the accuracy of the measurement device, the correct use of the device, and the representativeness of samples. All instruments should be handled and used in strict compliance with their manufacturers' recommendations.

One source of error is disturbance of the air stream by the instrument, its probe, and its user. That factor limits use of many of these devices to very large openings. Table 9-5 lists some characteristics of typical air velocity instruments designed for field use.

In addition, if a swinging vane, thermal anemometer, or other device is used to estimate airflow through grille openings, the average velocity inside the grill openings (V_{grille}) is the velocity through the reduced area of the grille. Each grille type blocks different fractions of the opening. For example, a strip grille may obstruct roughly 27% of its opening. Thus the airflow through a strip with a total unobstructed plus obstructed area of A_{total} would be estimated as:

$$Q_{grille} = 0.73 \times V_{grille}\, A_{total}$$

The degree of obstruction produced by different grilles varies greatly from one type to the next and for different manufacturers of the same nominal type. Hence, the obstruction factor provided by the manufacturer should be used in these calculations.

For most applications where the grille is small enough for them, volume devices have replaced measurements at the grille for estimating airflow.

Thermal Anemometers: These instruments (see Figure 9-14) respond to the amount of heat removed by an air stream passing a heated probe, allowing calibration to the velocity of the air stream for a given density. Since heat transfer to the air is a function of the number of molecules of air moving by a fixed monitoring point, the sensing element can be calibrated as a mass flow meter as well as a velocity recorder. Commercial instruments use a probe which consists of two integral sensors: a velocity sensor and a temperature sensor. The velocity sensor is heated to a constant temperature—typically about 75 F above ambient conditions—by a battery powered amplifier. The electrical current required to maintain the

TABLE 9-5. Characteristics of Flow Instruments

Instrument	Range, fpm	Hole Size (for ducts)	Range, Temp.	Dust, Fume Difficulty	Calibration Requirements	Ruggedness	General Usefulness and Comments
PITOT TUBE with inclined manometer or other calibrated pressure sensor of similar accuracy							
Standard	> 1500	3/8"	Wide	Some	None	Good	Good except at low velocities.
Small size	> 1500	3/16"	Wide	Yes	Once	Good	Good except at low velocities.
Double (type S)	600 - up	3/4"	Wide	Small	Once	Good	Dirty air stream.
SWINGING VANE ANEMOMETER							
	25-10,000	1/2" - 1"	Medium	Some	Frequent	Fair	Good
ROTATING VANE ANEMOMETER							
Mechanical	30-10,000	Not for duct use	Narrow	Yes	Frequent	Poor	Special; limited use
Electronic	25-200 25-500 25-2,000 25-5,000	Not for duct use	Narrow	Yes	Frequent	Poor	Special; can connect to computer
THERMAL ANEMOMETER							
	30-6,000	Yes	Narrow	Yes	Frequent	Poor	Can connect to computer

FIGURE 9–14. TSI thermal anemometer

probe temperature above ambient levels is proportional to the air velocity, allowing display of either mass flow rate or velocity on a digital or analog meter.

Air velocity often fluctuates rapidly, and the instrument can respond much quicker than one can read the display. Many instruments have a "hold" button to display a value until the user releases the button. In some units, the user can set the time constant (i.e., averaging time) and later push a button to "hold" the running average just computed. However, some instruments display the instantaneous response when the hold button is activated, which is much less useful.

In using the device, the user should note that:

1. The sensor is fragile and should be protected from shock. Avoid placing it in hot environments or corrosive, explosive, or dusty atmospheres.

2. Attachments are available to measure static pressure. The attachments allow air from a hole in the duct to pass through a calibrated orifice and the sensor. The velocity through the orifice is then related to static pressure by calibration.

3. The probe diameter is small enough and the range of the instruments is high enough to allow use of the instrument in measuring duct velocities for ducts larger than 10 inches. For smaller ducts the middle of the sensor is too far from the tip to reach points close to the skin of the duct opposite the insertion hole.

4. When used for low velocity measurements, substantial error can be introduced by inadvertent movement of the probe tip. Movement of the sensor may produce values that represent hand tremor more than environmental conditions. For that reason, one should hold the probe in an adjustable stand (e.g., camera tripod or ring stand)

to achieve the greatest accuracy. For cases where lower accuracy is acceptable it may be sufficient to steady the wand by holding it against a fixed object (e.g., a side of the hood.)

5. When used at hood faces it can be difficult both to decide which plane is the face of the enclosing hood and to hold the probe exactly in that plane. For many hoods, small deviations from the plane of the face can produce substantial changes in the measured velocity.

6. When used at supply or exhaust openings covered by grilles (see preceding discussion), the correction coefficient listed in Table 9-6 should be used.

7. Like all other devices, it should be zeroed before use and its calibration should be verified frequently (see Calibration).

8. Measurements may become incorrect if the battery charge level is low.

9. Thermal anemometers can measure from 30 fpm and up with reasonable accuracy if properly calibrated. At lower velocities instrument response can be erratic or it may simply display zero.

Thermal anemometers can measure both high and low velocities, which is convenient. However, calibrating them requires production of a known velocity, which is much more difficult to verify than a known static pressure. Therefore, static pressure measuring devices are more reliable in measuring high velocities. If possible, one should always determine airflow from Pitot traverses in ducts and compute average hood velocity from that airflow divided by the area of the hood face.

If leakage from the hood or just downstream of the hood is suspected, one could compare the results of a duct traverse and a hood face traverse. However, observing released smoke at possible leak points may be more reliable.

TABLE 9-6. Corrections for Velocity Readings through Grille Openings

Grille Openings	Correction Factor, %
Pressure	
More than 4 in. wide and up to 600 sq in area, free opening 70% or more of the gross area, no directional vanes. Use free open area.	93
Suction	
Square punched grille (use free open area)	88
Bar grille (use gross area)	78
Strip grille (use gross area)	73
Free open, no grille	100

FIGURE 9–15. Rotating vane anemometer

Rotating Vane Anemometers: Rotating vane anemometers (see Figure 9-15) can be used to determine air flow through large (greater than 4 ft^2) supply and exhaust openings. Where possible the cross-sectional area of the instrument should not exceed 5.0% of the cross-sectional area of the duct or hood opening. These instruments are fragile and are not suitable for dusty or corrosive atmospheres.

The standard instrument consists of a propeller or revolving vane connected through a gear train to a set of recording dials that convert the number of rotations to total distance traveled by the air during the sampling time. By dividing the total distance by time recorded elsewhere (e.g., on a stop watch), one can compute the estimated velocity of the air that passed through the instrument. The dial readings are seldom accurate as read. General practice is to tape a table of conversions based on the most recent calibration to the side of the instrument. The user uses those values to "correct" dial readings. Note that the calibration is for one direction of flow only. The instrument can be made in various sizes with 2", 3", 4", and 6" being the most common for purely mechanical versions. The standard instrument can have a useful range of 50-3,000 fpm but specially built models can read lower velocities. It is not intended for use in small ducts but it can be used in very large ducts, mine shafts, and large enclosing hoods.

Electronic rotating vane anemometers are also available. These instruments generally are much smaller than the mechanical devices but are too large for traversing any but the largest ducts (e.g., greater than 3 ft in diameter.) These instruments record and meter electrical pulses developed by a capacitance or inductive transducer. The impulses are fed to the indicator unit where they are integrated to operate a conventional meter dial or an electronic readout. These instruments also measure time so they can compute velocity and display it. Readings as low as 25 fpm can be measured and recorded.

Swinging Vane Anemometers: This instrument was once used extensively in the field because of its portability, versatility, and wide-scale range. However, it has been supplanted by thermal anemometers for low velocities and by digital manometers for both high velocities and static pressures. Calibration and maintenance of the instrument are concerns for the following reasons:

1. The presence of dust, moisture, or corrosive material in the atmosphere presents a problem since the air passes through the instrument case. It does have filters to remove particulates, but dust loading of the filter changes instrument response, as does removing and replacing the filter. Hence, filter loading is a source of error.

2. The instrument requires periodic calibration and adjustment but the instrument cannot be calibrated by the user.

3. The actual sensing device is a calibrated spring. For that reason, it is crucial that the instrument be held vertically while being calibrated and when used in the field—a difficult proposition while standing on a ladder. Furthermore, mechanical shocks can extend the spring, changing its calibration.

4. The length and inside diameter of the connecting tubing affect the calibration of the meter. When replacement is required, one can use only connecting tubing of the same length and inside diameter as that originally supplied with the meter.

5. The instrument does not actually measure static pressure. It measures the reduction in flow through the instrument when a fitting with a calibrated orifice impedes the flow. For that reason, loading of the filter also affects its static pressure readings and its readings must be corrected for air density.

The instrument has wide application. By use of a variety of fittings it can be used to check static pressure and air velocity over a wide range of values. The instrument can be used to measure velocities through supply air grilles large enough (roughly 3 ft^2) that the instrument does not introduce errors by blocking airflow. It is important to correct such readings using the calibration factors listed by the manufacturer for each grille type.

FIGURE 9–16. Flow hoods

FIGURE 9–17. Flow hood in use

The instrument can be used to measure hood face velocities when the specified fitting is attached. However, that fitting is attached directly to the body of the instrument so that both must be placed in the air stream, introducing error as the air flows around it. Worse, the user often must place his or her head and torso into the air stream to read the instrument. Finally, the instrument must be held vertically so the minimum height above a surface at which one can measure is roughly six inches.

Before using this instrument, check the meter for its zero setting by holding it vertically and covering both ports so that no air can flow through. If the pointer does not come to rest at zero, adjust it to read zero.

Although the instrument includes a probe intended to measure velocities in ducts, its large size precludes accurate measurements in smaller ducts (<6 inches). Its large diameter blocks airflow excessively and its probe tip cannot reach the outermost traverse points. Used in place of a Pitot tube for velocity or total pressure measurements, it necessitates a much larger hole in the duct—a potential source of substantial leaks.

Like many other instruments, its readings must be corrected if air density is non-standard (see Equation 9.9b).

Devices to Measure Volumetric Flows Through a Diffuser ("Flow Hoods"): Flow hoods are devices that channel all air from a diffuser or other sources through the device (see Figures 9-16 and 9-17). By sensing the velocities at several points at a fixed cross-section of known area, it is possible for the devices to compute the airflow through them. The sensor in most instruments is a thermal anemometer, but units are available that measure a matrix of pressures across an orifice with a low pressure digital manometer. At least one manufacturer uses a rotating vane and timer to measure airflow.

It is important that all of the air from the source flow through the device, so one should tightly seal the entrance to the device to the source outlet. The range of airflows a device can measure depends on the size of the device's entrance and the range of velocities it can measure with acceptable accuracy. A typical range is 25 to 2,000 cfm for devices using rotating vanes and timers to sense flow (see Figures 9-16 and 9-17) but sizes capable of higher and lower ranges are available.

The readout of most instruments should be corrected for air density. For a mechanical device (e.g., rotating vane or swinging vane, readouts should be corrected using Equation 9.9a. If the velocity is sensed with a thermal anemometer or other heat transfer device, Equation 9.9b should be employed. At least one instrument actually measures barometric pressure and temperature and compensates for their effects automatically.

9.6.2 Pressure Sensors: Several types of pressure sensors can be used in conjunction with the Pitot tube to measure velocity and static pressures within ventilation systems.

U-Tube Manometers: The vertical U-tube (see Figure 9-18) is the simplest type of pressure gauge. Usually calibrated in inches water gauge, it is used with various fluid media such as alcohol, mercury, oil, water, kerosene, or special manometer fluids. The manufacturer's specified gauge fluid must be used or the instrument will almost certainly have a gain error. The U-tube may be used for either portable or stationary applications. Available commercial units offer a wide variety of ranges and styles. Tubes are usually constructed of plastic to minimize breakage. One leg may be replaced by a reservoir or well (well-type manometer) for easier reading.

The precision of readings depends on the resolution of the scale markings. The accuracy of readings depends on the accuracy of the scale markings and how precisely vertical the measurement column is. The verticality can be verified with a spirit level or plumb line.

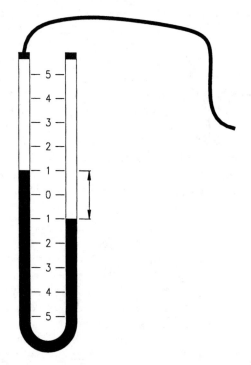

FIGURE 9–18. U-tube manameter

FIGURE 9–19. Hook guage

Hook Gauges: A hook gauge is a highly precise (0.001 "wg) form of a U-tube manometer intended for calibration of other pressure devices. Two reservoirs of gauge fluid are mounted on a stand one above the other and connected by tubing (see Figure 9-19). Rising from the bottom of each reservoir is a vertical "hook" (a sharpened point) connected to a micrometer. The user adjusts both micrometers until each hook just breaks the surface of the fluid, then reads the micrometer scales. The gauge pressure is the sum of the two micrometer readings. The micrometers are zeroed in the same fashion.

Inclined Manometers: By inclining a U-tube manometer one spreads out the vertical rise in fluid level over a broader scale, allowing more precise visual discrimination. The broader the scale for a given vertical rise, the greater the potential resolution. If the scale length is calibrated initially the instrument can serve as a high quality secondary standard if it is filled with the correct density gauge fluid and its orientation to gravity is set properly using a factory installed integrated spirit level or a plumb line and a calibrated ruler.

In commercial versions, only one tube is inclined and the other leg is replaced by a reservoir. The better gauges are equipped with a built-in spirit level, leveling adjustment, and a means of adjusting either the scale or the fluid level to zero. Some models include over-pressure safety traps to prevent loss of fluid in the event of pressure surges beyond the manometer range.

As will be discussed later in this section, under field conditions, even units marketed for field use are awkward to carry and set up and are time consuming and difficult to use. Ideally, one would mount a highly precise inclined manometer on the wall and employ it to verify more convenient pressure sensing devices (e.g., electronic manometers) for use in the field.

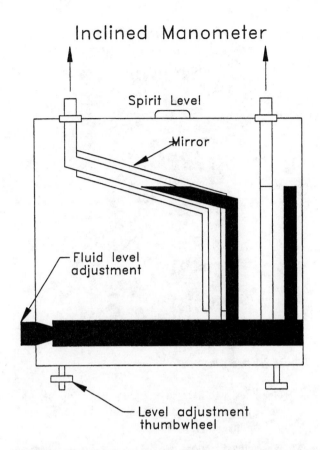

FIGURE 9–20. Inclined manometer with intergrated vertical section

A modification of the inclined manometer is the combined inclined and vertical gauge in which the indicator leg is bent or shaped to give both a vertical and inclined portion (see Figure 9-20). The advantage is the greater upper range provided by the vertical section and higher precision in the crucial lower pressures covered by the inclined section. Unfortunately, the vertical readings are sometimes inaccurate because some of the fluid remains in the horizontal section. For example, if the vertical section starts at 1.0 "wg, the manometer could produce a bias error of 0.1 "wg for all readings from 1.0 "wg to full scale. The closer the level to the inclined range, the greater the relative error since the magnitude of error does not vary.

Whether on the wall or in the field, proper use of any manometer requires the following:

1. Like the U-tube manometer, it must contain the correct gauge fluid and nothing else. Its chamber must have sufficient fluid and it must be replaced periodically with clean fluid.

2. The manometer must be aligned with gravity, usually aided by a built-in spirit level.

3. It must be zeroed before each use by the person who will use it (individuals read them differently).

4. The instrument cannot be read accurately until bubbles in the fluid have disappeared.

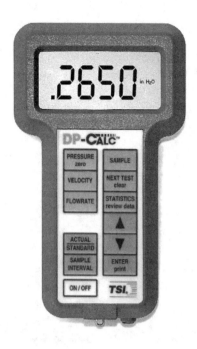

FIGURE 9–21. Digital manameter

5. One must wait from several seconds to a minute for a stable reading, depending on the size of the manometer and the magnitude of the pressure.

6. For inclined sections, the right-most edge of the meniscus should be read in both calibration and use. For vertical sections, the bottom of the meniscus should be read.

7. The meniscus and its mirror image on the device should be aligned before reading the scale. It is difficult to do this using both eyes, so shut one.

8. Values below 0.2 "wg are difficult to read with better than 10% precision.

Portable Digital (Electronic) Manometers: Digital manometers (see Figure 9-21) are electronic devices that use piezo-resistance or strain gauges to sense pressure changes. The calibration is set within the electronics. These devices hold their calibration well, but do show zero drift, especially after first turning them on (wait 30 minutes to zero and use) and with temperature changes. Within their range of application, their advantages compared to other ventilation devices are compelling:

1. As is true for all pressure sensors, the contaminants inside the ducts are not allowed to flow through the device.

2. Battery powered versions can be small and light-weight enough to use in the field with much greater convenience than other pressure gauges. Some will fit in a shirt pocket.

3. Orientation to gravity and movement are irrelevant— unlike mechanical devices.

4. They respond to pressure changes quickly (hence, user selectable time-averaging is a crucial feature).

5. Their accuracy often is superior to other devices suitable for field use.

6. Some have data logging and computer communication capabilities.

Computer communication with a digital manometer can facilitate much faster data collection, analysis, and reporting than is possible with non-computer enabled devices. Computer data acquisition can eliminate most data input errors and allows storage of the data in forms easily accessible to other computer programs for later analysis and reporting. It is also possible for specially written computer software to analyze values as they are received and provide "real time" feedback to the user.

Real time feedback can help the user catch errors as they are made, and it focuses attention on components for which data suggest there are problems requiring action. Data logging is less useful since it requires the user to log the circumstance of each reading elsewhere using an assigned number as an identifier. There is reduced potential for immediate feedback to the user.

Aneroid Gauges: Perhaps the best known device of this type is the Magnehelic™ gauge (Figure 9-22) produced by Dwyer®. They are inexpensive, extremely rugged pressure sensing devices that keep their calibration well. They can be purchased in ranges from low to high and with scales for pressure, velocity, or both. For example, one could use a 0-0.5" "wg range for low velocities in ducts; 0-1 "wg for moderate velocities in ducts; 0-2 "wg for high velocities in ducts; 0-5 "wg for low static pressures; and 0-15 "wg for high static pressures.

In using these devices, one should:

1. Select the gauge with the mid-range value closest to the value you expect to measure.

FIGURE 9–22. Aneroid manameter

FIGURE 9–23. Aneroid Anemometer must be held vertically

2. Zero and use the device in the vertical orientation if at all possible. Note that tilting the device changes the reading substantially (see Figure 9-23).

3. Zero the device before each use while it is positioned as it will be read (i.e., vertical or horizontal). See Figure 9-23.

4. Verify readings against a manometer frequently.

5. Since it measures pressures, the velocities displayed on the face are correct only for standard density. For non-standard densities, note the pressure and calculate the velocity (see Equation 9.9a). Pressure readings are not affected by density and should not be "corrected".

9.6.3 Temperature Measurement Devices: Temperature is an important factor for determining air density—which one must know to determine the true velocity of air when using most measurement devices. There are many types of devices or thermometers commonly used to measure temperature, including liquid-in-glass, bimetallic, thermocouple, and resistance.

In liquid-in-glass thermometers, liquid alcohol or mercury is contained in a bulb and expands into a capillary within the stem. Since mercury and liquid alcohol expand with increasing temperatures, the length of mercury or alcohol in the capillary tube can indicate the temperature if properly calibrated. Thermometers are awkward to use in the field because they (1) are usually fragile, (2) respond slowly to changes in temperature, (3) must be kept upright, and (4) are often difficult to read, especially in poor light. Other temperature measurement devices usually are more suitable for field use. The one advantage of liquid-in-glass thermometers is that their calibration should not change unless they are damaged.

Other types of thermometers suffer from none of the disadvantages of liquid-in-glass but do require frequent calibration. Bimetallic thermometers bind two metals with dissimilar thermal expansion coefficients at one end and measure the movement of the other ends due to different lengths of expansion as the temperature changes. Thermometers with dial indicators are often bimetallic.

Resistance thermometers measure the changes in electric resistance with a sensor with changes in temperature using a wheatstone bridge or galvanometer. A typical resistance ther-

FIGURE 9–24. Digital thermometer

mometer consists of a fine platinum wire wrapped around a mandrel and covered with a protective coating. A thermistor is a resistance thermometer whose sensor is a ceramic semiconductor. Thermistors release heat—which can interfere with measurements in still air. Their temperature range (-40 F to 300 F, -40 C to 150 C) is more limited than metallic resistance types.

Thermocouples (Figure 9-24) respond to the electromotive force produced when two dissimilar metals join. The magnitude of the electromotive force varies with temperature. If one metal is kept a constant reference temperature, one can calibrate the relationship between voltage or current and the temperature difference. Thermocouples are frequently used in electronic devices.

A two-point calibration can be done by the user over a range that is sufficient for most conditions inside both ducts and occupied spaces. The freezing point of distilled water is 32 F, a temperature achieved by letting ice come to equilibrium temperature in cold water. The boiling point of water at sea level is 212 F, providing the other test point. Since the boiling point temperature falls with barometric pressure, it is important to determine the boiling point at the altitude at which one is doing the calibration.

It is also possible to calibrate measurement devices over the range of temperatures of interest using a thermometer whose calibration over that range can be traced to a primary device.

9.6.4 Humidity Devices: Humidity usually is not an important factor in determining air density unless the air temperature is well above 100 F and the humidity is very high. However, ambient levels of humidity are sometimes important for processes, comfort, and control of heat stress—especially when the temperature is also elevated.

Humidity can be determined indirectly with psychrometers, which are inexpensive devices that pass air over a dry-bulb

FIGURE 9–25. Tachometer

and wet-bulb thermometer at a controlled velocity. The velocity is controlled with a battery-operated fan in some devices and by the user forcing the device to swing about one end in "sling" psychrometers. Psychrometric charts provided by the manufacturer allow determination of relative humidity from the dry-bulb and wet-bulb readings. In both types, air is driven across the thermometer bulbs until equilibrium is reached, while taking care that the sock covering the wet-bulb remains wet. In the battery powered devices the fan speed may vary with battery charge, so it is important to check the batteries before taking readings.

Hygrometers respond directly to the water vapor in the sampled air. Organic hygrometers are inexpensive and inaccurate devices that measure the change in length of organic materials with change in humidity. Electronic hygrometers, which can be much more accurate and are relatively expensive, measure the change in conductance of a sulfonated polystyrene strip.

9.6.5 Tachometers: Tachometers are used to measure the rotational speed of fans. If the rotational speed is different from the expected, the cause should be investigated. The most common causes are discussed below.

1. Reduced rates may indicate belt slippage or the wrong type of belt. With the fan motor locked out, one should test whether the belt is as taut as the manufacturer recommended.

2. If pulleys are used, their sizes may be different than intended (check design specifications).

3. If a variable frequency drive is used, the frequency may be set incorrectly (check design specifications).

Tachometers may count rotations per time directly (see Figure 9-25) or stroboscopically. The former should be placed on the center of the end of a rotating shaft. For the latter, white paint or chalk on the side of the shaft provides the reference point. It is useful to verify both the motor and fan rotation rates when analyzing conditions.

FIGURE 9–26. Using smoke to evaluate air movement

9.6.6 Use of Visible Smoke in Examining Hood Performance: "Smoke" will follow the path of the air with little deviation, allowing the visualization of air flow. The trail of streaming smoke and the path of a single puff of smoke are both useful in visualizing airflow behavior. They allow one to see cross-drafts, disruptive eddy currents, and stagnant zones—all of which are thought to be strongly associated with poor hood performance (see Figure 9-26). They also can be used for checking air movement and direction in plant space.

In addition, low velocity measurements may be made by timing the travel of smoke clouds through a known distance. Smoke trail observations are limited to velocities less than 150 fpm since higher air velocities disperse the smoke too rapidly. Smoke commonly is generated by heating a vegetable oil to sufficiently high temperatures or by reacting chemicals that give off a visible "smoke." The former can generate great quantities of smoke for sustained periods, but the heat of the cloud they release produces a vertical rise that makes interpretation more difficult. The chemically created smokes can be neutrally buoyant. A copious but short-term plug of smoke is released by smoke "bombs." Puffs of smoke also can be generated by manually pumping air through a tube filled with a reagent (e.g., titanium tetrachloride).

In using smoke, it is important to note that:

1. The visible plumes from some smoke tubes are corrosive and should be used with care near people, sensitive processes, or food preparation. Avoid exposing others to the smoke or to skin or eye contact with the corrosive materials. Acetic acid may be less objectionable than the HCL from titanium tetrachloride tubes. Smoke tubes should be disposed of properly.

2. Smoke candles are incendiary and thus cannot be used in flammable atmospheres and should not be hand held. All smoke sources (including smoke tubes) may set off fire alarms.

3. Alternative methods of observing airflow patters include the use of soap bubbles, water vapor cooled by dry ice (CO_2), and heated vegetable oil. None of these methods create neutrally buoyant "smokes."

4. Visible "smoke" will sometimes appear to show that a hood is functioning well when it is actually marginal or unacceptable. This is unfortunate but understandable if one considers that:

   a. Smoke that escapes the hood will mix with work-room air thus diluting the smoke concentration so that it is difficult to see. Unless lighting conditions are ideal it is difficult to observe small amounts of smoke, leading to false "observation" that "virtually all" of the smoke entered the hood. Thus one can be misled into believing that one has "demonstrated" that a hood is highly effective in cases where it is only 90-95% effective.

   b. One may have observed "almost all" (i.e., 80-95%) of the smoke enter the hood and falsely conclude that the hood functions well. A 5-20% escape rate may be excessive in other cases. For example, if 99% collection efficiency is required, a 5% rate of escape is 5 times too high!

   c. The user may have released the smoke when the operator is not present and performing normal motions. Operator (and all other) motions almost always reduce the collection efficiency of a hood.

   d. It is quite possible to have over-exposure without any contaminant escaping the hood—especially if the worker's head is inside the hood and the con-taminant is released close to the worker. An obvious example is a worker standing well inside of a walk-in hood while the contaminant is released at the hood face. Less obvious, but extremely common, are cases where the workers are handling the con-taminant source while leaning into or standing inside of the hood. Since air cannot flow through the worker's back, it must flow around him, creating a stagnant zone in front of his body. Smoke released just in front of the worker's body will tend to linger in the stagnant zone. If the worker leans over or if the source is over waist high, then body and arm movements will spread the smoke into the workers' breathing zone.

5. For the purposes of ventilation design, there is negligi-ble difference between the path taken by a neutrally buoyant smoke and the contaminant of concern. There-fore, it is important to observe the worker's body motions and the location of the worker's head in rela-tion to the location of the source as well as the interac-tive effect of disruptive airflow patterns.

Soap bubbles also can be very useful. They may survive and remain visible long after a puff of smoke would have dispersed to the point of invisibility. That persistence can be very helpful when evaluating large hoods or determining cross-draft veloc-ities. A disadvantage is that bubbles created with air and soap

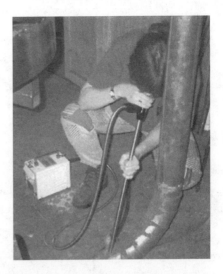

FIGURE 9–27. Dust inspection with borescope

are denser than air and will tend to fall to the floor. However, by creating very small bubbles (e.g., 1 mm diameter) with a helium-air mixture, it is possible to create neutrally buoyant bubbles. Since the toughness of bubbles is inversely related to diameter, these small bubbles can be remarkably persistent, further enhancing their usefulness.

9.6.7 Use of Borescopes in Examining the Interiors of Ventilation Components: Borescopes (Figure 9-27) are devices designed to allow one to view down their length into otherwise hidden spaces. Typically they employ fiberoptics to convey light into the space and arrangements of mirrors to allow reflection of the image back to the viewer. Those used for ventilation system inspections should have the following characteristics:

1. A 0.75 inch barrel, which is small enough that the access hole is reasonably small. Transmission losses increase dramatically with smaller diameters, dra-matically increasing the required lumens from the light source and reducing the maximum clear view-ing distance.

2. A view that is 90 degrees from the barrel.

3. A light source that is relatively light-weight. Note that the light source requires too much power for battery operation so alternating current is required for ventila-tion applications.

4. If interior photography is desired, connections for still or video cameras should be available.

Although units can be extremely useful in detecting hidden objects and plugging, they can mislead the user into thinking that nothing is present in a duct when an obstruction is actual-ly there. This can happen because:

1. Even light coatings of settled materials can make objects blend into the picture.

2. The optics can give the viewer the sense that he or she is viewing much further into a duct than is the case. The greatest distance for accurate impressions is probably less than 10 ft even in clean ducts and can be considerably less for ducts with coatings or settled material in them. For borescopes with barrel diameters less than 0.75 inches, the useful viewing distance is dramatically reduced.

9.7 CALIBRATION

Every sampling device must have both a sensor and a meter. The sensor reacts to the environment and the meter reports that reaction in terms understandable to the user. For example, a manometer reacts to pressure by vertical displacement of a fluid. The height of the fluid is directly related to magnitude of the pressure applied to the device. The column of gauge oil is the sensor; the scale is the meter. A Magnehelic™ gauge, on the other hand, has a spring that is deformed by pressure, causing a magnet to rotate and turn a meter needle in front of a calibrated scale. The spring reacts to the pressure, the rotating magnet reacts to the spring's deflection; together they are the pressure sensor. The instrument may have a probe to reach sites distant from the sensor. A Pitot tube simply conducts pressure to a pressure sensor such as an oil manometer or Magnehelic™ gauge.

Almost everything except simple manometers need regular calibration because their responses can be changed by shock (dropping, jarring), dust, high temperatures, and corrosive atmospheres. Meters should be calibrated regularly. It may be prudent to calibrate them before each use if they will not adjust to zero properly or if the have been subjected to rough handling or adverse atmospheres.

Determination of a gauge's accuracy requires calibration against an appropriate known quantity of known precision. For a manometer filled with distilled water to be accurate, it is necessary only that the vertical distance be marked accurately. If another fluid replaces distilled water then the density of that fluid and scale together must be calibrated for equivalent water displacement. If the gauge fluid is manufactured with an unchanging density, and the scale is marked carefully on a non-deforming surface with a scale calibrated with a National Bureau of Standards calibrated scale, the manometer need not be calibrated again, assuming that the manometer markings will not deviate due to damage. If its markings are invariant and the initial factory calibration can be traced back to a National Bureau of Standards primary standard, the manometer can be used to calibrate other instruments. Simple manometers are the only ventilation measurement devices currently in use that can be used as if they were primary standards. All others should be recalibrated periodically against a primary standard or against a secondary standard that is frequently calibrated against a primary standard.

The Magnehelic™ gauge, for example, should be periodically calibrated against a known level of pressure. It is subject to metal fatigue of its spring and to mechanical dislocations which could change the level shown on its scale face. Since the Magnehelic™ gauge reading can drift between calibrations, it cannot be a primary standard. Likewise, so-called "velometers", which are calibrated orifices, vanes, etc., and thermal anemometers must be calibrated against primary standards.

If during calibration one finds that the instrument has been reading incorrectly, one cannot be certain when the error occured after the last calibration. Hence, all data taken since the last calibration is suspect until a new calibration check confirms the accuracy of the instrument. Thus the optimal frequency of calibration depends on the cost of calibration as compared to the cost of incorrect measurements and the likelihood the instrument's accuracy will deteriorate unacceptably in the interim between calibration checks.

A great advantage of manometers is their ease of calibration. Practitioners can easily and quickly verify calibration in the office or lab using relatively inexpensive devices (see following section). This saves the cost of "factory" recalibration and reduces the time the instrument is out of service. Most digital manometers and Magnehelic™ gauges should not experience substantial errors unless subjected to sharp impacts or other harsh treatment or conditions. For that reason, unless the instrument has been dropped, immersed in liquids or otherwise abused, it may be adequate to rely on monthly calibration checks. However, given the low time cost of calibrating pressure devices, it would be prudent to check their calibration more frequently—perhaps even before and after a day of use if the measurements are crucial or will be difficult to repeat.

A great disadvantage of velocity devices is the difficulty of establishing a known velocity to verify calibration. A following section describes a calibrating wind tunnel that can be used for that purpose. Most practitioners will find it less costly to send the instrument back to the manufacturer for calibration rather than doing it themselves. The cost of "factory" calibration is typically very high (typically greater than 25% of the cost of the instrument) and the turn-around times are very long—often 4 to 6 weeks. For that reason, practitioners often have the calibration done annually or less frequently. Since vendors typically do not report the degree of error found prior to re-setting the device, the user generally has no idea whether the measurements taken prior to recalibration were accurate or not.

9.7.1 Calibrating Pressure Reading Devices: Calibrating pressure devices can be inexpensive and quick. All that is required is a device that can serve as a primary standard, a method to vary the test pressure, and connecting apparatus (i.e., plastic tubing). As shown in Figure 9-28,[9.5] a typical setup would include a hand pump, an on-off air valve (e.g., needle valve), an inclined manometer, and the device to be calibrated.

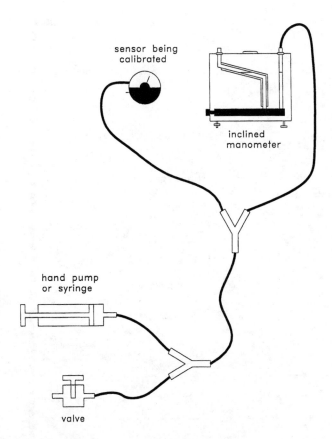

FIGURE 9–28. Pressure device calibration

A standard field manometer is not truly a primary calibration device, but the potential for error using one is very low as long as the following are true:

1. The manometer is aligned vertically using an integrated spirit level or an external spirit level and a plumb line.

2. The correct gauge fluid is used (follow manufacturer's specifications).

3. The internal volume is clean and the gauge fluid is free of debris.

4. The manometer is zeroed properly.

5. Inclined manometers with vertical elements are used only in the inclined range and not in the first values in vertical range which can be inaccurate due to retention of fluid in the inclined section. For pressures above the inclined range it is better to use a separate simple U-tube manometer

9.7.2 Design of a Calibrating Wind Tunnel for Practitioner Use:
Air velocity instruments must be calibrated against a known velocity. This requires that one must be able to produce a range of airflows and measure their velocities with a different instrument that is known to be accurate and precise for that velocity range. For high velocities (> 1500 fpm), readings from a velocity instrument can be compared to values in ducts determined using a Pitot tube and a calibrated pressure sensor. The difficulty is in calibrating velocity instruments for much lower velocities.

The best course for many practitioners may be to pay the manufacturer to check and recalibrate the instruments. For those with many instruments to check, it may be worth considering finding or constructing a small wind tunnel to calibrate instruments. The wind tunnel setup must include the following:[9.16, 9.17]

1. A relatively large, low velocity section for testing low velocity instruments. This chamber must have highly uniform airflow at the test cross-section and the velocities should vary little if the measurement location is moved short distances up or downstream. The latter precludes use of laboratory hoods. Their face velocities can vary radically as the measurement device is moved into or out of the plane of the opening.

2. The chamber inlet should have a smooth curved, bell shaped entry which directs the air into the duct over a 180 degree angle (see Figure 9-29). It must be free of obstructions and the air entering it should have no significant momentum lateral or vertical to the open face.

3. For calibrating larger instruments such as the lower velocity swinging vane anemometer and the rotating vane anemometer,[9.16, 9.18] a large rectangular test section of transparent plastic at least 2.5 cfm in cross-sectional area can be constructed with curved air foil inlets as shown in Figure 9-30. A fine mesh screen placed deep in the enclosure will assist in providing a uniform airflow in the test section.

4. Low velocities must be measured by a calibrated low velocity instrument that is placed in the test cross-section. If the low velocity section has highly uniform velocities, the test and tested instruments may be used side-by-side if one takes care not to obstruct the movement of air with one's body or with the instrument. Otherwise, a traverse should be performed using each instrument and the average values compared.

    If the low-velocity section does not have highly uniform velocities, the average from a traverse by the low velocity device should be used to estimate the airflow through the test cross-section and that value should be compared to the result of a velocity pressure traverse in the high velocity section.

5. A high velocity section, preferably downstream of the low velocity section, and a Pitot tube and calibrated pressure sensor to conduct a velocity pressure traverse. For velocity measurements below 2,000 fpm a micromanometer (e.g., hook gauge) should be used to measure pressures.[9.7]

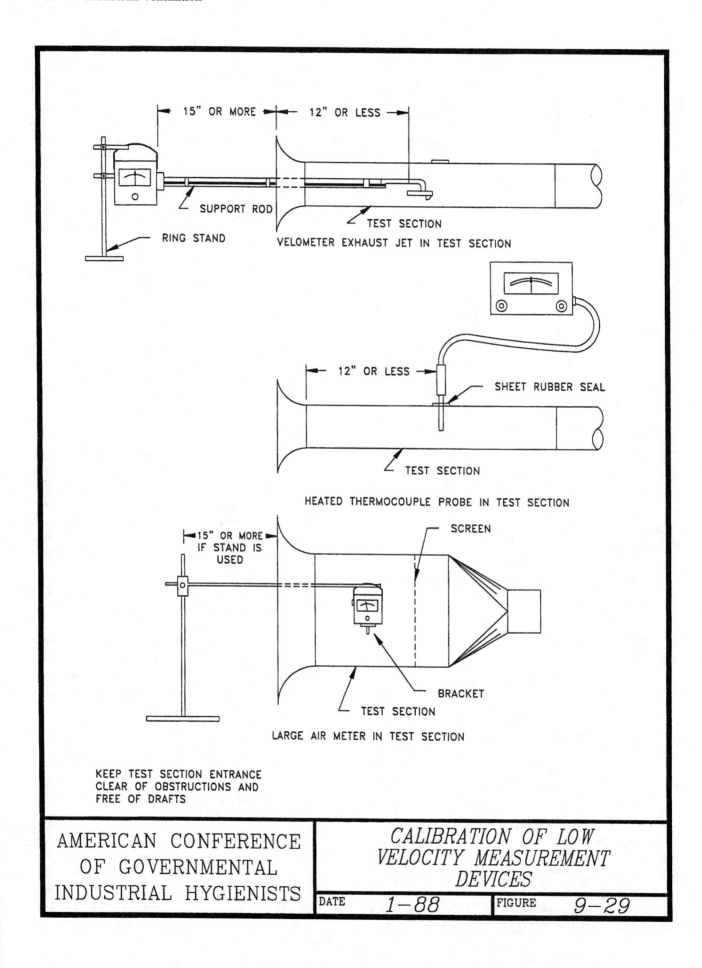

15" OR MORE — 12" OR LESS

SUPPORT ROD

RING STAND

TEST SECTION

VELOMETER EXHAUST JET IN TEST SECTION

12" OR LESS

SHEET RUBBER SEAL

TEST SECTION

HEATED THERMOCOUPLE PROBE IN TEST SECTION

15" OR MORE
IF STAND IS
USED

SCREEN

BRACKET

TEST SECTION

LARGE AIR METER IN TEST SECTION

KEEP TEST SECTION ENTRANCE
CLEAR OF OBSTRUCTIONS AND
FREE OF DRAFTS

AMERICAN CONFERENCE OF GOVERNMENTAL INDUSTRIAL HYGIENISTS	CALIBRATION OF LOW VELOCITY MEASUREMENT DEVICES	
	DATE 1-88	FIGURE 9-29

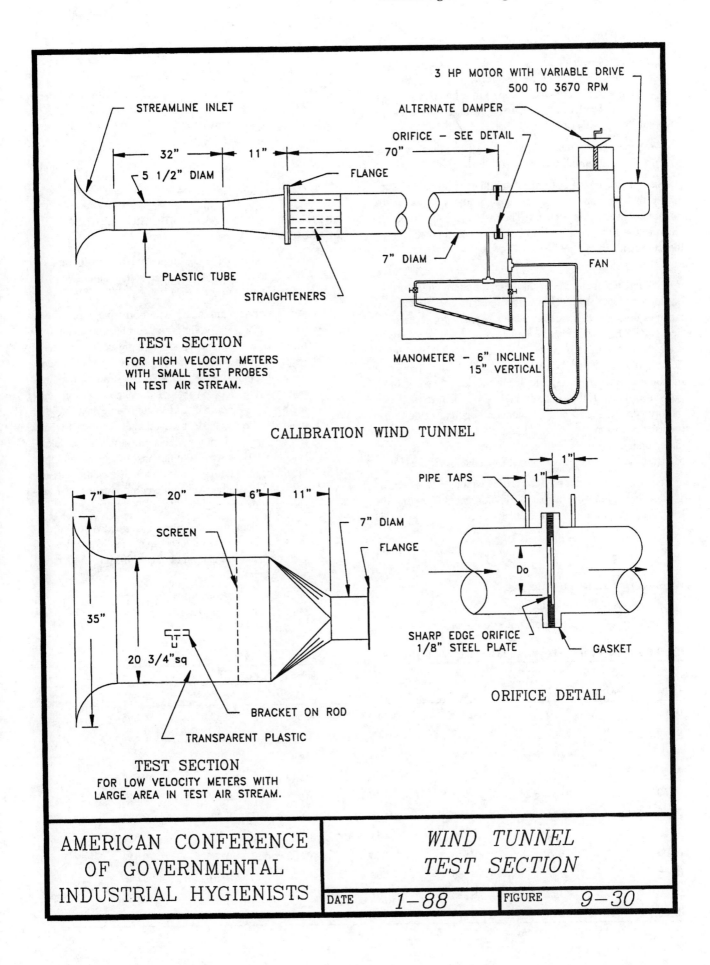

3 HP MOTOR WITH VARIABLE DRIVE
500 TO 3670 RPM

STREAMLINE INLET

ALTERNATE DAMPER

ORIFICE — SEE DETAIL

32"   11"   70"

5 1/2" DIAM

FLANGE

PLASTIC TUBE

STRAIGHTENERS

7" DIAM

FAN

MANOMETER — 6" INCLINE
15" VERTICAL

TEST SECTION
FOR HIGH VELOCITY METERS
WITH SMALL TEST PROBES
IN TEST AIR STREAM.

CALIBRATION WIND TUNNEL

7"   20"   6"   11"

SCREEN

7" DIAM

FLANGE

35"

20 3/4"sq

BRACKET ON ROD

TRANSPARENT PLASTIC

TEST SECTION
FOR LOW VELOCITY METERS WITH
LARGE AREA IN TEST AIR STREAM.

PIPE TAPS

1"
1"

D_o

SHARP EDGE ORIFICE
1/8" STEEL PLATE

GASKET

ORIFICE DETAIL

AMERICAN CONFERENCE OF GOVERNMENTAL INDUSTRIAL HYGIENISTS	*WIND TUNNEL TEST SECTION*
	DATE *1–88* FIGURE *9–30*

6. A fan and control system that allows variation of air velocities over the desired range in the test section. A variable frequency drive controller is preferred but a damper (e.g., slide-gate damper) may be employed if it is located well downstream of the low velocity and high velocity test sections.

7. Apparatus to measure temperature, barometric pressure, and humidity in the test room.

Note that the tested instrument should be supported in such a way that the support does not change the velocity at the instrument inlet by its presence. The instrument should be oriented to the flow as specified by the manufacturer for taking measurements in the field.

A sharp-edged orifice, Venturi meter or a flow nozzle can be used as a metering device.[9.18] Of these, the sharp-edged orifice has more resistance to flow but is more easily constructed, and it can be designed to be readily interchangeable for several orifice sizes. The orifice can be mounted between two flanged sections sealed with gaskets as shown in Figure 9-30. Each orifice should be calibrated using a standard Pitot tube and manometer prior to use. Table 9-7 lists calculations for three sizes of orifices: 1.400", 2.625", and 4.900" diameters. When the orifices are placed in a 7" diameter duct and made to the precise dimensions given, no calibration is needed and the tabulated data in Table 9-7 will give volumetric flow rates within 5% over the range of values shown for standard air density.

The airflow for a sharp-edged orifice with pipe taps located 1" on either side of the orifice can be computed from the following equation for 2" to 14" diameter ducts:

$$Q = 6KD^2_{orifice} \sqrt{\frac{SP_{orifice}}{\rho}} \qquad [9.13]$$

Where: Q = airflow rate, cfm

K = coefficient of airflow

$D_{orifice}$ = in diameter of open portion of orifice, inches

$SP_{orifice}$ = pressure drop across orifice, "wg

ρ = density, lbm/ft^3

The coefficient, K, is affected by the Reynolds number—a dimensionless value expressing flow conditions in a duct. The following equation gives a simplified method of calculating Reynolds number for standard air:

$$Re = 8.4D_{orifice}V_{orifice} \qquad [9.14]$$

The coefficient, K, can be selected from Table 9-7.

9.8 PRACTICAL ISSUES IN VENTILATION SYSTEM MEASUREMENT

Conditions inside ducts are important in considering the type of device to use and the corrections that should be made to its readings:

1. Air heavily contaminated with corrosive gases, dusts, fumes, mists, or products of combustion cannot be measured using some devices and presents problems in using all instruments. Fragile probes can be corroded, abraded, or otherwise damaged by airborne contaminants in the duct. Probes that contain sensors may report values incorrectly if coated with dust or other materials. Probes that act as a conduit for gases to reach the sensor may become blocked or allow these deleterious materials to reach the instrument where they block, coat, or damage it. Probes that conduct pressure only will pass along very little contaminant to the sensor, but they can become plugged.

2. High temperature conditions require density corrections for some devices (see Equations 9.9a and 9.9b), and most sensors can be damaged if high temperature gases reach them.

3. High concentrations of water vapor and mist can plug probes so quickly that measurement becomes impractical.

TABLE 9-7. Values of K in Equation 9.13 for Different Orifice Sizes

d/D	Reynolds Number in Thousands						
	25	50	100	230	500	1,000	10,000
0.100	0.605	0.601	0.598	0.597	0.596	0.595	0.595
0.200	0.607	0.603	0.600	0.599	0.598	0.597	0.597
0.300	0.611	0.606	0.603	0.603	0.601	0.600	0.600
0.400	0.621	0.615	0.611	0.610	0.609	0.608	0.608
0.450	0.631	0.624	0.619	0.617	0.615	0.615	0.615
0.500	0.644	0.634	0.628	0.626	0.624	0.623	0.623
0.550	0.663	0.649	0.641	0.637	0.635	0.634	0.634
0.600	0.686	0.668	0.658	0.653	0.650	0.649	0.649
0.650	0.717	0.695	0.680	0.674	0.670	0.668	0.667
0.700	0.755	0.723	0.707	0.699	0.694	0.692	0.691
0.750	0.826	0.773	0.747	0.734	0.726	0.723	0.721

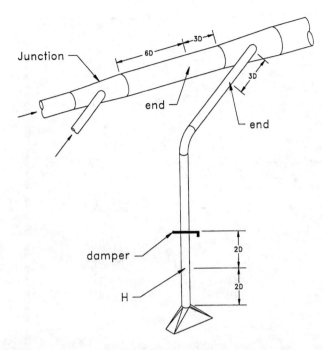

FIGURE 9–31. Minimum distances from disturbances for S.P. measurements

4. All field instruments have difficulty with very low velocities. Devices that measure pressure (including velocity pressure) for field use generally have degraded accuracy at static or velocity pressures below 0.15 "wg. Thermal anemometers developed for field use become increasingly unreliable below 30 fpm.

5. It is difficult to measure accurately where airflow is extremely non-uniform. Such locations include near the discharges of process equipment and fans and near elbows, sudden expansions or contractions, and downstream of junction fittings.

6. In some systems, measurements may vary substantially over relatively short periods of time. Systems with automatic control of dampers or fan speeds sometimes change so frequently that the measurements taken on the same day at different locations in the system may present a misleading picture of system behavior. Velocity sampling for isokinetic sampling of stacks is often plagued by variable air volume systems, particularly when one stack is used in common for several fans. It is therefore important to log the insertion depth or setting of all dampers before tests are done and confirm that they have not changed during the tests (see Figure 9-31).

9.9 MONITORING A SYSTEM

This section describes practical procedures for preparing a system for taking necessary measurements. It is oriented to using a Pitot tube with a digital manometer but would apply to velocity traverses of ducts done with a thermal anemometer or other devices.

9.9.1 Prepare Measurement Locations:

1. Select locations for measurements (see Table 9.3 and Figure 9-32).

2. Drill the entry hole using a drill bit that is slightly larger than the Pitot tube's stem diameter. Larger holes are unnecessary. When drilling, rock the bit back and forth inline with the duct to create a slot shape. The slot shape is ideal for inserting the Pitot tube without requiring an excessively large hole. When using an existing hole that is unnecessarily large, cover the hole with duct tape and cut a longitudinal slit to allow entry of the Pitot tube.

3. Label measurement points on a sketch or drawing of the system.

4. Label each measurement location with (1) item or test-point number; (2) ID of duct; (3) diameter of the duct; (4) SP_h, SP_{end}, VP; (5) date; and (6) initials of individual responsible.

5. If possible, install a measurement port for SP_h and for SP_{end}.

9.9.2 Immediate Preparation Each Day of Measurement:

1. Turn on digital manometer (if one is used) at least 30 minutes before use.

2. Check Pitot stems for misalignment with the probe.

3. Prepare computer (if used) or data collection sheet (see example sheets in the Appendix.)

4. Zero manometer.

5. Verify manometer calibration against an inclined manometer if it has not been checked within an acceptable time period (see Section 9.7).

9.9.3 Taking Measurements:

1. To avoid subconscious bias, when reading an instrument with fluctuating values, look away then look back and record the second value you see.

2. Insertion depths for measurements:

   a. for SP_h and SP_{end}, measure at centerline or at installed nipple;

   b. for VP, do 8 or 10 point traverse of each traverse diameter. Prepare to do two perpendicular traverses if the measurement cross-section is less than 7 D from adverse upstream conditions.

3. Time constants for digital manometers:

   a. for SP—average over 5 seconds (digital manometer) or take the median of three readings taken at least 2 seconds apart.

   b. for VP—average over 1.5 to 2 seconds (digital manometer).

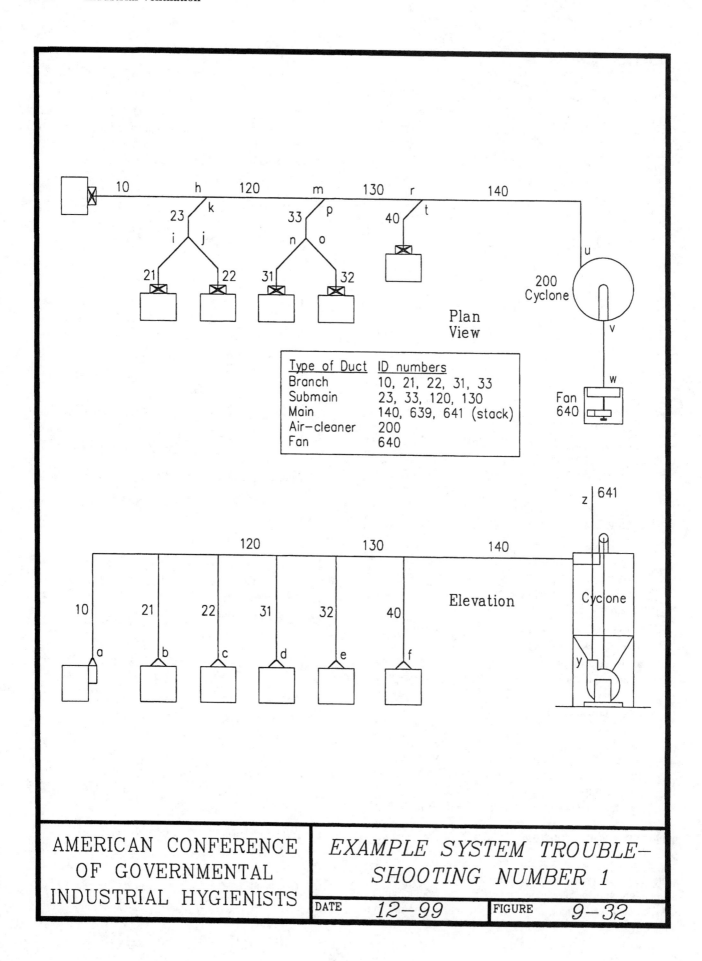

Plan
View

Type of Duct	ID numbers
Branch	10, 21, 22, 31, 33
Submain	23, 33, 120, 130
Main	140, 639, 641 (stack)
Air-cleaner	200
Fan	640

Elevation

AMERICAN CONFERENCE
OF GOVERNMENTAL
INDUSTRIAL HYGIENISTS

*EXAMPLE SYSTEM TROUBLE-
SHOOTING NUMBER 1*

DATE   *12-99*   FIGURE   *9-32*

4. Input or write comments on

    a. measurement conditions, if not good;

    b. condition of duct (defects, wear, plugging)

    c. known or suspected alterations;

    d. expected and observed pressure differential across the air cleaning device;

    e. special loss factors

    f. setting of blast gate or other damper (e.g., % open);

    g. other notes.

5. Compare to previous values, if available. If substantially different (>10%):

    a. re-measure;

    b. note need to investigate for alterations.

6. Recheck zero as frequently as experience with the device suggests.

9.10 USING PRESSURE AND FLOW DATA TO DETECT AND LOCATE OBSTRUCTIONS, LEAKS, AND ALTERATIONS

It can be difficult to troubleshoot installed systems by comparing observed pressures and flows to values expected from the original design or from "as is" computations from published loss coefficients. The coatings, abrasion, dents, and general wear of older systems can profoundly alter resistances to flow throughout the system so that published loss coefficients do not accurately model the system. The solution is to measure pressures and flows throughout the system and use those values as baselines for future comparisons. This does not allow one to locate defects and obstructions that existed before the initial measurements were taken, but it does allow detection

and location of new alterations to the system. Following sections describe procedures for troubleshooting existing systems by conditions and to meet different expectations of reliability and levels of effort.

Thresholds for each method's parameter are shown in Table 9-8.[9.15] Thresholds lower than those recommended for the Hood SP Method will produce modest gains in sensitivity at the cost of large increases in pointless searches. Use somewhat lower thresholds only if failure to detect even modest obstructions and leaks would be disastrous.

The Hood SP Method is the simplest and quickest but may detect only very large obstructions reliably[9.15] unless measurements and repairs are made frequently. Even when monitoring is infrequent, the other methods will detect roughly 90% of "moderate" and larger obstructions and roughly 50% of conditions capable of producing less than 5% shifts in airflow (i.e., "modest" obstructions). The Branch Pressure Ratio Method is the most reliable but requires somewhat more effort than the Reference Ratio Method. The Equivalent Resistance Method is the most time consuming but unlike the other methods can be applied to any part of a system not just branch ducts.[9.13–9.15]

9.10.1 Alteration Detection by the Hood Static Pressure Method: A change in SP_h indicates a change somewhere in the system. If the change in SP_h is great, it is likely that the alteration or obstruction was in the duct in which SP_h was measured and not somewhere else in the system. However, it is quite possible for a clean branch duct to experience large changes in SP_h due to events in other ducts, especially events in nearby ducts, the air cleaning device, or the fan.[9.14] Nevertheless, SP_h can be a useful troubleshooting parameter, especially if the system is monitored very frequently (e.g., daily) or is unusually free of problems.

TABLE 9-8. Recommended Thresholds for Parameters

Parameter	Eq. No.	% Threshold for FPR[1] of: 20%	% Threshold for FPR[1] of: 10%	Recommended Usage
% SP_h	15	35	46	Discovery of plugging and other drastic problems in systems that are unlikely to develop more than one problem between rounds of monitoring
% SP_h	15	10[2]	15[2]	Continuous monitoring, especially for hoods with overspray filters. Indication of need for SP_{end}, VP
%BrRatio	18	8	12	When investigating a single branch duct or when SP_{end} values are already available
%RefRatio	19	11	22	When many branches are to be checked and the main is conveniently located.
%X_{br}	23	17	26	As a check on %BrRatio when velocity traverse and SP_{end} values are already available.
%X_{sub}	25	35	50	Submains
%X_{cum}	24	17[2]	26[2]	Determining if cumulative resistance has changed
%X_{run}	26	30[2]	40[2]	Determining if exhaust duct is obstructed

[1]False positive rate   [2]A plausible value not determined empirically

TABLE 9-9. Response of Different Parameters to Alterations

Alteration	% SP_h	%BrRatio	%RefRatio	%X_h	%X_{br}	%X_{sub}	%X_{inlet}
Branch Ducts							
Obstruction upstream of H	+	+	−	+	+	0	V_s+
Obstruction between H & end	−	−	−	0	+	0	V_s+
Leak upstream of H	V_s+	V_s+	V_s+	−	−	0	V_s−
Leak between H & end	−	−	−	0	−	0	V_s−
Positive error in SP_h meas	+	+	+	+	0	0	0
Negative error in SP_h meas	−	−	0	0	0	0	0
Positive error in SP_{end}	0	−	0	0	+	−	0
Neg. error in SP_{end} meas	0	+	0	0	−	+	0
Positive error in VP	0	0	0	−	−	+	V_s−
Negative error in VP	0	0	0	+	+	−	V_s+
Submain ducts							
Obstruction upstream of end	−	0	V_s−	0	0	+	V_s+
Leak upstream of end	−	−	V_s+	0	0	−	−V_s−

+ Positive change

− Negative change

V_s Very small change except possibly in very small systems

A decline in SP_h can be due to an obstruction downstream of H, a leak anywhere upstream of END, or to an obstruction downstream of the junction fitting or a reduction in fan performance (see Table 9-9). SP_h may increase due to removal of an obstruction downstream of H or anywhere downstream of the junction fitting, a leak upstream of H or disconnection of the hood from the duct (if the hood has a high resistance to flow) or an obstruction in a different branch duct.

Since baseline level of pressure values can differ radically from one system to another, it is the relative change in SP that should be considered, not the magnitude:

$$\%SP_h = \left(\frac{SP_{h_2} - SP_{h_1}}{SP_{h_1}} \right) \times 100\% \qquad [9.15]$$

Where: $\%SP_h$ = relative change in SP_h

SP_{h_2} = current value of SP_h

SP_{h_1} = previous value of SP_h

Since increases and decreases in SP_h can indicate problems, both positive and negative changes in SP_h should be considered evidence of unwanted changes to the system.

At the thresholds recommended in Table 9-8, use of $\%SP_h$ correctly identify less than half of "moderate" obstructions and only 80% of "heavy" obstructions in a 4-year field study of systems operating in challenging environments,[9.15] while falsely indicating that 20% of clean ducts were obstructed. Use of lower thresholds increased sensitivity modestly at the cost of dramatic increases in false positives. That poor performance suggests that the method is unacceptable for systems used to protect workers from toxic exposures.

If used with a lower threshold rate (e.g., 10%), the hood static pressure method may be a reliable *negative* indicator in some very stable systems. It is unlikely that such constancy is obtained in many industrial systems, but it may be true for systems that operate in relatively benign environments (e.g., no particulates or mists) and are very well maintained. Even in those systems, the hood static pressure method should not be used alone to make the decision to do a time-consuming or invasive inspection. The other methods described here should be employed to verify the need for that action unless taking the duct apart is unusually quick and painless.

For well maintained, frequently monitored systems that are unlikely to sustain more than one deleterious change at a time, one can sometimes derive additional information by considering the pattern of changes to $\%SP_h$ for different hoods. For example, if all $\%SP_h$ values have changed by roughly the same percentage, the cause must be downstream of the last junction fitting. If all $\%SP_h$ values upstream of a particular junction have changed by the same percentage but those downstream have changed in the opposite direction, the alteration must be in the submain just downstream of that junction or in the next branch downstream.

It is unlikely that the same approach will work in finding anything less than gross obstructions if system measurements are taken so infrequently that multiple alterations or obstructions have occurred since the last set of measurements. Multiple changes to a system can produce complex patterns of effects that can confuse and mislead even the most experienced practitioner.

TABLE 9-10. First Example Problem Using SPh Method

ID	Duct	SP_{h_1}	SP_{h_2}	%SP_h	Altered?	Measure SP_h
					Thresh = 35%	Thresh = 10%
10	Branch a-h	2.830	1.867	-34%	Maybe	Yes
21	Branch b-i	1.912	1.487	-22%	Probably not	Yes
22	Branch c-j	1.912	1.283	-33%	Probably not	Yes
31	Branch d-n	2.368	1.819	-23%	Probably not	Yes
32	Branch e-o	2.368	2.118	-11%	Probably not	Yes
40	Branch f-t	3.728	2.481	-33%	Probably not	Yes

TABLE 9-11. Second Example Problem Using SPh Method

ID	Duct	SP_{h_1}	SP_{h_2}	%SP_h	Altered?	Measure SP_{end}
					Thresh = 35%	Thresh = 10%
10	Branch a-h	2.830	3.11	10%	Probably not	Maybe
21	Branch b-i	1.912	3.02	58%	Maybe	Yes
22	Branch c-j	1.912	2.01	5%	Probably not	No
31	Branch d-n	2.368	2.65	12%	Probably not	No
32	Branch e-o	2.368	2.25	5%	Probably not	No
40	Branch f-t	3.728	3.99	7%	Probably not	No

Example 1: Consider a system in Figure 9-32 with 6 branch ducts with the "before" and "after" observed values shown in Table 9-10. Use change in SP_h values to decide whether to look inside the duct or to take additional measures (to allow use of a different method).

Note that in this example the SP_h values make it clear that something has happened to the system. Since the pressures generally declined by about the same percentage, it is unlikely that these branch ducts have been altered.

Example 2: Consider a system with 6 branch ducts with the "before" and "after" observed values shown in Table 9-11.

Note that in this example the SP_h values make it clear that Branch 21 has been altered and that the other branches probably have not changed.

9.10.2 Alteration Detection by the Branch Pressure Ratio Method: The ratio of any two pressures in a ventilation system should remain constant unless the section of the system that includes both measurement locations has been altered or obstructed.[9.14] That independence makes the ratio of SP_h to SP_{end} within the same branch duct (BrRatio) suitable for use as a parameter to detect changes to branch ducts (see Figure 9-33).

$$BrRatio = \left(\frac{SP_h}{SP_{end}}\right) \qquad [9.16]$$

Where: SP_{end} = the value measured at the end of the same branch duct where SP_h was measured.

If one is comparing BrRatio values determined with current values to those previously collected, one would look at the percentage of change in the parameter's values from Time 1 to Time 2:

$$\%BrRatio = \left(\frac{BrRatio_2 - BrRatio_1}{BrRatio_1}\right) \times 100\% \qquad [9.17]$$

As listed in Table 9-9, the direction of change in %BrRatio values depends on the nature and location of the alteration to the branch duct. Alterations elsewhere should have no effect.

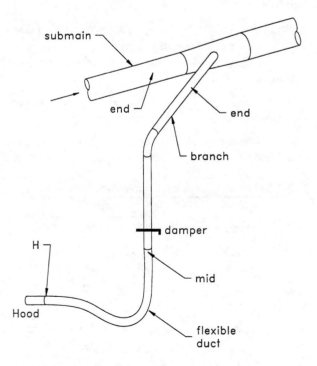

FIGURE 9–33. SP_h measurement location

TABLE 9-12. Example Problem Using BrRatio Method

ID	Points	Time 1			Time 2			Change	
		SP_h	SP_{end}	BrRatio	SP_h	SP_{end}	BrRatio	%BrRatio	Altered?
									Thresh = 10%
10	Branch a-	2.83	4.38	0.65	1.87	3.02	0.62	-4%	No
21	Branch b-i	1.91	2.50	0.77	1.49	1.70	0.87	14%	Very likely
22	Branch c-j	1.91	2.50	0.77	1.28	1.72	0.75	-3%	No
31	Branch d-	2.37	2.66	0.89	1.82	2.46	0.74	-17%	Very likely
32	Branch e-	2.37	2.66	0.89	2.12	2.44	0.87	-2%	No
40	Branch f-t	3.73	5.23	0.71	2.48	3.73	0.67	-6%	Not likely

The value of BrRatio cannot be less than zero and can exceed unity only if the cross-sectional area at H is less than at the END location—an atypical condition. If the initial value is near zero or unity, the method may not indicate the presence of some obstructions. The value will be near unity if the losses upstream of H account for almost all of the resistance. In that case, a new obstruction upstream of H will have little effect on BrRatio. For example, if the initial value is 0.98, the most it can increase is only 2% no matter how profound the obstruction.

Likewise, the value of BrRatio will be near zero if the losses downstream of H account for almost all of the resistance, and an obstruction downstream of H cannot decrease BrRatio significantly. If the BrRatio is 0.02, the maximum possible reduction is 2%. Thus when BrRatio is near unity or zero in initial readings, the Branch Ratio Method is of little value and the Equivalent Resistance Method should be employed.

Example 3: Consider the data for Example 1 branch ducts, this time with the addition of "before" and "after" observed values of SP_{end} allowing computation and comparison of BrRatio values (see Table 9-12).

Note that in this example the BrRatio values make it clear that something has happened to Branches 21 and 31.

9.10.3 Alteration Detection by the Reference Pressure Ratio Method: The Reference Pressure Ratio Method is based on the same principle[9.15] as the Branch Pressure Ratio Method. Unlike the Branch Ratio Method, the Reference Ratio Method employs a single value (SP_{ref}) for the whole system as the denominator in a pressure ratio.[9.14]

$$RefRatio = \left(\frac{SP_h}{SP_{ref}} \right)$$

Where: SP_{ref} = Static pressure at the end of a duct as a common reference measurement for all branch ducts.

$$\%RefRatio = \left(\frac{RefRatio_2 - RefRatio_1}{RefRatio_1} \right) \times 100\% \qquad [9.19]$$

The most convenient and useful reference pressure is generally the static pressure taken just upstream of the air cleaning device or the fan (whichever is most upstream). The pressures downstream of the air cleaning device are less useful because they would be strongly affected by the air cleaner.

As listed in Table 9-9, the direction of change in %RefRatio values depends on the nature and location of the alteration to the branch duct.

The Reference ratio method may give misleading results for branches if there are large obstructions or leaks in submains or main ducts. If branch ducts are free of obstructions and leaks, the method may spotlight obstructions and leaks in submain ducts.

TABLE 9-13. Example Problem Using RefRatio Method

ID	Points	Time 1			Time 2			Change	
		SP_h	SP_{ref}	RefRatio	SP_h	SP_{ref}	BrRatio	%BrRatio	Altered?
									Thresh = 10%
10	Branch a-h	2.8	6.02	0.47	1.9	4.11	0.45	-3%	No
21	Branch b-i	1.9	6.02	0.32	1.5	4.11	0.36	14%	Probably
22	Branch c-j	1.9	6.02	0.32	1.3	4.11	0.31	-2%	No
31	Branch d-n	2.4	6.02	0.39	1.8	4.11	0.44	-12%	Maybe
32	Branch e-o	2.4	6.02	0.39	2.1	4.11	0.52	-31%	Very likely
40	Branch f-t	3.7	6.02	0.62	2.5	4.11	0.60	-3%	No

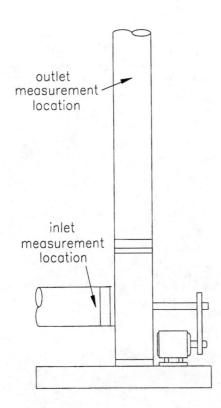

inlet
measurement
location

outlet
measurement
location

FIGURE 9–34. Fan

Example for RefRatio Method

Consider the data for Example 1 branch ducts, this time with the addition of "before" and "after" observed values of SP_h and SP_{ref}. The latter was a value of SP_{end} measured for a duct just upstream of the air cleaning device. The measurements were repeated later (Time 2) and the values of %RefRatio were computed (see Table 9-13).

As shown in Table 9-13, %RefRatio exceeded the recommended threshold for action (13%) in Branches 21 and 32.

9.10.4 Alteration Detection by the Equivalent Resistance Method: Equivalent resistance (X) is the ratio of the dissipated energy rate divided by the kinetic energy rate.[9.14] As with static pressure ratios, the equivalent resistance value for a given portion of the system (e.g., a branch duct) should vary little with changes to airflow, including changes induced by alterations to other parts of a system. Conversely, a substantial change in an X value is a strong indication that an obstruction or alteration has occurred. Those properties make observed values of X useful for troubleshooting. For a single flow in a duct, X is approximately the same as the sum of loss coefficients for the components in that section of duct. Indeed, velocity pressure coefficients can be considered as the X-values for individual components (e.g., elbows, hood entries to ducts, etc.)

Unlike the static pressure ratios described in the previous section, which work well only for branch ducts, equivalent

resistance can be applied usefully to any contiguous section of ducts, including branch ducts (X_{br}), submains (X_{sub}), many air cleaning devices (X_{clean}), the entire system of ducts upstream of the fan inlet (X_{inlet}), and the ducts connected to the exhaust side of the fan (X_{outlet}).

As listed in Table 9-9, the direction of change in %X values depends on the nature and location of the alteration to a given duct or component. Alterations elsewhere should have no effect.

The values for the various parts of a system can be computed from the following relationships:[9.14]

Fan Inlet: $X_{inlet} = \dfrac{-(SP_{inlet} + VP_{inlet})}{VP_{inlet}}$ [9.20a]

Where: SP_{inlet} = Static pressure measured just upstream of the fan inlet (see Figure 9-34)

X_{inlet} = Equivalent cumulative resistance upstream of the fan inlet

Hood: $X_h = \dfrac{-(SP_h + VP)}{VP}$ [9.20b]

Where: X_h = Cumulative resistance upstream of "H"

Branch: $X_{br} = \dfrac{-(SP_{end} + VP_{end})}{VP_{end}}$ [9.21a]

Where: X_{br} = Cumulative resistance of the branch upstream of "end"

Submain:

$X_{sub} = \dfrac{Q_a (SP_a + VP_a) + Q_b (SP_b + VP_b) - Q_m(SP_m + VP_m)}{Q_m VP_m}$ [9.21b]

Where: X_{sub} = Equivalent resistance of the volume bounded by cross-sections a, b, and m (see Figure 9-35)

a, b = Cross-section near the end of the upstream ducts terminating at the junction fitting

m = Cross-section near the end of the Submain duct

Air Cleaner:

$X_{clean} = \dfrac{Q_{up}(SP_{dn} + VP_{dn}) - Q_{dn}(SP_{dn} + VP_{dn})}{Q_{dn}(VP_{dn})}$ [9.22a]

Where: X_{clean} = Equivalent resistance of the air cleaning device

up = Cross-section just upstream of the air cleaning device (see Figure 9-36)

dn = Cross-section just downstream of the air cleaning device (see Figure 9-36)

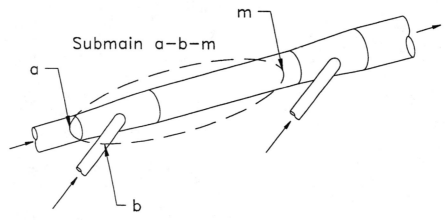

FIGURE 9–35. Submain

If the densities at up and dn are roughly the same (as is usually true), Equation 9.22a can be simplified to:

$$X_{clean} = \frac{Q_{up}(SP_{dn} + VP_{dn}) - Q_{dn}(SP_{dn} + VP_{dn})}{Q_{dn}(VP_{dn})} \qquad \textbf{[9.22b]}$$

Note that the pressures across some air cleaning devices (notably baghouses) vary linearly with airflow, not VP. Hence a change in airflow would produce a change in X for a baghouse even if the baghouse had experienced no changes that would affect resistance to flow. For that reason, an alternative way of evaluating air cleaning devices is shown as equation 9.24.

For all of the various forms of equivalent resistance, an increase or decrease in resistance can indicate an unwelcome

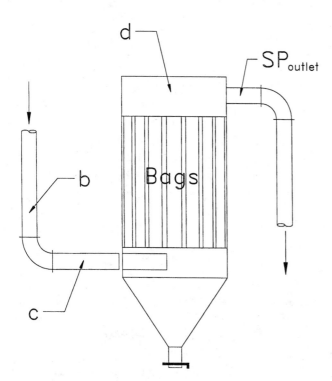

FIGURE 9–36. Air-cleaning device

development. For that reason one should look at the percentage change in the parameter's values.

$$\%X = \left(\frac{X_2 - X_1}{X_1}\right) = 100\% \qquad \textbf{[9.23]}$$

Where $\%X$ = Percentage change in X for a section of a system.

In evaluating changes to X_{values}, judicious consideration can reveal additional information. For example:

1. An obstruction upstream of H should increase X_h and X_{br} by about the same deviation (not percentage) since X_{br} includes the losses up to H. For example, an obstruction that increases X_h by 0.5 should also increase X_{br} by roughly 0.5. If X_h increases substantially and X_{br} does not, it is likely that SP_h was measured incorrectly.

2. If X_h and X_{br} change by roughly the same percentage and BrRatio has changed little, the value of VP is probably incorrect.

3. X_{sub} is less reliable than X_{br} because it is affected by errors in VP_a, VP_b, SP_a, and SP_m. The uncertainty associated with a value of X_{sub} is high because it is computed using the difference between large numbers. This is especially true if X_{sub} is relatively small. To reduce false positives, it is important to consider not only the percentage change in X_{sub} but the magnitude of the deviation. For example, if the observed value of X_{sub} increases from 0.15 to 0.30, it produces a percentage change of 100% even though the deviation is only 0.15—a very small increase in observed resistance that could easily be due to measurement errors.

4. Obstructions can be located by noting where X first increases. If X_h hs not changed and X_{br} has increased substantially, the obstruction must be between H and END (assuming SP_{end} is correct.)

TABLE 9-14. Example Problem Using X_{inlet}

		Time 1			Time 2			Change	
ID	Points	VP	SP_{end}	X_{inlet}	VP	SP_{end}	X_{inlet}	$\%X_{br}$	Check fan or ducts?
640	Fan inlet	0.95	8.01	7.43	0.68	6.02	7.85	6	Fan

TABLE 9-15. Example Problem Using X_{br}

		Time 1			Time 2			Change	
ID	Points	VP	SP_{end}	X_{br}	VP	SP_{end}	X_{br}	$\%X_{br}$	Check
10	Branch a-h	1.95	4.38	1.25	1.28	3.02	1.36	8	No
21	Branch B-i	1.32	2.50	0.89	1.03	1.70	0.66	-26	Yes
22	Branch c-j	1.32	2.50	0.89	0.89	1.72	0.94	6	No
31	Branch d-n	1.36	2.66	0.95	1.05	2.46	1.35	42	Yes
32	Branch e-o	1.36	2.66	0.95	1.22	2.44	1.00	5	No

EXAMPLE USING X_{INLET}

The observed fan inlet mean velocity pressure (VP) and SP_{end} values for Times 1 and 2 are shown in Table 9-14. By comparing the changes to X_{inlet} it is possible to determine whether the reduction in fan airflow is due to changes in resistance in the system or to problems with the fan.

A 6% change in resistance to flow could be attributable to random measurement error. In addition, it is unlikely that a 28% drop in VP (and thus a 15% change in fan airflow) could be produced by a 6% increase in resistance to flow. It is most likely that the problem is with the fan itself. Note, also, that lack of substantial change in X_{inlet} does not imply that nothing has

changed anywhere in the duct system. Even profound alteration to a single branch may have very small effects on X_{inlet} if there are many branches in the system. A small change in X_{inlet} does imply that any changes that did occur in the duct system upstream of the fan should have had little effect on fan output.

EXAMPLE USING X_{br}

The observed velocity pressures (VP) and SP_{end} values for Times 1 and 2 are shown in Table 9-15. By comparing the changes to X_{br}, it is possible to determine which branches are most likely to have become obstructed or have been altered from Time 1 to Time 2.

TABLE 9-16. Example Problem Using X_{sub}

Time	ID	Type	Dia	Q	VP	SP_{end}	TP_{end}	$Q*TP_{end}$	$Q*VP$	Down to	X_{sub}
1	10	Branch	9	2510	1.945	4.38	2.44	6117	4882	Sub 120	
2	10	Branch	9	2036	1.283	3.02	2.74	3545	2612	Sub 120	
1	21	Branch	5	637	1.320	2.50	2.28	750	841	Sub 23	
2	21	Branch	5	561	1.026	2.70	0.67	378	576	Sub 23	
1	22	Branch	5	637	1.320	2.50	1.18	750	841	Sub 23	
2	22	Branch	5	521	0.885	1.72	0.84	436	461	Sub 23	
1	23	Submain	7	278	1.378	4.01	2.64	3368	1761	Sub 120	1.06
2	23	Submain	7	1085	0.995	2.77	1.77	1924	1080	Sub 120	1.03
Spr Sib,aom 23: ΔX_{sub} = 1.03 - 1.06 = -0.03					X_{sub} = -0.03/1.06*100 = -3%						
1	31	Branch	6	933	1.364	2.66	1.30	1208	1273	Sub 33	
2	31	Branch	6	817	1.047	2.46	1.41	1155	856	Sub 33	
1	32	Branch	6	933	1.364	2.66	1.30	1208	1273	Sub 33	
2	32	Branch	6	882	1.220	2.44	1.22	1074	1076	Sub 33	
1	33	Submain	8	1874	1.733	5.29	3.56	6668	3248	Sub 130	1.31
2	33	Submain	8	1703	1.436	3.78	2.34	3988	2446	Sub 130	0.72
For Submain 33: ΔX_{sub} = 1.03 - 1.06 = -0.03					$\%X_{sub}$ = -0.03/1.06*100 = -3%						
1	120	Submain	10	3803	2.918	6.16	3.25	12345	11097	Sub 130	0.26
2	120	Submain	10	3129	1.983	4.30	2.32	7253	6205	Sub 130	0.29
For Submain 120: ΔX_{sub} = 0.29 - 0.26 = -.03					$\%X_{sub}$ = 0.03/0.26*100 = 12%						

The values of X_{br} changed from 5% to 42% from Time 1 to Time 2. Deviations that are above 20% are likely to correspond to significant obstructions or alterations. Branch 21 showed a 26% drop in value which indicates that between Times 1 and 2 a leak appeared, an obstruction was removed, or the duct was altered otherwise in a manner that reduced resistance to flow. The value of X_{br} for Branch 31 increased substantially, which is consistent with an increase in resistance due to an obstruction or alteration.

EXAMPLE USING X_{SUB}

Computations of X_{sub} requires determination of airflow and measurement of SP_{end} in the ducts upstream of the junction fitting as well as measurement of SP_{end} in the submain. The observed velocity pressures and SP_{end} values for the test system at Times 1 and 2 are shown in the Table 9-16. Note that both the magnitude and the percentage change in X_{sub} should be considered.

Note that it is convenient to list the product of Q and TP_{end} as well as Q and VP. For example, when computing the value of X_{sub} for the junction of branches 21 and 22 with Submain 23:

For Submain 23:

$$X_{sub} = \frac{Q_{21}(TP_{21}) + Q_{22}(TP_{22}) - Q_{23}(TP_{23})}{Q_{23}(VP_{23})}$$

$$X_{sub_1} = \frac{-750 - 750 - (-3368)}{1761} = 1.06$$

$$X_{sub_2} = \frac{-378 - 436 - (-1924)}{1080} = 1.03$$

For Submain 33:

$$X_{sub} = \frac{Q_{31}(TP_{31}) + (Q_{32}(TP_{32}) - Q_{23}(TP_{23})}{Q_{33}(VP_{33})}$$

$$X_{sub_1} = \frac{-1208 - 1208 - (-6668)}{3248} = 1.31$$

$$X_{sub_2} = \frac{-1155 - 1074 - (-3988)}{2446} = 0.72$$

For Submain 120:

$$X_{sub} = \frac{Q_{10}(TP_{10}) + (Q_{23}(TP_{23}) - Q_{120}(TP_{120})}{Q_{120}(VP_{120})}$$

$$X_{sub_1} = \frac{-6117 - 3368 - (-12345)}{11097} = 0.26$$

$$X_{sub_2} = \frac{-3545 - 1924 - (-7553)}{6205} = 0.29$$

The results of similar computations shown on Table 9-16 indicate that Submain 33 probably accrued an obstruction between Times 1 and 2. The conditions for other submains were probably not changed.

EXPECTED PRESSURE METHOD FOR AIR CLEANING DEVICES

The Equivalent Resistance Method can be useful for air cleaning devices whose pressures change with the square of airflow (e.g., cyclones) but is of little value for devices whose pressures do not (e.g., filters). For the latter, one should use the deviation between the observed and expected relationship between pressures and flows to detect changes in resistance:

$$\%\text{Deviation} = \left[\left(\frac{SP_2}{SP_1}\right)\left(\frac{Q_1}{Q_2}\right)^y\left(\frac{df_1}{df_2}\right) - 1\right] \times 100\% \qquad [9.24]$$

Where: $y = 1$ to 2

The value of the exponent "y" in the equation should be selected based on the characteristics of the air cleaning device. For a loss induced by laminar flow (e.g., across bags in a baghouse), the appropriate value is unity. For a device with turbulent flow (e.g., cyclones, electrostatic precipitators, and most other devices) a value of 2 should be used.

EXAMPLE

The median pressure (measured over several cleaning cycles) across the bags in a baghouse changed from 2.33 "wg to 2.10 "wg as the actual airflow through it changed from 11,500 cfm to 12,100 cfm and the density factor fell from 0.95 to 0.86. Is it likely that either leakage or blinding have occurred in the interval between measurements?

$$\%\text{Deviation} = \left[\left(\frac{2.10}{2.33}\right)\left(\frac{11,500}{11,900}\right)^y\left(\frac{0.94}{0.86}\right) - 1\right](100\%) = -5\%$$

Solution: A reduction in %Deviation may indicate leakage. However, the reduction in this example was well within the uncertainty one would expect from measurements needed to determine the airflow, pressure, and density. It is unlikely that anything has happened to produce major changes in resistance across the bags. Thus one could rule significant blinding and substantial leakage. Some leakage is possible, but not proven.

EXAMPLE

For the same system at a later time, the median pressure across the bags in a baghouse changed from 2.33 "wg to 3.02 "wg as the actual airflow through it changed from 11,500 cfm to 10,900 cfm and the density factor fell from 0.94 to 0.86. Is it likely that either leakage or blinding have occurred in the interval between measurements?

$$\%\text{Deviation} = \left[\left(\frac{3.02}{2.33}\right)\left(\frac{11,500}{10,900}\right)^y\left(\frac{0.94}{0.86}\right) - 1\right](100\%) = +49\%$$

Solution: This substantial increase in %Deviation probably indicates a developing problem with blinding or other problems in the unit. However, one should re-measure the parameters and re-compute %Deviation before acting on that guidance.

9.11 TESTING FOR ACCEPTANCE

A newly installed system should be tested for compliance with construction specifications and success in meeting design goals. However, the practitioner must use judgement in evaluating both. It is sometimes difficult to install a system exactly as designed, and some deviations may be unavoidable or unimportant. Ideally, in case of major deviations from design, the installer would inform the designer of changes before installation and the designer would modify the design to meet the new conditions. However, there may be instances where no such communication occurs and deviations are not reported—perhaps because the installer deemed them unimportant or was unaware of them or had no communication with the designer.

When deviations are discovered after installation is complete, the cost of remediation may be high and the installer correspondingly reluctant to accept that the deviation is important. Indeed, it is true that not all deviations will be important to system functioning. When testing for acceptance the purchaser must be prepared to present justification for rework if deviations are discovered. The installer, too, should be prepared to either rework or demonstrate that it is not necessary. In searching for and evaluating the importance of deviations, it may be useful to place deviations in one of the categories discussed below: [9.14]

1. Clearly adversely affects longevity, safety, maintainability, or reliability: should be reworked even if no deleterious effects have been presented. An obvious example affecting longevity is the use of thinner gauge material for an abrasive dust application. An obvious example for the fan and motor would be use of a non-approved fan for a potentially flammable effluent.

2. Clearly adversely affects performance of the air cleaner or the fan: should be remediated even if no deleterious effects are currently observed. Examples for the fan would include installation of the wrong fan and incorrect material or coating.

3. Clearly will adversely affect duct system functioning: should be remediated, but the effects of the deviations can and should be documented from observed pressures and flows. Examples include installing a substantially incorrect duct size (particularly in systems ventilating dusty processes), connecting ducts together differently from the design or other major deviations from prescribed layout, and use of substandard components (e.g., mitered elbows instead of radiused elbows).

4. May or may not adversely affect duct velocity, airflow distribution, etc., depending on the severity of the deviation, the interaction of all duct resistances, and the fan performance: should require rework only if observed airflow and pressure or modeling demonstrate unacceptable results (e.g., shift airflow by more than 5%). Examples include moderate deviations from layout that change duct lengths by moderate amounts, small deviations from prescribed duct sizes (e.g., less than 5%), and moderate changes to components (e.g., elbow with slightly smaller radius or curvature).

5. Missed by visual inspection but adversely affect pressures and flows. Should require rework if they shift airflow by 5% or more or if they raise system pressures unacceptably.

The following section discusses visual inspection of systems, and later sections describe procedures and methods for making reliable comparisons between design and observed values of pressures and flows.

9.11.1 Examine the System for Apparent Deviations from Design or Good Practice: It is important to determine what was specified. For that the evaluator should obtain as much of the following information as possible:

1. Design drawings and blueprints

2. Construction specifications

3. Specified fan rotation rate and motor power rating

4. Reports (verbal or otherwise) of constraints to installation

5. Design calculation worksheets

The next step is to determine obvious and known deviations from construction specifications. The installer may be aware of some deviations and unaware of others. The evaluator may find it useful to re-compute the system including only the known deviations. If those results are not definitive, more comprehensive examination of the physical layout will be necessary.

In cases where there is inadequate information from the installer or when the design specifications are either lost or not clear, the evaluator should then trace the system and compare actual installation to drawings and listed specifications. Mark off important items as they are measured or otherwise observed. Particularly important to airflow distribution are:

1. Duct connections as designed (e.g., branches A and B upstream of Submain S1).

2. Duct diameter (should be the nominal size; no larger, no smaller), duct shape (e.g., round), and duct construction and materials (e.g., 18 gauge galvanized steel).

3. Sub-standard, high-resistance components, especially mitered elbows and lateral junction entries.

4. Components not shown on the drawings of blueprints (e.g., fire dampers, flow dampers, drop boxes).

5. Number of elbows and gross lengths of runs of ducts.

6. Components that deviate from specifications (e.g., mitered instead of radiused elbows, flanged takeoffs from hoods).

9.11.2 Compare Observed to Predicted Airflows and Pressures:

To compare actual airflows and pressures to expected values one must measure the observed values and determine from knowledge of design goals and calculations what values to expect. The actual pressures and flows can be determined using the methods and instruments described earlier in this Chapter. The design values are: (1) the target airflows at the branches, (2) the predicted pressures throughout the system, and (3) the predicted fan airflow.

With these values in hand one can compute the percentage differences between design and observed values. However, interpreting the significance of computed differences requires careful consideration, mainly because there will not always be good agreement between predicted and observed values even when construction deviations from design are accounted for. There are several reasons for this uncertainty. Mathematical models and the published loss coefficients used in ventilation design procedures are not perfect, and uncertainty in field measurements can easily contribute deviations of 5% between predicted and observed values of airflows and pressures. Changes anywhere in the system affect all pressures and airflows, making it confusing to determine the causes of the changes. If the fan is set to a rotation rate that is 5% higher than the design value, pressures throughout the system will be roughly 10% higher than calculated.

There may be less uncertainty if equivalent resistances or pressure ratios are compared instead of pressures (but airflows should always be compared to target values). For that reason, the procedure below suggests comparing equivalent resistances or pressure ratios as well as comparing the observed values of hood airflows to the minimum design values.

The steps necessary to evaluate a new duct system for unexplained differences between observed and expected airflows are listed below:

1. Visually inspect the system for deviations from construction specifications and determine the reasons for them.

2. Complete Pitot traverses for each branch duct and near the fan inlet. Measure SP_h values for branches and SP_{end} values for every branch, submain, and main duct.

3. Compute actual airflows at the fan and for each branch duct from the Pitot traverses. Further investigation is indicated if:

   a. Any branch airflow is unacceptably lower than its design value.

   b. The airflow at the fan ("total" airflow) is unacceptably higher than the value computed during design.

c. The pressure at the fan inlet is unacceptably high.

   d. The standard airflow computed at the fan inlet is substantially greater than the sum of the branch airflows, indicating substantial leakage or measurement errors.

   e. The pressure across the air cleaning device is outside the expected range.

4. Compute predicted airflows and pressures for the system "as installed" using the new system calculations described in Chapter 5 with the modifications described in following sections.

5. Compute the percentage of total airflows going through each branch duct and the equivalent resistance at the fan inlet.

6. If the distribution of airflows to the branches is reasonably close to the expected values and the equivalent resistance at the fan inlet is within 15% of design values then the problem is limited to the fan. If so, inspect the fan.

7. If the predicted airflow distribution does not match the observed distribution, determine equivalent resistances for all branches and submains and the BrRatio or RefRatio values for each branch. Investigate each duct whose pressure ratio or equivalent resistance values are substantially different from expected values.

In following the procedure above, one should keep in mind that predictions based on published loss coefficients almost certainly will produce inaccurate values for duct systems with life experiences that include coatings, wear, dents, additions, and removals of branches, etc. Indeed, the predictions may be substantially inaccurate even for some newly installed systems. For that reason, the threshold values listed in Table 9-8 should be nearly doubled when comparing measured to predicted values than when comparing two rounds of measured values on the same system.

The sections that follow discuss elements of the procedure above in greater detail.

9.11.3 Modifications of the Calculation Procedure to Increase Accuracy:

In comparing predicted to observed values one must keep in mind that the computational methods described in Chapter 5 are intended to aid in selection of duct sizes and to provide information needed to select the fan and air cleaning devices. To predict "measurable" values one would have to add several complicating steps to the computations including:[9.20]

- Re-computing SP_h for the "corrected" velocity pressure

- Computation for SP_h and SP_{end} at measurable locations (e.g., 3 diameters from the hood connection and junction fitting connection)

- Rigorous use of density factors even for conditions that vary only modestly from "standard" conditions

- Computation of effects of "corrected" submain volumetric flows on pressures and flows for all ducts upstream of that submain

- More rigorous computation of losses due to straight duct.

It is relatively simple to account for effects of altitude, temperature, and modest humidity levels using spreadsheet computer software. However, precise computation of friction losses and accounting for effects of duct pressure on density (and vice versa) both require iterative computations and are therefore difficult to set up on currently available spreadsheet software. Likewise, accounting for upstream effects of airflow "corrections" is complex enough on many systems that it may be feasible only on properly programmed ventilation-design software. However, computing pressures just upstream of junction fittings and downstream of hood connections are relatively simple:

$$SP_h = VP (1 + F_h) + F_s VP_s - SP_{filter} + SP_{offset} \qquad [9.25]$$

$$SP_{end} = SP_{gov} - F_{en} VP - SP_{offset} \qquad [9.26]$$

Where: VP and VP_s are computed using the "corrected" volumetric flowrate.

SP_{filter} is the median pressure requirement for a hood filter, if present.

SP_{offset} is the friction loss for 3 diameters length of duct.

As is demonstrated in an example problem, these modifications should produce more accurate comparisons. However, one should expect to sometimes find significant differences between predicted and observed, even with all known computation issues resolved. In practice there would be larger differences between predicted and observed values due to:

Unavoidable Factors
- Small differences between the ideal fan speed and actual operating speed.

- Small differences between the design layout and the installed system.

- Measurement imprecision and inaccuracy.

- Fluctuations in observed values during normal operations.

Avoidable factors
- Substantial deviations between ideal and actual fan speed as well as reduced fan performance due to damage, coatings, or poor inlet and outlet conditions.

- Important deviations between the design layout and the installed system.

- Intentional alterations made since the system was designed (e.g., adding another branch duct).

- Larger or smaller than expected pressure requirements for air cleaning devices.

- Damage, obstructions, leaks, and maintenance mistakes.

9.11.4 Evaluating the Fan: Fans develop problems frequently enough that if problems appear to afflict more than one branch it may be cost-effective to investigate the fan before individual ducts—especially given the greater time and effort required to thoroughly investigate the duct system. Fan output can fall due to many causes such as (1) reduced shaft speed caused by belt slippage; (2) wear or accumulation of contaminant on the fan wheel or casing; (3) obstructions near the fan inlet or outlet or other system effects that can effect fan performance; (4) maintenance errors; and (5) increased resistance to flow through the ducts or air cleaning device.

If external inspection of the fan has not revealed a potential cause of reduced airflow, it is often more convenient to determine whether increased resistance to flow caused the reduction rather than stopping the fan and inspecting its internal condition. To determine if the duct system has the expected resistance to flow, compute X_{inlet} and X_{outlet} (Equations 9.25 and 9.26) for the observed values and the expected values and compare them.

The minimum information required to evaluate X_{inlet} and X_{outlet} is the information needed to select the fan: the static pressures (SP) and average velocity pressures (VP) at the fan inlet and outlet, and the flow rate (Q) and density (ρ) of the airflow at the fan inlet. To determine those values, one should measure the following:

1. SP_{inlet}, VP_{inlet} traverse, temperature humidity ratio, and duct diameter measured in straight duct at least 3 diameters upstream of the fan and 5 diameters downstream of any elbow or other upstream disturbance.

2. SP_{outlet} and duct diameter, measured in straight duct at least 6 diameters downstream of the fan and 2 diameters upstream of any elbow or other downstream disturbance.

3. Barometric pressure outside the building.

In comparing observed and expected values, it is helpful to note the following:

1. The output of a fan is strongly affected by the total resistance of the system, which is the sum of X_{inlet} and X_{outlet}.

2. A deviation in X of 0.20 is equivalent to adding or removing one 90 degree elbow.

3. For most systems, it should be possible to detect 15% changes in X_{inlet} reliably.

If the total resistance of the system is substantially the same as predicted values, the duct system is not the cause of degraded fan performance.

Whether or not the duct system is the sole source of reduced airflow, one can determine if the fan is performing at its rated level by comparing the observed fan performance to values in the fan's performance table at its rotation rate. The rotation rate can be measured directly at the end of the fan shaft using a tachometer or stroboscope. The amperage consumed by the

TABLE 9-17. Actions to Take Based Solely on %SP_h

ID	— SP_h — 1st	— SP_h — 2nd	%Dev	Thresh = 10% Meas SP_end?	Thresh = 35% Take Apart?
1	3.94	3.95	0	No	No
2	1.96	2.29	17	Yes	No
3	1.72	1.77	3	No	No
5	1.56	1.89	21	Yes	No
6	1.84	2.26	23	Yes	No
7	1.83	2.04	12	Yes	No
8	2.53	1.89	−25	Yes	No
9	2.08	1.45	−30	Yes	No
10	2.71	3.43	27	No	OK
12	1.79	1.73	−3	Yes	False Neg

motor and its voltage can be measured to compute the expected power requirement of the fan which can be compared to the value published in the fan table (or otherwise specified by the manufacturer) for the same observed conditions. Amperage should be measured with an ammeter starting with the highest scale and working down until the correct range is reached. The values on the three leads of a 3-phase service should be averaged and compared to the rating listed on the motor nameplate. If the measured amperage exceeds the expected value by more than 15% (the portion lost to drive inefficiencies), the fan inlet conditions may be poor or the fan wheel may be misaligned, dirty, or damaged.

9.11.5 Example Commissioning Problem: The following example problem is based on the second example design problem in Chapter 5. The Time 1 values are values predicted using Chapter 5 and the "corrections" of Equations 9.25 and 9.26. The calculations were done for standard density air.

The Time 2 values are measurements taken 2 weeks after the installation. The conditions affecting density were 60 F, 250 ft altitude, and 50% relative humidity. Given the predicted values and the observed values shown in each of Tables 9-17–9-19, determine the likely location of substantial obstructions and possible deviations from design specifications using %SP_h, % BrRatio, and %X_{br}.

Solution for %SP_h: As shown in Table 9-17, values of SP_h varied by 0 to 30%. As shown on the table, all but two branch duct values changed at least 10% suggesting that further investigation is needed, but not implying that a problem is definitely established. None exceeded 35%, the value one might consider a threshold for intervention on systems that are frequently monitored and kept in repair.

Solution for %BrRatio: as shown in Table 9-18, values of BrRatio varied by 3 to 29% from predicted values. Branches 2 and 12 exceeded the 9% threshold for intervention and Branches 3 and 8 were borderline. If intervention would be particularly costly or time consuming, one would do well to corroborate the positive findings with %X_{br}. The ambiguous findings for 3 and 8 should be corroborated with %X_{br} before discounting them.

Solution for %X_{br}: as shown in Table 9-19, values of X_{br} varied by 3 to 100% from predicted values. Branches 2, 3, 6, 9, and 12 exceeded the 17% threshold for intervention. If intervention would be particularly costly or time consuming, one would do well to corroborate the findings with %BrRatio. Note that both methods agreed on Branches 2 and 12. The %X_{br} findings strengthen the ambiguous findings from %BrRatio for Branches 3 and 9. The two methods disagreed on Branch 6. This most likely indicates a measurement error in either SP_h or VP.

REFERENCES

9.1   American Society of Heating, Refrigerating and Air Conditioning Engineers, Practices for Measurement, Testing, Adjusting, and Balancing of Building Heating, Ventilation, Air Conditioning and Refrigeration Systems, ANSI/ASHRAE Standard 111-1988.

TABLE 9-18. Actions to Take Based Solely on %BrRatio

ID	— Time 1 — SP_h	— Time 1 — SP_end	— Time 1 — BrRatio	— Time 2 — SP_h	— Time 2 — SP_end	— Time 2 — BrRatio	Thres = 9% %BrRatio	Action Take Apart?
1	3.94	5.12	0.77	3.95	5.05	0.78	1	No
2	1.96	2.45	0.80	2.29	2.56	0.89	12	Yes
3	1.72	2.22	0.78	1.77	2.52	0.70	−9	Maybe
5	1.56	1.98	0.79	1.89	2.31	0.82	4	No
6	1.84	2.15	0.86	2.26	3.56	0.88	3	No
7	1.83	2.99	0.61	2.04	3.45	0.59	−3	No
8	2.53	3.50	0.72	1.89	2.76	0.68	−5	No
9	2.08	2.95	0.70	1.45	2.23	0.65	−8	Maybe
10	2.71	2.88	0.94	3.43	3.80	0.90	−4	No
12	1.79	2.33	0.77	1.73	3.20	0.54	−29	Yes

TABLE 9-19. Actions to Take Based Solely on %X$_{br}$

ID	— Time 1 —			— Time 2 —			Thres = 17%	Action
	SP$_{end}$	VP	X$_{br}$	SP$_{end}$	VP	Xbr	%Xbr	Take Apart?
1	5.12	2.58	0.98	5.05	2.64	0.91	-7	No
2	2.45	1.54	0.59	2.56	1.37	0.88	48	Yes
3	3.22	1.37	0,62	2.52	1.25	1.02	64	Yes
5	1.98	1.19	0.67	2.31	1.35	0.71	7	No
6	2.15	0.89	1.40	2.56	1.31	0.96	-32	Yes
7	2.99	0.95	2.16	3.45	1.05	2.27	5	No
8	3.50	1.63	1.14	2.76	1.27	1.17	3	No
9	2.95	1.67	0.77	2.23	1.09	1.05	37	Yes
10	2.88	2.01	0.43	3.80	2.52	0.51	17	No
12	2.33	1.41	0.66	3.20	1.38	1.31	100	Yes

9.2   American Society of Heating, Refrigerating and Air Conditioning Engineers. ASHRAE Handbook–1997 Fundamentals.

9.3   American Society of Heating, Refrigerating and Air Conditioning Engineers. Standard Method for Temperature Measurement. ANSI/ASHRAE standard 41.2-1987 (RA 9).

9.4   American Society of Heating, Refrigeration and Air Conditioning Engineers, Standard Methods for Laboratory Measurement. ANSI/ASHRAE Standard 41.2-1987 (RA 92).

9.5   Guffey, S.E.: Simplifying Pitot Traverses. Applied Occup. Environ. Hyg., 5(2): 95-100(1990).

9.6   American Society of Heating, Refrigeration and Air Conditioning Engineers. Standard Method for Pressure Measurement. ANSI/ASHRAE Standard 41.3-1989).

9.7   American Society of Mechanical Engineers, ASME Power Test Codes, Chapter 4, Flow Measurement, P.T.C., 19.5:4-1959.

9.8   American Society of Mechanical Engineers, Fluid Meters–Their Theory and Applications, 1959.

9.9   Booth, D.W.: Comparison of Three Methods for Troubleshooting Ventilation Duct Systems Using Measured Pressure and Flows, Ph.D. Dissertation, Dept. of Environmental Health, University of Washington, 1998.

9.10   Farant, J.P.; McKinnon, D.L.; and McKenna, T.A.: Tracer Gases as a Ventilation Tool: Methods and Instrumentation, Ventilation'85–Proceedings of the First International Symposium of Ventilation for Contaminant Control, pp. 263-274, October 1-3, 1985, Toronto, Canada.

9.11   First, N.W.; Silverman, L.: Airfoil Pitometer, Industrial and Engineering Chemistry, 42, Feb., 1950, pp. 301-308.

9.12   Guffey, S.E.; Booth, D.W.: Comparison of Pitot Traverses Taken at Varying Distance Downstream of Obstructions, Am. Ind. Hyg. Assoc. J. (In Press).

9.13   Guffey, S.E.; Spann, J.G.: Experimental Investigation of Power Loss Coefficients and Static Pressure Ratios in an Industrial Exhaust System, Am. Ind. Hyg. Assoc. J., 60: 367-376, 1999.

9.14   Guffey, S. E.: Quantitative Troubleshooting of Industrial Exhaust Ventilation Systems, Applied Occup. Environ. Hyg., 9(4):267-280, (1994).

9.15   Guffey, S. E.: Final Report of Field Validation of Ventilation Troubleshooting Methods, Grant Number: 1 RO1 OH03165; Project Dates: 4/1/94 to 10/30/97.

9.16   Hama, G.: A Calibrating Wind Tunnel for Measuring Instruments, Air Engr. 41:18-20, (December, 1967).

9.17   Hama, G.: Calibration of Alnor Velometers, Am. Ind. Hyg. Assoc. J., Dec., 1958.

9.18   Hama, G.; Curley, L.S.: Instrumentation for the Measurement of Low Velocities with a Pitot Tube, Air Engr., July, 1967, and Am. Ind. Hyg. Assoc. J., May-June, 1967.

9.19   Wang, L.S.: Repeatability of Velocity Pressure Traverses and Static Pressure Measurements in Five Working Ventilation Systems, MS Thesis, Dept. of Env. Health, University of Washington, 1997.

9.20   Guffey, S.E.: Modeling Existing Ventilation Systems Using Measured Values. Am. Ind. Hyg. Assoc. J., 54(6):293-306 (1993).

APPENDIX A.9.1: NEED FOR CORRECTIONS TO CHAPTER 5 PROCEDURES

This section is intended to illustrate the need for Equations 9.25 and 9.26 to correct the computations made in Chapter 5 and to show the combined effects of ignoring "trivial" effects of density. The following example problem is based on the second example design problem in Chapter 5. It compares a set of fictitious measurements taken two weeks after installation to the values show in Chapter 5. To illustrate the deviations between observed and computed pressures one might encounter in testing installed systems, the results from Example 2 (non-dampers) were recomputed using a ventilation software program that accounts for all of the complications listed in the preceding section including those difficult to do with a calculator or spreadsheet software.

To make the comparisons even more interesting, the more complex computations were done for environmental conditions most practitioners would treat as "standard": temperature of 60 F (possible winter room temperature), 250 ft altitude, and 50% relative humidity. It was assumed that the new system had been in operation insufficient time to achieve the roughness employed in the Chapter 5 computations, so a roughness of 0.0004 ft was employed. It also was assumed that the fan speed was set at 5% above the ideal level one selected for the solution shown in Chapter 5. Finally, it was assumed that the system was installed in perfect compliance with specifications, all loss coefficients were exactly correct, and all measurements were perfectly accurate.

As shown in Table A.9.1, all of the observed troubleshooting parameters varied substantially from the values predicted in Chapter 5. Indeed, the deviations between predicted and "observed" frequently exceeded the thresholds for action shown in Table 9-8 even though all measurements were perfectly accurate. Hence, using the unmodified predictions from Chapter 5, it would be possible to reliably detect only gross obstructions or deviations from design.

TABLE A.9.1. Deviation from "Perfect Measurements if Solution in Chapter 5 Were Employed

%Q	%SP$_h$	%BrRatio	%RefRatio	%X$_{br}$
6	−33	25	51	−3
−1	−12	23	14	−38
−2	−21	40	28	−21
−1	−11	21	14	−21
−3	−9	12	11	−1
−2	−9	14	11	−10
8	−24	8	33	−2
3	−27	36	38	−19
5	−37	39	59	−4
−1	−11	22	14	−22

Chapter 10
SPECIFIC OPERATIONS

The following illustrations of hoods for specific operations are intended as guides for design purposes and apply to usual or typical operations. In most cases, they are taken from designs used in actual installations of successful local exhaust ventilation systems. Technology and shop equipment change over the years. Some drawings in Chapter 10 show ventilation solutions for older types of shop equipment. Manufacturers, designers, and end-users are encouraged to submit improved designs to the Industrial Ventilation Committee for inclusion in future editions of the manual. All conditions of operation cannot be categorized, and because of special conditions (i.e., cross-drafts, motion, differences in temperature, or use of other means of contaminant suppression), modifications may be in order. Using principles discussed in earlier chapters, manual users are encouraged to cautiously adapt the existing drawings to their specific needs. For instance, there are presently no drawings for fiberglass lay-up and spray-up operations. To collect the solvent vapors, the manual user could adapt a paint booth for these operations. The designer should also recommend Low Volume-High Velocity (vacuum) tools and a separate collection system if workers also perform grinding in the same shop.

The flow rates specified in the various VS-prints are to be considered actual flow rates (ACFM) at the local conditions existing at the places used.

Unless it is specifically stated, the design data are not to be applied indiscriminately to materials of high toxicity, e.g., beryllium and radioactive materials. Thus the designer may require higher or lower air flow rates or other modifications because of the peculiarities or the process in order to adequately control the air contaminant.

10.05 BATTERY CHARGING

Operations using rechargeable batteries are increasing in industry, commercially, and even in the home, as regulatory agencies encourage the move away from petroleum fuels. Traditional battery operated vehicles, such as warehouse forklifts and golf carts, are now joined by battery charging facilities in automotive, bus, and light vehicle fleet garages. The telecommunications industry, ships, and submarines also rely on rechargeable batteries. Operations requiring an uninterrupted power source (UPS) sometimes use rechargeable batteries as a back-up power source. This section does not address manufacturing, reclaiming, and recycling operations.

10.05.1 End-user Operations: End-user battery maintenance operations are usually limited to inspections, electrolyte level adjustment, adding water, recharging, and battery replacement. The most commonly found rechargeable batteries are lead-acid and nickel-cadmium. The primary hazard is the build-up of hydrogen that could lead to an explosion if there is sufficient quantity and an ignition source. Charging lead-acid batteries also can produce sulfuric acid mists. Charging nickel-cadmium batteries can produce alkaline mists. Arsine and stilbine have been reported in poorly ventilated battery charging rooms. If the end-user makes frequent battery repairs (e.g., lead post maintenance and lead plate work), consider modifying a welding hood shown in VS-90-01 or VS-90-02.

Battery out-gassing occurs by inducing charging currents in excess of those needed to charge the cells, thereby converting the water to oxygen and hydrogen which are released into the room. When charging a large quantity of batteries in the same room, hydrogen gas can build up to the LEL. The LEL of hydrogen is 4.1%. In some cases, regulatory requirements, local practice or consensus standards require a lower safety factor. Typical safety factors are 25, 10, or 1% of the LEL.

Many modern rechargeable batteries are valve-regulated or sealed and they do not release gasses. However, they have a pressure release valve and the batteries can leak hydrogen if they are overcharged or charged in a hot (> 80 F) environment. Many newer batteries are able to absorb the hydrogen generated internally. When charging older-style batteries, more hydrogen is generated as batteries age. Contact the manufacturer to determine the proper ventilation rates for older batteries.

10.05.2 Battery Charging Ventilation: Some code organizations require mechanically supplied replacement air. The user should move the battery to a ventilated table when performing operations such as electrolyte addition and post welding.

Dilution Ventilation: Typical electric and fire codes permit the use of the building's ventilation without local exhaust ventilation for the following:

- The engineered ventilation system (HVAC) approved by local fire officials that is intended to maintain a gas-air mixture of less than 25% (or 10% in certain cases) of the lower flammable limit.

- The charger system is approved for indoor charging of batteries by a testing or consensus organization such as Factory Mutual or the National Electric Code. These are normally a charger/battery combination that does not emit hydrogen (e.g., pagers, cell phones, etc.)

TABLE 10.05.1. Minimum Dilution Ventilation Requirements per Electric Vehicle

Branch Circuit Ampere Rating	Minimum Ventilation Required in Cubic Feet per Minute (cfm) for Each of the Total Number of Electric Vehicles that Can Be Charged at One Time						
	Branch Circuit Voltage						
	Single Phase			Three Phase			
	120V	108V	240V or 120/240V	208V or 208Y/120V	240V	480V or 480Y/277V	600V or 600Y/347V
15	37	64	74				
20	49	85	99	148	117	342	427
30	74	128	148	222	256	512	641
40	99	171	197	296	342	683	854
50	123	214	246	370	427	854	1066
60	148	256	296	444	512	1025	1281
100	246	427	493	740	854	1708	2165
150				1110	1281	2562	3203
200				1480	1708	3416	4270
250				1850	2135	4270	5338
300				2221	2562	5125	6406
350				2591	2989	5979	7473
400				2961	3416	6832	8541

- Open garages, carports, and other structures with two or more sides open.

Small Battery Charging Room or Small Battery Charging Areas in Large Rooms: To determine the amount of ventilation required for compliance with the health and safety requirements, follow the battery manufacturer's recommendation and the local building codes. The National Electric Code also cites the criteria for minimum mechanical ventilation in cubic feet per minute required for each parking space that is equipped to charge an electric vehicle.

For voltages and currents not shown on Table 10.05.1, use the following formula:

$$Q_{singlephase} = \frac{(volts)(amperes)}{48.7} \qquad [10.05.1]$$

$$Q_{threephase} = \frac{1.732(volts)(amperes)}{48.7} \qquad [10.05.2]$$

The above calculated ventilation rate ($Q_{calculated}$) assumes efficient mixing of the air inside the battery charging facility. In most cases, this does not occur and a safety factor (K), to allow for incomplete mixing, must be used to determine the actual ventilation required. Values for K can be found in Chapter 2, Figure 2.1.

A properly designed industrial ventilation system will assist in completely mixing the air inside the battery charging facility, lowering the K value, and lowering the actual ventilation rate. Industrial ventilation design considerations to include in the battery charging facility are:

- High level and low level dilution exhaust. High level exhaust should ventilate all roof pockets. Low level exhaust should be a maximum of 12 inches above the floor.

- Exhaust all air directly outdoors. Consider the required air pollution permits.

- The supply air rate should be approximately 95% of the exhaust ventilation rate to maintain a slightly negative room static pressure (relative to outside) to prevent fumes and gases from migrating outside the battery charging facility.

Passive Exhaust Systems: In temperate climates, some facilities employ passive ventilation systems where the stack effect of varying densities and rising heat carries the hydrogen to the uppermost point in the facility. Providing a supply air opening low in the building and a covered opening in the roof peak/opening usually provides sufficient natural ventilation. Since these systems depend on natural ventilation, it is impossible to predict a constant amount of airflow through the building. Passive systems generally are not recommended and some local code organizations prohibit them.

10.05.3: End-user Electrolyte Maintenance Hood: Electrolyte changing is usually a short term operation. Industrial ventilation is generally not required for this operation. However, personal protective equipment (i.e., apron, gloves, safety glasses, and shield) is imperative. A small laboratory hood (VS-35-01 or VS-35-02) can be adapted when the operator mixes and dispenses large quantities of electrolyte.

10.05.4: Supply Air Systems:

Small Dilution Ventilation Type Systems: The designer should evaluate the local supply air system balance in small battery recharging operations, such as forklift and electric cart recharging areas, to ensure that the system provides a sufficient air volume. Check the ventilation control cycle to ensure that at least a small amount of air is available even when the plant ventilation system is off such as night and weekend setback conditions. When only a few batteries are charged simultaneously, a dedicated supply air system may not be required.

Larger Operations with Dedicated Exhaust Hoods: Depending on the operation, supply air can be by a perforated plenum covering the whole room or through a low hanging diffuser providing laminar flow. The key point in supplying the replacement air is that air/contaminant mixing does not occur in the workers breathing zone or the contaminant does not bounce back into the worker's breathing zone.

Do not recirculate air from a ventilation system installed to remove hydrogen.

REFERENCES

10.05.1 National Institute for Occupational Safety and Health, NIOSH Health Hazard Evaluation Report HETA 95-0097-2661, October, 1997.

10.05.2 California Building Code, Section 1202.2.2.2.1; California Building Officials, 2215 21st Street, Sacramento, CA 95818.

10.05.3 National Fire Protection Association, National Electric Code Handbook, Section 6.25, 1999.

RELATED LITERATURE

Naval Facilities Engineering Service Center, Battery Charging Facilities Ventilation Rates, Information Bulletin 425.114, October, 1997.

Minor, Cheryl L., State of the Art Ventilation Engineering Principles of Laminar Flow and Recirculation in the Battery Industry. Ventilation '91, Cincinnati, OH, September, 1991.

Personal Communication from Melvin Cassidy, Cooperative Assessment Program Manual for the Battery Manufacturing Industry, U. S. Department of Labor, February, 1986.

10.10 CLEANROOMS

U. S. Federal Standard 209E[10.10.1] establishes standard classes of air cleanliness for airborne particulate levels in cleanrooms and clean zones. This standard is issued by the General Services Administration of the United States. While nominally a publication for use by federal agencies, FED-STD-209E has been adopted by American industry. It prescribes methods for class verification and monitoring of air cleanliness. It also addresses certain other factors that affect control of airborne contaminants.

FED-STD-209E does not address the physical, chemical, radiological, or viable nature of airborne contaminants. It also does not address the occupational health concerns of employees working in clean room environments.

A cleanroom class is the statistically allowable number of particles, greater than or equal to 0.5 micrometers in size, per cubic foot of air. Cleanroom classes are shown in Table 10.10.1.

In order to meet the class limits, a High Efficiency Particulate Air (HEPA) or Ultra Low Penetration Air (ULPA) filter is required. A HEPA filter is a disposable, extended-media, dry-type filter in a rigid frame with a minimum particle collecting efficiency of 99.97% for 0.3 micrometer, thermally generated dioctylphthlate (DOP), or specified alternate, aerosol particles at a maximum clean resistance of 1.0 "wg when tested at rated airflow capacity. An ULPA filter is a disposable, extended-media, dry-type filter in a rigid frame with a minimum particle collecting efficiency of 99.999% for particulate diameters between 0.1 and 0.2 micrometers in size.

Military specifications[10.10.2] and publications[10.10.3] by the Institute of Environmental Sciences (IES) define HEPA and ULPA filter construction. Filters having an efficiency even higher than an ULPA filter are available from some companies specializing in cleanrooms and air filtration.

The primary design considerations for cleanrooms are the supply airflow rate, the airflow patterns within the clean room, the method for recirculating the air from the clean room, and the filter efficiency.

Air is supplied to the cleanroom by an air handling system containing the components needed for heating, cooling, and humidity control. Noise is readily transmitted to the clean room so very slow fan speeds, vibration isolation, and noise control devices are important design considerations. The air circulation system will also contain two or three stages of pre-filtration. This allows the final filters in the cleanroom ceiling to remain in place for very long periods of time. A final filter life of ten years or more is typical for Class 100 and better cleanrooms.

Air from the supply system enters the cleanroom through either a ducted module or a pressurized plenum. VS-10-01 shows the ducted module arrangement. Ducted modules containing HEPA or ULPA filters are connected to the main air supply duct by flexible branch ducts. The modules usually contain an internal baffle for balancing the air exhaust which must be at a uniform velocity across the face of the filter. The ducted modules are mounted in a T-bar grid and sealed with either solid gaskets or a liquid gel sealant. The ducted modules, because of long filter life, usually are considered to be throwaway items; however, some arrangements do permit the replacement of filters from within the cleanroom. A ducted module system offers maximum flexibility for clean room modification.

VS-10-02 shows a pressurized plenum arrangement. A heavy duty grid system is suspended from the ceiling with suspension rods and the HEPA or ULPA filters sealed in the grid with liquid gel or solid gaskets. The entire plenum is pressurized by the air supply system to allow a uniform flow of air through the filters to the cleanroom below. A pressurized plenum system will usually cost less than a ducted module system for large cleanrooms.

VS-10-03 shows raised floor and low sidewall arrangements. Air is returned through a utility chase to the cleanroom supply air system. To provide better particulate control, the raised floor arrangement is preferred. The low sidewall return should not be used for vertical downflow cleanrooms more than 14 feet wide in order not to disrupt laminar flow at the work area.

TABLE 10.10.1. Class Limits in Particles per Cubic Foot of Size Equal to or Greater than Particle Sizes Shown.*

	Measured Particle Size (Micrometers)				
Room Class	0.1	0.2	0.3	0.5	5.0
1	35	7.5	3	1	NA
10	350	75	30	10	NA
100	NA	750	300	100	NA
1000	NA	NA	NA	1000	7
10,000	NA	NA	NA	10,000	70
100,000	NA	NA	NA	100,000	700

*The class limit particle concentrations shown are defined for class purposes only and do not necessarily represent the size distribution to be found in any particular situation.

IES-RP-CC-006-84[10.10.4] contains testing methods for characterizing the performance of cleanrooms. It defines terms having special meaning and describes test procedures to assure proper clean room operation. Uniform airflow is defined as unidirectional with all velocity readings within 20% of the average velocity of the work area. The air velocity at the work area is generally about 100 fpm; however, design conditions may require velocities of 10 fpm or lower.

REFERENCES

10.10.1 FED-STD-209E, Federal Standard, Cleanroom and Work Station Requirements, Controlled Environment, Federal Supply Service, General Services Administration, Washington, DC (June 15, 1988).

10.10.2 MIL-F-51068(EA), Specification Filters, Particulate, High-Efficiency, Fire Resistant, Biological Use, General Specifications For, Commander, U.S. Army Armament Research and Development Command, ATTN: DRDAR-TSC-S, Aberdeen Proving Ground, MD (October 4, 1982).

10.10.3 IES-RP-CC-001.3, HEPA and ULPA Filters, Institute of Environmental Sciences, Mount Prospect, IL.

10.10.4 IES-RP-CC-006, Testing Cleanrooms, Institute of Environmental Sciences, Mount Prospect, IL.

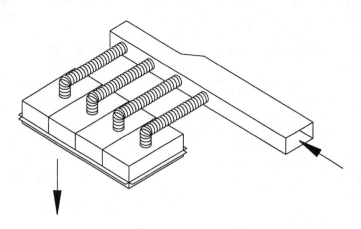

Air is supplied to the ducted modules from the air distribution duct through flexible branch ducts, which are secured at the bottom ends by clamps.   A damper (not shown) on the inside of the collar allows balancing of the air flowing from the module to the cleanroom.

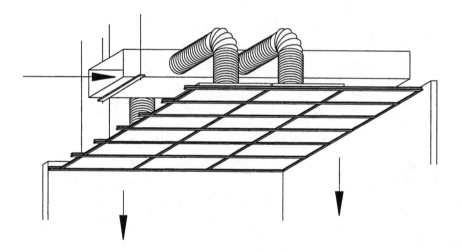

Ducted modules are mounted in 2' x 4' grids and sealed with gaskets or a liquid gel sealant.   Tear drop or recessed lighting (shown) provides illumination.

AMERICAN CONFERENCE OF GOVERNMENTAL INDUSTRIAL HYGIENISTS	CLEANROOM DUCTED MODULE	
	DATE *12-90*	FIGURE *VS-10-01*

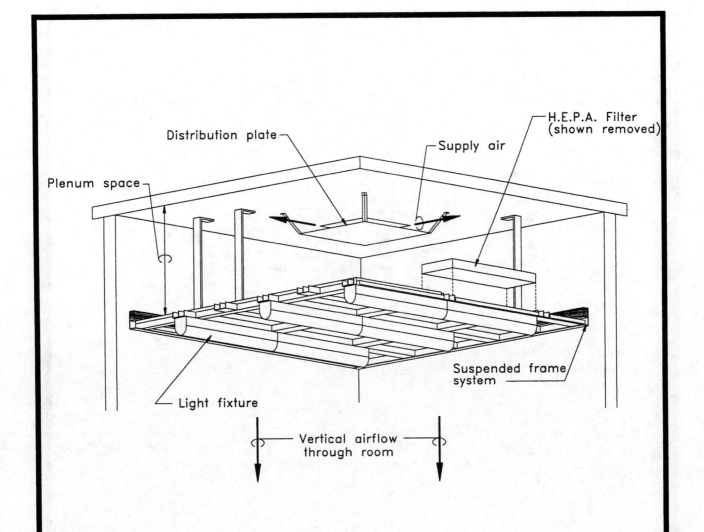

Supply air enters a pressurized plenum and strikes a distribution plate. Each 2' x 4' opening in the support structure contains a HEPA filter. Filters are sealed around the perimeter with gaskets or a fluidic sealant. The framing structure is supported from the plenum ceiling by suspension rods. Tear drop lighting is shown.

AMERICAN CONFERENCE OF GOVERNMENTAL INDUSTRIAL HYGIENISTS	CLEANROOM PRESSURIZED PLENUM	
	DATE 12-90	FIGURE VS-10-02

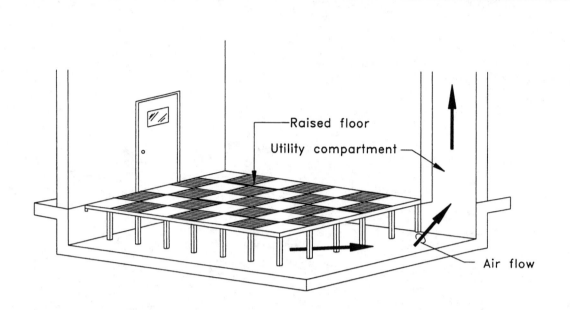

Raised floor with depressed slab. Air is returned through a utility compartment to the air supply system.

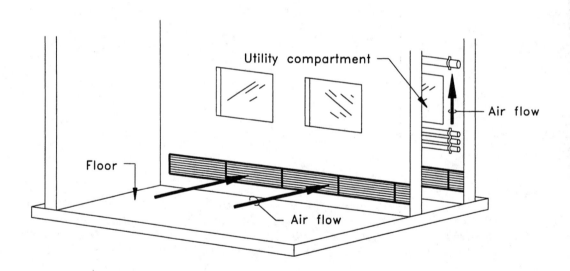

Low sidewall grille return through a utility compartment to the air supply system. Room width is limited to 14 feet if laminar air flow is to be achieved. The distance from the top of the grille to the floor should not exceed 18 inches.

AMERICAN CONFERENCE OF GOVERNMENTAL INDUSTRIAL HYGIENISTS	CLEANROOM RETURN AIR ARRANGEMENTS	
	DATE 12-90	FIGURE VS-10-03

10.15 FILLING OPERATIONS

Filling operations have special considerations that should be addressed when designing hoods. An enclosed space is not empty but rather is filled with air. When material enters the space, it forces the air out which in turn can carry some of the material with it. Also, additional air can be entrained by the material stream entering the enclosed space. This effect is a function of the size of the particles and the distance the material must fall. These two effects must be considered when designing hoods for material handling situations.

If there are any openings in the walls of the container which is being filled, some "splashing" of the material can occur. This can lead to loss of material through cracks and openings in the receiving vessel. The design of the ventilation system should take this effect into account.

The proper choice of exhaust flow rate is critical. If too little air is exhausted, the air displaced by the falling material may exceed the exhaust rate and the contaminant may not be adequately controlled. If too much air is exhausted, excess material could be entrained into the exhaust air stream. As this material often is the product, excess product loss could occur.

VS-15-01 illustrates four different ways of controlling barrel or drum filling operations. VS-15-02 illustrates bag filling and weighing. VS-15-03 depicts a bag tube packer. VS-15-10 and VS-15-11 depict a weighing hood where dry materials are removed from a bulk pack and weighed into smaller bags.[10.15.3]

These smaller bags are then packed into a container. Bags containing toxic materials can be opened within an enclosing hood such as shown on VS-15-20.[10.15.4]

VS-15-30 shows how to extract a toxic liquid from a process line or vessel for analysis and VS-15-21 shows a possibility of controlling leaks around rotating shafts that enter containers.[10.15.5]

REFERENCES

10.15.1   Hama, G.M.: Ventilation Control of Dust from Bagging Operations, Heating and Ventilating. p. 91 (April, 1948).

10.15.2   Cooper, T. C.: Control Technology for a Dry Chemical Bagging and Filling Operations. Monsanto Agricultural Products Co., Cincinnati, OH (1983).

10.15.3   Gressel, M. G.; Fischback, T. J.: Workstation Design Improvements for the Reduction of Dust Exposures During Weighing of Chemical Powders. Applied Industrial Hygiene, 4:227-233 (1989).

10.15.4   Goldfield, J.; Brandt, F. E.: Dust Control Techniques in the Asbestos Industry. A paper presented at the American Industrial Hygiene Conference, Miami Beach, FL (May 12-17, 1974).

10.15.5   Langner, R. R.: How to Control Carcinogens in Chemical Production. Occupational Health and Safety, (March-April 1977).

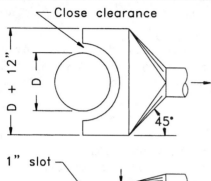

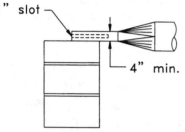

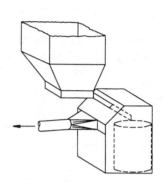

$Q = 100$ cfm/ft^2 barrel top (minimum)
Minimum duct velocity = 3500 fpm
$h_e = 1.78$ VP$_s$ + 0.25 VP$_d$

$Q = 150$ cfm/ft^2 of open face area
Minimum duct velocity = 3500 fpm
$h_e = 0.25$ VP$_d$ (45° taper)

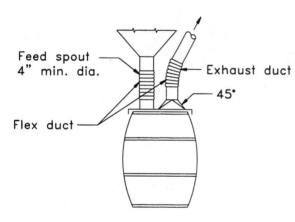

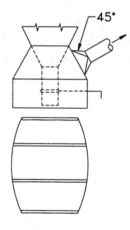

$Q = 50$ cfm x drum diam. (ft)
Minimum duct velocity = 3500 fpm
$h_e = 0.25$ VP$_d$

$Q = 300-400$ cfm
Minimum duct velocity = 3500 fpm
$h_e = 0.25$ VP$_d$

Note 1: Air displaced by material feed rate may require higher exhaust flow rates.

Note 2: Excessive air flow can cause loss of product.

Reference: 10.15.1

AMERICAN CONFERENCE OF GOVERNMENTAL INDUSTRIAL HYGIENISTS	*BARREL FILLING*	
	DATE *1-91*	FIGURE *VS-15-01*

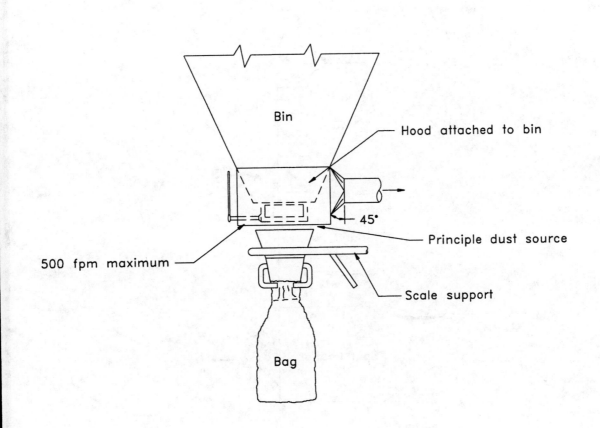

Bin

Hood attached to bin

Principle dust source

45°

500 fpm maximum

Scale support

Bag

Q = 400–500 cfm – non–toxic dust
1000–1500 cfm – toxic dust

Minimum duct velocity = 3500 fpm
$h_e = 0.25\ VP_d$

Note: Care must be taken such that too much air
is not used, as valuable product will be
pulled into the exhaust system.

Reference: 10.15.2

AMERICAN CONFERENCE OF GOVERNMENTAL INDUSTRIAL HYGIENISTS	*BAG FILLING*	
	DATE *1–91*	FIGURE *VS–15–02*

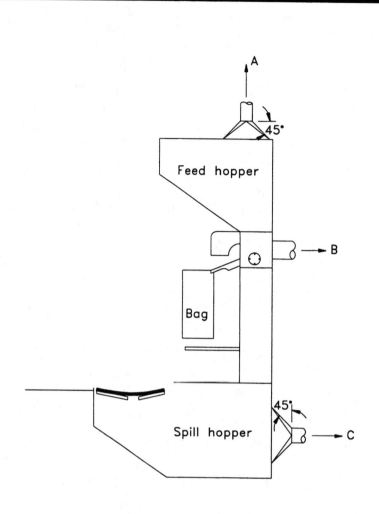

Q = 500 cfm per filling tube
  = 500 cfm at Feed hopper
  = 950 cfm at Spill hopper

Minimum duct velocity = 3500 fpm

h_e = 0.25 VP_d for take-off at A and C
      1.0 VP_d for take-off at B

Reference: 10.15.2

AMERICAN CONFERENCE OF GOVERNMENTAL INDUSTRIAL HYGIENISTS	*BAG TUBE PACKER*	
	DATE *1-91*	FIGURE *VS-15-03*

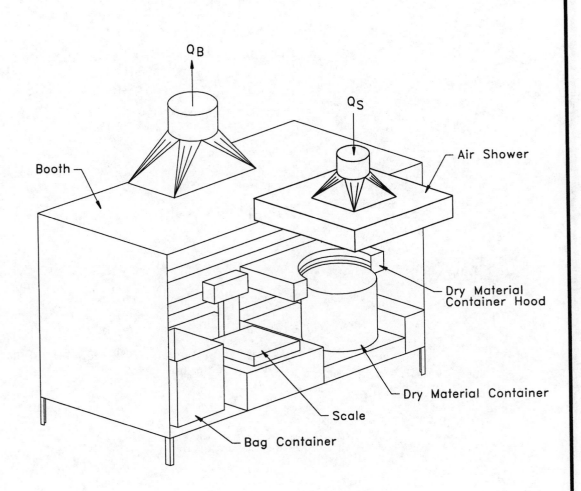

NOTE: See VS—15—11 for design details

Reference 10.15.3

AMERICAN CONFERENCE OF GOVERNMENTAL INDUSTRIAL HYGIENISTS	*WEIGH HOOD ASSEMBLY DRY MATERIAL*	
	DATE *1—91*	FIGURE *VS—15—10*

BOOTH

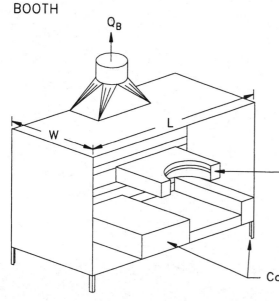

Q_B = 50 cfm/ft^2 of face open area.

L and W to fit operation

Minimum duct velocity = 3500 fpm

h_e = 1.78 VP$_s$ + 0.25 VP$_d$

Dry material container hood is extension of booth slot

Configure to fit equipment.

AIR SHOWER

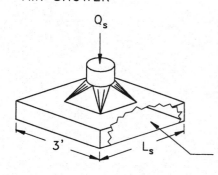

Q_s = 100 L$_s$ cfm

L$_s$ = 3 feet. (Can be longer if required to fit workstation but do not exceed 1/2 booth length; L)

0.25" pegboard or equivalent, 20 percent maximum open area.

DRY MATERIAL CONTAINER HOOD

Hood is extension of booth slot. An additional takeoff(s) may be used if required for hood air flow distribution.

Airflow and hood slot design per VS-15-01

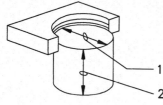

12" to 24" Diameter

24" Maximum

Reference 10.15.3

AMERICAN CONFERENCE OF GOVERNMENTAL INDUSTRIAL HYGIENISTS	*WEIGH HOOD DETAILS DRY MATERIAL*	
	DATE *2-91*	FIGURE *VS-15-11*

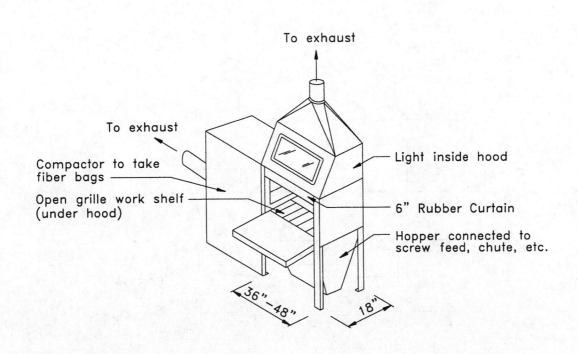

To exhaust

To exhaust

Compactor to take fiber bags

Open grille work shelf (under hood)

Light inside hood

6" Rubber Curtain

Hopper connected to screw feed, chute, etc.

36"–48"   18"

Q = minimum 250 cfm/ft² of open area
Minimum duct velocity = 3500 fpm
$h_e = 0.25\ VP_d$

Reference: 10.15.4

AMERICAN CONFERENCE OF GOVERNMENTAL INDUSTRIAL HYGIENISTS	*TOXIC MATERIAL BAG OPENING*	
	DATE *1–91*	FIGURE *VS–15–20*

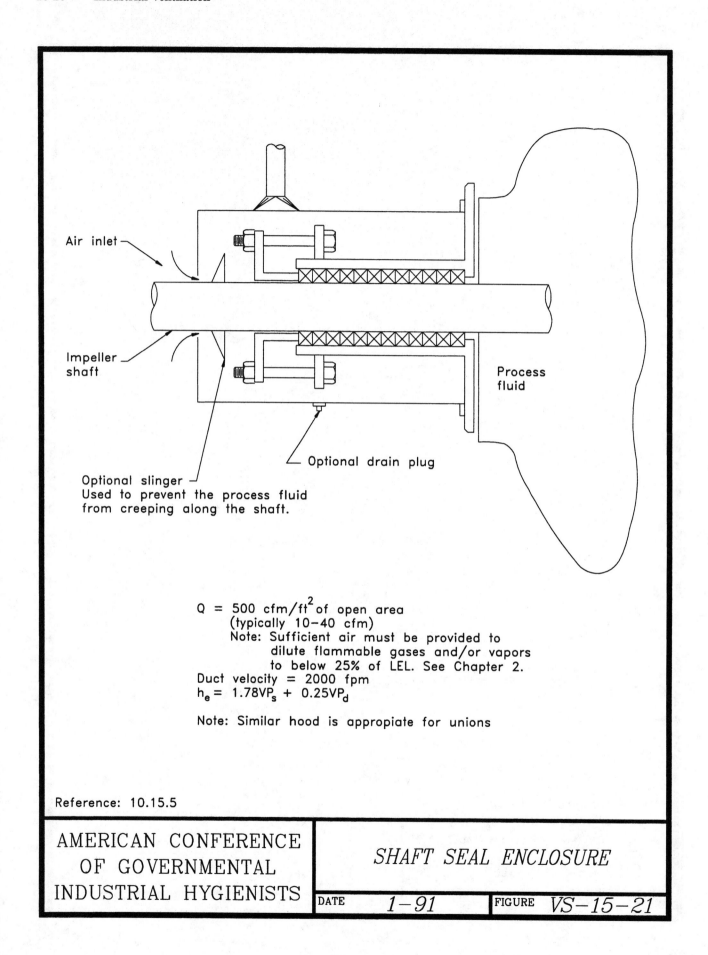

Air inlet

Impeller
shaft

Optional drain plug

Optional slinger
Used to prevent the process fluid
from creeping along the shaft.

Process
fluid

$Q = 500$ cfm/ft^2 of open area
(typically 10–40 cfm)
Note: Sufficient air must be provided to
dilute flammable gases and/or vapors
to below 25% of LEL. See Chapter 2.
Duct velocity = 2000 fpm
$h_e = 1.78VP_s + 0.25VP_d$

Note: Similar hood is appropiate for unions

Reference: 10.15.5

AMERICAN CONFERENCE OF GOVERNMENTAL INDUSTRIAL HYGIENISTS	*SHAFT SEAL ENCLOSURE*	
	DATE *1–91*	FIGURE *VS–15–21*

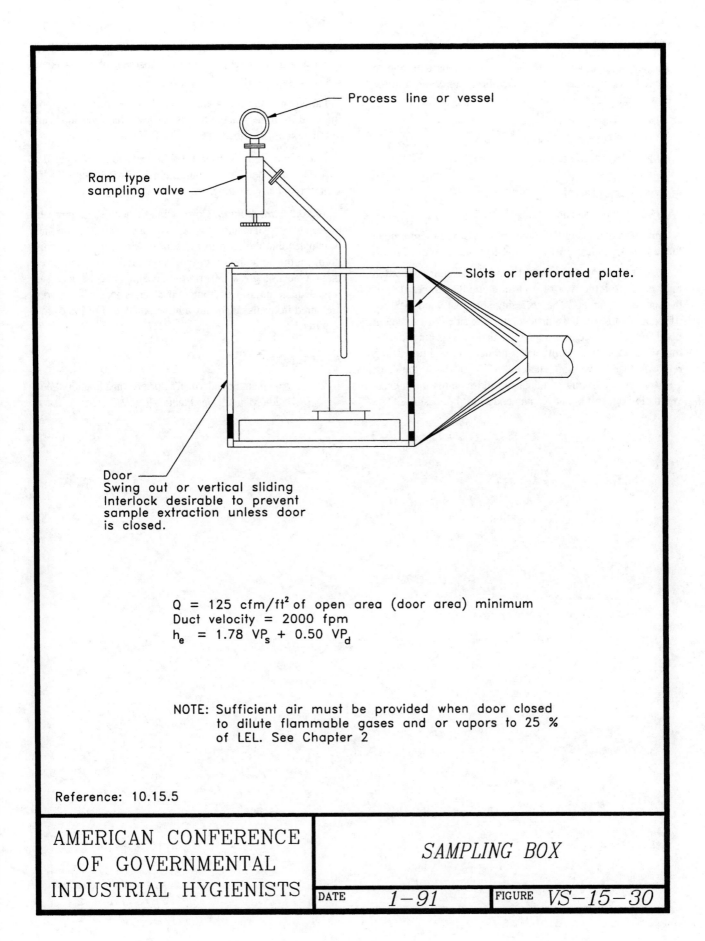

Process line or vessel

Ram type
sampling valve

Slots or perforated plate.

Door
Swing out or vertical sliding
Interlock desirable to prevent
sample extraction unless door
is closed.

Q = 125 cfm/ft² of open area (door area) minimum
Duct velocity = 2000 fpm
$h_e = 1.78\ VP_s + 0.50\ VP_d$

NOTE: Sufficient air must be provided when door closed
to dilute flammable gases and or vapors to 25 %
of LEL. See Chapter 2

Reference: 10.15.5

AMERICAN CONFERENCE
OF GOVERNMENTAL
INDUSTRIAL HYGIENISTS

SAMPLING BOX

DATE   1-91   FIGURE   VS-15-30

10.20 FOUNDRY OPERATIONS

Foundry operations include many operations common to other industries. Some of these operations are covered in the following subsections of this chapter:

10.45   Machining

10.50   Material Transport

10.55   Metal Melting

10.60   Mixing

10.80   Surface Cleaning

10.90   Welding and Cutting

This subsection addresses operations that are more unique to the foundry industry: casting shakeout and core making.

10.20.1 Casting Shakeout: Foundry shakeout ventilation rates depend on the type of enclosure and the temperature of the sand and castings. The enclosing shakeout hood (VS-20-01) requires the smallest airflow rate. The side draft shakeout hood (VS-20-02) requires additional airflow rates but provides improved access for casting and sand delivery and for casting removal. The downdraft shakeout (VS-20-03) is the least effective in controlling contaminant and requires the highest ventilation rates. It is not recommended for hot castings. The shakeout hopper below the shakeout table requires additional exhaust ventilation equivalent to 10 percent of the shakeout hood exhaust rate.

Particular attention should be paid to the conveyor removing sand from the shakeout. This conveyor requires hoods and ventilation as described in Section 10.55.

Rotary tumble mills used for shakeout should be treated as an enclosing hood with a minimum inward velocity of 150 fpm through any opening.

10.20.2 Core Making: Core making machines require ventilation to control reactive vapors and gases such as amines and isocynates that are used in the core making process. A minimum capture velocity of 75 fpm is required. However, a ventilation rate as high as 250 cfm/ft^2 of opening may be necessary for adequate control of contaminant emissions. When cores are cured in ovens, adequate ventilation control of the oven is required.

REFERENCES

10.20.1   American Foundrymen's Society, Inc., Foundry Ventilation Manual, Des Plaines, IL (1985).

ENCLOSING HOOD

Provides best control with least flow rate
Minimum duct velocity = 4000 fpm
$h_e = 0.25\ VP_d$

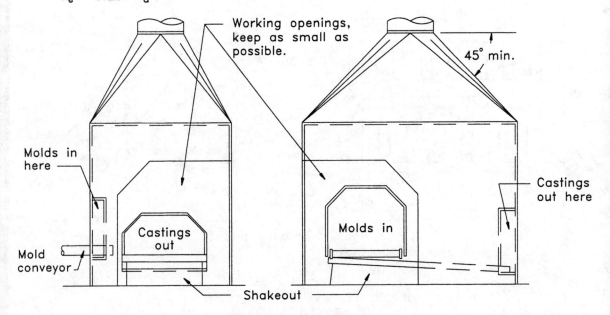

Working openings, keep as small as possible.

45° min.

Molds in here

Castings out here

Mold conveyor

Castings out

Molds in

Shakeout

Shakeout exhaust, minimum*

Type of hood	Hot castings	Cool castings
Enclosing ** VS-20-01	200 cfm/ft^2 opening At least 200 cfm/ft^2 grate area	200 cfm/ft^2 opening At least 150 cfm/ft^2 grate area
Two sides and 1/3 top area enclosed ** VS-20-02	300 cfm/ft^2 grate area	275 cfm/ft^2 grate area
Side hood (as shown or equivalent) ** VS-20-02	400-500 cfm/ft^2 grate area	350-400 cfm/ft^2 grate area
Double side hood ** VS-20-02	400 cfm/ft^2 grate area	300 cfm/ft^2 grate area

*Choose higher values when
   (1) Castings are quite hot
   (2) Sand to metal ratio is low
   (3) Cross-drafts are high

**Shakeout hoppers require an additional 10% exhaust.

AMERICAN CONFERENCE OF GOVERNMENTAL INDUSTRIAL HYGIENISTS	*FOUNDRY SHAKEOUT ENCLOSING*	
	DATE *10-90*	FIGURE *VS-20-01*

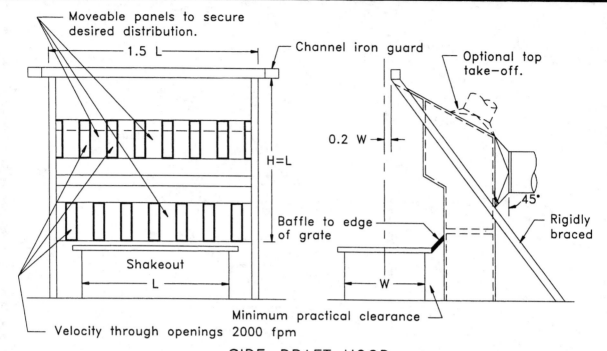

Moveable panels to secure desired distribution.

1.5 L

Channel iron guard

Optional top take-off.

0.2 W

H=L

Baffle to edge of grate

Rigidly braced

45°

Shakeout

L

W

Minimum practical clearance

Velocity through openings 2000 fpm

Minimum practical clearance

SIDE-DRAFT HOOD

Minimum duct velocity = 4000 fpm.

$$h_e = 1.78\ VP_s + 0.25\ VP_d$$

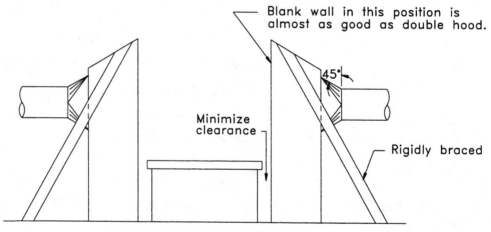

Blank wall in this position is almost as good as double hood.

45°

Minimize clearance

Rigidly braced

DOUBLE SIDE-DRAFT

Proportions same as single side-draft hood except for overhang.

Minimum duct velocity = 4000 fpm
Slots sized for 2000 fpm
$$h_e = 1.78\ VP_s + 0.25\ VP_d$$

See VS-20-01 for exhaust rates

AMERICAN CONFERENCE OF GOVERNMENTAL INDUSTRIAL HYGIENISTS	*FOUNDRY SHAKEOUT SIDE DRAFT*	
	DATE *10-90*	FIGURE *VS-20-02*

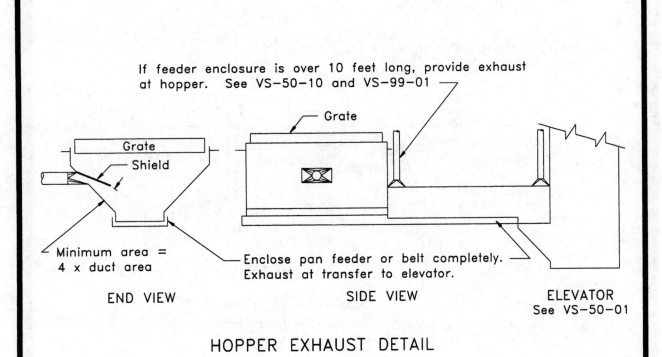

If feeder enclosure is over 10 feet long, provide exhaust at hopper. See VS-50-10 and VS-99-01

Grate

Grate

Shield

Minimum area =
4 x duct area

Enclose pan feeder or belt completely.
Exhaust at transfer to elevator.

END VIEW

SIDE VIEW

ELEVATOR
See VS-50-01

HOPPER EXHAUST DETAIL

AMERICAN CONFERENCE OF GOVERNMENTAL INDUSTRIAL HYGIENISTS	*FOUNDRY SHAKEOUT*	
	DATE *11-90*	FIGURE *VS-20-03*

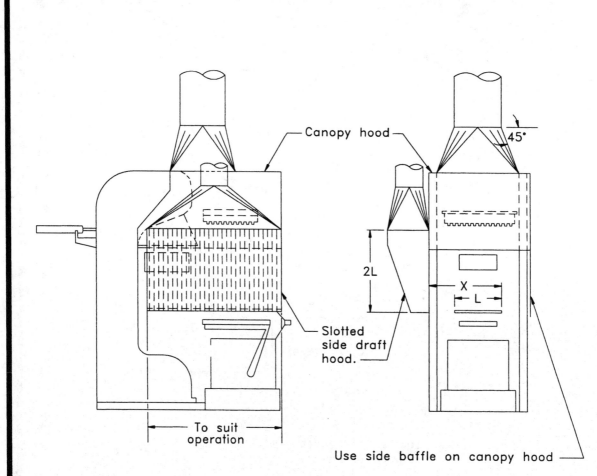

Canopy hood

45°

2L

X

L

Slotted
side draft
hood.

To suit
operation

Use side baffle on canopy hood

Canopy hood: $Q = 250$ cfm/ft^2 canopy − single unit
150 cfm/ft^2 canopy − double unit
$h_e = 0.25$ VP$_d$

Note: Slotted side draft hoods required to remove
smoke as hot cores emerge from machine.
Minimum capture velocity = 150 fpm

Side draft hood: $Q = 150(10X^2 + A)$ where A equals hood area
$h_e = 1.78$ VP$_s$ + 0.25 VP$_d$

Note: Conveyor or cooling area require ventilation for
large cores. Scrap conveyor or tote boxes may also
require additional ventilation.
Minimum duct velocity = 3500 fpm

AMERICAN CONFERENCE OF GOVERNMENTAL INDUSTRIAL HYGIENISTS	*SHELL CORE MAKING*	
	DATE *10−90*	FIGURE *VS−20−10*

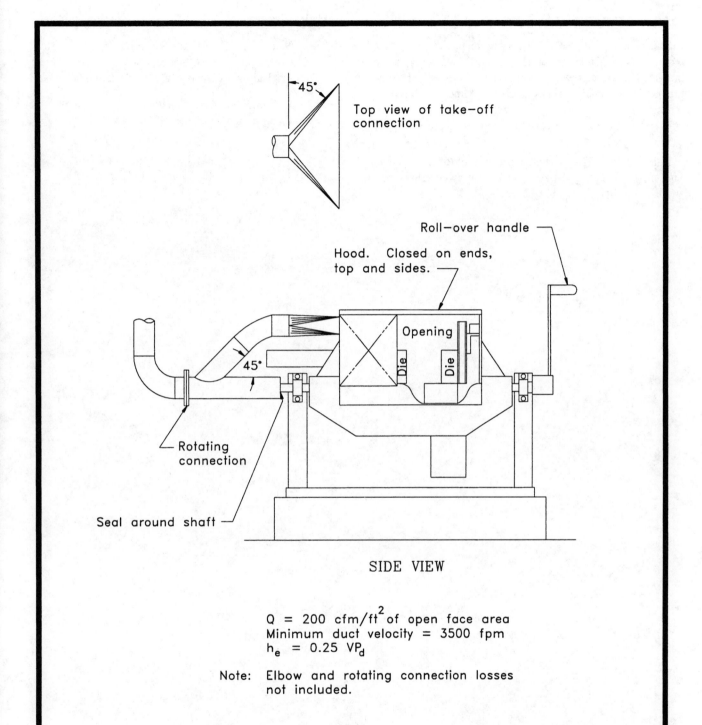

45°

Top view of take−off
connection

Roll−over handle

Hood. Closed on ends,
top and sides.

Opening

Die

Die

45°

Rotating
connection

Seal around shaft

SIDE VIEW

$Q = 200$ cfm/ft^2 of open face area
Minimum duct velocity = 3500 fpm
$h_e = 0.25$ VP_d

Note: Elbow and rotating connection losses
not included.

AMERICAN CONFERENCE
OF GOVERNMENTAL
INDUSTRIAL HYGIENISTS

*CORE MAKING MACHINE
SMALL ROLL−OVER TYPE*

DATE *10−90*   FIGURE *VS−20−11*

10.25 GAS TREATMENT

The handling of gas cylinders for industrial operations requires special attention. In addition to the potential safety problems associated with transportation and use of compressed gas cylinders, the gas inside the cylinders can escape through leaky valves and fittings. During connection and disconnection of the gas lines, due to the operating pressures, gas can be released.

This section of VS-prints illustrates uses of toxic gases during fumigation (VS-25-01 and -02) and during ethylene oxide sterilization (VS-25-10, -11, -12, and -13).

REFERENCES

10.25.1   Mortimer, V. D.; Kercher, S. L.; O'Brien, D. M.: Effective Controls for Ethylene Oxide—A Case Study. Applied Industrial Hygiene, 1(1):15-20 (1986).

10.25.2   Hama, G. M.: Ventilation for Fumigation Booths. Air Engineering (December 1964).

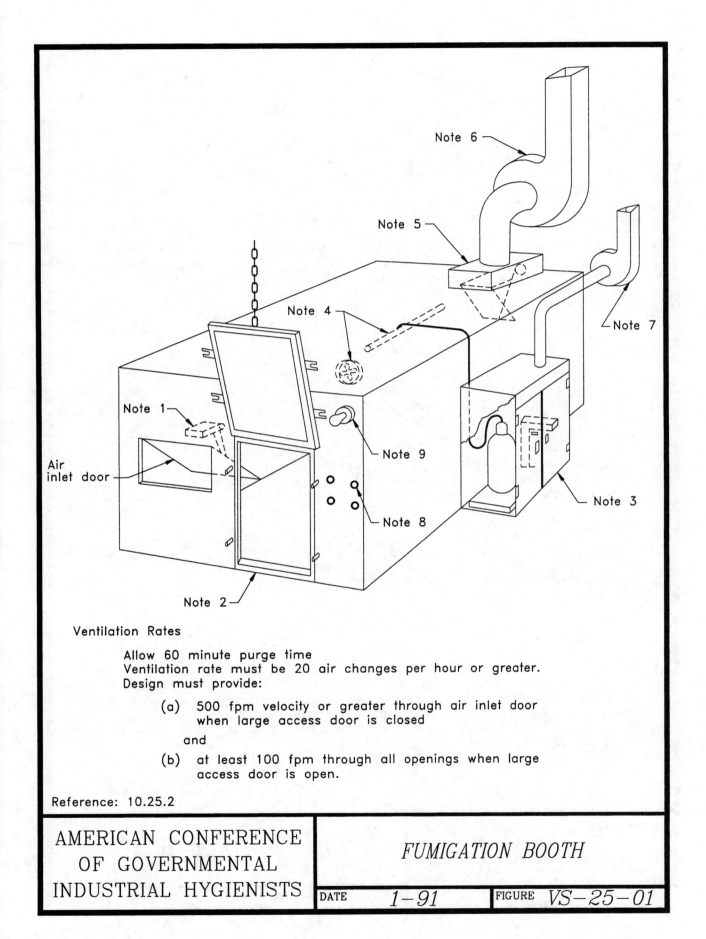

Ventilation Rates

Allow 60 minute purge time
Ventilation rate must be 20 air changes per hour or greater.
Design must provide:

(a)   500 fpm velocity or greater through air inlet door
when large access door is closed

and

(b)   at least 100 fpm through all openings when large
access door is open.

Reference: 10.25.2

AMERICAN CONFERENCE OF GOVERNMENTAL INDUSTRIAL HYGIENISTS	*FUMIGATION BOOTH*	
	DATE *1-91*	FIGURE *VS-25-01*

NOTES:

1. Provide an air inlet with automatic damper closure; damper must be interlocked with fan circuit to open only when fan is turned on. Size opening for a minimum velocity of 500 fpm. Air inlet must be located so purge air sweeps entire booth.

2. Loading door must be opened only when booth has been completely purged. Provide gaskets, screw clamps, and brackets for applying uniform pressure for a gas—tight fit.

3. Provide ventilated cabinet for gas cylinders in use and being stored. Fan must be on continuously and exhaust approximately 500cfm to produce a negative pressure in the cabinet when the doors are closed.

4. Provide nozzle openings for introducing fumigant gas. A circulating cabinet fan should also be provided for obtaining good mixture of fumigant gas.

5. Mechanical fan damper must be provided that closes tightly when fan is shut off during fumigation and opens when fan is turned on. Damper controls should be interlocked with fan controls.

6. Fan for ventilating fumigation booth must be sized to dilute air to safe limit in required time. Use vertical, outside, discharge stack away from windows, doors, and air intakes.

7. Fumigant gas cylinder cabinet fan must run continuously.

8. Control switches for fan and lights and an air flow switch—actuated pilot light are recommended.

9. Red warning light to indicate booth is under fumigation as a protection against careless entry is recommended.

10. To facilitate penetration of fumigant gas and subsequent airing out, mattresses should be loaded with separators to allow free air space around each mattress.

11. Fumigants with no odor—warning properties should be used together with an order—indicating chamical.

12. Where toxic fumigants are used, a leak test should be made on the booth. The booth first should be tested by lighting several large smoke candles in it with doors and dampers closed. Leaks can be noted by the presence of smoke at the point of escape. Where highly diffusible toxic gases are used, an additional test should be made with the booth under charge, at doors and dampers, with a sensitive detecting meter or sampling device.

AMERICAN CONFERENCE OF GOVERNMENTAL INDUSTRIAL HYGIENISTS	FUMIGATION BOOTH NOTES	
	DATE *1—91*	FIGURE *VS—25—02*

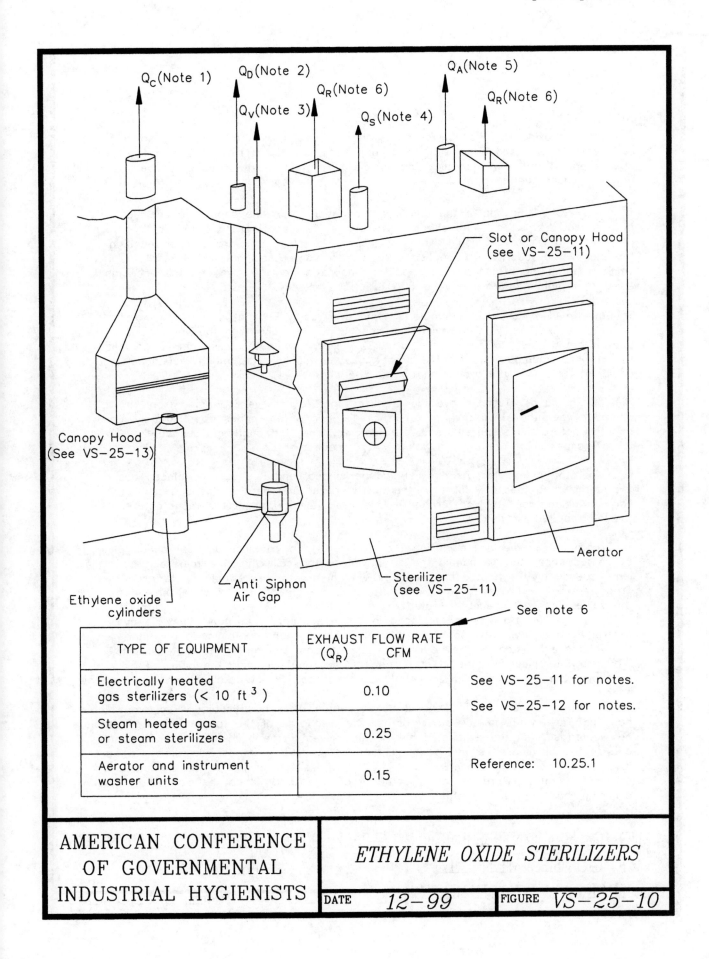

Q_C(Note 1) Q_D(Note 2) Q_A(Note 5)

Q_V(Note 3) Q_R(Note 6) Q_R(Note 6)

Q_S(Note 4)

Slot or Canopy Hood
(see VS-25-11)

Canopy Hood
(See VS-25-13)

Ethylene oxide
cylinders

Anti Siphon
Air Gap

Sterilizer
(see VS-25-11)

Aerator

See note 6

TYPE OF EQUIPMENT	EXHAUST FLOW RATE (Q_R) CFM
Electrically heated gas sterilizers (< 10 ft^3)	0.10
Steam heated gas or steam sterilizers	0.25
Aerator and instrument washer units	0.15

See VS-25-11 for notes.

See VS-25-12 for notes.

Reference: 10.25.1

AMERICAN CONFERENCE
OF GOVERNMENTAL
INDUSTRIAL HYGIENISTS

ETHYLENE OXIDE STERILIZERS

DATE   *12-99*   FIGURE   *VS-25-10*

NOTES:

1. The ethylene oxide (EtO) supply cylinders should be placed in a ventilated cabinet or a partially enclosed hood with an exhaust rate, Q_C, of at least 100 cfm/ft^2 of open area. Install a hinged plexiglass shield to protect maintenance personnel during cylinder change out.

2. The anti-syphon air gap in the sterilizer evacuation drain line should be enclosed and ventilated. The enclosure should have one or two openings to allow air, Q_D, to enter and to prevent liquid, which might back up from the drain, from reaching the sterilizer evacuation line. In lieu of a greater value specified by the sterilizer/ vacuum pump manufacturer, Q_D, should be approximately 50 cfm and the openings sized to maintain approximately a 600 fpm face velocity.

3. The overpressure relief valve should be vented to carry EtO out of the building if it should ever open. With a sealed line connecting the valve with the ventilation duct, there will be no ventilation volume, Q_V, except when the valve opens. Consult the sterilizer manufacturer for the proper size of this line; too much resistance could interfere wiht the proper venting of the chamber.

4. A hood should be placed above the sterilizer door to remove EtO rising from the chamber when the sterilizer door is "cracked" open a few inches approximately 15 minutes before the sterilized items are removed from the chamber. See VS-25-12 for a discussion of the exhaust volume, Q_S, requirements.

5. If an aerator is installed, its door should be hinged, and it should be placed beside the sterilizer so that the doors of the gas sterilizer and aerator opens away from each other to facilitate transferring the sterilized items. Consult the manufacturer for the required air flow, Q_A.

6. The room behind the wall enclosing the sterilizer(s) and other equipment should be exhausted adequately to handle the air driven to the ceiling by the thermal grad- ients caused by the heated equipment. The ideal arrangement would be to have a properly sized vent above each piece of heated equipment. The total Q_R should be the values for each piece of heated equipment (see VS-25-10) plus 100 cfm/ft^2 of open area for transfer vents placed in the upper portion of the room. However, federal hospital standards specify that, for a recess room containing a gas sterilizer, the volume exhausted in one hour should be at least ten times the room volume. Transfer vents placed in the lower portion of the room will help the influx of air to supply the thermal air currents and would not add to the total exhaust requirement.

7. All air that could contain EtO should be exhausted through a ventilation system which does not have vents in any other rooms. The discharge of the fan on the roof should be located so that the exhausted air will not re-enter the building or expose people outside the building. This ventilation system should have a flow sensor/alarm to warn if it is not functioning properly. If there is the possibility of lint in the exhausted air use a different pressure sensor or some other type that will not be clogged or stuck open by the accumulation of lint.

AMERICAN CONFERENCE	ETHYLENE OXIDE STERILIZER
OF GOVERNMENTAL	NOTES
INDUSTRIAL HYGIENISTS	DATE 12-99	FIGURE VS-25-11

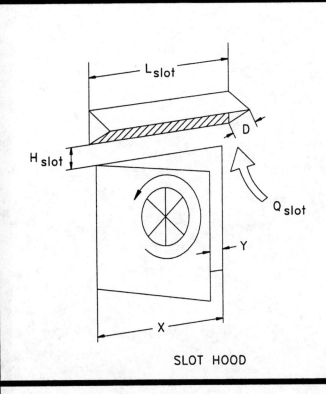

$H_{slot} \leq 3"$

$L_{slot} = X + 0.66H_{slot}$

$D = 1"$
   slot face to be at 45°–90°
   angle with plane of enclosure

$Q_{slot} = 75$ cfm/ft slot length

$Y = 2"$ for airing out sterilizer
   chamber.

SLOT HOOD

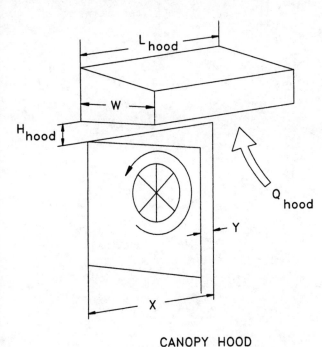

$Q_{hood} = 100\ L_{hood}W$

$H_{hood} = 12"$ to $24"$

$W = \dfrac{H_{hood}}{3}$

$L_{hood} = X + 0.66H_{hood}$

$Y = 2"$ for airing out sterilizer
   chamber.

CANOPY HOOD

AMERICAN CONFERENCE OF GOVERNMENTAL INDUSTRIAL HYGIENISTS	*ETHYLENE OXIDE STERILIZER HOOD DETAILS*	
	DATE *02–91*	FIGURE *VS–25–12*

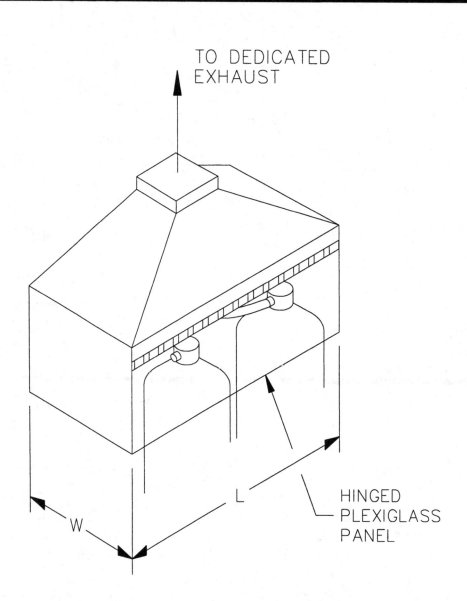

TO DEDICATED
EXHAUST

W

L

HINGED
PLEXIGLASS
PANEL

The recommended cylinder hood design features a hinged
Plexiglass panel which can be raised to remove the empty
cylinder and slide in the new cylinder. In the down position,
the panel protects the worker's face from spray while
allowing the worker to see the connection point while the
empty cylinder is being disconnected and then the new
cylinder is connected to the supply line.

AMERICAN CONFERENCE OF GOVERNMENTAL INDUSTRIAL HYGIENISTS	ETHYLENE OXIDE STERILIZER HOOD DESIGN	
	DATE *01–00*	FIGURE *VS–25–13*

10.30 KITCHEN EQUIPMENT

The purpose of an exhaust system for kitchen equipment is to control heat, humidity, and grease vapor released into the space by cooking or dishwashing equipment. A secondary consideration is the control of combustion products associated with the heat source which may be vented separately or through the hood itself.

National Fire Protection Association (NFPA) Standard 96[10.30.1] describes grease filter construction as well as hood construction necessary to maintain hood integrity in the event of a fire. Welded seam construction is preferred and sometimes required by public health authorities to assure cleanability and ease of maintenance. The National Sanitation Foundation Standard No. 4[10.30.2] also lists hood construction requirements for cleanability and integrity in the cooking and food zones within the hood. In all cases, the local health authorities having jurisdiction should be consulted for construction requirements prior to hood fabrication.

Fire is a primary concern with all cooking equipment. Each hood will require some type of fire suppression consistent with local fire code requirements. The system selected must not compromise sanitation or endanger workers due to location or system activation. Hood or duct penetrations by fire suppression piping, etc., must be sealed to prevent short circuiting of air or loss of fire arrestance.

For high temperatures situations such as exposed flames or charcoal, the grease filters must be sufficiently removed from the heat source to prevent ignition. Fan selection may require use of high temperature fan components and consideration of the effect of change in air density.

REFERENCES

10.30.1 National Fire Protection Association Standard: Standard for the Installation of Equipment for the Removal of Smoke and Grease-Laden Vapors from Commercial Cooking Equipment. NFPA, Quincy, MA (1987).

10.30.2 National Sanitation Foundation: Commercial Cooking and Hot Food Storage Equipment. Ann Arbor, MI (1986).

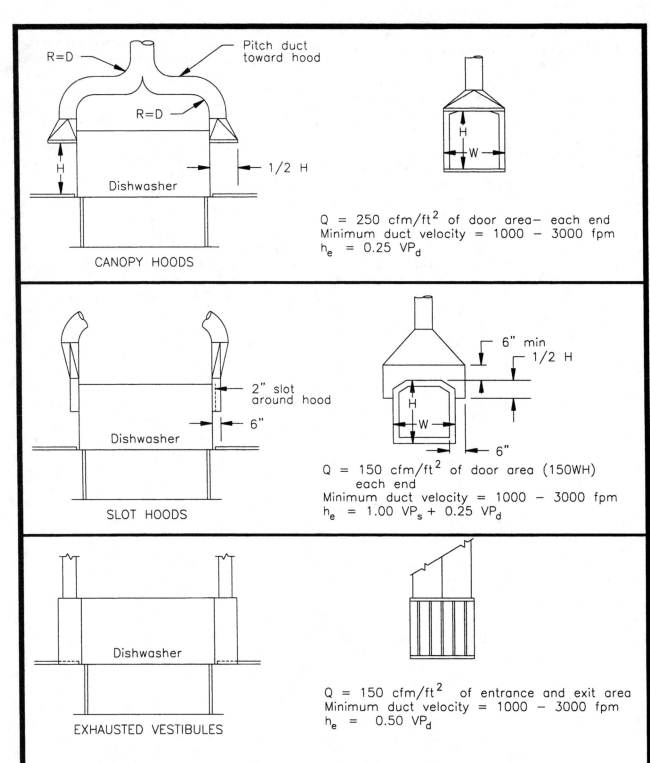

CANOPY HOODS

$Q = 250$ cfm/ft^2 of door area— each end
Minimum duct velocity = 1000 − 3000 fpm
$h_e = 0.25$ VP$_d$

SLOT HOODS

2" slot around hood
6"

$Q = 150$ cfm/ft^2 of door area (150WH)
        each end
Minimum duct velocity = 1000 − 3000 fpm
$h_e = 1.00$ VP$_s$ + 0.25 VP$_d$

6" min
1/2 H
6"

EXHAUSTED VESTIBULES

$Q = 150$ cfm/ft^2 of entrance and exit area
Minimum duct velocity = 1000 − 3000 fpm
$h_e = 0.50$ VP$_d$

Note: If direct exhaust connections are provided from dishwasher body, cap these
        connections and use external hoods.

AMERICAN CONFERENCE OF GOVERNMENTAL INDUSTRIAL HYGIENISTS	*DISHWASHER VENTILATION*	
	DATE *10-90*	FIGURE *VS-30-01*

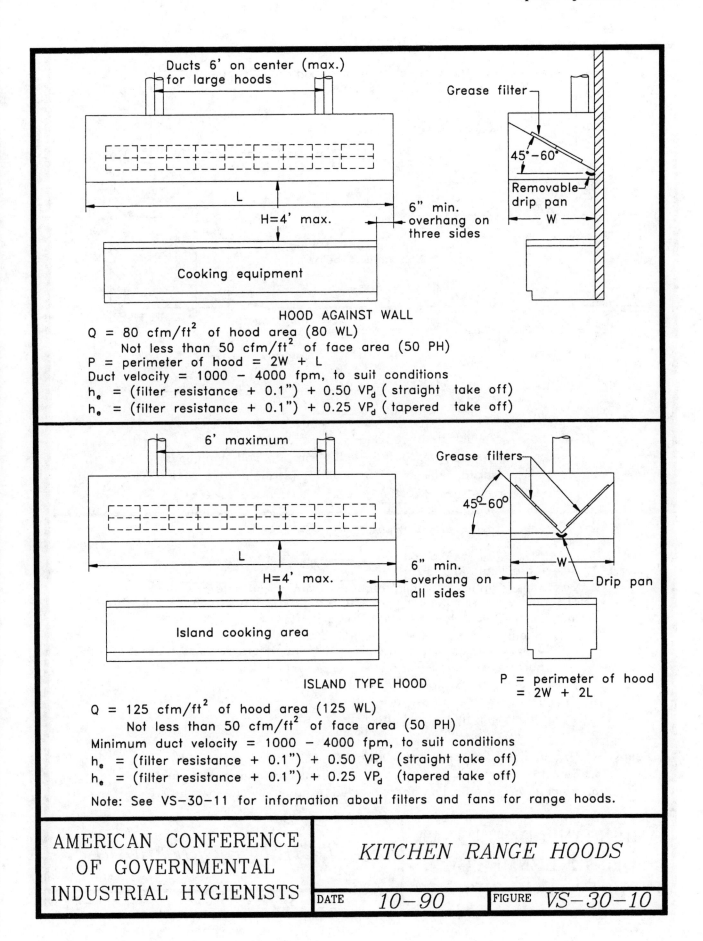

HOOD AGAINST WALL

Q = 80 cfm/ft^2 of hood area (80 WL)
  Not less than 50 cfm/ft^2 of face area (50 PH)
P = perimeter of hood = 2W + L
Duct velocity = 1000 – 4000 fpm, to suit conditions
h_e = (filter resistance + 0.1") + 0.50 VP_d (straight take off)
h_e = (filter resistance + 0.1") + 0.25 VP_d (tapered take off)

ISLAND TYPE HOOD

Q = 125 cfm/ft^2 of hood area (125 WL)
  Not less than 50 cfm/ft^2 of face area (50 PH)
Minimum duct velocity = 1000 – 4000 fpm, to suit conditions
h_e = (filter resistance + 0.1") + 0.50 VP_d (straight take off)
h_e = (filter resistance + 0.1") + 0.25 VP_d (tapered take off)

Note: See VS–30–11 for information about filters and fans for range hoods.

AMERICAN CONFERENCE OF GOVERNMENTAL INDUSTRIAL HYGIENISTS	*KITCHEN RANGE HOODS*	
	DATE *10-90*	FIGURE *VS–30–10*

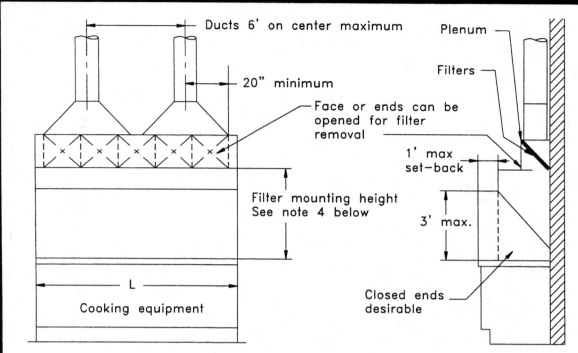

Ducts 6' on center maximum

20" minimum

Face or ends can be opened for filter removal

Filter mounting height See note 4 below

L

Cooking equipment

Plenum

Filters

1' max set-back

3' max.

Closed ends desirable

LOW SIDE WALL HOOD

Q = 200 cfm/lineal ft of cooking surface (200L)

Minimum duct velocity = 1000 – 4000 fpm, to suit conditions

h_e = (filter resistance + 0.1") + 0.50 VP_d (straight take off)

h_e = (filter resistance + 0.1") + 0.25 VP_d (tapered take off)

NOTES FOR KITCHEN HOODS

Filters:
1. Select practical filter size.
2. Determine number of filters required from manufacturer's data. (Usually: 2 cfm maximum exhaust for each square inch of filter area.)
3. Install at 45°–60° to horizontal. Never horizontal.
4. Filter mounting height (Reference 10.30.1)
   a. No exposed cooking flame ––– 18" minimum to lowest edge of filter.
   b. Charcoal and similar fires ––– 4' minimum to lowest edge of filter.
5. Shield filters from direct radiant heat.
6. Provide removable grease drip pan.
7. Clean pan and filters regularly.

Fan:
1. Use upblast discharge fan. Downblast is not recommended.
2. Select fan for design Q and SP resistance of filters and duct.
3. Adjust fan specification for expected exhaust air temperature.

AMERICAN CONFERENCE OF GOVERNMENTAL INDUSTRIAL HYGIENISTS	*KITCHEN RANGE HOOD*	
	DATE *10–90*	FIGURE *VS–30–11*

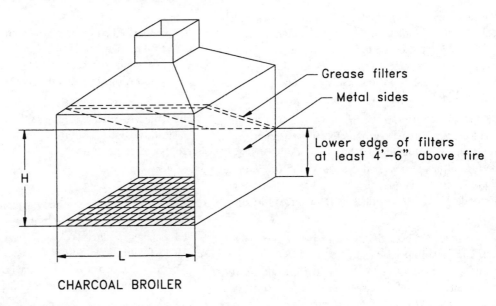

CHARCOAL BROILER

Grease filters
Metal sides
Lower edge of filters
at least 4'-6" above fire

Q = 100 LH
Minimum duct velocity = 1000 - 3000 fpm
h_e = (filter resistance + 0.1") + 0.50 VP (straight take off)
h_e = (filter resistance + 0.1") + 0.25 VP (tapered take off)

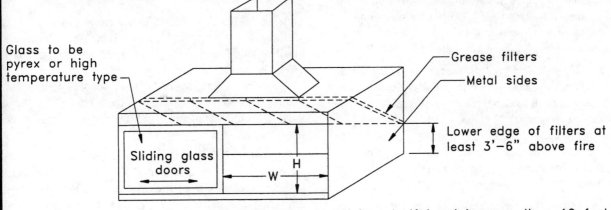

Glass to be
pyrex or high
temperature type

Grease filters
Metal sides

Lower edge of filters at
least 3'-6" above fire

Sliding glass
doors

BARBEQUE PITS

Notes: 1. If hood is more than 12 feet
long use multiple takeoffs 6
feet on center.

2. See VS-30-11 for information
about filters and fans for
range hoods.

Q = 100 WH (maximum open door area, ft^2)
Minimum duct velocity = 1000 - 3000 fpm
h_e = (filter resistance + 0.1") + 0.50 VP (straight take off)
h_e = (filter resistance + 0.1") + 0.25 VP (tapered take off)

AMERICAN CONFERENCE OF GOVERNMENTAL INDUSTRIAL HYGIENISTS	CHARCOAL BROILER AND BARBEQUE PIT VENTILATION	
	DATE *10-90*	FIGURE *VS-30-12*

10.35 LABORATORY VENTILATION

The primary method of contaminant control within the laboratory is exhaust ventilation and, in particular, laboratory hoods. This section presents information on laboratory hoods but expands to other types of ventilation control such as biological safety cabinets, clean benches, and other local exhaust systems found in the laboratory.

10.35.1 Laboratory Hoods: In most cases, laboratory hoods will be purchased from manufacturers specializing in the design and construction of laboratory hoods. VS-35-01 shows a typical laboratory hood design. VS-35-02 describes general use laboratory hoods and VS-35-03 describes perchloric acid hoods. VS-35-04 describes work practices for laboratory hoods.

Several features are essential to the proper performance of the hood. The most important aspect of the hood is the aerodynamic entry characteristics. For the hood to adequately control contaminants, the entry must be smooth. This usually is achieved with an airfoil sill at the leading edge of the work bench. Often, beveled jambs at the side wall entry will improve the airflow.

In many cases, good performance correlates with uniform face velocity. To achieve a uniform face velocity, many hood manufacturers provide adjustable slots in the plenum at the back of the hood. Although the adjustment will allow for unusual conditions such as large hot plates for sample digestions, inappropriate adjustment of the slots can have a detrimental effect on hood performance.[10.35.1]

Supply Air Distribution: For typical operation of a laboratory hood, the worker stands at the face of the hood and manipulates the apparatus in the hood. The indraft at the hood face creates eddy currents around the worker's body which can drag contaminants in the hood along the worker's body and up to the breathing zone. The higher the face velocity, the greater the eddy currents. For this reason, higher face velocities do not result in greater protection as might be supposed.

Room air currents have a large effect on the performance of the hood. Thus, the design of the room air supply distribution system is as important in securing good hood performance as is the face velocity of the hood. American Society of Heating, Refrigeration and Air Conditioning (ASHRAE) research project RP-70 results, reported by Caplan and Knutson,[10.35.2] concludes in part:

1. Lower breathing zone concentrations can be attained at 50 cfm/ft^2 face velocities with good air supply distribution than at 150 cfm/ft^2 with poor air distribution. With a good air supply system and tracer gas released at 8 liters per minute inside the hood, breathing zone concentrations can be kept below 0.1 ppm and usually below 0.05 ppm.

2. The terminal throw velocity of supply air jets should be no more than one-half the hood face velocity; such terminal throw velocities are far less than conventional practice.

3. Perforated ceiling panels provide a better supply system than grilles or ceiling diffusers in that the system design criteria are simpler and easier to apply, and precise adjustment of the fixtures is not required.

For the reasons described, an increased hood face velocity may be self-defeating because the increased air volume handled through the room makes the low-velocity distribution of supply air more difficult.

Selection of Hood Face Velocity: The interaction of supply air distribution and hood face velocity makes any blanket specification of hood face velocity inappropriate. Higher hood face velocities will be wasteful of energy and may provide no better or even poorer worker protection. The ANSI/ASHRAE Hood Performance Test[10.35.3] may be used as a specification. The specified performance should be required of both the hood manufacturer and the designer of the room air supply system.

The specification takes the form: AU_{yyy}, AI_{yyy}, or AM_{yyy}

where: AU identifies an "as used" test.

AI identifies an "as installed" test and

AM identifies an "as manufactured" test

yyy = control level, ppm, at the breathing zone of the worker.

Any well-designed airfoil hood, properly balanced, can achieve < 0.10 ppm control level when the supply air distribution is good. Therefore, it would seem appropriate that the "AM" requirements would be < 0.10 ppm. The "AU" requirement involves the design of the room supply system and the toxicity of the materials handled in the hood. The "AU" specification would be tailored to suit the needs of the laboratory room location.

For projected new buildings, it is frequently necessary to estimate the cost of air conditioning early—before the detailed design and equipment specifications are available. For that early estimating, the guidelines listed in Table 10.35.1 can be used.

10.35.2 Biological Safety Cabinets: Biological safety cabinets (BSCs) are classified as Class I, Class II; Types A, B1, B2, and B3; and Class III.

Class I BSC provides personnel and environmental protection but does not protect the product. The front panel can be open, allowing room air to enter the cabinet, sweep the inner surfaces, and exhaust out the duct. A front closure panel with glove ports may be installed. If gloves are installed, air is drawn through a secondary opening equipped with a roughing filter. A laboratory hood, as shown in VS-35-20, could be considered a Class I BSC if the exhausted air is passed through HEPA filters prior to release to the atmosphere.

Class II BSCs provide personnel, product and environmental protection. Class II cabinets differ in the proportion of air recirculated within the cabinet; velocity of airflow to the work

TABLE 10.35.1. Laboratory Hood Ventilation Rates

Condition	cfm/ft² Open Hood Face
1. Ceiling panels properly located with average panel face velocity < 40 fpm[10.35.2]. Horizontal sliding sash hoods. No equipment in hood closer than 12 inches to face of hood. Hoods located away from doors and trafficways.*	60
2. Same as 1 above; some traffic past hoods. No equipment in hoods closer than 6 inches to face of hood. Hoods located away from doors and trafficways.*	80
3. Ceiling panels properly located with average panel face velocity < 60 fpm [10.35.2] or ceiling diffusers properly located; no diffuser immediately in front of hoods; quadrant facing hood blocked; terminal throw velocity < 60 fpm. No equipment in hood closer than 6 inches to face of hood. Hoods located away from doors or trafficways.*	80
4. Same as 3 above; some traffic past hood. No equipment in hood closer than 6 inches to face of hood.	100
5. Wall grilles are possible but not recommended for advance planning of new facilities.	

*Hoods near doors are acceptable if 1) there is a second safe egress from the room; 2) traffic past hood is low; and 3) door is normally closed.

surface; where the exhausted air is discharged; and whether the contaminated air plenum is under positive pressure. A Type A cabinet (VS-35-10) may discharge the exhausted air, after HEPA filtration, directly into the room. Type A cabinets which discharge into the work area are not recommended for use with gases or vapors. A primary application is for sterile packaging. Care is required while decontaminating the cabinet.

Type B hoods (VS-35-11) discharge the exhaust but may recirculate within the cabinet. Type B1 cabinets recirculate about 30% of the air within the BSC and typically exhaust the remainder outside the laboratory (i.e., exhaust air is not discharged back into the room). The contaminated plenum is under negative pressure. Type B2 cabinets are referred to as "total exhaust" cabinets as the contaminated air is exhausted to the atmosphere after HEPA filtration without recirculation in the cabinet or return to the laboratory room air. Type B3 BSCs have HEPA filtered downflow air that is a portion of the mixed downflow and inflow air from a common exhaust plenum.

Class III BSCs (VS-35-20) provide the highest level of protection to personnel and the environment. The cabinet is totally enclosed with operations conducted through attached gloves. See "National Sanitation Foundation Standard No. 49"[10.35.4] for descriptions and requirements of the various classes of BSCs.

10.35.3 Clean Benches: Clean benches can be divided into laminar flow and exhausted clean benches.

Laminar flow clean benches provide product protection only. In a laminar flow clean bench, room air is HEPA-filtered, directed across the work area, and discharged back to the room. Air may be directed horizontally as depicted in VS-35-30 or vertically as in VS-35-31. Neither of these hoods provide worker protection. Workers using the Horizontal Laminar Flow Clean Bench are exposed to the product as the air sweeps across the product into the worker's face. Workers's arms or other objects protruding into the Vertical Laminar Flow Clean Bench opening may cause contaminated air to spill into the room. Personal protective equipment or general ventilation should be provided as needed.

Other types of clean benches incorporate the same general principles of biological safety cabinets and utilize HEPA filtered laminar flow within the hood to provide product protection and exhaust sufficient air to ensure flow into the hood at the face to provide operator protection.

10.35.4 Laboratory Equipment: Some laboratory equipment such as evaporation hoods (VS-35-40), discharge from instruments such as ICP or AA, and some ovens (VS-35-41) require local exhaust ventilation to adequately control contaminant releases. Often, especially designed ventilation specific to the operation provides better control than using a laboratory hood to control these releases.

REFERENCES

10.35.1 Knutson, G. W.: Effect of Slot Position on Laboratory Fume Hood Performance. Heating, Piping and Air Conditioning. (February 1984).

10.35.2 Caplan, K. J.; Knutson, G. W.: Influence of Room Air Supply on Laboratory Hoods. American Industrial Hygiene Association Journal.

10.35.3 American Society of Heating, Refrigerating and Air Conditioning Engineers, ANSI/ASHRAE Standard 110-1985, Method of Testing the Performance of Laboratory Fume Hoods. ASHRAE, Atlanta, GA (1985).

10.35.4 National Sanitation Foundation: Standard 49, Class II (Laminar Flow) Biohazard Cabinetry. NSF, Ann Arbor, MI (1987).

10.35.5 U. S. Air Force Technical Order 00-25-203: Standards and Guidelines for Design and Operation of Clean Rooms and Clean Work Stations. Office of Technical Services, Department of Commerce, Washington, DC, (July 1963).

10.35.6 Harris, W. P.; Christofano, E.E.; Lippman, M.: Combination Hot Plate and Hood for Multiple Beaker Evaporation. American Industrial Hygiene Association Journal, 22, 4, (August 1961).

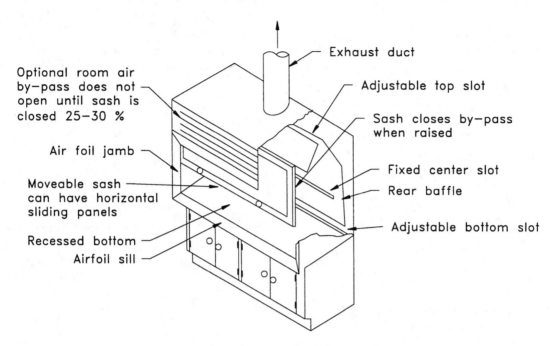

Optional room air by-pass does not open until sash is closed 25-30 %

Air foil jamb

Moveable sash can have horizontal sliding panels

Recessed bottom

Airfoil sill

Exhaust duct

Adjustable top slot

Sash closes by-pass when raised

Fixed center slot

Rear baffle

Adjustable bottom slot

VERTICAL SASH AIRFOIL HOOD

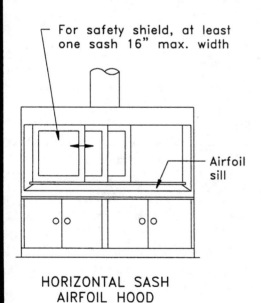

For safety shield, at least one sash 16" max. width

Airfoil sill

HORIZONTAL SASH
AIRFOIL HOOD

$Q = 80-100$ cfm/ft^2 full open area depending on quality of supply air distribution and uniformity of face velocity

$h_e = 0.5$ VP_d

Duct velocity = 1000-2000 fpm to suit conditions

Design specifications:

General use laboratory hoods—See VS-35-02

Perchloric acid —See VS-35-03

"Auxiliary Air" or "Compensating" hoods furnish some replacement air at hood face, design varies with vendor.

Work practices — See VS-35-04

AMERICAN CONFERENCE OF GOVERNMENTAL INDUSTRIAL HYGIENISTS	*TYPICAL LABORATORY HOOD*	
	DATE *02-91*	FIGURE *VS-35-01*

GENERAL USE LABORATORY HOODS:

A. Provide uniform exhaust air distribution in hood. Adjust baffles and air flow for ≤ 10% variation in point—to—point face velocity with sash in maximum open position.

B. Locate hood away from heavy traffic aisles and doorways. Hoods near doors are acceptable if: 1) there is a second safe means of egress from room, 2) traffic past hood is low, and 3) door is normally closed.

C. Use corrosion—resistant materials suitable for expected use.

D. Provide air cleaning on exhaust air if necessary and adequate stack height to minimize re—entry of contaminants or to comply with air pollution regulations.

E. Avoid sharp corners at jambs and sill. Tapered or round hood inlets are desirable an airfoil shroud at sill is important.

F. Provide filters for radioactive materials in greater than "exempt" quantities.

G. By—pass opening in hood is desirable to avoid excessive indraft under partially closed sash condition. Opening to be baffled to prevent splash from eruption in hood as shown in VS—35—01.

H. Provide tempered or conditioned replacement air to laboratory. Replacement air volume to be selected for desired air balance with adjoining spaces.

I. In order to reduce air flow volumes, local exhaust hood should be considered instead of laboratory bench hoods for fixed setups.

J. For air conservation, use horizontal sliding sash with airfoil sill.

K. All bench hoods should have a recessed work surface and airfoil sill.

AMERICAN CONFERENCE OF GOVERNMENTAL INDUSTRIAL HYGIENISTS	GENERAL USE LABORATORY HOODS	
	DATE *02—91*	FIGURE *VS—35—02*

PERCHLORIC ACID HOODS

Perchloric acid is extremely dangerous because it is a very strong oxidizer. When the acid reacts with organic material, an explosive reaction product may be formed.

1. Do not use perchloric acid in a hood designed for other purposes. Identify perchloric acid hoods with large warning signs.

2. Provide exhaust ventilation and room supply air with minimal challenge to the hood.

3. Utilize local exhaust ventilation within the hood to minimize condensation of vapors inside the hood.

4. Locate all utility controls outside the hood.

5. Materials of construction for this type of hood and duct must be nonreactive, and acid resistant, and relatively impervious. AVOID ORGANIC MATERIALS unless known to be safe. Stainless steel type 316 with welded joints is preferred. Unplasticized polyvinyl chloride or an inorganic ceramic coating, such as porcelain, is acceptable.

6. Ease of cleanliness is paramount. Use stainless steel within accessible rounded corners and all—welded construction.

7. The work surface should be watertight with a minimum of 0.5—inch dished front and sides and an integral trough at the rear to collect the washdown water.

8. Design washdown facilities into the hood and duct. Use daily or more often to thoroughly clean perchloric acid from the exhaust system surfaces.

9. Each perchloric acid hood should have an individual exhuast sytem. Slope horizontal runs to drain. Avoid sharp turns.

10. Construct the hood and duct to allow easy visual inspection.

11. Where required, use a high—effciency (greater than 80%) wet collector constructed for perchloric acid service. Locate as close to the hood as possible to minimize the accumulation of perchloric acid in the exhaust duct.

12. Use only an acid—resistant metallic fan protected by an inorganic coating of an air injector.

13. Lubricate the fan with fluorocarbon—type grease.

14. Locate the fan outside the building.

15. The exhaust discharge must terminate out-of-doors, preferably using a vertical discharge cap that extends well above the roof eddy zone. See Figure 5.30.

AMERICAN CONFERENCE OF GOVERNMENTAL INDUSTRIAL HYGIENISTS	PERCHLORIC ACID HOOD DATA	
	DATE *02—91*	FIGURE *VS—35—03*

WORK PRACTICES FOR LABORATORY HOODS

No large, open-face hood with a low face velocity can provide complete safety for a worker standing at the face against all events that may occur in the hood. The hood may not adequately protect the worker from volatile or otherwise airborne contaminants with a TLV in the low part-per-billion range. For more ordinary exposures, a properly designed hood in a properly ventilated room can provide adequate protection. However, certain work practices are necessary in order for the hood to perform capably. The following work practices are generally required; more stringent practices may be necessary in some circumstances.

1. Conduct all operations that may generate air contaminants at or above the appropriate TLV inside a hood.

2. Keep all apparatus at least 6 inches back from the face of the hood. A stripe on the bench surface is a good reminder.

3. Do not put your head in the hood when contaminants are being generated.

4. Do not use the hood as a waste disposal mechanism except for very small quantities of volatile materials.

5. Do not store chemicals or apparatus in the hood. Store hazardous chemicals in an approved safety cabinet.

6. Keep the hood sash closed as much as possible.

7. Keep the slots in the hood baffle free of obstruction by apparatus or containers.

8. Minimize foot traffic past the face of the hood.

9. Keep laboratory doors closed (exception: some laboratory designs require lab doors to be open).

10. Do not remove hood sash or panels except when necessary for apparatus set-up; replace sash or panels before operating.

11. Do not place electrical recepticals or other spark sources inside the hood when flammable liquids or gases are present. No permanent electrical recepticals are permited in the hood.

12. Use an appropriate barricade if there is a chance of explosion or eruption.

13. Provide adequate maintenance for the hood exhaust system and the building supply system. Use static pressure gauges on the hood throat, across any filters in the exhaust system, or other appropriate indicators to ensure flow is appropriate.

14. If hood sash is supposed to be partially closed for the operation, the hood should be so labeled and the appropriate closure point clearly indicated.

AMERICAN CONFERENCE OF GOVERNMENTAL INDUSTRIAL HYGIENISTS	*WORK PRACTICES FOR LABORATORY HOODS*
	DATE *02-91* FIGURE *VS-35-04*

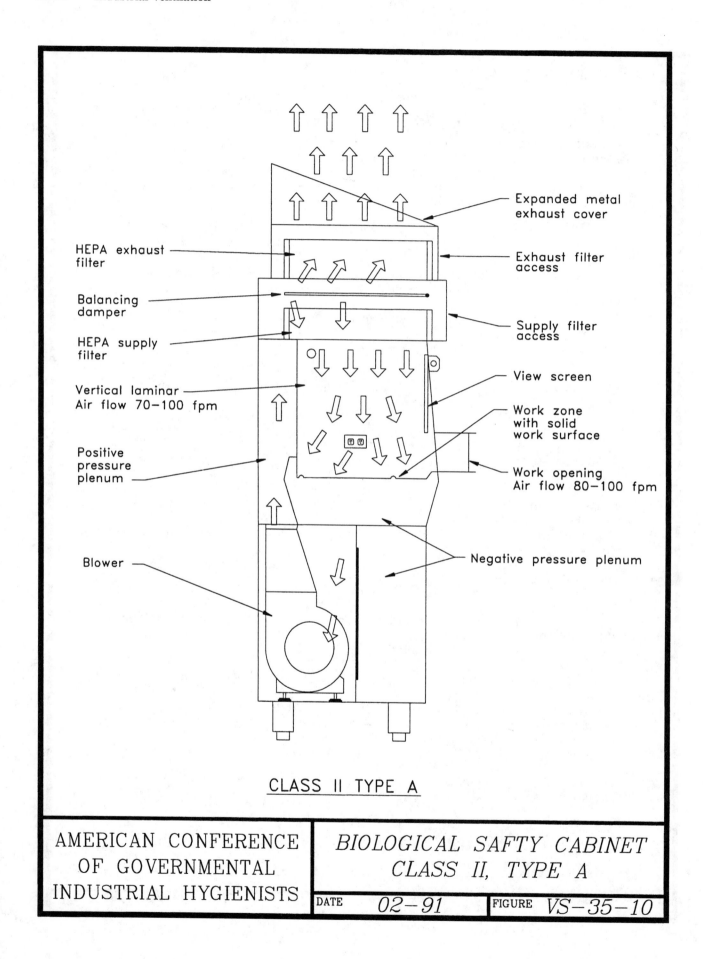

Expanded metal
exhaust cover

HEPA exhaust
filter

Exhaust filter
access

Balancing
damper

Supply filter
access

HEPA supply
filter

Vertical laminar
Air flow 70–100 fpm

View screen

Work zone
with solid
work surface

Positive
pressure
plenum

Work opening
Air flow 80–100 fpm

Negative pressure plenum

Blower

CLASS II TYPE A

AMERICAN CONFERENCE OF GOVERNMENTAL INDUSTRIAL HYGIENISTS	BIOLOGICAL SAFTY CABINET CLASS II, TYPE A	
	DATE 02–91	FIGURE VS–35–10

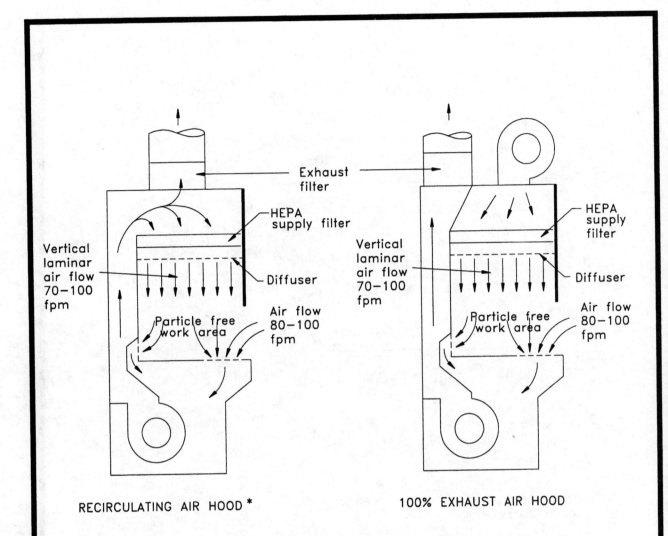

RECIRCULATING AIR HOOD *   100% EXHAUST AIR HOOD

* Recirculating Air Hoods are not recommended for use with gases or vapors.

Note: See "National Sanitation Foundation Standard 49" (10.35.4) for
requirements and definitions of classes.

For product protection only, see VS−35−30 and VS−35−31.

AMERICAN CONFERENCE OF GOVERNMENTAL INDUSTRIAL HYGIENISTS	BIOLOGICAL SAFETY CABINET CLASS II, TYPE B	
	DATE 02−91	FIGURE VS−35−11

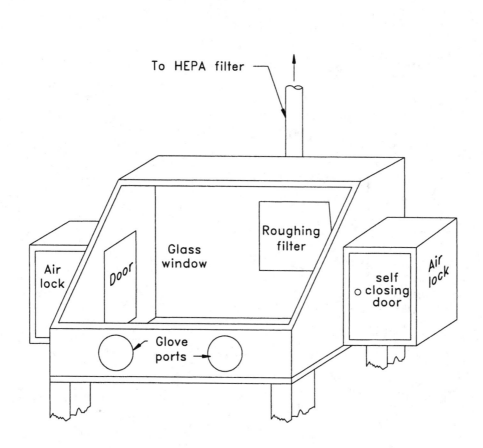

To HEPA filter

Roughing filter

Air lock

Door

Glass window

self o closing door

Air lock

Glove ports

$Q = 50$ cfm/ft^2 of open door area and 0.25" wg SP
on a closed system.
$h_e = 0.50$ VP$_d$
Duct velocity = 2000−4000 fpm
Filters : 1. Inlet air filters in doors.
       2. Roughing filter at exhaust connection to hood.
       3. HEPA filter
All facilities totally enclosed in hood. Exterior controls may be advisable.
Arm length rubber gloves are sealed to glove port rings.
Strippable plastic on interior and air cleaner on exhaust outlet may be
      used to facilitate decontamination of the system.
Filter units may be installed in the doors to allow the air flow necessary
      for burners etc.
For filters, see Chapter 4.

AMERICAN CONFERENCE OF GOVERNMENTAL INDUSTRIAL HYGIENISTS	*DRY BOX OR GLOVE HOOD FOR HIGH TOXICITY & RADIOACTIVE MATERIALS*	
	DATE *02−91*	FIGURE *VS−35−20*

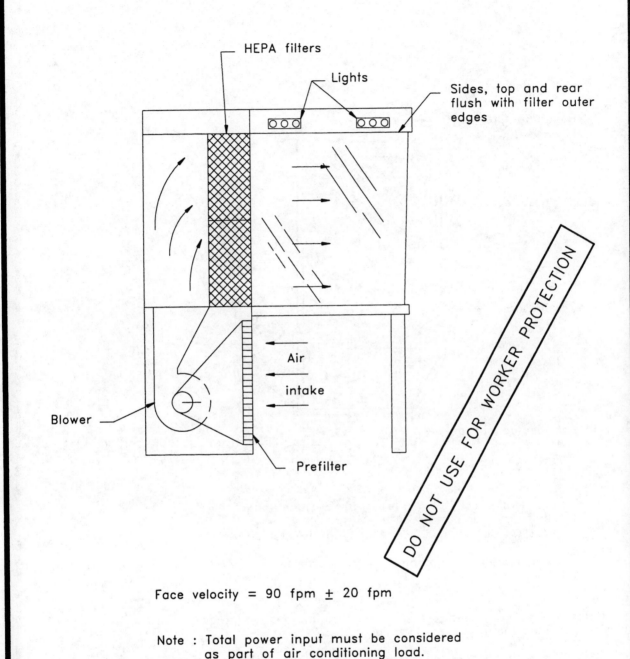

HEPA filters

Lights

Sides, top and rear
flush with filter outer
edges

Blower

Air

intake

Prefilter

DO NOT USE FOR WORKER PROTECTION

Face velocity = 90 fpm ± 20 fpm

Note : Total power input must be considered
as part of air conditioning load.

This hood does not provide protection
for the operator.

Reference 10.35.5

AMERICAN CONFERENCE OF GOVERNMENTAL INDUSTRIAL HYGIENISTS	HORIZONTAL LAMINAR FLOW CLEAN BENCH (PRODUCT PROTECTION ONLY)	
	DATE *02-91*	FIGURE *VS-35-30*

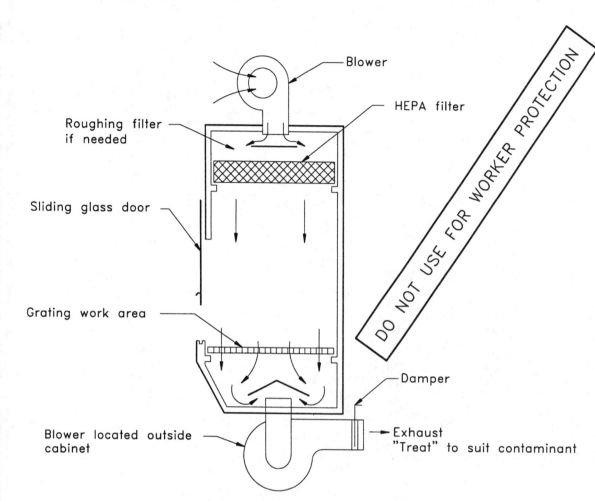

Blower

HEPA filter

Roughing filter
if needed

Sliding glass door

Grating work area

DO NOT USE FOR WORKER PROTECTION

Damper

Blower located outside
cabinet

Exhaust
"Treat" to suit contaminant

Vertical velocity = 90 fpm with average minimum
uniformity ± 20 fpm
Duct velocity = 2000 – 4000 fpm to suit conditions

Clean station for control of air particles

Notes: Supply and exhaust should be maintained equal by
flow meter control techniques.

This hood does not provide protection for the operator.

Do not use with toxic material.

AMERICAN CONFERENCE OF GOVERNMENTAL INDUSTRIAL HYGIENISTS	VERTICAL LAMINAR FLOW CLEAN BENCH (PRODUCT PROTECTION ONLY)	
	DATE 92–91	FIGURE VS–35–31

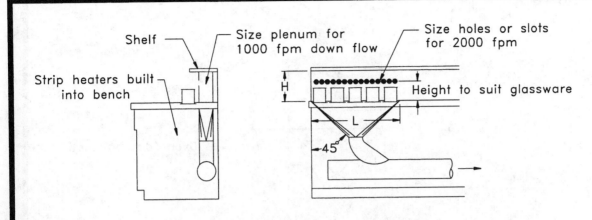

EVAPORATION BENCH

Q= 20 cfm/foot of hood or 50 HL
Minimum duct velocity = 2000 fpm
$h_e = 1.78VP_s + 0.25VP_d$

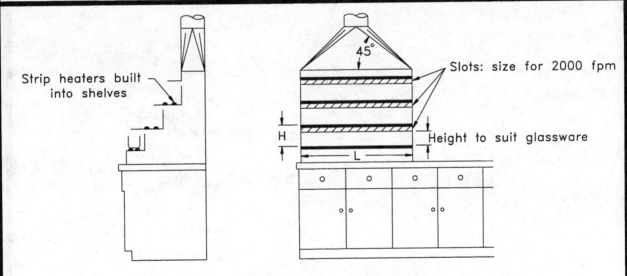

EVAPORATION HOOD

Q = 20 cfm/foot of shelf or 50 HL for each shelf
Minimum duct velocity = 2000 fpm
$h_e = 1.78VP_s + 0.25VP_d$

Reference 10.35.6

AMERICAN CONFERENCE OF GOVERNMENTAL INDUSTRIAL HYGIENISTS	SPECIALIZED LABORATORY HOOD DESIGNS	
	DATE 02-91	FIGURE VS-35-40

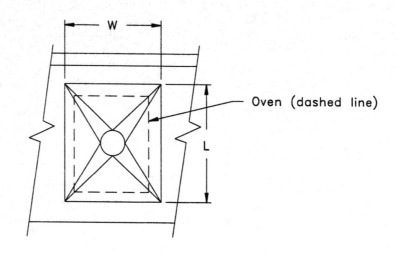

Oven (dashed line)

Top View

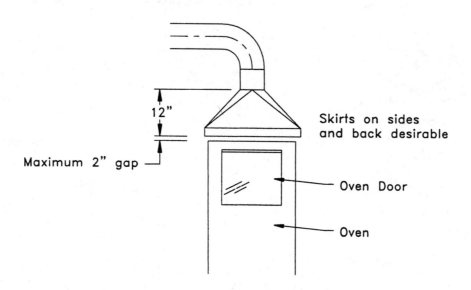

12"

Maximum 2" gap

Skirts on sides
and back desirable

Oven Door

Oven

Q = 200 − 400 cfm

Minimum duct velocity 1000 − 3000 fpm

$h_e = 0.25\ VP_d$

AMERICAN CONFERENCE OF GOVERNMENTAL INDUSTRIAL HYGIENISTS	*OVEN EXHAUST*	
	DATE *02−91*	FIGURE *VS−35−41*

10.40 LOW VOLUME-HIGH VELOCITY EXHAUST SYSTEMS

The low volume-high velocity (LVHV) exhaust system is a unique application of exhaust which uses small volumes of air at high velocities to control dust from portable hand tools and machining operations. Control is achieved by exhausting the air directly at the point of dust generation using close-fitting, custom-made hoods. Capture velocities are relatively high but the exhaust volume is low due to the small distance required. For flexibility, small diameter, light-weight plastic hoses are used with portable tools. This results in very high duct velocities but allows the application of local exhaust ventilation to portable tools which otherwise would require larger flow rates and large duct sizes when controlled by conventional exhaust methods. The resulting additional benefit is the reduction of replacement air requirements.

This technique has found a variety of applications although its use is not common. Rock drilling dust has been controlled by using hollow core drill steel with suitable exhaust holes in the drill bits. Air is exhausted either by a multi-stage turbine of the size generally used in industrial vacuum cleaners or, in the case of one manufacturer,[10.40.1] by the exhaust air from the pneumatic tool which operates a Venturi to withdraw air from the drill. Some applications use flexible connections to a central vacuum system to aid in the control of graphite dust at conventional machining operations. One- to two-inch diameter flexible hose was used with simple exhaust hoods mounted directly at the cutting tool. In a similar application for the machining of beryllium,[10.40.2] a central vacuum system utilizing 1.5-inch I.D. flexible hoses was employed. The exhaust hoods were made of lucite or transparent material and were tailor-made to surround the cutting tools and much of the work. Exhaust flow rates vary from 120 to 150 cfm with inlet velocities of 11,000 to 14,000 fpm. In another application,[10.40.3] a portable orbital sanding machine has been fitted with a small exhaust duct surrounding the edge of the plate. A fitting has been provided to connect this to the flexible hose of a standard domestic vacuum cleaner.

VS-40-01 to VS-40-06 illustrate a custom-made line of exhaust hoods available.[10.40.4] The required airflow rates range from 60 cfm for pneumatic chisels to 380 cfm for swing grinders. Due to the high entering velocities involved, static pressures are in the range of 7" to 14" of mercury (95 to 290 "wg). This high pressure is necessary to create the high capture velocities at the source to control the dust. However, there are disadvantages associated with high velocities: (1) small metal parts can be sucked into the hood; (2) coolants may be disturbed; and (3) very high noise levels may be produced.

10.40.1 Design—Calculations: With the exception of the proprietary system mentioned which can be purchased as a "package," the design calculations for these systems are largely empirical and little performance data are available for the user. In normal ventilation practice, air is considered to be incompressible since static pressures vary only slightly from atmospheric pressure. However, in LVHV systems the extreme pressures required introduce problems of air density, compressibility, and viscosity which are not easily solved. Also, pressure drop data for small diameter pipe, especially flexible tubing, is not commonly available. For practical purposes, the turbine exhauster should be selected for the maximum simultaneous exhaust flow rate required. Resistance in the pipe should be kept as low as possible; flexible tubing of less than 1-1.5-inch diameter should be limited to 10 feet or less. In most applications this is not a severe problem.

The main consideration in piping for such systems is to provide smooth internal configuration so as to reduce pressure loss at the high velocities involved and to minimize abrasion. Ordinary pipe with threaded fittings is to be avoided because the lip of the pipe or male fitting, being of smaller diameter than the female thread, presents a discontinuity which increases pressure loss and may be a point of rapid abrasion.

For dust exhaust systems, a good dust collector and primary separator should be mounted ahead of the exhauster to minimize erosion of the precision blades and subsequent loss in performance. Final balance of the system can be achieved by varying the length and diameters of the small flexible hoses.

It must be emphasized that although data are empirical, LVHV systems require the same careful design as the more conventional ones. Abrupt changes of direction, expansions and contractions must be avoided and care must always be taken to minimize pressure losses.

REFERENCES

10.40.1 Thor Power Tool Company, Aurora, IL.

10.40.2 Chamberlin, Richard I.: The Control of Beryllium Machining Operations. A.M.A. Archives of Industrial Health, 19, No. 2, (February 1959).

10.40.3 Master Power, Inc., Westminster, MD.

10.40.4 Hoffman Air and Filtration Div., Clarkson Industries, Inc., New York.

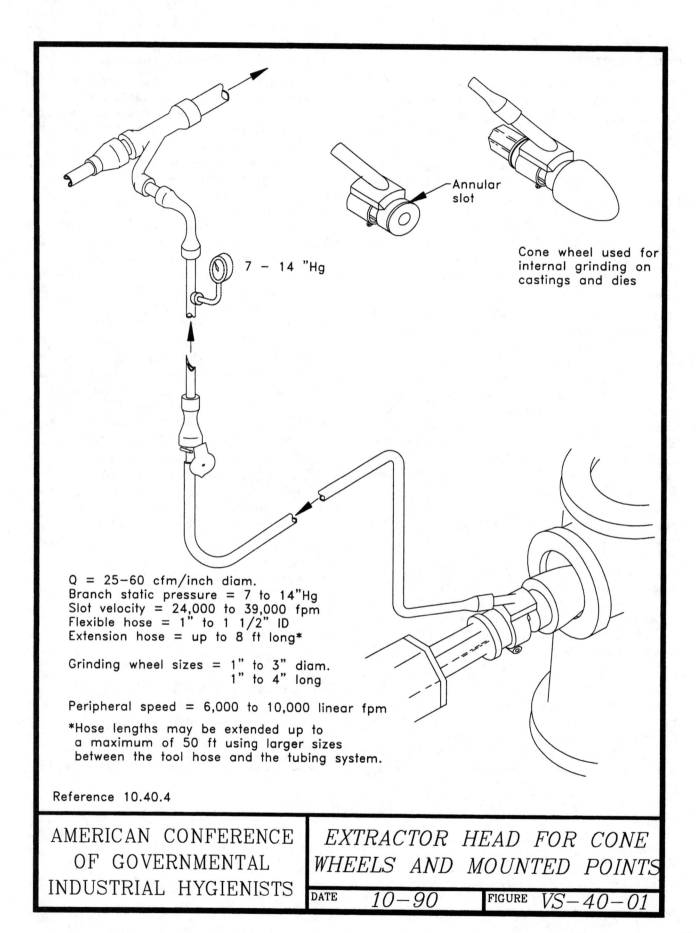

7 – 14 "Hg

Annular slot

Cone wheel used for internal grinding on castings and dies

Q = 25–60 cfm/inch diam.
Branch static pressure = 7 to 14"Hg
Slot velocity = 24,000 to 39,000 fpm
Flexible hose = 1" to 1 1/2" ID
Extension hose = up to 8 ft long*

Grinding wheel sizes = 1" to 3" diam.
                       1" to 4" long

Peripheral speed = 6,000 to 10,000 linear fpm

*Hose lengths may be extended up to
a maximum of 50 ft using larger sizes
between the tool hose and the tubing system.

Reference 10.40.4

AMERICAN CONFERENCE OF GOVERNMENTAL INDUSTRIAL HYGIENISTS	EXTRACTOR HEAD FOR CONE WHEELS AND MOUNTED POINTS
	DATE 10-90 FIGURE VS-40-01

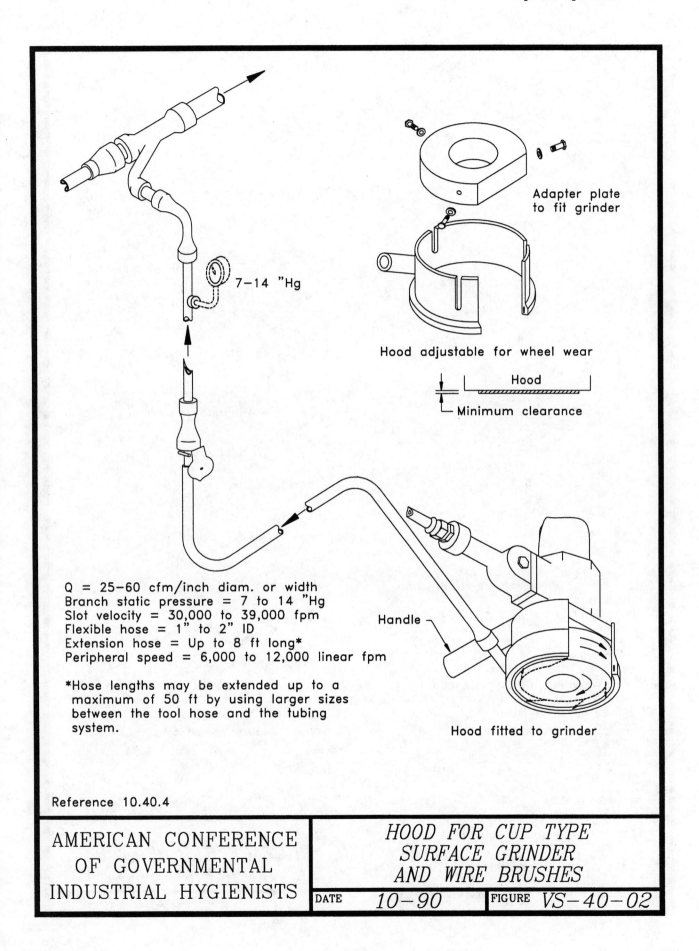

7–14 "Hg

Adapter plate
to fit grinder

Hood adjustable for wheel wear

Hood

Minimum clearance

Q = 25–60 cfm/inch diam. or width
Branch static pressure = 7 to 14 "Hg
Slot velocity = 30,000 to 39,000 fpm
Flexible hose = 1" to 2" ID
Extension hose = Up to 8 ft long*
Peripheral speed = 6,000 to 12,000 linear fpm

*Hose lengths may be extended up to a
 maximum of 50 ft by using larger sizes
 between the tool hose and the tubing
 system.

Handle

Hood fitted to grinder

Reference 10.40.4

AMERICAN CONFERENCE OF GOVERNMENTAL INDUSTRIAL HYGIENISTS	*HOOD FOR CUP TYPE SURFACE GRINDER AND WIRE BRUSHES*	
	DATE *10–90*	FIGURE *VS–40–02*

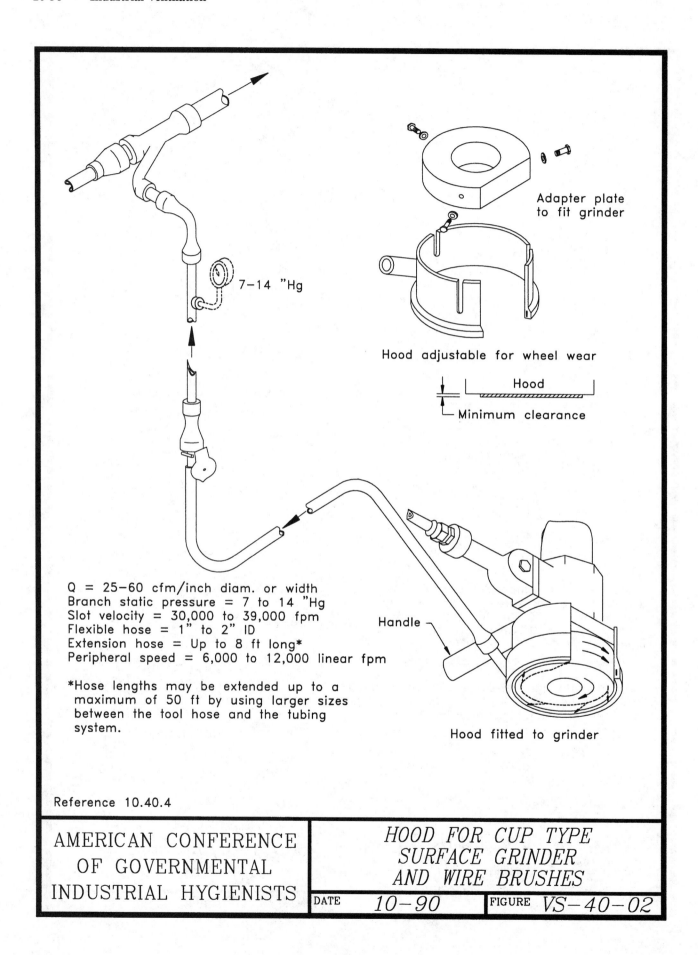

7-14 "Hg

Adapter plate
to fit grinder

Hood adjustable for wheel wear

Hood

Minimum clearance

Q = 25–60 cfm/inch diam. or width
Branch static pressure = 7 to 14 "Hg
Slot velocity = 30,000 to 39,000 fpm
Flexible hose = 1" to 2" ID
Extension hose = Up to 8 ft long*
Peripheral speed = 6,000 to 12,000 linear fpm

*Hose lengths may be extended up to a
 maximum of 50 ft by using larger sizes
 between the tool hose and the tubing
 system.

Handle

Hood fitted to grinder

Reference 10.40.4

AMERICAN CONFERENCE OF GOVERNMENTAL INDUSTRIAL HYGIENISTS	HOOD FOR CUP TYPE SURFACE GRINDER AND WIRE BRUSHES	
	DATE 10–90	FIGURE VS–40–02

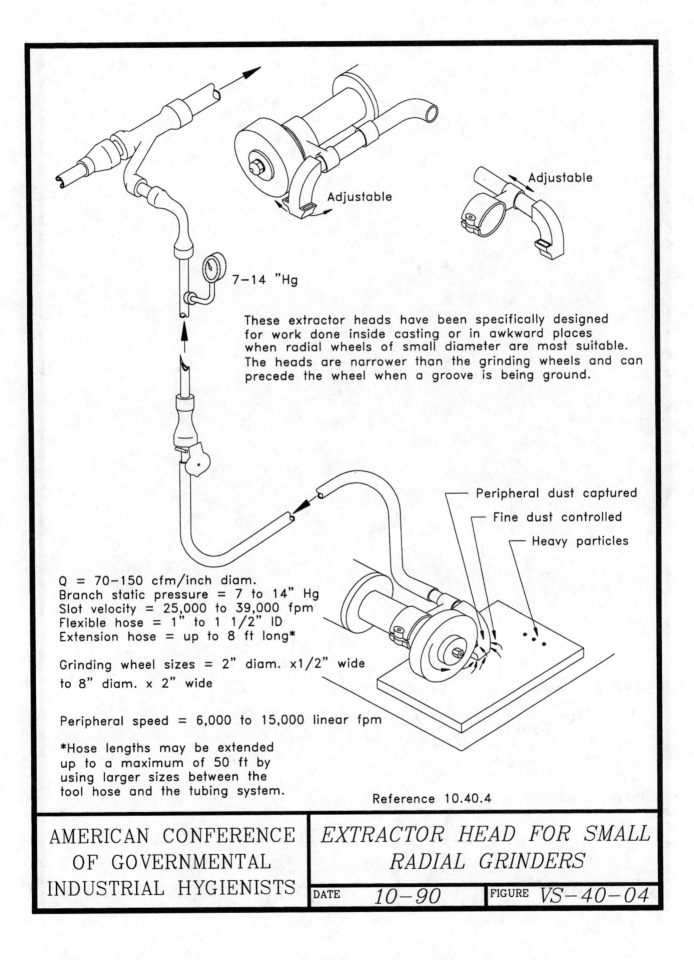

Adjustable

Adjustable

7-14 "Hg

These extractor heads have been specifically designed for work done inside casting or in awkward places when radial wheels of small diameter are most suitable. The heads are narrower than the grinding wheels and can precede the wheel when a groove is being ground.

Peripheral dust captured

Fine dust controlled

Heavy particles

Q = 70-150 cfm/inch diam.
Branch static pressure = 7 to 14" Hg
Slot velocity = 25,000 to 39,000 fpm
Flexible hose = 1" to 1 1/2" ID
Extension hose = up to 8 ft long*

Grinding wheel sizes = 2" diam. x1/2" wide
to 8" diam. x 2" wide

Peripheral speed = 6,000 to 15,000 linear fpm

*Hose lengths may be extended
up to a maximum of 50 ft by
using larger sizes between the
tool hose and the tubing system.

Reference 10.40.4

AMERICAN CONFERENCE OF GOVERNMENTAL INDUSTRIAL HYGIENISTS	EXTRACTOR HEAD FOR SMALL RADIAL GRINDERS	
	DATE *10-90*	FIGURE *VS-40-04*

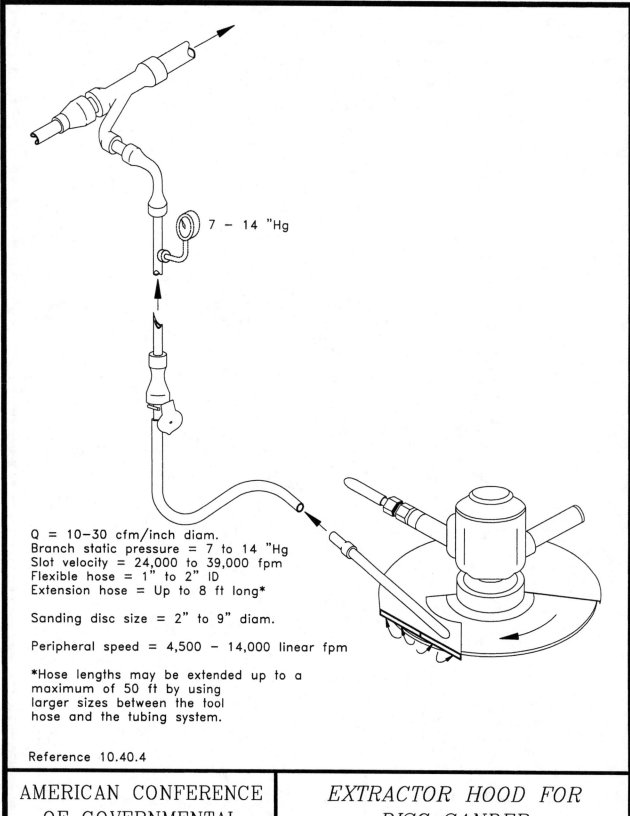

7 – 14 "Hg

Q = 10–30 cfm/inch diam.
Branch static pressure = 7 to 14 "Hg
Slot velocity = 24,000 to 39,000 fpm
Flexible hose = 1" to 2" ID
Extension hose = Up to 8 ft long*

Sanding disc size = 2" to 9" diam.

Peripheral speed = 4,500 – 14,000 linear fpm

*Hose lengths may be extended up to a
maximum of 50 ft by using
larger sizes between the tool
hose and the tubing system.

Reference 10.40.4

AMERICAN CONFERENCE	EXTRACTOR HOOD FOR	
OF GOVERNMENTAL	DISC SANDER	
INDUSTRIAL HYGIENISTS		
	DATE 10-90	FIGURE VS-40-05

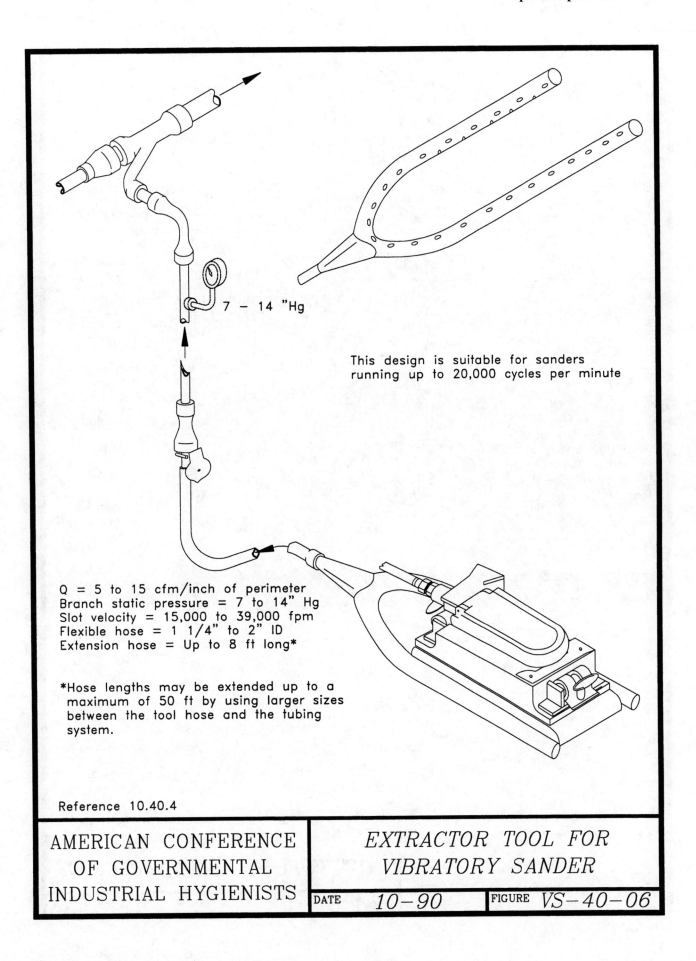

7 – 14 "Hg

This design is suitable for sanders
running up to 20,000 cycles per minute

Q = 5 to 15 cfm/inch of perimeter
Branch static pressure = 7 to 14" Hg
Slot velocity = 15,000 to 39,000 fpm
Flexible hose = 1 1/4" to 2" ID
Extension hose = Up to 8 ft long*

*Hose lengths may be extended up to a
maximum of 50 ft by using larger sizes
between the tool hose and the tubing
system.

Reference 10.40.4

AMERICAN CONFERENCE OF GOVERNMENTAL INDUSTRIAL HYGIENISTS	EXTRACTOR TOOL FOR VIBRATORY SANDER	
	DATE 10-90	FIGURE VS-40-06

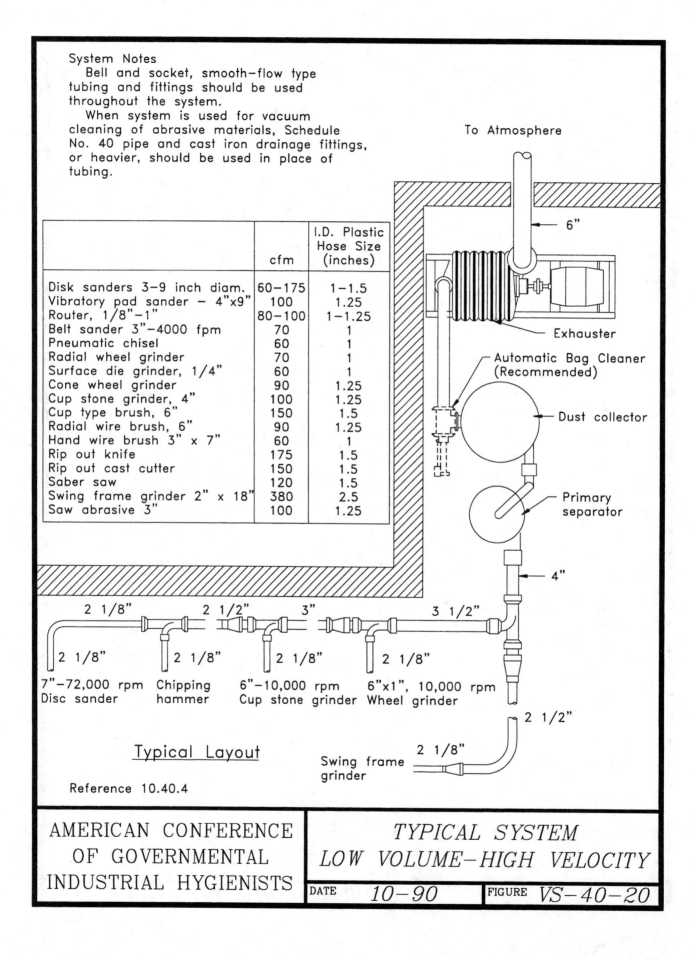

System Notes

Bell and socket, smooth—flow type tubing and fittings should be used throughout the system.

When system is used for vacuum cleaning of abrasive materials, Schedule No. 40 pipe and cast iron drainage fittings, or heavier, should be used in place of tubing.

	cfm	I.D. Plastic Hose Size (inches)
Disk sanders 3–9 inch diam.	60–175	1–1.5
Vibratory pad sander – 4"x9"	100	1.25
Router, 1/8"–1"	80–100	1–1.25
Belt sander 3"–4000 fpm	70	1
Pneumatic chisel	60	1
Radial wheel grinder	70	1
Surface die grinder, 1/4"	60	1
Cone wheel grinder	90	1.25
Cup stone grinder, 4"	100	1.25
Cup type brush, 6"	150	1.5
Radial wire brush, 6"	90	1.25
Hand wire brush 3" x 7"	60	1
Rip out knife	175	1.5
Rip out cast cutter	150	1.5
Saber saw	120	1.5
Swing frame grinder 2" x 18"	380	2.5
Saw abrasive 3"	100	1.25

To Atmosphere

6"

Exhauster

Automatic Bag Cleaner (Recommended)

Dust collector

Primary separator

4"

2 1/8"   2 1/2"   3"   3 1/2"

2 1/8"   2 1/8"   2 1/8"   2 1/8"

7"–72,000 rpm   Chipping   6"–10,000 rpm   6"x1", 10,000 rpm
Disc sander   hammer   Cup stone grinder   Wheel grinder

2 1/2"

2 1/8"

Swing frame grinder

Typical Layout

Reference 10.40.4

AMERICAN CONFERENCE OF GOVERNMENTAL INDUSTRIAL HYGIENISTS	*TYPICAL SYSTEM LOW VOLUME–HIGH VELOCITY*	
	DATE *10–90*	FIGURE *VS–40–20*

10.45 MACHINING

The primary purpose of metal cutting machines is to finish rough parts formed by other processes to specific dimensions. Finishing and shaping may be accomplished by a variety of cutting tools such as saws, broaches, and chisel-shaped tool bits held in fixtures with fixed or movable drives. Cutting is accomplished by creating relative motion between the tool edge and the material blank. Chips of varying sizes are produced; chip size depends on the material being cut, feed rate of the tool, and relative speed or feed between the tool and the metal being shaped.

Non-traditional methods of metal cutting and shaping include electrochemical, electrodischarge, wire electrodischarge, and laser beam machining. With the exception of the laser beam, each of the processes utilizes a circulating oil or water-base dielectric to facilitate molecular erosion as well as to remove process heat and particulate debris. The rate of metal removal is controlled carefully by regulating the flow of electrical current between the shaped anode or wire and the workpiece. The laser beam is used in a dry environment and metal cutting is accomplished by vaporizing the workpiece along the cutting edge with a focused beam of high energy light. The process is flexible and a variety of metallic and non-metallic materials can be shaped by this means.[10.45.1]

It is estimated that up to 97% of the work involved in conventional metal cutting results in heat. The rate of heat removal must be controlled carefully in order to protect both the cutting tool and the metallurgy of the work being cut. Where convection or radiant cooling is insufficient, a cutting fluid can be used to reduce friction, carry away generated heat, and, more commonly, flush away metal chips produced by the cutting process. Cutting fluids include straight chained and synthetic mineral oils as well as soluble oil emulsions in water. A variety of water soluble lubri-coolants (1 to 5% mixture of lubricants, emulsifiers, rust inhibitors and other chemicals in water) are used commonly, particularly for high speed metal working machines. In some applications the lubri-coolant mixture is applied as a mist by using a small volume of liquid in a high velocity air stream. In the more usual situation, liquid is applied by flooding the tool in the cutting zone to flush away cutting debris. The latter type system requires a low pressure pump with valves; filters; settling chamber to separate the fluid from the chips; and a reservoir which permits recirculation. Where liquids cannot be used, low temperature nitrogen or carbon dioxide gas can be used as a cooling media for both the tool and the cutting surface as well as a means of dispersing particulate debris.

The hazards created by skin exposure to the water lubri-coolant mixtures, particulates, and oil mist/vapor produced in the transfer of heat is best handled with engineering controls—primarily ventilation. An additional health concern is the fact that soluble oil emulsions provide a breeding ground for bacteria and, therefore, it is common practice to add biocides to prevent odor generation and decomposition of the oil mixture.

Biocides and other additives may be primary skin irritants or cause hypersensitive dermatitis. It is for these reasons that mist, vapors, and particulates must be controlled adequately.[10.45.2]

Mist and vapors from machining operations can be controlled by a combination of machine enclosure and local exhaust ventilation. Exhaust hoods and enclosures should be designed so the machine can be serviced easily and the operation observed when required. Hood sides should act as splash guards since an indraft of air will not stop liquid directly thrown from rotating parts. All components should be robust and rigidly supported. To facilitate maintenance, service and tool adjustment portions of the hood enclosure which are not permanently fixed should be designed for easy removal. Thought should be given also to the use of sliding, hinged, or bellows-connected panels in locations where frequent access is required. All windowed openings must be shatter-proof with appropriate internal lighting. All non-fixed panels should be designed with overlapping, drip-proof edges. The use of gaskets or seals on abutting panels is not recommended. Ventilation rates vary; however, a minimum of 100 fpm indraft usually is required to prevent vapor and mist from exiting the enclosure. A typical machine enclosure will require a volumetric flow rate of from 400-500 cfm. Additional air may be required to control heat generated within the enclosure as well as to maintain adequate vision. Where coolant flumes are used for chip transport, additional exhaust ventilation is required to control air entrainment. Baffles above the liquid level are beneficial and flumes should be enclosed to the extent possible.

Local ventilation control is the preferred method—particularly in machine environments which are temperature controlled with refrigerated air conditioning systems. In more open workrooms, the use of dilution ventilation may be adequate to control air contaminants. For further information on dilution ventilation, see Chapter 2 of this manual.

REFERENCES

10.45.1 Rain, Carl: Non-traditional Methods Advance Machining Industry. High Technology, (November/December 1957).

10.45.2 O'Brien, Dennis; Frede, John C.: Guidelines for the Control of Exposure to Metal Working Fluids. National Institute for Occupational Safety and Health, (February 1978).

10.45.3 Schulte, H. F.; Hyatt, E.C.; Smith, Jr., F.S.: Exhaust Ventilation for Machine Tools Used on Materials of High Toxicity. American Medical Association Archives of Industrial Hygiene and Occupational Medicine, 5, 21, (January 1952).

10.45.4 Mitchell, R. N.; Hyatt, E. C.: Beryllium—Hazard Evaluation and Control Covering a Five-Year Study. American Industrial Hygiene Quarterly, 18, 3, (September 1957).

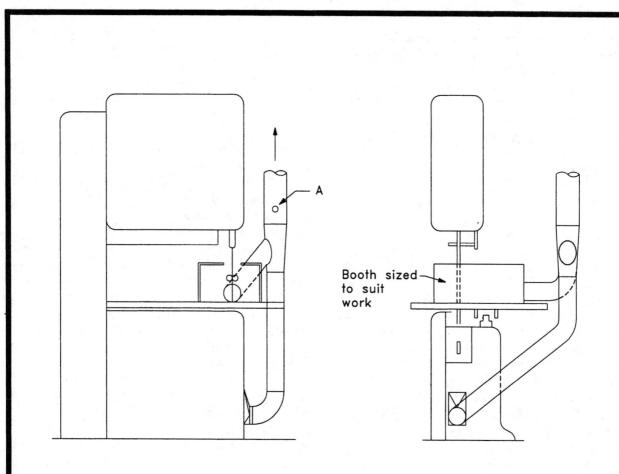

A

Booth sized
to suit
work

Q at booth = 225 cfm/ft^2 open area
Q at bottom = 350 cfm

Minimum duct velocity = 4000 fpm

h_e = 1.75 VP_d , at point A

AMERICAN CONFERENCE OF GOVERNMENTAL INDUSTRIAL HYGIENISTS	*METAL CUTTING BANDSAW*	
	DATE *10−90*	FIGURE *VS−45−01*

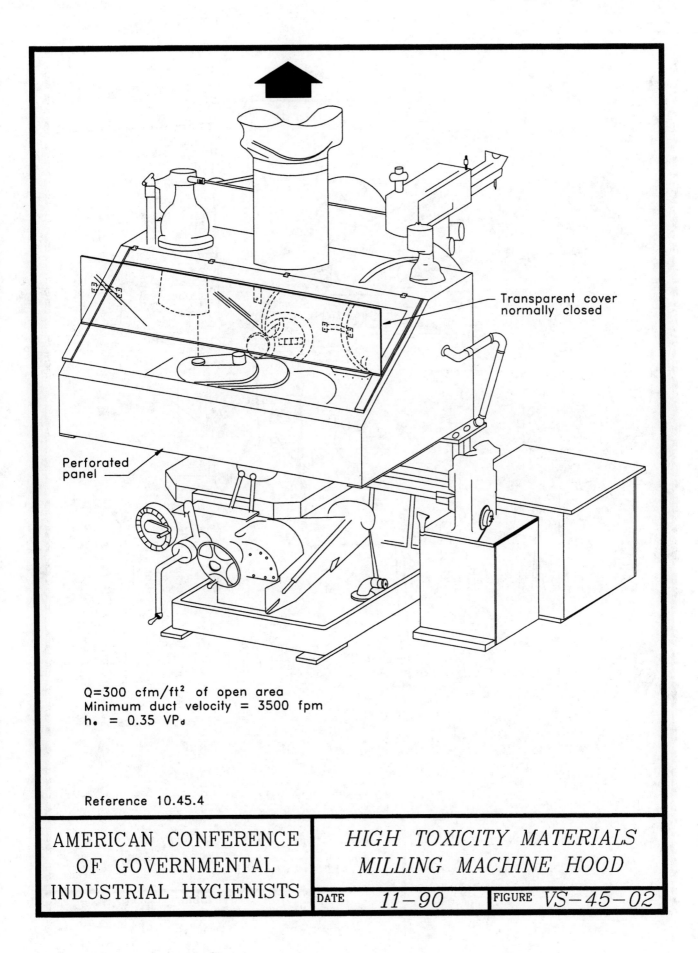

Transparent cover
normally closed

Perforated
panel

$Q = 300$ cfm/ft² of open area
Minimum duct velocity = 3500 fpm
$h_e = 0.35$ VP$_d$

Reference 10.45.4

AMERICAN CONFERENCE OF GOVERNMENTAL INDUSTRIAL HYGIENISTS	HIGH TOXICITY MATERIALS MILLING MACHINE HOOD	
	DATE *11—90*	FIGURE *VS—45—02*

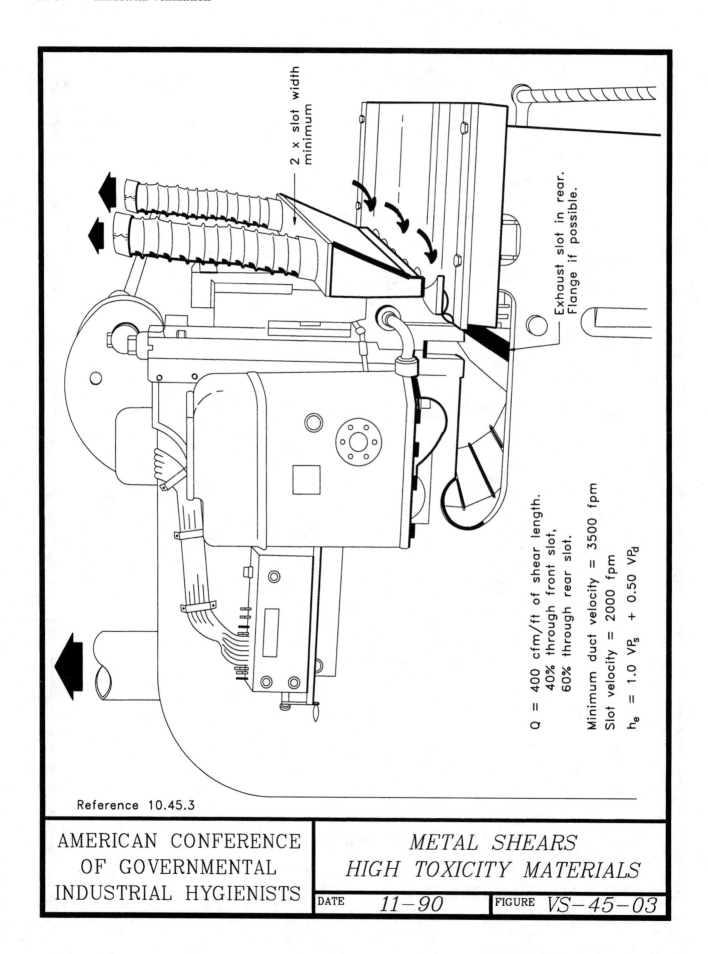

2 x slot width minimum

Exhaust slot in rear. Flange if possible.

Q = 400 cfm/ft of shear length.
40% through front slot,
60% through rear slot.

Minimum duct velocity = 3500 fpm

Slot velocity = 2000 fpm

$h_e = 1.0\ VP_s + 0.50\ VP_d$

Reference 10.45.3

AMERICAN CONFERENCE OF GOVERNMENTAL INDUSTRIAL HYGIENISTS	*METAL SHEARS* *HIGH TOXICITY MATERIALS*	
	DATE *11—90*	FIGURE *VS—45—03*

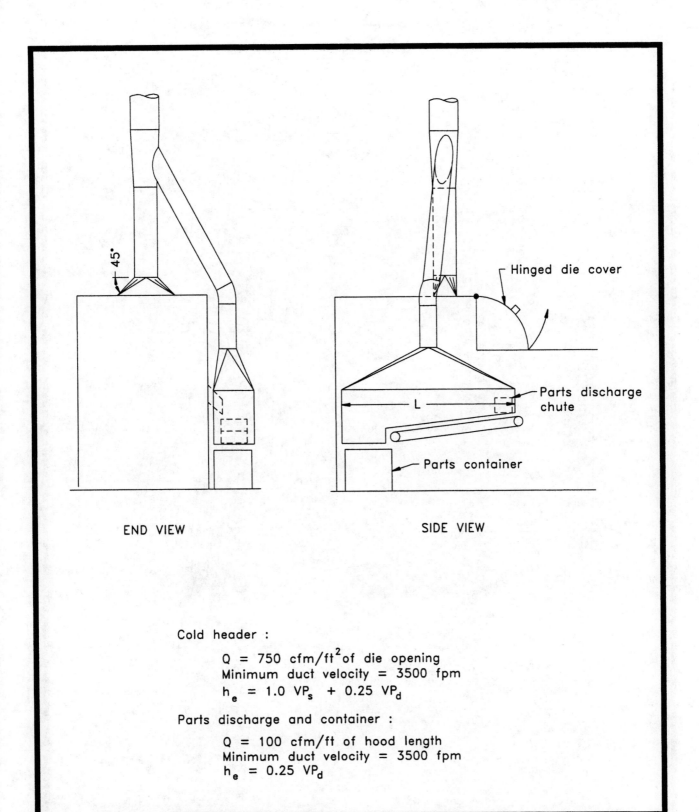

END VIEW

SIDE VIEW

Hinged die cover

Parts discharge chute

Parts container

45°

L

Cold header :

$Q = 750$ cfm/ft^2 of die opening
Minimum duct velocity = 3500 fpm
$h_e = 1.0$ VP_s + 0.25 VP_d

Parts discharge and container :

$Q = 100$ cfm/ft of hood length
Minimum duct velocity = 3500 fpm
$h_e = 0.25$ VP_d

AMERICAN CONFERENCE OF GOVERNMENTAL INDUSTRIAL HYGIENISTS	COLD HEADING MACHINE VENTILATION	
	DATE 11-90	FIGURE VS-45-04

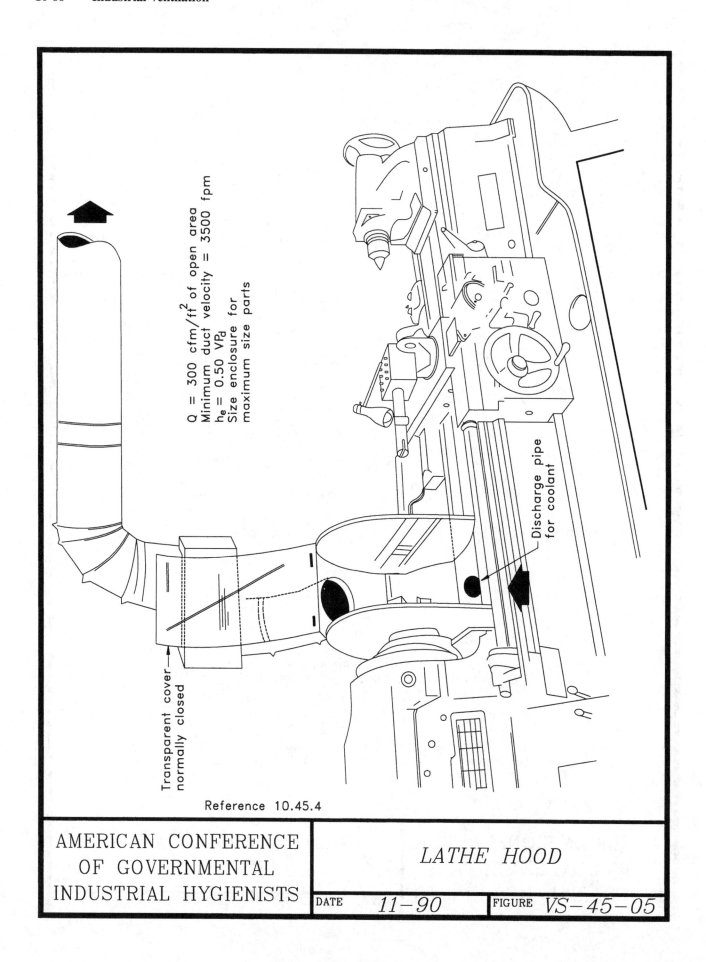

$Q = 300 \text{ cfm/ft}^2$ of open area
Minimum duct velocity = 3500 fpm
$h_e = 0.50 \text{ VP}_d$
Size enclosure for maximum size parts

Transparent cover normally closed

Discharge pipe for coolant

Reference 10.45.4

AMERICAN CONFERENCE
OF GOVERNMENTAL
INDUSTRIAL HYGIENISTS

LATHE HOOD

DATE *11-90*   FIGURE *VS-45-05*

10.50 MATERIAL TRANSPORT

Ventilation of material transport systems generally requires the use of an exhausted enclosure because of the motion and quantity of material involved. If the enclosure were perfectly air tight there would be no need for exhaust. However, there usually are cracks and other leak points in addition to the openings necessary for personnel and material access.

For enclosures where there is little motion and low material quantity, the exhaust rate is the product of the total openings in square feet and some velocity between 50 and 200 fpm. However, in some cases the inward flow of material and entrained air can overwhelm the exhaust flow rate calculated on the basis of enclosure openings. In such cases the material flow rate, the dustiness of the material, and the height of fall in transferring from one surface to another must be considered in the system design.[10.50.1, 10.50.2] Other design factors include:

1. The rate of air induction into the space.

2. The location of cracks or other openings in relation to the "splash" or agitation of material during transfer.

3. The need to avoid excessive product withdrawal.

4. Adequate airflow for dilution of interior concentrations for visibility or safety from explosions.

10.50.1 Bucket Elevators: Air motion caused by the bucket moving within the elevator is not significant. The motion of buckets in one direction is offset by the opposite flow. Consequently, an exhaust rate of 100 cfm/ft^2 of elevator cross-section is adequate for most elevator applications (see VS-50-01 for details). Additional ventilation is required as materials enter and leave the elevator (see VS-50-10, VS-50-20, and VS-50-21). Handling hot material often causes significant thermal bouyancy which requires increased exhaust ventilation to overcome this challenge.

10.50.2 Conveyors: Dust from the operation of belt conveyors originates mainly at the tail pulley where material is received and at the head pulley where material is discharged. The exhaust requirement at the head pulley is generally small because air is induced downward and away from this transfer point. An exhaust rate of 150-200 cfm/ft^2 of opening often is adequate.

At the tail pulley, the exhaust requirements are determined by the amount of air induced by the delivery chute. An exhaust of 350 cfm/ft^2 of belt width often is adequate where the material does not fall more than 3 feet. The exhaust point should be located at least twice the belt width away from the point where the material hits the belt. Where the material falls more than 3 feet, additional exhaust is required (see VS-50-20 for details). Note that very dry or dusty material may require flowrates 1.5 to 2.0 times these values.

Belt conveyors should be covered and exhausted at 30 foot intervals at a rate of 350 cfm/ft of belt width. Vibrating feeders should be exhausted at a rate of 500 cfm/ft of feeder width. Rubber or canvas flexible seals should be provided from the feeder sides and end to the hopper sides and end.

The conveying of toxic material requires additional care in enclosure design to ensure that no air leaks out and that sufficient access is available for inspection and cleanout. The head pulley should be equipped with a scraper or brush (see VS-50-21).

10.50.3 Bin and Hopper Ventilation: For the mechanical loading of bins and hoppers, the exhaust rates previously listed for belt conveyors are appropriate. An exhaust rate of 150 cfm/ft^2 of hopper is adequate for manual loading operations. The enclosure should cover as much of the hopper opening as possible.

10.50.4 Loading and Unloading: For loading and unloading operations, a ventilation rate of 150-200 cfm/ft^2 of enclosure opening is adequate *provided the enclosure is large enough to accommodate the "splash" effect.* The entrance to enclosure for truck dumps should be covered with flaps to minimize ventilation requirements. Rotary or bottom car dumps generally are exhausted at the rate of 50-100 cfm/ft^2 of hopper area.

REFERENCES

10.50.1   DallaValle, J. M.: Exhaust Hoods, Industrial Press. New York (1946).

10.50.2   Hemeon, W. C. L.: Plant and Process Ventilation. Industrial Press, (1963).

10.50.3   Rajhans, G. S.; Bragg, G. M.: Engineering Aspects of Asbestos Dust Control. Ann Arbor Science Publications, Inc., Ann Arbor, MI, (1978).

10.50.4   National Grain and Feed Association, Dust Control for Grain Elevators. Washington, DC, (1981).

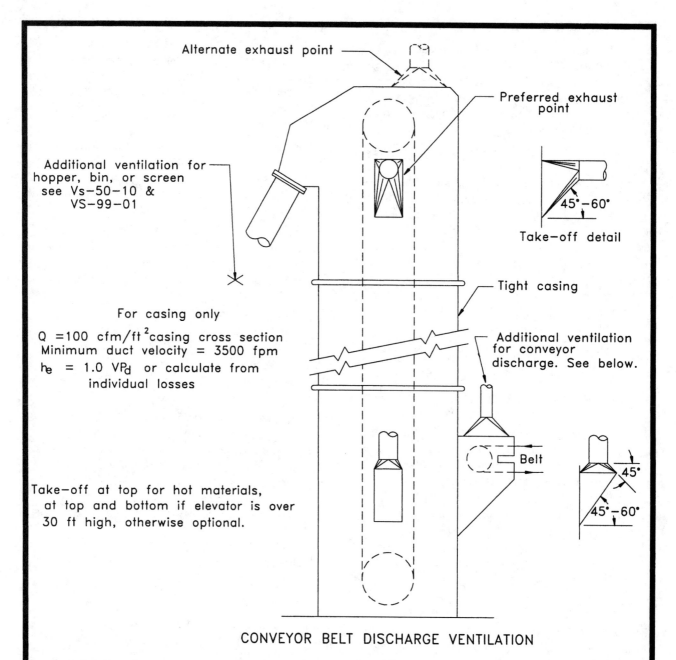

Alternate exhaust point

Preferred exhaust point

Additional ventilation for hopper, bin, or screen see Vs-50-10 & VS-99-01

45°-60°

Take-off detail

Tight casing

For casing only

$Q = 100$ cfm/ft^2 casing cross section
Minimum duct velocity = 3500 fpm
$h_e = 1.0$ VP$_d$ or calculate from individual losses

Additional ventilation for conveyor discharge. See below.

Belt

45°

45°-60°

Take-off at top for hot materials, at top and bottom if elevator is over 30 ft high, otherwise optional.

CONVEYOR BELT DISCHARGE VENTILATION

BELT SPEED	FLOWRATE
Less than 200 fpm	350 cfm/ft of belt width. Not less than 150 cfm/ft^2 of opening.
Over 200 fpm	500 cfm/ft of belt width. Not less than 200 cfm/ft^2 of opening.

AMERICAN CONFERENCE OF GOVERNMENTAL INDUSTRIAL HYGIENISTS	*BUCKET ELEVATOR VENTILATION*	
	DATE *1-91*	FIGURE *VS-50-01*

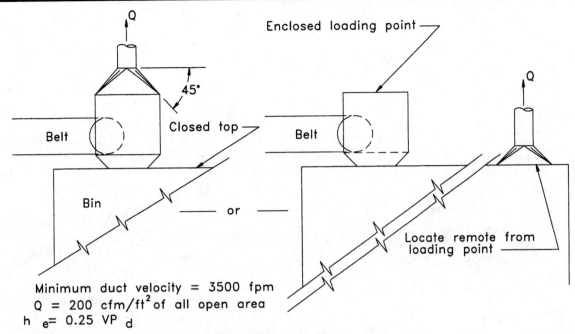

Minimum duct velocity = 3500 fpm

$Q = 200$ cfm/ft^2 of all open area

$h_e = 0.25 VP_d$

MECHANICAL LOADING

Belt speed	Flowrate
Less than 200 fpm ————	350 cfm/ft of belt width, Not less than 150 cfm/ft^2 of opening.
Over 200 fpm ————	500 cfm/ft of belt width, Not less than 200 cfm/ft^2 of opening.

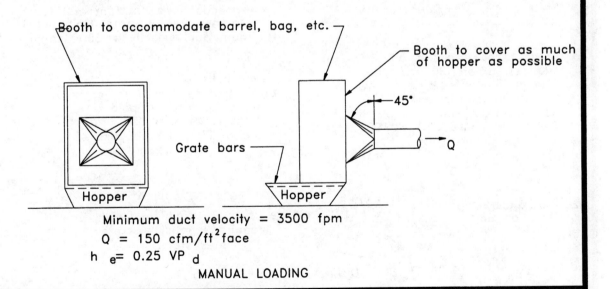

Minimum duct velocity = 3500 fpm

$Q = 150$ cfm/ft^2 face

$h_e = 0.25 VP_d$

MANUAL LOADING

AMERICAN CONFERENCE OF GOVERNMENTAL INDUSTRIAL HYGIENISTS	*BIN & HOPPER VENTILATION*	
	DATE *1-91*	FIGURE *VS-50-10*

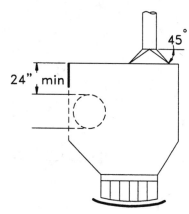

45°

24" min

1. Conveyor transfer less than 3' fall. For greater fall, provide additional exhaust at lower belt. See 3 below.
$h_e = 0.25\ VP_d$

45°

24" min

Close face to bottom of belt

Elevator exhaust (See VS-50-01)

As close as practical

Tote box

2. Conveyor to elevator with magnetic separator.
$h_e = 0.25\ VP_d$

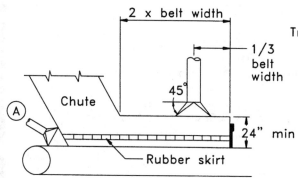

2 x belt width

1/3 belt width

45°

Chute

A

24" min

Rubber skirt

3. Chute to belt transfer and conveyor transfer, greater than 3' fall. Use additional exhaust at Ⓐ for dusty material as follows:
Belt width 12"-36", Q=700 cfm
Belt width above 36", Q=1000 cfm
$h_e = 0.25\ VP_d$

DESIGN DATA

Transfer points:

Enclose to provide 150 — 200 fpm indraft at all openings. (Underground mining tunnel ventilation will interfere with conveyor exhaust systems.)

Q = 350 cfm/ft belt width for belt speeds under 200 fpm. (minimum)
= 500 cfm/ft belt width for belt speeds over 200 fpm and for magnetic separators. (minimum)
Minimum duct velocity = 3500 fpm
$h_e = 0.25\ VP_d$

Conveyor belts:

Cover belt between transfer points
Exhaust at transfer points
Exhaust additional 350 cfm/ft. of belt width at 30' intervals. Use 45° tapered connections.

Note: Dry, very dusty materials may require exhaust flowrates 1.5 to 2.0 times stated values.

2" clearance for load on belt

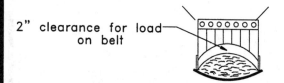

DETAIL OF BELT OPENING

AMERICAN CONFERENCE OF GOVERNMENTAL INDUSTRIAL HYGIENISTS

CONVEYOR BELT VENTILATION

DATE *2-00*   FIGURE *VS-50-20*

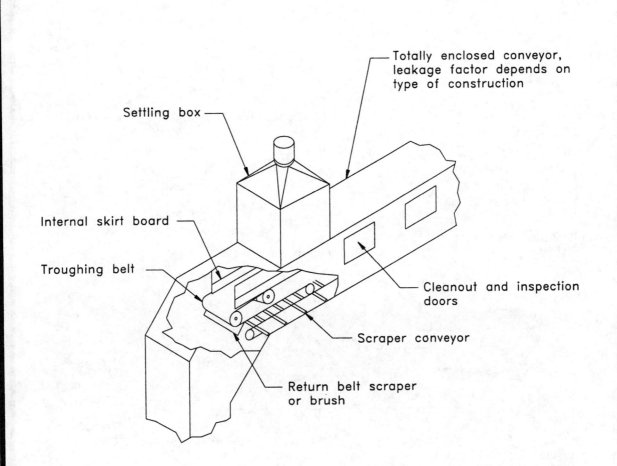

Settling box

Totally enclosed conveyor,
leakage factor depends on
type of construction

Internal skirt board

Troughing belt

Cleanout and inspection
doors

Scraper conveyor

Return belt scraper
or brush

$Q = 250$ cfm/ft^2 of open area
Minimum duct velocity = 3500 fpm
$h_e = 0.4$ VP_d

Reference: 10.50.3

AMERICAN CONFERENCE OF GOVERNMENTAL INDUSTRIAL HYGIENISTS	*TOXIC MATERIAL BELT CONVEYING HEAD PULLEY*	
	DATE *1-91*	FIGURE *VS-50-21*

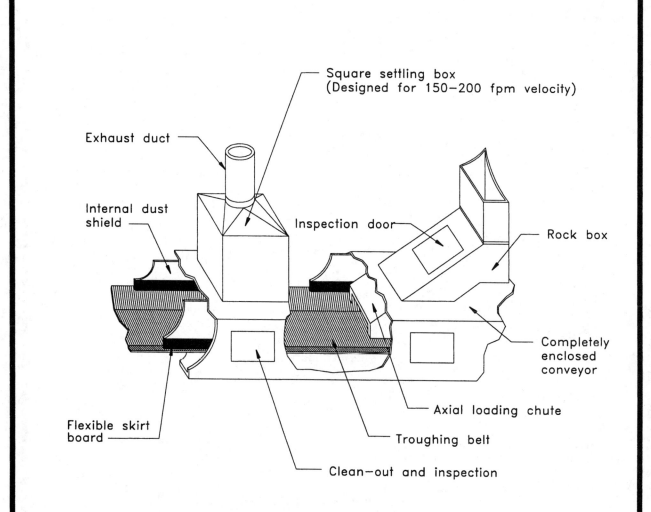

Exhaust duct

Square settling box
(Designed for 150–200 fpm velocity)

Internal dust shield

Inspection door

Rock box

Flexible skirt board

Clean-out and inspection

Troughing belt

Axial loading chute

Completely enclosed conveyor

$Q = 250 \text{ cfm/ft}^2$ of open area
Minimum duct velocity = 3500 fpm
$h_e = 0.4 \text{ VP}_d$

Reference: 10.50.3

AMERICAN CONFERENCE OF GOVERNMENTAL INDUSTRIAL HYGIENISTS	*TOXIC MATERIAL CONVEYOR BELT LOADING*	
	DATE *1–91*	FIGURE *VS–50–22*

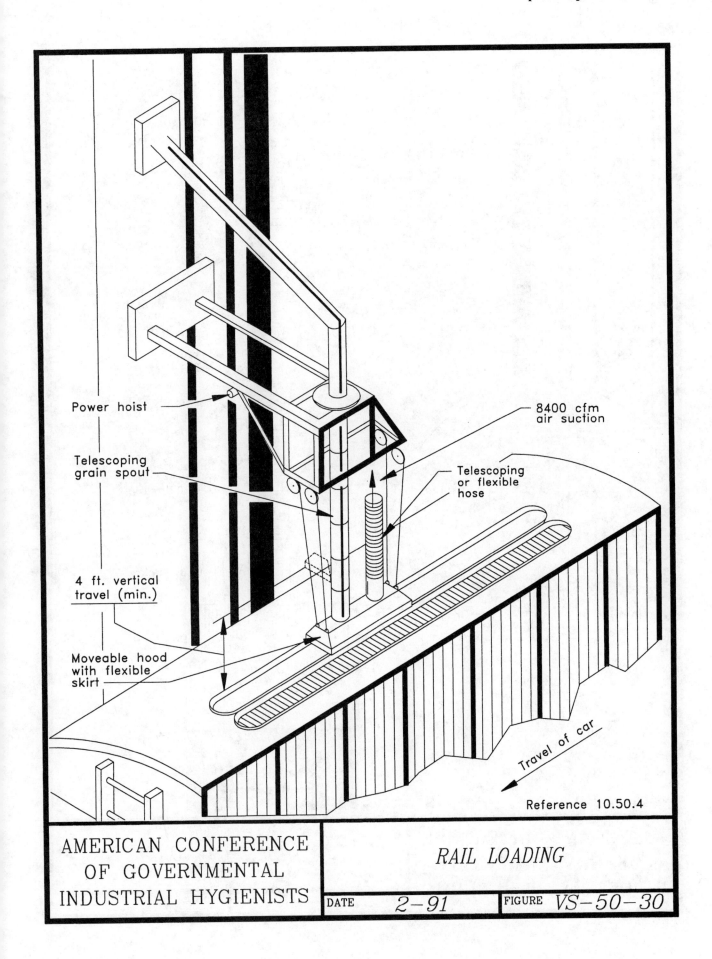

Power hoist

Telescoping
grain spout

4 ft. vertical
travel (min.)

Moveable hood
with flexible
skirt

8400 cfm
air suction

Telescoping
or flexible
hose

Travel of car

Reference 10.50.4

AMERICAN CONFERENCE	RAIL LOADING	
OF GOVERNMENTAL		
INDUSTRIAL HYGIENISTS		
DATE 2-91	FIGURE VS-50-30	

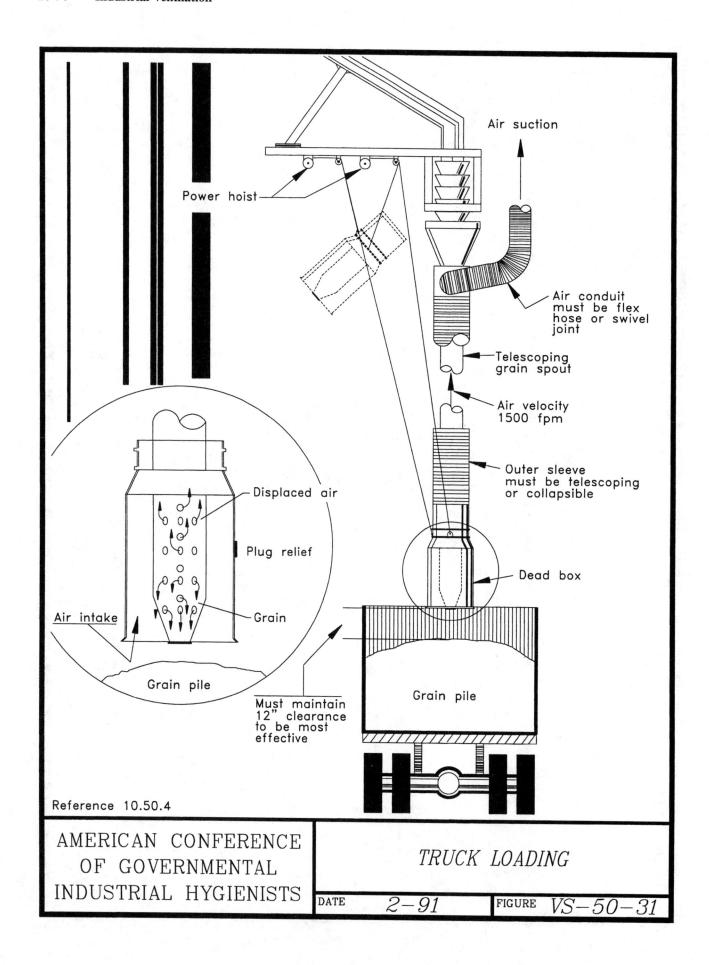

Power hoist

Air suction

Air conduit
must be flex
hose or swivel
joint

Telescoping
grain spout

Air velocity
1500 fpm

Outer sleeve
must be telescoping
or collapsible

Dead box

Displaced air

Plug relief

Grain

Air intake

Grain pile

Grain pile

Must maintain
12" clearance
to be most
effective

Reference 10.50.4

AMERICAN CONFERENCE
OF GOVERNMENTAL
INDUSTRIAL HYGIENISTS

TRUCK LOADING

DATE   2-91

FIGURE   VS-50-31

10.55 METAL MELTING FURNACES

This set of VS-prints describes hood designs for a variety of metal melting furnaces, including electric induction, carbon arc, convention, and crucible, which use natural gas or electric resistance elements as the heat source. Exhaust ventilation usually is required to control specific oxides associated with the metal being melted or contaminants carried in the scrap charge. In some cases, a single hood will suffice for charging, melting, and pouring. In other cases, a separate hood, remote from the primary melter, may be required for charging because of the nature of the charge or the large open area necessary at this phase of the operation. This is true particularly of electric arc furnaces which are completely open for charging. After charging, the port exhaust can be used to achieve control during the remainder of the melting and pouring cycles.

All metal melting will produce a slag which must be removed prior to pouring. This activity may produce a significant release of oxides and may require a separate exhaust system for oxide and/or dross control. Where metal purification is performed directly within the furnace or melting vessel, such as the addition of oxygen or chlorine, additional exhaust may be required to contain the rapidly generated plume.

All systems must be designed to include the increase in air temperature under operating conditions to insure an adequate airflow into the hood. The air temperature rise is usually relatively low except where metal innoculants or oxidizers are added to the molten charge. During this phase of metal melting, a significant temperature rise will occur and it is customary to provide a large hood in which gas expansion can take place.

REFERENCES

10.55.1   American Air Filter Co., Rotoclone Dust Control. (January 1946).

10.55.2   Kane, J. M.: Foundry Ventilation. The Foundry (February and March 1946).

10.55.3   Kane, J. M.: The Application of Local Exhaust Ventilation to Electric Melting Furnaces. In: Transactions of the American Foundrymen's Association, 52, p 1351 (1945).

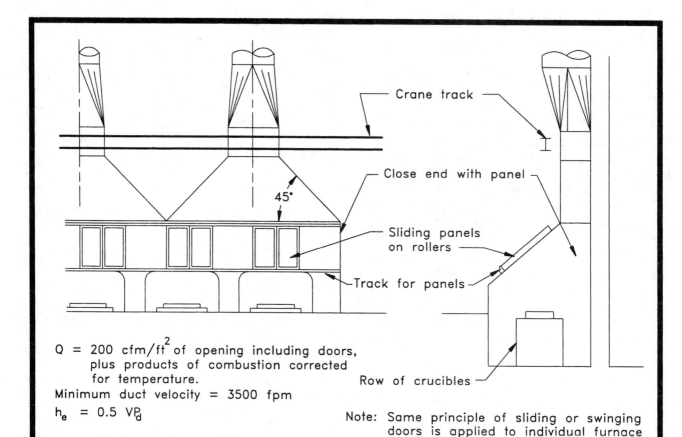

Q = 200 cfm/ft^2 of opening including doors,
    plus products of combustion corrected
    for temperature.
Minimum duct velocity = 3500 fpm
$h_e = 0.5 \ VP_d$

Note: Same principle of sliding or swinging
      doors is applied to individual furnace
      enclosures.

— Exhaust stack

— Fireproof drop panel from roof.

— Canopy to clear crane; or provide slot for crane bridge;
  or separate cranes inside and outside; or use
  manual crucible removal.

7' – 8'

Q = 200 cfm/ft^2 of total opening, minimum, plus
products of combustion corrected for temperature.

AMERICAN CONFERENCE OF GOVERNMENTAL INDUSTRIAL HYGIENISTS	*MELTING FURNACE CRUCIBLE, NON–TILT*
DATE *02–91*	FIGURE *VS–55–01*

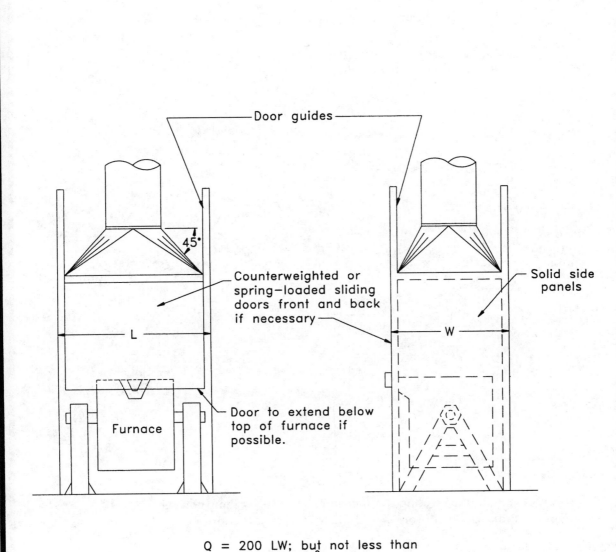

Door guides

45°

Counterweighted or
spring—loaded sliding
doors front and back
if necessary

Solid side
panels

L

W

Door to extend below
top of furnace if
possible.

Furnace

$Q = 200\ LW$; but not less than
200 cfm/ft^2 of all openings
with doors open. Correct for products
of combustion and temperature.
Minimum duct velocity = 3500 fpm
$h_e = 0.25\ VP_d$

AMERICAN CONFERENCE OF GOVERNMENTAL INDUSTRIAL HYGIENISTS	*MELTING FURNACE TILTING*	
	DATE *02—91*	FIGURE *VS—55—02*

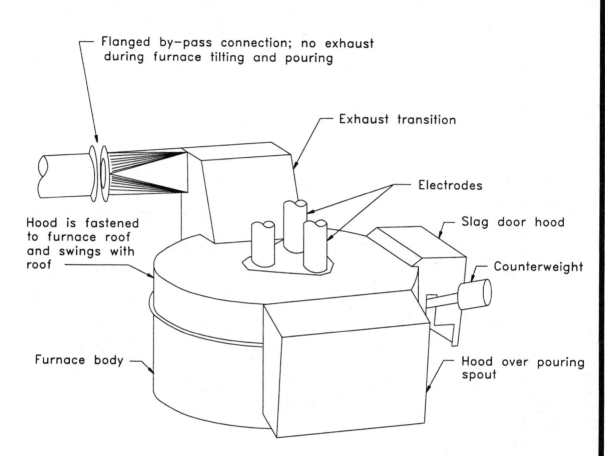

Flanged by-pass connection; no exhaust during furnace tilting and pouring

Exhaust transition

Electrodes

Hood is fastened to furnace roof and swings with roof

Slag door hood

Counterweight

Furnace body

Hood over pouring spout

Close Capture:

For Q, SP and operating temperature, consult manufacturer
Approximate exhaust rate = 2500 scfm/ton of charge

Alternate designs:

1. Some exhaust designs utilize direct furnace roof tap. For details consult manufacturer.

2. Canopy hoods require large exhaust and are not recommended Canopy hoods can be used as secondary hoods to capture fugitive emissions.

References 10.55.1, 10.55.2, 10.55.3

AMERICAN CONFERENCE OF GOVERNMENTAL INDUSTRIAL HYGIENISTS	*MELTING FURNACE ELECTRIC, TOP ELECTRODE*	
	DATE *02-91*	FIGURE *VS-55-03*

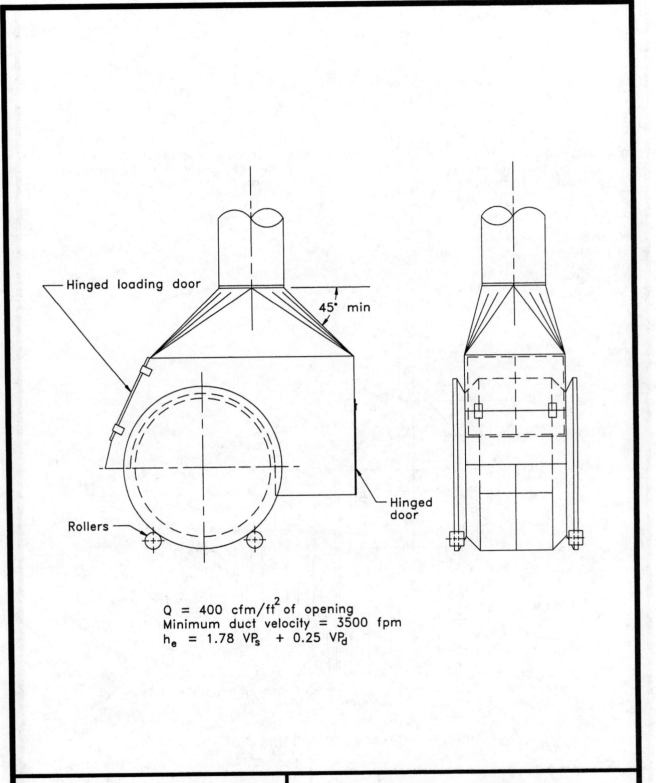

Hinged loading door

45° min

Rollers

Hinged
door

$Q = 400$ cfm/ft^2 of opening
Minimum duct velocity = 3500 fpm
$h_e = 1.78$ VP$_s$ + 0.25 VP$_d$

AMERICAN CONFERENCE OF GOVERNMENTAL INDUSTRIAL HYGIENISTS	MELTING FURNACE ELECTRIC ROCKING	
	DATE 02-91	FIGURE VS-55-04

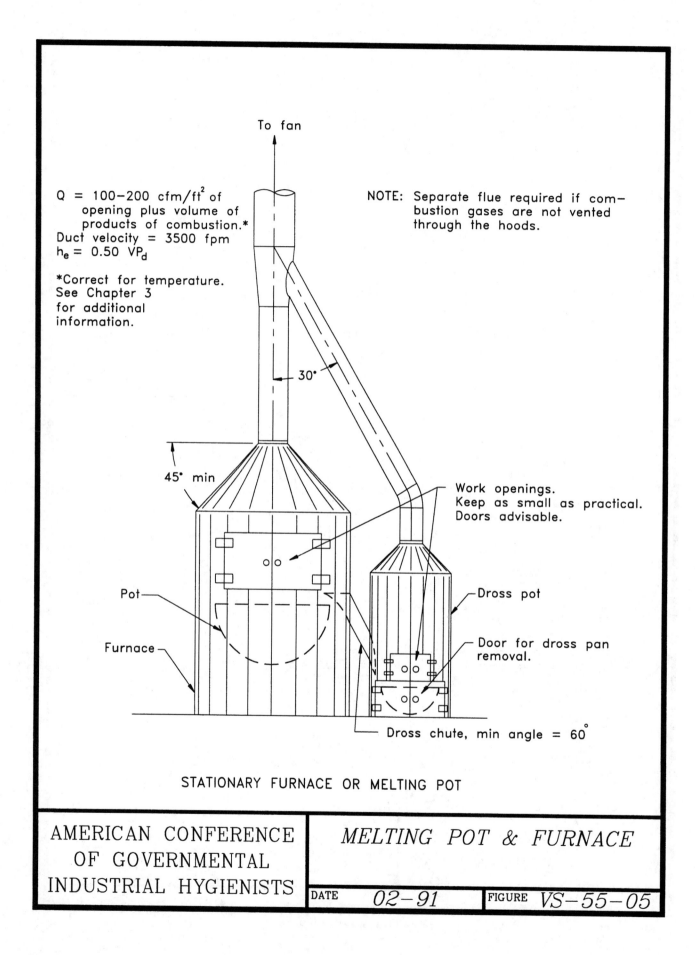

To fan

Q = 100–200 cfm/ft^2 of
    opening plus volume of
    products of combustion.*
Duct velocity = 3500 fpm
$h_e = 0.50 \ VP_d$

*Correct for temperature.
See Chapter 3
for additional
information.

NOTE: Separate flue required if combustion gases are not vented
through the hoods.

30°

45° min

Work openings.
Keep as small as practical.
Doors advisable.

Pot

Dross pot

Furnace

Door for dross pan
removal.

Dross chute, min angle = 60°

STATIONARY FURNACE OR MELTING POT

AMERICAN CONFERENCE
OF GOVERNMENTAL
INDUSTRIAL HYGIENISTS

MELTING POT & FURNACE

DATE   02–91

FIGURE   VS–55–05

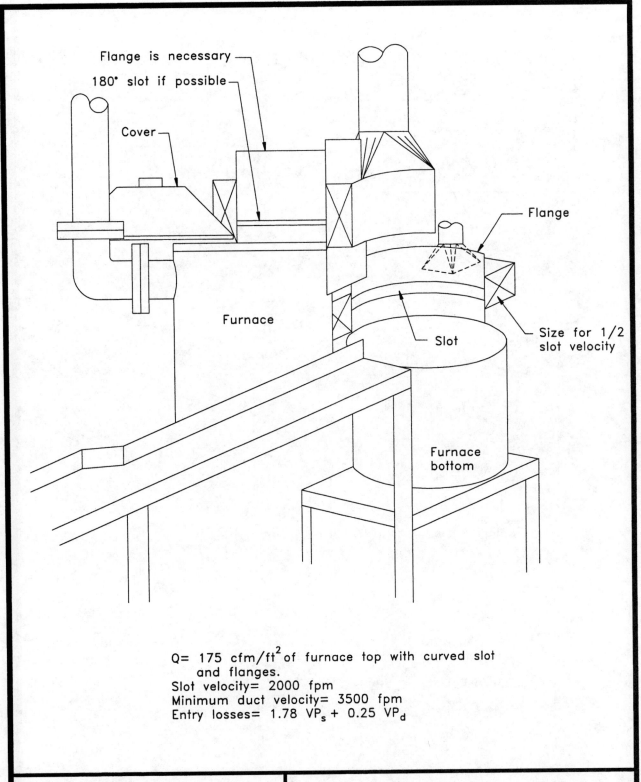

Flange is necessary

180° slot if possible

Cover

Flange

Furnace

Slot

Size for 1/2 slot velocity

Furnace bottom

$Q = 175$ cfm/ft^2 of furnace top with curved slot and flanges.
Slot velocity= 2000 fpm
Minimum duct velocity= 3500 fpm
Entry losses= 1.78 VP_s + 0.25 VP_d

AMERICAN CONFERENCE OF GOVERNMENTAL INDUSTRIAL HYGIENISTS	CRUCIBLE MELTING FURNACE HIGH TOXICITY MATERIAL
	DATE 02-91 FIGURE VS-55-06

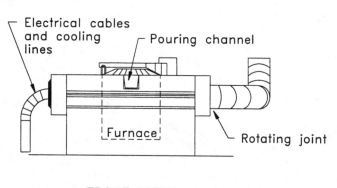

FRONT VIEW

SIDE VIEW

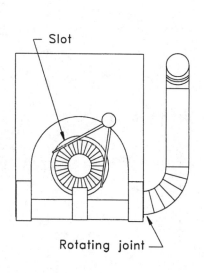

TOP VIEW

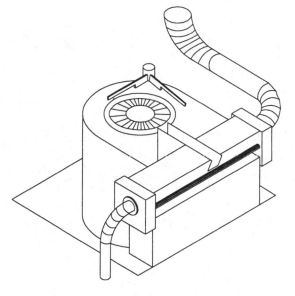

ISOMETRIC VIEW

$Q = 350$ cfm/ft.^{2} open area. Correct for temperature and combustion products.

Entry loss $= 1.78\ VP_s + 0.5\ VP_d$

Slot velocity $= 2000$ fpm

Minimum duct velocity $= 3500$ fpm

AMERICAN CONFERENCE OF GOVERNMENTAL INDUSTRIAL HYGIENISTS	INDUCTION MELTING FURNACE —TILTING	
	DATE *02—91*	FIGURE *VS—55—07*

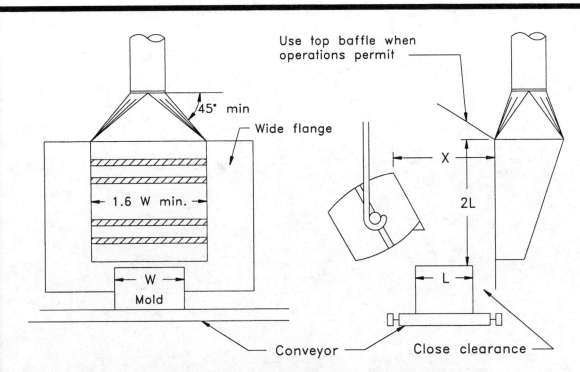

SMALL MOLDS

$Q = 200 (10 X^2 + A)$ where A equals hood area.
Minimum duct velocity = 3500 fpm
$h_e = 1.78 VP_s + 0.25 VP_d$
Use slots for uniform distribution, size slots
for 2000 fpm

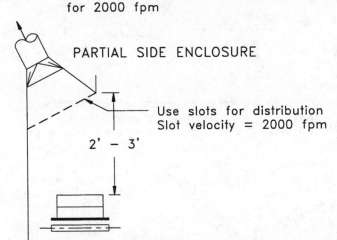

PARTIAL SIDE ENCLOSURE

Use slots for distribution
Slot velocity = 2000 fpm

Note:
For large molds and ladles
provide large – draft hood
similar to shakeout.
$Q = 400$ cfm/ft^2 working area.

$Q = 200 - 300$ cfm/ft of hood length.

AMERICAN CONFERENCE OF GOVERNMENTAL INDUSTRIAL HYGIENISTS	POURING STATION	
	DATE *02–91*	FIGURE *VS–55–10*

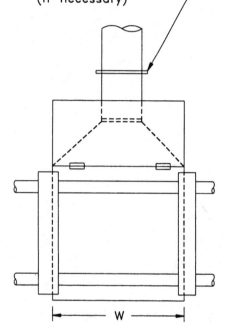

Flange type fitting for
easy removal of hood
(if necessary)

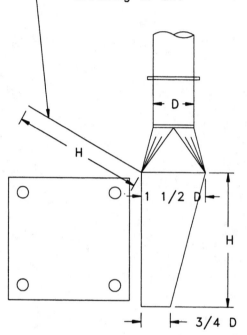

Hinged baffle for preventing short
circuiting of air.

Note: Place hood as close to machine as
possible. If more than 4 inches
from back of machine, hinged side
baffles should be used.

Note: Products of combustion
require separate flue or
may be vented into hood.

$$Q = 300WH$$
$$h_e = 0.25 \ VP_d$$
Minimum duct velocity = 2000 fpm.

AMERICAN CONFERENCE OF GOVERNMENTAL INDUSTRIAL HYGIENISTS	*FIXED POSITION DIE CASTING HOOD*	
	DATE *02-91*	FIGURE *VS-55-20*

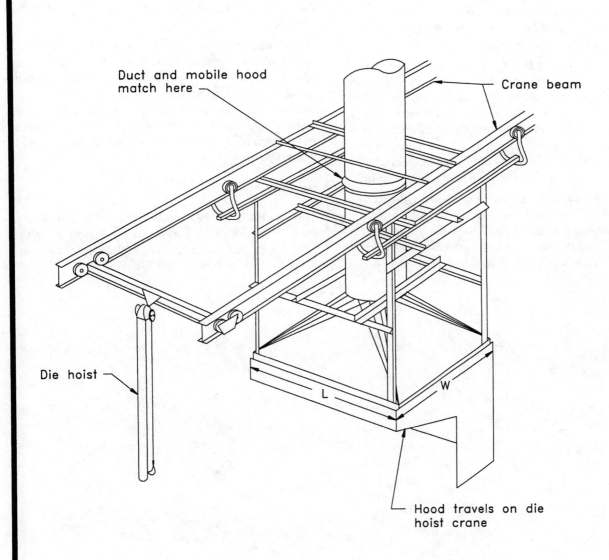

Duct and mobile hood match here

Crane beam

Die hoist

Hood travels on die hoist crane

Q = 300WL
Minimum duct velocity = 2000 fpm
h_e = 0.25 VP_d

AMERICAN CONFERENCE OF GOVERNMENTAL INDUSTRIAL HYGIENISTS	MOBILE HOOD DIE CASTING	
	DATE *02-91*	FIGURE *VS-55-21*

10.60 MIXING

Mixing operations combine a large variety of materials, usually without significant chemical reactions. This section includes categories of mixing operations.

10.60.1 Mixing and Mulling: Mixers and mullers require exhaust ventilation to provide a minimum velocity of 150 fpm through all openings. Additional ventilation may be required when flammable solvents are used. The dilution ventilation rates should maintain concentrations within the muller below 25% of the Lower Explosive Limit (LEL). Some codes or standards may require ventilation rates which ensure the concentration of flammable vapor is maintained below 20% of the LEL.

10.60.2 Roll Mixing: The machinery shown in this subsection is used to mix and blend quantitie of viscid materials, such as rubber and plastic, with additives that are dry powders or liquids. Emissions of gases and vapors may evolve due to chemical reactions or may be caused by the elevated temperature of the mixed materials. Particulate emissions can occur during additions as well as during mechanical blending.

The roller mill ventilation shown in VS-60-12 encloses the roller mill to the maximum extent possible except for a front opening of sufficient height and width to permit operator access and material entry/removal. An air curtain directed upward towards the top of the enclosure provides a barrier to contaminant escape but still permits operator access and material entry/removal. The design values provided are critical for proper operation.

REFERENCES

10.60.1   Hampl, V.; Johnston, O. E.; Murdock, D.M.: Application of an Air Curtain Exhaust System at a Milling Process. American Industrial Hygiene Association Journal, 49, 4, pp. 167-175 (1988).

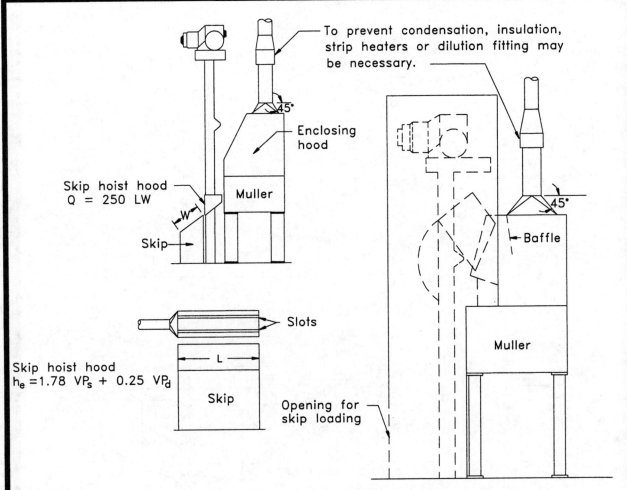

Skip hoist hood
Q = 250 LW

Skip hoist hood
$h_e = 1.78\ VP_s + 0.25\ VP_d$

To prevent condensation, insulation, strip heaters or dilution fitting may be necessary.

Enclosing hood

Muller

Slots

Skip

Baffle

Muller

Opening for skip loading

$Q = 150\ cfm/ft^2$ through all openings but not less than:

Muller diam. feet	Exhaust, cfm
4	750
6	900
7	1050
8	1200
10	1575

Minimum duct velocity = 4000 fpm
$h_e = 0.25\ VP_d$

Notes: 1. Other types of mixers: enclose as much as possible and provide 150 cfm/ft^2 of remaining openings
2. When flammable solvents are used in mixer, calculate minimum exhaust rate for dilution to 25% of the LEL. See Chapter 2
3. For air cooled mullers see VS-60-02

AMERICAN CONFERENCE OF GOVERNMENTAL INDUSTRIAL HYGIENISTS

MIXER AND MULLER HOOD

DATE *11-90*   FIGURE *VS-60-01*

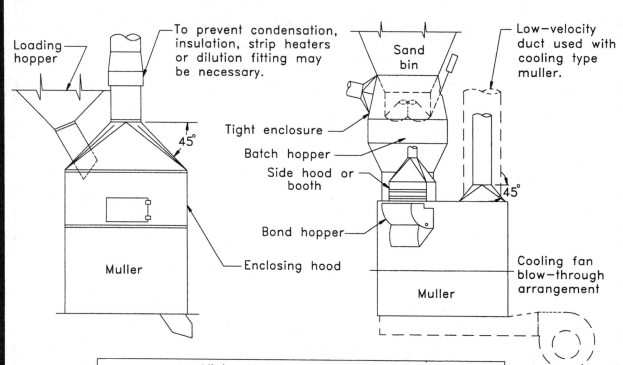

Minimum exhaust rate, cfm			
Location	Muller type		
	No cooling	Blow-though cooling	Draw-though cooling
Batch hopper	Note 1	600	Note 1
Bond hopper	600	600	600
Muller:	Note 2	Note 3	Note 3
4' diameter	750	”	”
6' diameter	900	”	”
7' diameter	1050	”	”
8' diameter	1200	”	”
10' diameter	1575	”	”

Minimum duct velocity = 4500 fpm
$h_e = 0.25 \, VP$

Notes:
1. Batch hopper requires separate exhaust with blow-through cooling. With other fan arrangement (muller under suction), separate exhaust may not be required. (If skip hoist is used, see VS-60-01)
2. Maintain 150 fpm velocity through all openings in muller hood. Exhaust flow rates shown are the minimum for control.
3. Cooling mullers do not require additional exhaust if maintained in dust tight condition. Blow-through fan must be off during loading. If muller is not dust tight, exhaust as in note 2 plus cooling air flow rate.
4. When flammable solvents are used in mixer, calculate minimum exhaust flow rate for dilution to 25% of the LEL. See Chapter 2.

AMERICAN CONFERENCE OF GOVERNMENTAL INDUSTRIAL HYGIENISTS	*AIR COOLED MIXER AND MULLER*	
	DATE *11-90*	FIGURE *VS-60-02*

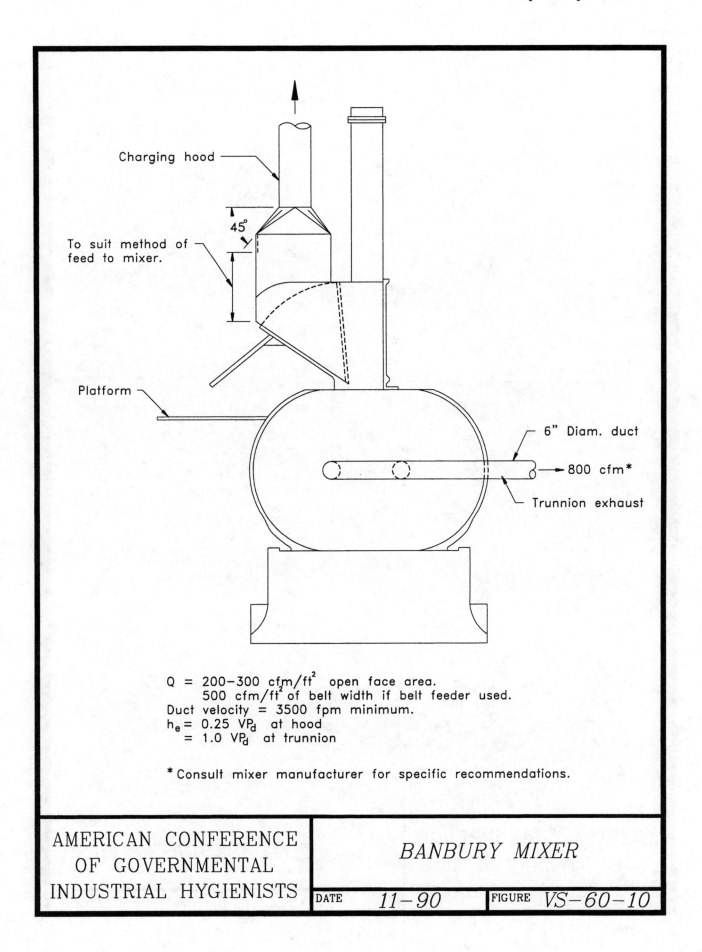

Charging hood

45°

To suit method of feed to mixer.

Platform

6" Diam. duct

→ 800 cfm*

Trunnion exhaust

Q = 200–300 cfm/ft² open face area.
    500 cfm/ft² of belt width if belt feeder used.
Duct velocity = 3500 fpm minimum.
h_e = 0.25 VP_d at hood
    = 1.0 VP_d at trunnion

*Consult mixer manufacturer for specific recommendations.

AMERICAN CONFERENCE OF GOVERNMENTAL INDUSTRIAL HYGIENISTS	*BANBURY MIXER*	
	DATE *11–90*	FIGURE *VS–60–10*

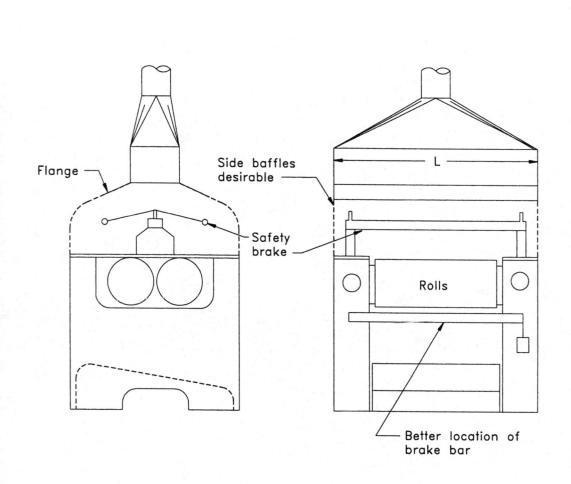

Flange

Side baffles
desirable

Safety
brake

Rolls

L

Better location of
brake bar

Q = 125 cfm/ft^2 open face area
Minimum duct velocity = 2000 fpm
$h_e = 0.25 \ VP_d$

NOTE: Both sides may be open

AMERICAN CONFERENCE OF GOVERNMENTAL INDUSTRIAL HYGIENISTS	*RUBBER CALENDER ROLLS*	
	DATE *11-90*	FIGURE *VS-60-11*

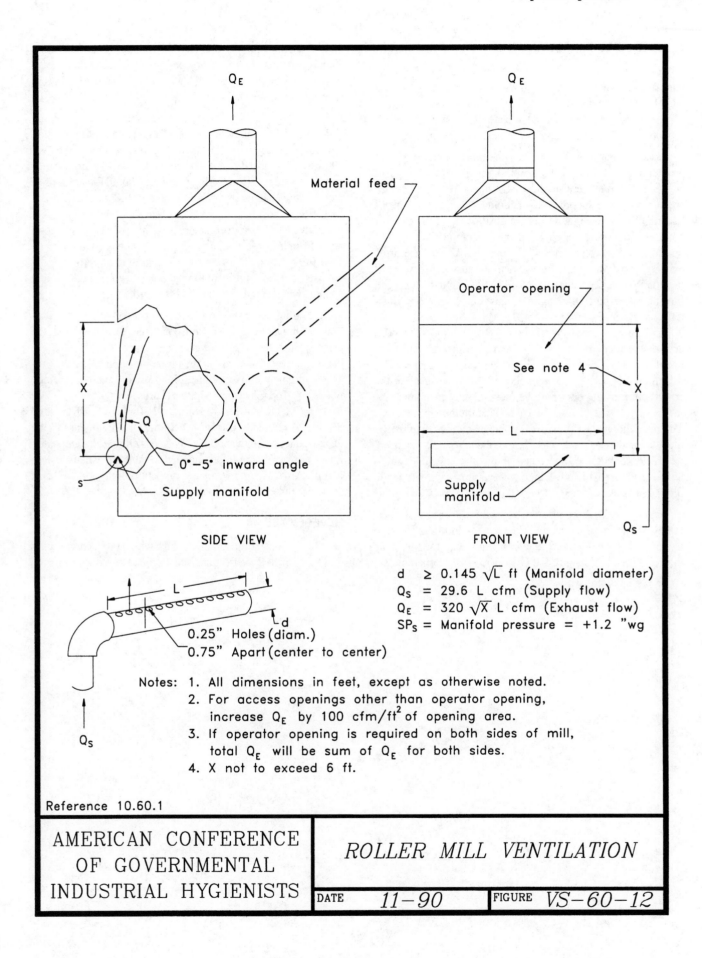

$d \geq 0.145 \sqrt{L}$ ft (Manifold diameter)
$Q_S = 29.6$ L cfm (Supply flow)
$Q_E = 320 \sqrt{X}$ L cfm (Exhaust flow)
$SP_S =$ Manifold pressure $= +1.2$ "wg

SIDE VIEW

FRONT VIEW

0.25" Holes (diam.)
0.75" Apart (center to center)

Notes: 1. All dimensions in feet, except as otherwise noted.
2. For access openings other than operator opening, increase Q_E by 100 cfm/ft^2 of opening area.
3. If operator opening is required on both sides of mill, total Q_E will be sum of Q_E for both sides.
4. X not to exceed 6 ft.

Reference 10.60.1

AMERICAN CONFERENCE
OF GOVERNMENTAL
INDUSTRIAL HYGIENISTS

ROLLER MILL VENTILATION

DATE   11-90

FIGURE   VS-60-12

10.65 MOVABLE EXHAUST HOODS

Movable exhaust hoods provide control for moving contaminant sources. In general, movable hoods are associated with flexible exhaust ducts, traveling exhaust hoods, swivel, slip or telescoping joints in duct sections, or systems which separate the hood from the duct for access to the process.

Flexible exhaust duct is possibly the most common way of providing a movable exhaust hood. A section of flexible duct connects to a relatively small exhaust hood. The duct section and hood may be supported by a counter-weighted or spring-loaded, hinged arm that allows the positioning of the exhaust hood near the source of contaminant generation. This type of device is known as "snorkel," "elephant trunk," or "flex-arm" exhaust. Illustrations of this type of exhaust in Chapter 10 include Welding Exhaust (VS-65-01) and Granite Cutting and Finishing (VS-65-02). Flexible exhaust duct use is also illustrated in Barrel Filling (VS-15-01), Metal Spraying (VS-90-30) and Service Garage Ventilation (VS-85-01 and VS-85-02) and low volume/high velocity systems (Section 10.40). Frictional resistance can be very high in the flexible duct section as can the negative pressure or suction. Materials used in the construction of the duct may be metal or non-metal and the losses vary over a wide range and depend on the type and use. The application data provided by the manufacturer must be included in the design development of the system. When used, flexible duct should be non-collapsible with minimal length to reduce undesirable bends which will result in excessive static pressure losses.

Traveling exhaust hoods may be used for a variety of operations where the contaminant source moves from one point to another. This type is more suited to heavy duty requirements than the flexible exhaust duct. Examples of these operations include flame and plasma cutting, foundry pouring, heavy abrasive cutting, and similar operations. An illustration of a traveling exhaust hood is the Hawley Trav-L-Vent (VS-65-03). (See reference 10.65.1.)

Telescoping or slip joints are duct sections that overlap, slide, or rotate to allow a section of one exhaust duct to slide into or rotate around another section of duct. This arrangement allows an exhaust hood to be moved from one position to another without disconnecting the duct or hood. Illustrations of the slip joint include the Core Grinder (VS-80-13) and Granite Cutting and Finishing (VS-65-02). This joint or duct section may include a swivel feature to permit rotation of the hood away from the process equipment being exhausted and may be used in the horizontal or vertical plane. Guide rails may be required for the horizontal application while pulleys and counter-weights may be required for vertical applications.

Separating exhaust duct sections is another method of providing a movable exhaust hood. This concept requires that the exhaust duct separate at or near the exhaust hood when the hood is moved for access to the process equipment or the process equipment moves. Illustrations of this method include hoods for Top Electrode Melting Furnace (VS-55-03), Core Making Machine—Small Roll-Over Type (VS-20-11) and Mobile Hood, Die Casting (VS-55-21). Alignment of the exhaust duct when the hood is in place is critical and any opening at this point should be included in the total exhaust calculations. Also, during the separation period, little or no exhaust control will be available at the contaminant source.

REFERENCES

10.65.1   Vulcan Engineering Co.: Hawley Trav-L-Vent Equipment Specifications and Layout, Helena, AL.

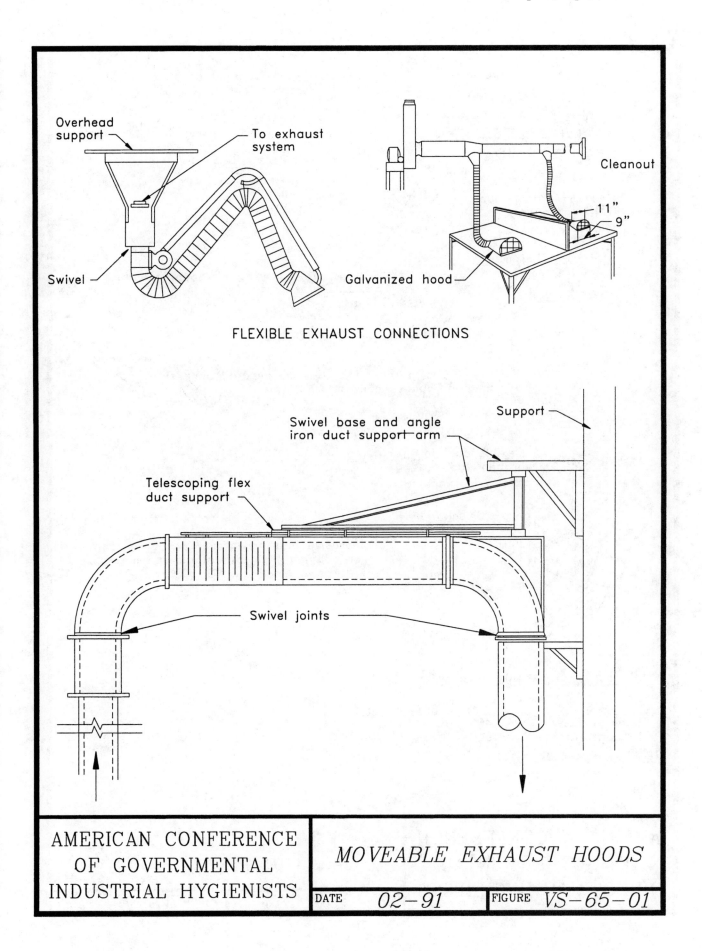

Overhead support

To exhaust system

Swivel

FLEXIBLE EXHAUST CONNECTIONS

Cleanout

11"

9"

Galvanized hood

Support

Swivel base and angle iron duct support arm

Telescoping flex duct support

Swivel joints

AMERICAN CONFERENCE OF GOVERNMENTAL INDUSTRIAL HYGIENISTS

MOVEABLE EXHAUST HOODS

DATE   *02-91*

FIGURE   *VS-65-01*

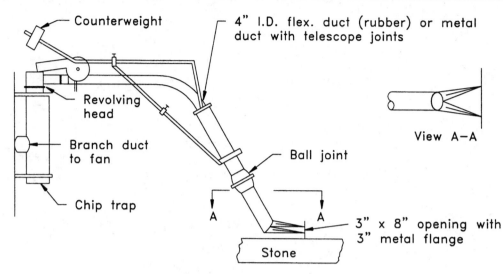

Counterweight

4" I.D. flex. duct (rubber) or metal duct with telescope joints

Revolving head

Branch duct to fan

Ball joint

View A–A

Chip trap

A   A

3" x 8" opening with 3" metal flange

Stone

PNEUMATIC HAND TOOLS

Q = 400 cfm minimum, tool 10" max distance from hood
Minimum duct velocity = 4000 fpm

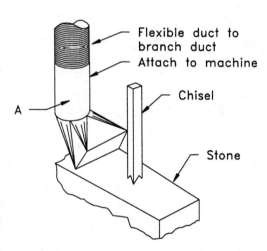

Flexible duct to branch duct

Attach to machine

Chisel

A

Stone

Abrasive blasting to be done in a room or cabinet; 500 fpm at all openings. See "Abrasive Blasting", VS–80–01

SURFACE MACHINE HOODS

Hood	cfm	Branch diam.
Baby surfacer	400	4"
Medium surfacer	600	5"

$h_e = 1.0\ VP_d$ (at point A)

AMERICAN CONFERENCE OF GOVERNMENTAL INDUSTRIAL HYGIENISTS	*GRANITE CUTTING AND FINISHING*	
	DATE *02–91*	FIGURE *VS–65–02*

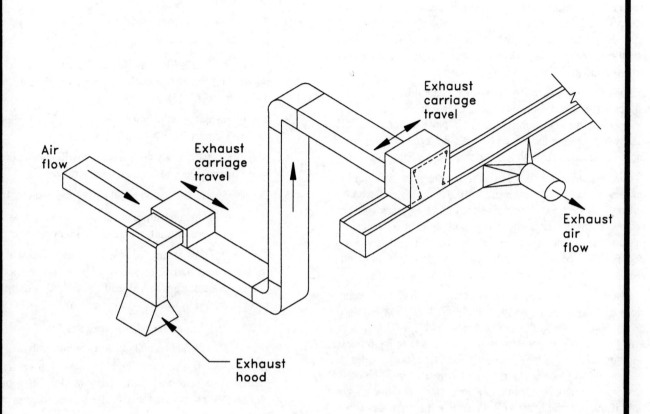

Typical Design Ranges

Q = 2500 — 10,000 cfm
V = 3500 — 4000 fpm
h_e = 6"wg approx. total
SP_h = calculate separately

Note: This is a patented system with many variations.
Consult manufacturer for applications.

See Reference 10.65.1

AMERICAN CONFERENCE OF GOVERNMENTAL INDUSTRIAL HYGIENISTS	*HAWLEY TRAV−L−VENT PERSPECTIVE LAYOUT*	
	DATE *02−91*	FIGURE *VS−65−03*

10.70 OPEN SURFACE TANKS

Ventilation rates for plating, cleaning, and other open surface tank operations will depend on a number of parameters which include materials, tank configuration and location, and type of ventilation system. This section describes four hood/ventilation types: enclosing and canopy hoods, lateral exhaust, and push-pull.

Enclosing hoods usually consist of a lateral hood with one end panel (two sides open) or panels at both tank ends (one side open). This hood configuration can provide increased efficiency by reducing the effects of cross-drafts and by directing more of the hood airflow over the tank open surface.

Canopy hoods may be open on four sides (free standing) or on three sides (such as against a wall). Control is achieved by airflow into the hood. It is, however, difficult in many cases to achieve sufficient control velocity without excessive airflow rates. Canopy hoods should not be used with highly toxic materials, in locations where high cross-drafts are unavoidable, or where the worker must bend over the tank.

Lateral exhaust consists of a slot hood which controls emissions by pulling air across the tank. A single slot may be used on one side of the tank where the tank width is 36 inches or less. For widths greater than 36 inches and where the process configuration will allow, two slot hoods on opposite sides of the tank or a slot hood along the tank centerline may be used. A single slot may be used up to a tank width of 48 inches but only if the material hazard class is low and if cross-drafts are not present.(See Section 10.70.1)

The airflow required will be that necessary to achieve a minimum control velocity determined by the hazard class of the material used for operation and the particular tank/ventilation system configuration. The procedure for determining the class and minimum control velocity for the three preceding hood types is provided in Tables 10.70.1 through 10.70.7 and the accompanying text. Exhaust flow for a canopy hood is determined from VS-99-03 and for a booth hood from Figure 3-11 where W is the total opening width. The exhaust flow for a lateral hood is determined from Table 10.70.4.

Air and/or mechanical agitation of the tank solution may be used as an aid to the plating or cleaning process. Mechanical agitation creates a rolling motion and usually will not affect tank emissions. However, air agitation creates a boiling-like condition and may significantly increase tank emissions, thus creating need for increased exhaust flow to provide effective control.

Push-pull ventilation consists of a push jet located on one side of a tank with a lateral exhaust hood on the other side.[10.70.1-10.70.3] Tank emissions are controlled by the jet formed over the tank surface. The jet captures the emissions and carries them into the hood. As the jet velocity, at all locations across the tank, is higher than the maximum control velocities specified for canopy, enclosing, or lateral exhaust hoods (Table 10.70.3), the push-pull exhaust flow is determined on the basis of that necessary to capture the jet flow and is independent of the hazard classification. Push-pull design criteria is provided in VS-70-10, -11 and -12.

10.70.1 Tank Design Considerations:

1. Duct velocity = any desired velocity (see Chapter 3).

2. Entry loss = 1.78 slot VP plus duct entry loss for slot hoods. For canopy or enclosure hoods, entry loss = duct entry loss.

3. Maximum slot hood plenum velocity = 1/2 slot velocity (see Chapter 3).

4. Slot velocity = 2,000 fpm unless distribution is provided by well-designed, tapered takeoff.

5. Provide ample area at the small end of the plenum.

6. If L = 6' or greater, multiple takeoffs are desirable. If L = 10' or greater, multiple takeoffs are necessary.

7. Tank width (W) means the effective width over which the hood must pull air to operate (e.g., where the hood face is set back from the edge of the tank, this setback must be added in measuring tank width).

    If W = 20", slot on one side is suitable.

    If W = 20 - 36", slots on both sides are desirable.

    If W = 36 - 48", use slots on both sides or along tank centerline or use push-pull. A single slot along one side should not be used unless all other conditions are optimum.

    If W = 48" or greater, local exhaust usually is not practical. Consider using push-pull.

    Enclosure can be used for any width tank if process will permit.

    It is not practicable to ventilate across the long dimension of a tank whose ratio W/L exceeds 2.0. It is undesirable to do so when W/L exceeds 1.0

8. Liquid level should be 6" to 8" below top of tank with parts immersed.

9. Lateral hood types A, C, D, and E (VS-70-01 and -02) are preferred. Plenum acts as baffle to room air currents.

10. Provide removable covers on tank if possible.

11. Provide duct with cleanouts, drains, and corrosion-resistant coating if necessary. Use flexible connection at fan inlet.

12. Install baffles to reduce cross-drafts. A baffle is a vertical plate the same length as the tank and with the top of the plate as high as the tank is wide. If the exhaust hood is on the side of the tank against a building wall or close to it, it is perfectly baffled.

13. Replacement air to the tank area must be supplied evenly and directed toward the tank from above or in front of the tank so that cross-drafts do not occur.

Flow Rate Calculation for Good Conditions: (No cross-crafts, adequate and well-distributed replacement air.)

1. Establish process class by determining hazard potential from Tables 10.70.1 and 10.70.2; information from Threshold Limit Values, Solvent Flash Point, Solvent Drying Time Tables in Appendices A and B and Tables 10.70.5 - 10.70.8.

2. Process class can also be established directly from Tables 10.70.5 - 10.70.8 if process parameters are known.

3. From Table 10.70.3, choose minimum control velocity according to hazard potential; evolution rate (process class); and hood design (see Table 10.70.5 for typical processes).

4. From Table 10.70.4, select the cfm/ft^2 for tank dimensions and tank location.

5. Multiply tank area by value obtained from Table 10.70.4 to calculate required air volume.

EXAMPLE

Given: Chrome Plating Tank 6' x 2.5'.

       High production decorative chrome.

       Free standing in room.

       No cross-drafts.

   a. Tank Hood. See VS-70-01. Use hood "A" long 6' side. Hood acts as baffle.

   b. Component—Chromic Acid.

      Hazard potential: A (from Table 10.70.1; from Appendix A: TLV = 0.05 mg/m^3; from Appendix A: Flash point = Negligible).

      Rate of Evolution: 1 from Table 10.70.2; from Table 10.70.6: Gassing rate = *high*)

Class: A-1

Control Velocity = 150 fpm (from Table 10.70.3)

Minimum Exhaust Rate = 225 cfm/ft^2 (from Table 10.70.4; Baffled tank, W/L = 0.42)

Minimum Exhaust Flow Rate = 225 × 15 = 3375 cfm

   c. Hood Design

Design slot velocity = 2000 fpm

Slot area = Q/V = 3375 cfm/2000 fpm = 1.69 ft^2

Slot Width = A/L = 1.69 ft2/6 ft = 0.281' = 3.375"

Plenum depth = (2)(slot width) = (2)(3.375) = 6.75"

Duct area = Q/V = 3375 cfm/2500 fpm = 1.35 ft^2.
      Use 16" duct, area = 1.396 ft2

Final duct velocity = Q/A = 337/1.396 = 2420 fpm

Hood SP = Entry loss + Acceleration

         = 1.78 VPs + 0.25 VPd + 1.0 VPd (see Chapter 3)

         = (1.78 × 0.25") + (0.25 × 0.37") + 0.37"

         = 0.45 + 0.09 + 0.37

Hood SP = 0.91"

REFERENCES

10.70.1 Huebener, D. J.; Hughes, R. T.: Development of Push-Pull Ventilation. American Industrial Hygiene Assoc. Journal, Vol. 46, pp. 262-267 (1985).

10.70.2 Hughes, R. T.: Design Criteria for Plating Tank Push-Pull Ventilation. Ventilation '85, Elsiever Press, Amsterdam (1986).

10.70.3 Sciola, V.: Private Communication, Hamilton Standard.

TABLE 10.70.1. Determination of Hazard Potential

HYGIENIC STANDARDS			
Hazard Potential	Gas and Vapor (see Appendix A)	Mist (see Appendix A)	Flash Point (see Appendix A)
A	0-10 ppm	0-0.1 mg/m^3	—
B	11-100 ppm	0.11-1.0 mg/m^3	Under 100 F
C	101-500 ppm	1.1-10 mg/m^3	100-200 F
D	Over 500 ppm	Over 10 mg/m^3	Over 200 F

TABLE 10.70.2. Determination of Rate of Gas, Vapor, or Mist Evolution

Rate	Liquid Temperature (F)	Degrees Below Boiling Point (F)	Relative Evaporation* (Time for 100% Evaporation	Gassing*
1	Over 200	0-20	Fast (0-3 hours)	High
2	150-200	21-50	Medium (3-12 hours)	Medium
3	94-149	51-100	Slow (12-50 hours)	Low
4	Under 94	Over 100	Nil (Over 50 hours)	Nil

*Dry time relation (see Appendix B), Below 5—Fast; 5-15—Medium; 15-75—Slow; 70-over—Nil.

**Rate of gassing depends on rate of chemical or electrochemical action and therefore depends on the material treated and the solution used in the tank and tends to increase with 1. amount of work in the tank at any one time, 2. strength of the solution in the tank, 3. temperature of the solution in the tank, and 4. current density applied to the work in electrochemical tanks.

TABLE 10.70.3 Minimum Control Velocity (FPM) for Undisturbed Locations

Class (see Tables 10.70.1 and 10.70.2)	Enclosing Hood		Lateral Exhaust (see VA-70-01 and 70-02) (Note 1)	Canopy Hoods (see Figures 3-6 and VS-90-03)	
	One Open Side	Two Open Sides		Three Open Sides	Four Open Sides
A-1 and A-2 (Note 2)	100	150	150	Do not use	Do not use
A-3 (Note 2), B-1, B-2, and C-1	75	100	100	125	175
B-3, C-2, and D-1 (Note 3)	65	90	75	100	150
A-4 (Note 1), C-3, and D-2 (Note 3)	50	75	50	75	125
B-4, C-4, D-3 (Note 3), and D-4—Adequate General Room Ventilation Required (see Chapter 2)					

Notes: 1. Use aspect ratio to determine air volume; see Table 10.70.4.
2. Do not use canopy hood for Hazard Potential A processes.
3. Where complete control of hot water is desired, design as next highest class.

TABLE 10.70.4 Minimum Rate, cfm/ft^2 of Tank Area for Lateral Exhaust

Required Minimum Control Velocity, fpm (from Table 10.70.3)	cfm/ft^2 to maintain required minimum control velocities at following $\dfrac{\text{tank width}}{\text{tank length}}\left(\dfrac{W}{L}\right)$ ratios				
	0.0-0.09	0.1-0.24	0.25-0.49	0.50-0.99	1.0-2.0 (Note 2)
Hood against wall or flanged (see Note 1 below and Section 10.70.1. Note 12). See VS-70-01 A and VS-70-02 D and E.					
50	50	60	75	90	100
75	75	90	110	130	150
100	100	125	150	175	200
150	150	190	225	[250] Note 3	[250] Note 3
Hood on free standing tank (see Note 1). See VS-70-01 B and VS-70-02 F.					
50	75	90	100	110	125
75	110	130	150	170	190
100	150	175	200	225	250
150	225	[250] Note 3	[250] Note 3	[250] Note 3	[250] Note 3

Note 1. Use W/2 as tank width in computing W/L ratio for hood along centerline or two parallel sides of tank. See VS-70-01 B and C and VS-70-02 F.
2. See Section 10.70.1, Notes 6 and 7.
3. While bracketed values may not produce 150 fpm control velocity at all aspect ratios, the 250 cfm/ft2 is considered adequate for control.

TABLE 10.70.5 Typical Processes Minimum Control Velocity (fpm) for Undisturbed Locations

Operation	Contaminant	Hazard	Contaminant Evolution	Lateral Exhaust Control Velocity (See VS-70-01 & VS-70-02)	Collector Recommended
Anodizing Aluminum	Chromic-Sulfuric Acids	A	1	150	X
Aluminum Bright Dip	Nitric + Sulfuric Acids	A	1	150	X
	Nitric & Phosphoric Acids	A	1	150	X
Plating–Chromium	Chromic Acid	A	1	150	X
Copper Strike	Cyanide Mist	C	2	75	X
Metal Cleaning (Boiling)	Alkaline Mist	C	1	100	X
Hot Water (if vent desired)					
Not boiling	Water Vapor	D	2	50*	
Boiling		D	1	75*	
Stripping–Copper	Alkaline-Cyanide Mists	C	2	75	X
Nickel	Nitrogen Oxide Gases	A	1	150	X
Pickling–Steel	Hydrochloric Acid	A	2	150	X
	Sulfuric Acid	B	1	100	X
Salt Solution					
Bonderizing & Parkerizing	Water Vapor	D	2	50*	
Not Boiling	Water Vapor	D	2	50*	
Boiling		D	1	75*	
Salt Baths (Molten)	Alkaline Mist	C	1	100	X

*Where complete control of water vapor is desired, design as next highest class.

TABLE 10.70.6. Airborne Contaminants Released by Metallic Surfaced Treatment, Etching, Pickling, Acid Dipping and Metal Cleaning Operations

Process	Type	Notes	Component of Bath Which May Be Released to Atmosphere(13)	Physical and Chemical Nature of Major Atmospheric Contaminant	Class (12)	Usual Temp. Range, F
Surface Treatment	Anodizing Aluminum		Chromic-Sulfuric Acids	Chromic Acid Mist	A-1	95
	Anodizing Aluminum		Sulfuric Acid	Sulfuric Acid Mist	B-1	60-80
	Black Magic	1	Conc. Sol. Alkaline Oxi-	Alkaline Mist, Steam	C-1	260-350
	Bonderizing		Boiling Water	Steam	D-2,1(14,15)	140-212
	Chemical Coloring		None	None	D-4	70-90
	Descaling	2	Nitric-Sulfuric, Hydrofluoric Acids	Acid Mist, Hydrogen Fluoide Gas, Steam	B-2,1(15)	70-150
	Ebonol		Conc. Sol. Alkaline Oxidizing Agents	Alkaline Mist, Steam	C-1	260-350
	Galvanic-Anodize	3	Ammonium Hydroxide	Ammonia Gas, Steam	B-3	140
	Hard-Coating Aluminum		Chromic-Sulfuric Acid	Chromic Acid Mist	A-1	120-180
	Hard-Coating Aluminum		Sulfuric Acid	Sulfuric Acid Mist	B-1	120-180
	Jetal		Conc. Sol. Alkaline Oxidizing Agents	Alkaline Mist, Steam	C-1	260-350
	Magcote	4	Sodium Hydroxide	Alkaline Mist, Steam	C-3,2(15)	105-212
	Magnesium Pre-Dye Dip		Ammonium Hydroxide-Ammonium Acetate	Ammonia Gas, Steam	B-3	90-180
	Parkerizing	1	Boiling Water	Steam	D-2,1(14,15)	140-213
	Zincete Immersion	5	None	None	D-4	70-90
Etching	Aluminum		Sodium Hydroxide-Soda Ash-Trisodium Phosphate	Alkaline Mist, Steam	C-1	160-180
	Copper	6	Hydrochloric Acid	Hydrogen Chloride Gas	A-2	79-90
	Copper	7	None	None	D-4	70
Pickling	Aluminum		Nitric Acid	Nitrogen Oxide Gases	A-2	70-90
	Aluminum		Chromic, Sulfuric Acids	Acid Mists	A-3	140
	Aluminum		Sodium Hydroxide	Alkaline Mist	C-1	140
	Cast Iron		Hydrofluoric-Nitric Acids	Hydrogen Fluoride-Nitrogen Oxide Gases	A-2,1(15)	70-90
	Copper		Sulfuric Acid	Acid Mist, Steam	B-3,2(15)	125-175
	Copper	8	None	None	D-4	70-175
	Duralumin		Sodium Fluoride, Sulfuric Acid	Hydrogen Fluoride Gas, Sulfuric Acid	A-3	70
	Inconel		Nitric, Hydrofluoric Acids	Nitrogen Oxide, HF Gases, Steam	A-1	150-165
	Inconel		Sulfuric Acid	Sulfuric Acid Mist, Steam	B-2	160-180
	Iron and Steel		Hydrochloric Acid	Hydrogen Chloride Gas	A-2	70
	Iron and Steel		Sulfuric Acid	Sulfuric Acid Mist, Steam	B-1	70-175
	Magnesium		Chromic-Sulfuric, Nitric Acids	Nitrogen Oxide Gases, Acid Mist, Steam	A-2	70-160
	Monel and Nickel		Hydrochloric Acid	Hydrogen Chloride Gas, Steam	A-2	180
	Monel and Nickel		Sulfuric Acid	Sulfuric Acid Mist, Steam	B-1	160-190
	Nickel Silver		Sulfuric Acid	Acid Mist, Steam	B-3,2(15)	70-140
	Silver		Sodium Cyanide	Cyanide Mist, Steam	C-3	70-210
	Stainless Steel	9	Nitric, Hydrofluoric Acid	Nitrogen Oxide, Hydrogen Fluoride Gases	A-2	125-180
	Stainless Steel	9,10	Hydrochloric Acid	Hydrogen Chloride Gas	A-2	130-140
	Stainless Steel	9,10	Sulfuric Acid	Sulfuric Acid Mist, Steam	B-1	180
	Stainless Steel Immunization		Nitric Acid	Nitrogen Oxide Gases	A-2	70-120
	Stainless Steel Passivation		Nitric Acid	Nitrogen Oxide Gases	A-2	70-120

TABLE 10.70.6. Airborne Contaminants Released by Metallic Surfaced Treatment, Etching, Pickling, Acid Dipping and Metal Cleaning Operations (Con't.)

Process	Type	Notes	Component of Bath Which May Be Released to Atmosphere(13)	Physical and Chemical Nature of Major Atmospheric Contaminant	Class (12)	Usual Temp. Range, F
Acid Dipping	Aluminum Bright Dip		Phosphoric, Nitric Acids	Nitrogen Oxide Gases	A-1	200
	Aluminum Bright Dip		Nitric, Sulfuric Acids	Nitrogen Oxide Gases, Acid Mist	A-2,1(15)	70-90
	Cadmium Bright Dip		None	None	D-4	70
	Copper Bright Dip		Nitric, Sulfuric Acids	Nitrogen Oxide Gases, Acid Mist	A-2,1(15)	70-90
	Copper Semi-Bright Dip		Sulfuric Acid	Acid Mist	B-2	70
	Copper Alloys Bright Dip		Nitric, Sulfuric Acids	Nitrogen Oxide Gases, Acid Mist	A-2,1(15)	70-90
	Copper Matte Dip		Nitric, Sulfuric Acids	Nitrogen Oxide Gases, Acid Mist	A-2,1(15)	70-90
	Magnesium Dip		Chromic Acid	Acid Mist, Steam	A-2	190-212
	Magnesium Dip		Nitric, Sulfuric Acids	Nitrogen Oxide Gases, Acid Mist	A-2,1(15)	70-90
	Monel Dip		Nitric, Sulfuric Acids	Nitrogen Oxide Gases, Acid Mist	A-2,1(15)	70-90
	Nickel and Nickel Alloys Dip		Nitric, Sulfuric Acids	Nitrogen Oxide Gases, Acid Mist	A-2,1(15)	70-90
	Silver Dip		Nitric Acid	Nitrogen Oxide Gases	A-1	70-90
	Silver Dip		Sulfuric Acid	Sulfuric Acid Mist	B-2	70-90
	Zinc and Zinc Alloys Dip		Chromic, Hydrochloric	Hydrogen Chloride Gas (If HCl attacks Zn)	A-4,3(15)	70-90
Metal Cleaning	Alkaline Cleaning	11	Alkaline Sodium Salts	Alkaline Mist, Steam	C-2,1(15)	160-210
	Degreasing		Trichloroethylene-Perchlorethylene	Trichlorethylene-Perchlorethylene Vapors	B(16)	188-250
	Emulsion Cleaning		Petroleum-Coal Tar Solvents	Petroleum-Coal Tar Vapors	B-3,2(15)	70-140
					(17)	70-140
	Emulsion Cleanign		Chlorinated Hydrocarbons	Chlorinated Hydrocarbon Vapors	(17)	70-140

Notes:
1 Also Aluminum Seal, Magnesium Seal, Magnesium Dye Set, Dyeing Anodized Magnesium, Magnesium Alkaline Dichromate Soak, Coloring Anodized Aluminum.
2 Stainless Steel before Electropolishing.
3 On Magnesium.
4 Also Manodyz, Dow-12.
5 On Aluminum.
6 Dull Finish.
7 Ferric Chloride Bath.
8 Sodium Dichromate, Sulfuric Acid Bath and Ferrous Sulfate, Sulfuric Acid Bath.
9 Scale Removal.
10 Scale Loosening.
11 Soak and Electrocleaning.
12 Class as described in Chapter 2 for use in Table 10.5-3 based on hazard potential (Table 10.5-1) and rate of evolution (Table 10.5-2) for usual operating conditions. Higher temperatures, agitation or other conditions may result in a higher rate of evolution.
13 Hydrogen gas also released by many of these operations.
14 Rate where essentially complete control of steam is required. Otherwise, adequate dilution ventilation may be sufficient.
15 The higher rate is associated with the higher value in the temperature range
16 For vapor degreasers, rate is determined by operating procedure. See VS-501.
17 Class of operation is determined by nature of the hydrocarbon. Refer to Appendix A.

10.70.7. Airborne Contaminants Released by Electropolishing, Electroplating and Electroless Plating Operations

Process	Type	Notes	Component of Bath Which May Be Released to Atmosphere (19)	Physical and Chemical Nature of Major Atmospheric Contaminant	Class (18)	Usual Temp. Range, F
Electropolishing	Aluminum	1	Sulfuric, Hydrofluoric Acids	Acid Mist, Hydrogen Flouride Gas, Steam	A-2	140-200
	Brass, Bronze	1	Phosphoric Acid	Acid Mist	B-3	68
	Copper	1	Phosphoric Acid	Acid Mist	B-3	68
	Iron	1	Sulfuric, Hydrochloric, Perchloric Acids	Acid Mist, Hydrogen Chloride Gas, Steam	A-2	68-175
	Monel	1	Sulfuric Acid	Acid Mist, Steam	B-2	86-160
	Nickel	1	Sulfuric Acid	Acid Mist, Steam	B-2	86-160
	Stainless Steel	1	Sulfuric, Hydrofluoric, Chromic Acids	Acid Mist, Hydrogen Fluoride Gas, Steam	A-2,1 (20)	70-300
	Steel	1	Sulfuric, Hydrochloric, Perchloric Acids	Acid Mist, Hydrogen Gas, Steam	A-2	68-175
Strike Solutions	Copper		Cyanide Salts	Cyanide Mist	C-2	70-90
	Silver		Cyanide Salts	Cyanide Mists	C-2	70-90
	Wood's Nickel		Nickel Chloride, Hydrochloric Acid	Hydrogen Chloride Gas, Chloride Mist	A-2	70-90
Electroless Plating	Copper	2	Formaldehyde	Formaldehyde Gas	A-1	75
	Nickel	2	Ammonium Hydroxide	Ammonia Gas	B-1	190
Electroplating Alkaline	Platinum		Ammonium Phosphate, Ammonia Gas	Ammonia Gas	B-2	158-203
	Tin		Sodium Stannate	Tin Salt Mist, Steam	C-3	140-170
	Zinc	3	None	None	D-4	170-180
Electroplating Fluoborate	Cadmium		Fluoborate Salts	Fluoborate Mist, Steam	C-3,2 (20)	70-170
	Copper		Copper Fluoborate	Fluoborate Mist, Steam	C-3,2 (20)	70-170
	Indium		Fluoborate Salts	Fluoborate Mist, Steam	C-3,2 (20)	70-170
	Lead		Lead Fluoborate-Fluoboric Acid	Fluoborate Mist, Hydrogen Fluoride Gas	A-3	70-90
	Lead-Tin Alloy		Lead Fluoborate-Fluoboric Acid	Fluoborate Mist	C-3,2 (20)	70-100
	Nickel		Nickel Fluoborate	Fluoborate Mist	C-3,2 (20)	100-170
	Tin		Stannous Fluoborate, Fluoboric Acid	Fluoborate Mist	C-3,2 (20)	70-100
	Zinc		Fluoborate Salts	Fluoborate Mist, Steam	C-3,2 (20)	70-170
Electroplating Cyanide	Brass, Bronze	4,5	Cyanide Salts, Ammonium Hydroxide	Cyanide Mist, Ammonia Gas	B-4,3 (20)	60-100
	Bright Zinc	5	Cyanide Salts, Sodium Hydroxide	Cyanide, Alkaline Mists	C-3	70-120
	Cadmium	5	None	None	D-4	70-100
	Copper	5,6	None	None	D-4	70-160
	Copper	5,7	Cyanide Salts, Sodium Hydroxide	Cyanide, Alkaline Mists, Steam	C-2	110-160
	Indium	5	Cyanide Salts, Sodium Hydroxide	Cyanide, Alkaline Mists	C-3	70-120
	Silver	5	None	None	D-4	72-120
	Tin-Zinc Alloy	5	Cyanide Salts, Potassium Hydroxide	Cyanide, Alkaline Mists, Steam	C-3,2 (20)	120-140
	White Alloy	5,8	Cyanide Salts, Sodium Stannate	Cyanide, Alkaline Mists	C-3	120-150
	Zinc	5,9	Cyanide Salts, Sodium Hydroxide	Cyanide, Alkaline Mists	C-3,2 (7)	70-120

10.70.7. Airborne Contaminants Released by Electropolishing, Electroplating and Electroless Plating Operations

Process	Type	Notes	Component of Bath Which May Be Released to Atmosphere (19)	Physical and Chemical Nature of Major Atmospheric Contaminant	Class (18)	Usual Temp. Range, F
Electroplating Acid	Chromium		Chromic Acid	Chromic Acid Mists	A-1	90-140
	Copper	10	Copper Sulfate, Sulfuric Acid	Sulfuric Acid Mist	B-4,3 (20,21)	75-120
	Indium	12	None	None	D-4	70-120
	Indium	13,14	Sulfamic Acid, Sulfamate Salts	Sulfamate Mist	C-3	70-90
	Iron		Chloride Salts, Hydrochloric Acid	Hydrochloric Acid Mist, Steam	A-2	190-210
	Iron	12	None	None	D-4	70-120
	Nickel	3	Ammonium Fluoride, Hydrofluoric Acid	Hydrofluoric Acid Mist	A-3	102
	Nickel and Black Nickel	12,15	None	None	C-4 (22)	70-150
	Nickel	9,12	Nickel Sulfate	Nickel Sulfate Mist	B-2	70-90
	Nickel	13,14	Nickel Sulfamate	Sulfamate Mist	C-3	75-160
	Palladium	15	None	None	D-4	70-120
	Rhodium	12,17	None	None	D-4	70-120
	Tin		Tin Halide	Halide Mist	C-2	70-90
	Tin	12	None	None	D-4	70-120
	Zinc		Zinc Chloride	Zinc Chloride Mist	B-3	75-120
	Zinc	12	None	None	D-4	70-120

Notes:

1   Arsine may be produced due to the presence of arsenic in the metal or polishing bath.
2   Alkaline Bath
3   On Magnesium
4   Also Copper-Cadmium Bronze
5   HCN gas may be evolved due to the acidic action of CO2 in the air at the surface of the bath
6   Conventional Cyanide Bath
7   Except Conventional Cyanide Bath
8   Albaloy, Spekwhite, Bonwhite (Alloys of Copper, Tin, Zinc)
9   Using Insoluble Anodes
10 Over 90 F
11 Mild Organic Acid Bath
12 Sulfate Bath
13 Sulfamate Bath
14 Air Agitated
15 Chloride Bath
16 Nitrite Bath
17 Phosphate Bath
18 Class as described in Chapter 2 for use in Table 10.70.3 based on hazard potential (Table 10.70.1) and rate of evolution (Table 10.70.2) for usual operating conditions. Higher temperatures, agitation, high current density or other conditions may result in a higher rate of evolution.
19 Hydrogen gas also released by many of these operations.
20 The higher rate is associated with the higher value in the temperature range.
21 Baths operated at a temperature of over 140 F with a current density of over 45 amps/ft2 and with air agitation will have a higher rate of evolution.
22 Local exhaust ventilation may be desired to control steam and water vapor.

TABLE 10.70-8. Airborne Contaminants Released by Stripping Operations

Coating to be Stripped	Base Metal (Footnote)		Component of Batch Which May be Released to Atmosphere (1)	Physical and Chemical Nature of Major Atmospheric Contaminant	Class (e)		Usual Temp Range F
Anodized Coatings	1,7		Chromic Acid	Acid Mist, Steam	A-2		120-200
Black Oxide Coatings	14		Hydrochloric Acid	Hydrogen Chloride Gas	A-3,2	(g)	70-125
Brass and Bronze	8,14	(a)	Sodium Hydroxide, Sodium Cyanide	Alkaline, Cyanide Mists	C-3,2	(g)	70-90
Cadmium	8,14	(a)	Sodium Hydroxide, Sodium Cyanide	Alkaline, Cyanide Mists	C-3,2	(g)	70-90
	2,4,14		Hydrochloric Acid	Acid Mist, Hydrogen Chloride Gas	A-3,2	(g)	70-90
Chromium	7,8,14	(a)	Sodium Hydroxide	Alkaline Mist, Steam	C-3		70-150
	2,4,8,14		Hydrochloric Acid	Hydrogen Chloride Gas	A-2		70-125
	2,4,8,18	(a)	Sulfuric Acid	Acid Mist	B-2		70-90
Copper	8,14		odium Hydroxide, Sodium Cyanide	Alkaline, Cyanide Mists	C-3,2	(g)	70-90
	7,12,14	(b)	None	None	D-4		70-90
	14	(a)	Alkaline Cyanide	Cyanide Mist	C-3,2	(g)	70-160
	1		Nitric Acid	Nitrogen Oxide Gases	A-1		70-120
	18	(a)	Sodium Hydroxide-Sodium Sulfide	Alkaline Mist, Steam	C-2		185-195
Gold	4,5,6,8,9,14	(a)	Sodium Hydroxide, Sodium Cyanide	Alkaline, Cyanide Mists	C-3,2	(g)	70-90
	4,5,18	(a)	Sulfuric Acid	Acid Mist	B-3,2	(g)	70-100
Lead	13	(c)	Acetic Acid, Hydrogen Peroxide	Oxygen Mist	D-3		70-90
	14	(a),(c)	Sodium Hydroxide	Alakaline Mist, Steam	C-3,2	(g)	70-140
Nickel	2,4		Sulfuric, Nitric Acids	Nitrogen Oxide Gases	A-2,1	(g)	70-90
	2,4	(a)	Hydrochloric Acid	Hydrogen Chloride Gas	A-3		70-90
	2,4,14	(a)	Sulfuric Acid	Acid Mist	B-3		70-90
	7		Hydrofluoric Acid	Hydrogen Fluoride Gas	A-3,2	(g)	70-90
	14		Fuming Nitric Acid	Nitrogen Oxide Gases	A-1		70-90
		(a),(d)	Hot Water	Steam	D-2	(h)	200
	1,18,19	(a)	Sulfuric Acid	Acid Mist, Steam	B-3,2	(g)	70-150
Phosphate Coatings	15		Chromic Acid	Acid Mist, Steam	A-3		165
	16		Ammonium Hydroxide	Ammonia Gas	B-3,2	(g)	70-90
Rhodium	10		Sulfuric, Hydrochloric Acids	Acid Mist, Hydrogen Chloride Gas	A-3,2	(g)	70-100
Silver	1		Nitric Acid	Nitrogen Oxide Gases	A-1		70-90
	2,11		Sulfuric, Nitric Acids	Nitrogen Oxide Gases, Steam	A-1		180
	8,14	(a)	Sodium Hydroxide, Sodium Cyanide	Alkaline, Cyanide Mists	C-3		70-90
	17	(a)	Sodium Cyanide	Cyanide Mist	C-3		70-90
Tin	2,3,4		Ferric Chloride, Copper Sulfate Acetic Acid	Acid Mist	B-4,3	(g)	70-90
		(a)	Sodium Hydroxide	Alkaline Mist	C-3		70-90
	2,14,14		Hydrochloric Acid	Hydrogen Chloride Gas	A-3,2	(g)	70-90
	14	(a)	Sodium Hydroxide	Alkaline Mist, Steam	C-2		70-200

TABLE 10.70-8. Airborne Contaminants Released by Stripping Operations (Con't)

Coating to be Stripped	Base Metal (Footnote)	Component of Batch Which May be Released to Atmosphere (1)	Physical and Chemical Nature of Major Atmospheric Contaminant	Class (e)	Usual Temp Range F
Zinc	1	Nitric Acid	Nitrogen Oxide Gases	A-1	70-90
	8,14	Sodium Hydroxide, Sodium	Alkaline, Cyanide Mists	C-3	70-90

Base Metal:

1. Aluminum
2. Brass
3. Bronze
4. Copper
5. Copper Alloys
6. Ferrous Metals
7. Magnesium

8. Nickel
9. Nickel Alloys
10. Nickel Plated Brass
11. Nickel Silver
12. Non-Ferrous Metals
13. Silver

14. Steel
15. Steel (Manganese Type Coatings)
16. Steel (Zinc Type Coatings)
17. White Metal
18. Zinc
19. Zinc Base Die Castings

Notes:

(a) Electrolytic Process
(b) Refers only to steel (14) when Chromic, Sulfuric Acids Bath is used.
(c) Also Lead Alloys
(d) Sodium Nitrate Bath
(e) Class as described in Chapter 2 for use in Table 3 based on hazard potential (Table 1) and rate of evolution (Table 2) for usual operating conditions. Higher temperatures, agitation or other conditions may result in a higher rate of evolution.

(f) Hydrogen gas also released by some of these operations.
(g) The higher rate is associated with the higher value in the temperature range.
(h) Rate where essentially complete control of steam is required. Otherwise, adequate dilution ventilation may be sufficient.

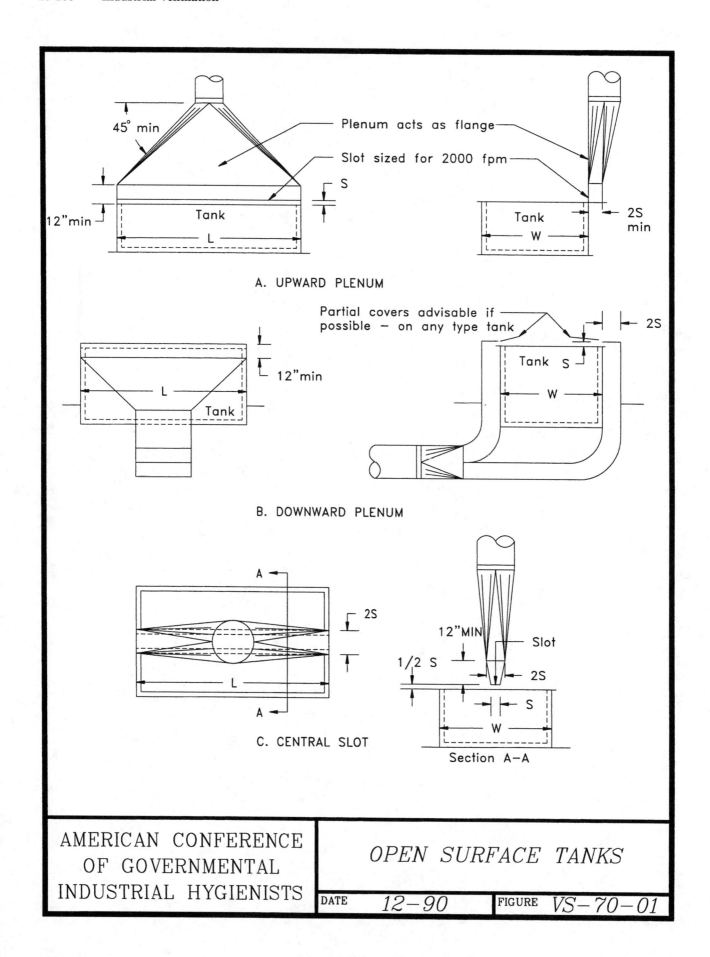

A. UPWARD PLENUM

Plenum acts as flange

Slot sized for 2000 fpm

45° min

12"min

Tank

L

S

Tank

W

2S min

Partial covers advisable if possible — on any type tank

2S

Tank S

W

L

12"min

Tank

B. DOWNWARD PLENUM

A

2S

L

A

C. CENTRAL SLOT

12"MIN

Slot

1/2 S

2S

S

W

Section A-A

AMERICAN CONFERENCE OF GOVERNMENTAL INDUSTRIAL HYGIENISTS

OPEN SURFACE TANKS

DATE *12-90*   FIGURE *VS-70-01*

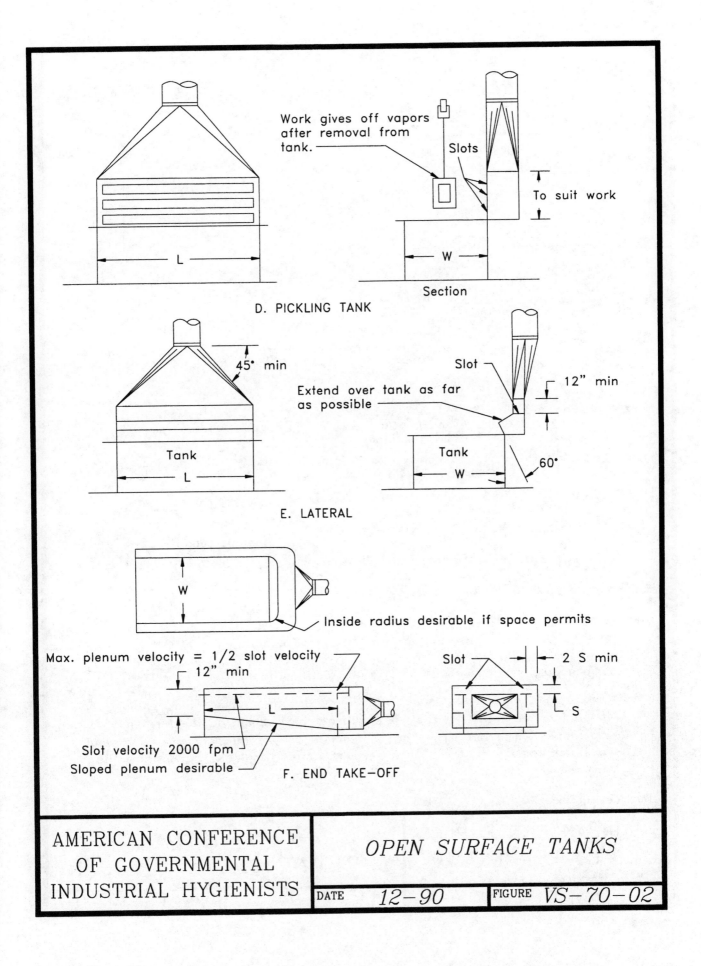

Work gives off vapors after removal from tank.

Slots

To suit work

L

W

Section

D. PICKLING TANK

45° min

Slot

Extend over tank as far as possible

12" min

Tank

Tank

L

W

60°

E. LATERAL

W

Inside radius desirable if space permits

Max. plenum velocity = 1/2 slot velocity

12" min

Slot

2 S min

L

S

Slot velocity 2000 fpm
Sloped plenum desirable

F. END TAKE-OFF

AMERICAN CONFERENCE OF GOVERNMENTAL INDUSTRIAL HYGIENISTS

OPEN SURFACE TANKS

DATE 12-90

FIGURE VS-70-02

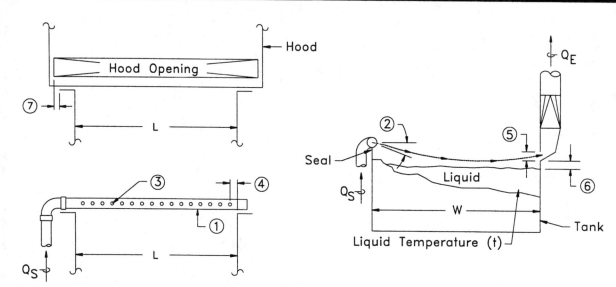

Push nozzle manifold ①–Circular, rectangular or square. Manifold cross–sectional area should be at least 2.5 times the total nozzle flow area.

Push nozzle angle ② – 0° to 20° down.

Nozzle openings ③ – 1/8" to 1/4" slot or 5/32" to 1/4" dia. holes with 3 to 8 dia. spacing. Outer holes or slot ends ④ must be 1/2" to 1" inside tank inner edges.

Exhaust opening ⑤ – Size to achieve 2000 fpm slot velocity. Outer edges of opening ⑦ must extend to edge of tank including flanges.

Liquid surface ⑥ – Tank freeboard must not exceed 8" with parts removed.

Push nozzle supply $Q_j = 243 \sqrt{A_j}$

where Q_j = push nozzle supply, cfm/ft manifold length

A_j = total nozzle opening per foot of manifold length

Total push supply $Q_S = Q_j \times L$ cfm

Exhaust flow $Q_E = 75$ cfm/ft^2 tank surface area for $t \leq 150$ F
$Q_E = (0.4\ T + 15)$ cfm/ft^2 tank surface area for $t > 150$ F.

Tank surface area = L (length of tank) x W (width of tank)

Note: This criteria applies to manual and automatic open surface tank plating operations which do not present significant obstructions to the push jet. Plating operations which use large parts containers and/or mechanisms which would obstruct and deflect the push jet require careful analysis to determine the method of application or applicability of push – pull.

Reference 10.70.1, 10.70.2, & 10.70.3

AMERICAN CONFERENCE OF GOVERNMENTAL INDUSTRIAL HYGIENISTS	*PUSH–PULL HOOD DESIGN DATA FOR WIDTHS UP TO 10'*	
	DATE *4–94*	FIGURE *VS–70–10*

In push—pull ventilation, a nozzle pushes a jet of air across the vessel surface into an exhaust hood. Effectiveness of a push jet is a function of its momentum which can be related to the product of the nozzle supply air flow (Q_j) and the nozzle exit velocity(V_j). For a jet used for plating tanks or other open surface vessels, a push supply flow can be determined from:

$$Q_j = 243 \sqrt{A_j}$$

Where Q_j = push nozzle supply, cfm per foot of push nozzle plenum length
A_j = nozzle exit area,   ft²/per foot of push nozzle plenum length

Using this approach, a push nozzle design is first selected and the nozzle area(A_j) determined.

The push nozzle manifold may be round, rectangular or square in cross—section. The push nozzle may be 1/8" to 1/4" horizontal slot or 5/32" to 1/4" diameter drilled holes on 3 to 8 diameters spacing.

It is important that the air flow from the nozzle be evenly distributed along the length of the supply plenum. To acheive this, the total nozzle exit area should not exceed 40% of the plenum cross—sectional area. Multiple supply plenum inlets should be used where practical.

The push nozzle manifold should be located as near the vessel edge as possible to minimize the height above the liquid surface. The manifold should be adjustable to optimize the push jet angle. The manifold axis can be angled down a maximum of 20° to permit the jet to clear obstructions and to maintain the jet at the vessel surface. It is essential any opening between the manifold and tank be sealed.

An exhaust flow of 75 cfm/ft² of vessel surface area should be used for tank liquid temperatures (t) of 150°F or lower. For tank liquid temperatures greater than 150°F use an exhaust flow of (0.4t+15)cfm/ft² . These flow rates are independent of the "class" used in determining exhaust flow for side draft hoods. "Control velocity" is achieved by the push jet blowing over the tank and will be considerably higher than that which can be achieved by a side draft hood. The purpose of the exhaust hood is to capture and remove the jet——not to provide capture velocity. A flanged hood design is to be used wherever practical. The exhaust hood should be located at the vessel edge so as not to leave a gap between the hood and the vessel.

Design and location of an open surface vessel encompasses a number of variables. In some cases vessel shape, room location, cross—drafts, etc., may create conditions requiring adjustment of the push and/or pull flow rates in order to achieve control. Cross draft velocities over 75 fpm, very wide vessels (8 feet or more), or very large or flat surface parts may require increased push and/or pull flows. To account for the effects of these variables, a flow adjustment of ±20% should be designed into the push and +20% into the pull flow system. Wherever practical, construction and evaluation of a pilot system is recommended. Once designed and installed, push—pull systems can be initially evaluated by use of a visual tracer technique and appropriate flow adjustments can be made as required.

The exhuast hood opening should be sized to assure even flow distribution across the opening. This can be achieved by sizing the slot for 2000 fpm slot velocity.

AMERICAN CONFERENCE OF GOVERNMENTAL INDUSTRIAL HYGIENISTS	*DESIGN DATA PUSH—PULL HOOD*
DATE *4—94*	FIGURE *VS—70—11*

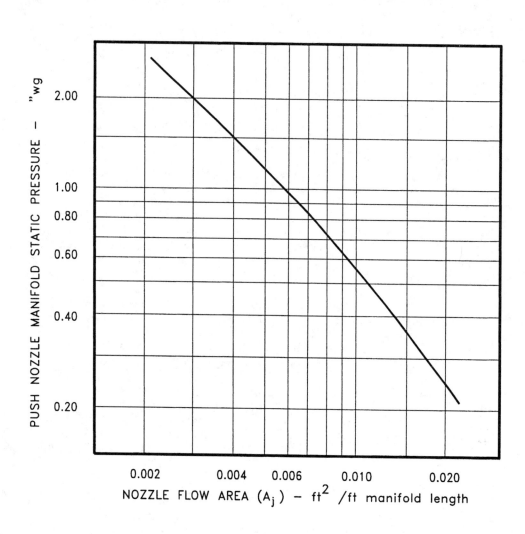

NOZZLE FLOW AREA (A$_j$) — ft^2 /ft manifold length

PUSH NOZZLE SUPPLY = 243 $\sqrt{A_j}$ cfm/ft of length for nozzles with 1/8 to 1/4 inch wide slots or 5/32 to 1/4 inch diameter holes on 3 to 8 diameter spacing.

For holes A$_j$ (ft^2/ft)=   0.065 x hole diameter (in)/hole spacing (no. of diameters (in).)

For slot A$_j$ (ft^2/ft)= $\frac{\text{slot width (in)}}{12}$ (See VS–70–10)

AMERICAN CONFERENCE OF GOVERNMENTAL INDUSTRIAL HYGIENISTS	*PUSH NOZZLE MANIFOLD PRESSURE*
DATE *4–94*	FIGURE *VS–70–12*

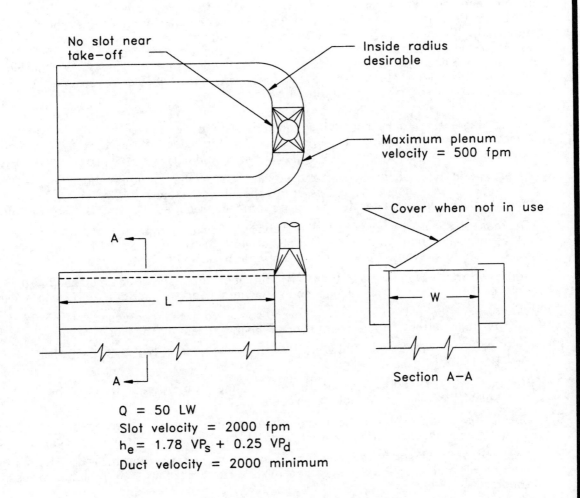

No slot near take-off

Inside radius desirable

Maximum plenum velocity = 500 fpm

Cover when not in use

A

L

W

A

Section A-A

$Q = 50 \ LW$
Slot velocity = 2000 fpm
$h_e = 1.78 \ VP_s + 0.25 \ VP_d$
Duct velocity = 2000 minimum

Also provide: 1. Separate flue for combustion products

2. For cleaning operation, appropriate respiratory protection is necessary.

3. For pit units, the pit should be mechanically ventilated.

4. For further safeguards, see VS–501.1

NOTE: Provide downdraft grille for parts that cannot be removed dry; $Q = 50 \ cfm/ft^2$ grille area.

AMERICAN CONFERENCE OF GOVERNMENTAL INDUSTRIAL HYGIENISTS	*SOLVENT DEGREASING TANKS*	
	DATE *12-90*	FIGURE *VS-70-20*

Solvent vapor degreasing refers to boiling liquid cleaning systems utilizing trichloroethylene, perchlorethylene, methylene chloride freons® or other halogentated hydrocarbons. Cleaning action is accomplished by the condensation of the solvent vapors in contact with the work surface producing a continuous liquid rinsing action. Cleaning ceases when the temperature of the work reaches the temperature of the surrounding solvent vapors. Since halogenated hydrocarbons are somewhat similar in their physical, chemical and toxic characteristics, the following safeguards should be provided to prevent the creation of a health or life hazard:

1. Vapor degreasing tanks should be equipped with a condenser or vapor level thermostat to keep the vapor level below the top edge of the tank by a distance equal to one-half the tank width or 36 inches, whichever is shorter.

2. Where water type condensers are used, inlet water temperature should not exceed 80°F (27°C) and the outlet temperature should not exceed 110°. For some solvent, lower water temperatures may be required.

3. Degreasers should be equipped with a boiling liquid thermostat to regulate the rate of vapor generation, and with a safety control at an appropriate height above the vapor line to prevent the escape of solvent in case of malfunction.

4. Tanks or machines of more than 4 ft² of vapor area should be equipped with suitable gasketed cleanout or sludge doors, located near the bottom, to facilitate cleaning.

5. Work should be placed in and removed slowly from the degreaser, at a rate of no greater than 11fpm., to prevent sudden disturbances of the vapor level.

6. CARE MUST BE TAKEN TO PREVENT DIRECT SOLVENT CARRYOUT DUE TO THE SHAPE OF THE PART.

7. Maximum rated workloads as determined by the rate of heat transfer (surface area and specific heat) should not be exceeded.

8. Special precautions should be taken where natural gas or other open flames are used to heat the solvent to prevent vapors* from entering the combustion air supply.

9. Heating elements should be designed and maintained so that their surface temperature will not cause the solvent or mixture to breakdown* or produce excessive vapors.

10. Degreasers should be located in such a manner that vapors* will not reach or be drawn into atmospheres used for gas or electrical arc welding, high temperature heat treating, combustion air or open electric motors.

11. Whenever spray or other mechanical means are used to disperse solvent liquids, sufficient enclosure or baffling should be provided to prevent direct release of air-bourne vapor to the top of the tank.

12. An emergency quick-drenching facility should be located in near proximity to the degreaser for use in the event of accidental eye contact with the degreasing liquid.

*Electric arcs, open flames and hot surfaces will thermally decompose halogenated hydrocarbons to toxic and corrosive substances (such as hydrochloric and/or hydrofluoric acid). Under some circumstances, phosgene may be formed.

AMERICAN CONFERENCE OF GOVERNMENTAL INDUSTRIAL HYGIENISTS	SOLVENT VAPOR DEGREASING	
	DATE 1-91	FIGURE VS-70-21

10.75 PAINTING OPERATIONS

Application of industrial paints and coatings usually is accomplished by one of three techniques: air-atomization, electrostatic, or airless methods. A fourth method used in high production automated systems uses a spinning disk mist generator. The paint or coating is introduced at the center of the disk and shears off at the disk edge due to centrifugal force. The process offers the advantage of uniform particle size which varies with the speed and disk diameter. Compressed air is used to shape the particles in a cone pattern and may be further enhanced by applying an electrostatic charge.

The device is frequently referred to as a "Bell" due to its shape. Potential health hazards exist from exposure to solid and liquid aerosols as well as to solvent vapors. In addition to the airborne exposures, hazards include the use of flammable and combustible liquids and the accumulation of flammable paint residues. Fire safety and proper electrical wiring are important concerns in most paint applications.[10.75.1, 10.75.2]

Control of airborne pollutants by ventilation may be accomplished through the use of spray booths such as shown on VS-75-01, VS-75-02, and VS-75-05. More specialized ventilation arrangements are shown on VS-75-03 and VS-75-04. The typical booth is a partial enclosure of sheet metal construction with openings for conveying the work piece into and out of the booth. Several factors are important in the performance of these booths. Booth depth is critical; spray rebound may escape from shallow booths and increase exposures. The size of the booth is governed principally by the size of the object being coated. Sufficient space must be provided to permit airflow on all sides of the object, to provide room to work, and to enable the air to enter the booth in a smooth, controlled manner without excessive wrap-around. In some cases, downdraft booths may be employed when large objects are painted.

VS-75-07 shows a cross-section of a typical High Production Downdraft Water Wash Paint Booth used to paint large objects such as automobiles, trucks and appliances. The booths may be several hundred feet long divided into zones for sequential coating applications. The zones are typically separated by vestibules to prevent coating drift between zones.

In air-atomization applications, the most common spray technique, it is important to use the minimum air pressure needed to accomplish the task. Excess air pressure results in increased dispersion of the paint and overspray as well as poor work quality.

Airless application results in aerosols with fewer particles in the respirable range. One study[10.75.3] suggests that approximately 20% of the particles in air-atomization applications are less than 12 microns while airless methods produce aerosols with only 2% less than this value. The larger aerosols produced by the airless technique will deposit more efficiently on the work piece, due to impaction, than the smaller particles produced by the compressed air method.

Electrostatic applications result in more efficient deposition of paint aerosols due to electrostatic forces. As a result, ventilation airflow requirements for control of electrostatic applications tend to be lower than for compressed air methods.

Many spray booths are equipped with disposable particulate filters which become loaded over time and result in increased pressure loss. This loss eventually can reduce airflow to unacceptable levels and, hence, system performance must be monitored. Water wash systems are available for cleaning particulate matter from the exhausted air but do little for solvent vapors. Fan selection is an important component of a spray booth installation. Often the fan is an integral part of the system when purchased and may be installed in a different configuration than originally designed. This can result in reduced airflow, particularly if additional system resistance is encountered in the actual installation.[10.75.4]

Work practices remain an important aspect of controlling exposure to paint aerosols and solvent vapors. The worker should not stand downstream of the object being sprayed. See section 3.4.6, Worker Position Effect. A turntable can help to facilitate easy access to all sides of the object without the worker having to move. Extension arms on spray guns should be employed for hard to reach cavities. Proper location of the booth with respect to replacement air and obstructions is essential. Locating booths in corners or near disruptive air currents can defeat the protection of these hoods. Poor location of the booth may result in turbulent airflow which may reduce the protection provided by the booth.

Respiratory protection may be required in applications using toxic materials. This includes heavy metal pigments and organics such as isocyanates in urethane paints and amines in epoxy paints.

REFERENCES

10.75.1   National Fire Protection Association: Flammable and Combustible Liquids Code. No. 30, NFPA, Boston, MA (1990).

10.75.2   National Fire Protection Association: National Electric Code. No. 70. Boston, MA (1990).

10.75.3   National Institute for Occupational Safety and Health, "An Evaluation of Engineering Control Technology for Spray Painting". DHHS (NIOSH) Pub. No. 81-121; NTIS Pub. No. PB-82-162-264. National Technical Information Service, Springfield, VA (1981).

10.75.4   Burgess, W.A.; Ellenbecker, M. J.; Treitman, R. D.: Ventilation for Control of the Work Environment, John Wiley and Sons, NY (1989).

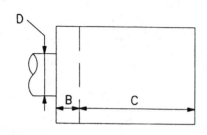

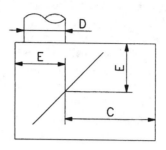

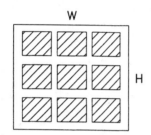

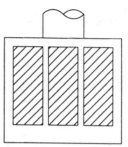

1. Split baffle or filters
   B = 0.75 D
   Baffle area = 0.75 WH
   For filter area, see note 2

2. Angular baffle
   E = D + 6"
   Baffle area = 0.40 WH
   For filter area, see note 2

Air spray paint design data.
   Any combination of duct connections and baffles may be used. Large, deep booths do not require baffles. Consult manufacturers for water-curtain designs. Use explosion proof fixtures and a non-sparking fan. Electrostatic spray booth requires automatic high-voltage disconnects for conveyor failure, fan failure or grounding.

Walk-in booth
  W = work size + 6'
  H = work size + 3' (minimum = 7')
  C = work size + 6'
  Q = 100 cfm/ft^2 booth cross section
    May be 75 cfm/ft^2 for very
    large, deep booth. Operator may
    require a NIOSH cerified respirator.
    h_e = 1.78 VP_s + 0.50 VP_d (baffles)
    h_e = Dirty filter resistance + 0.50 VP_d (filters)
    Duct velocity = 2000 fpm

Operator outside booth
  W = work size + 2'
  H = work size + 2'
  C = 0.75 x larger front dimension
  Q = 100 - 150 cfm/ft^2 of open
    area, including conveyor
    openings.

Airless spray paint design
  Q = 60 cfm/ft^2 booth cross
    section, walk-in booth
  Q = 60 - 100 cfm/ft^2 of
    total open area, operator
    outside of booth

Notes : 1. Baffle arrangements shown are for
      air distribution only.
    2. Paint arresting filters usually selected
      for 100 - 500 fpm, consult manu-
      facturer for specific details.
    3. For construction an safety, consult
      NFPA - See Reference 10.75.1.

AMERICAN CONFERENCE OF GOVERNMENTAL INDUSTRIAL HYGIENISTS	*LARGE PAINT BOOTH*	
	DATE *1-91*	FIGURE *VS- 75- 01*

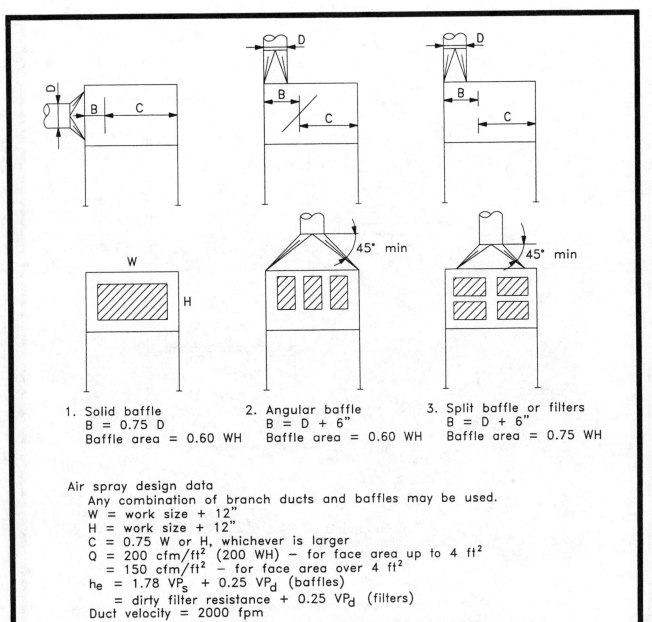

1. Solid baffle
   B = 0.75 D
   Baffle area = 0.60 WH

2. Angular baffle
   B = D + 6"
   Baffle area = 0.60 WH

3. Split baffle or filters
   B = D + 6"
   Baffle area = 0.75 WH

Air spray design data
    Any combination of branch ducts and baffles may be used.
    W = work size + 12"
    H = work size + 12"
    C = 0.75 W or H, whichever is larger
    Q = 200 cfm/ft^2 (200 WH) − for face area up to 4 ft^2
       = 150 cfm/ft^2 − for face area over 4 ft^2
    h_e = 1.78 VP_s + 0.25 VP_d (baffles)
       = dirty filter resistance + 0.25 VP_d (filters)
Duct velocity = 2000 fpm

Airless spray paint design data
    Q = 125 cfm/ft^2 (125 WH) − for face area up to 4 ft^2
       = 100 cfm/ft^2 − for face area over 4 ft^2

Notes: 1. Baffle arrangements shown are for air distribution only.

         2. Paint arresting filters usually selected for 100 − 500 fpm, consult
            manufacturer for specific details.

         3. For construction and safety, consult NFPA (Reference 10.75.1).

AMERICAN CONFERENCE OF GOVERNMENTAL INDUSTRIAL HYGIENISTS	*SMALL PAINT BOOTH*
	DATE *1−91* FIGURE *VS−75−02*

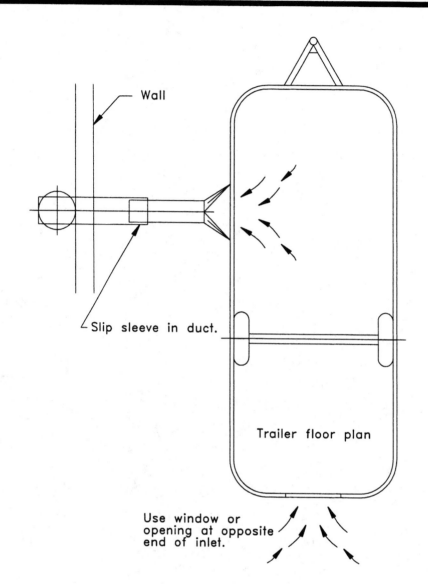

Wall

Slip sleeve in duct.

Trailer floor plan

Use window or
opening at opposite
end of inlet.

$Q = 50$ cfm/ft^2 of cross-sectional trailer area
$h_e = 0.25$ VP$_d$
Minimum duct velocity = 2000 fpm

Notes:
1. Paint arresting filters usually selected for 100–500 fpm,
   consult manufacturer for specific details.
2. For construction and safety, consult NFPA, Reference 10.75.1.
3. Operator must wear an appropriate, NIOSH certified respirator.

AMERICAN CONFERENCE OF GOVERNMENTAL INDUSTRIAL HYGIENISTS	TRAILER INTERIOR SPRAY PAINTING	
	DATE 1-91	FIGURE VS-75-03

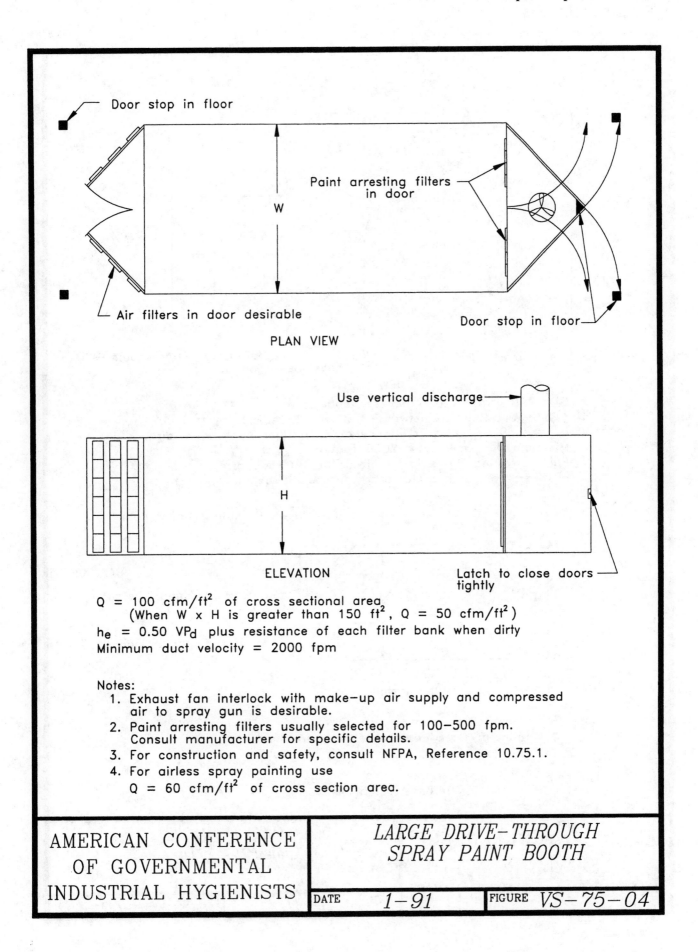

Door stop in floor

Paint arresting filters in door

W

Air filters in door desirable

Door stop in floor

PLAN VIEW

Use vertical discharge

H

ELEVATION

Latch to close doors tightly

$Q = 100$ cfm/ft^2 of cross sectional area
(When W x H is greater than 150 ft^2, $Q = 50$ cfm/ft^2)
$h_e = 0.50$ VP$_d$ plus resistance of each filter bank when dirty
Minimum duct velocity = 2000 fpm

Notes:
1. Exhaust fan interlock with make-up air supply and compressed air to spray gun is desirable.
2. Paint arresting filters usually selected for 100-500 fpm. Consult manufacturer for specific details.
3. For construction and safety, consult NFPA, Reference 10.75.1.
4. For airless spray painting use
   $Q = 60$ cfm/ft^2 of cross section area.

AMERICAN CONFERENCE OF GOVERNMENTAL INDUSTRIAL HYGIENISTS	LARGE DRIVE-THROUGH SPRAY PAINT BOOTH	
	DATE *1-91*	FIGURE *VS-75-04*

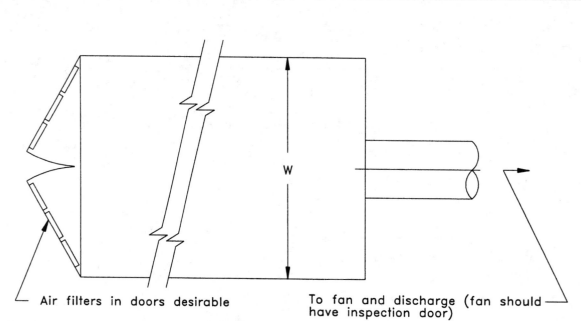

Air filters in doors desirable

To fan and discharge (fan should have inspection door)

PLAN VIEW

$Q = 100$ cfm/ft^2 of cross sectional area
(when W x H is greater than 150 ft , $Q = 50$ cfm/ft^2)
$h_e = 0.50$ VP$_d$ plus resistance of each filter bank when dirty
Minimum duct velocity = 2000 fpm
Paint arresting filters to be sized for 100–500 cfm/ft^2
of filter. Consult manufacturer for specific details.

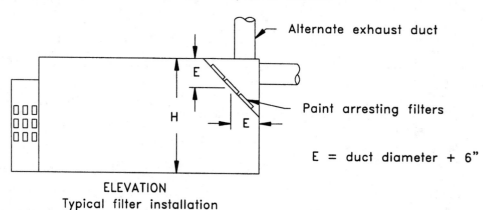

Alternate exhaust duct

Paint arresting filters

E = duct diameter + 6"

ELEVATION
Typical filter installation

Note: For airless spray painting use
$Q = 60$ cfm/ft^2 of cross-sectional area

For construction and safety
consult NFPA code (Reference 10.75.1).

AMERICAN CONFERENCE OF GOVERNMENTAL INDUSTRIAL HYGIENISTS	*PAINT BOOTH VEHICLE SPRAY*	
	DATE *1-91*	FIGURE *VS-75-05*

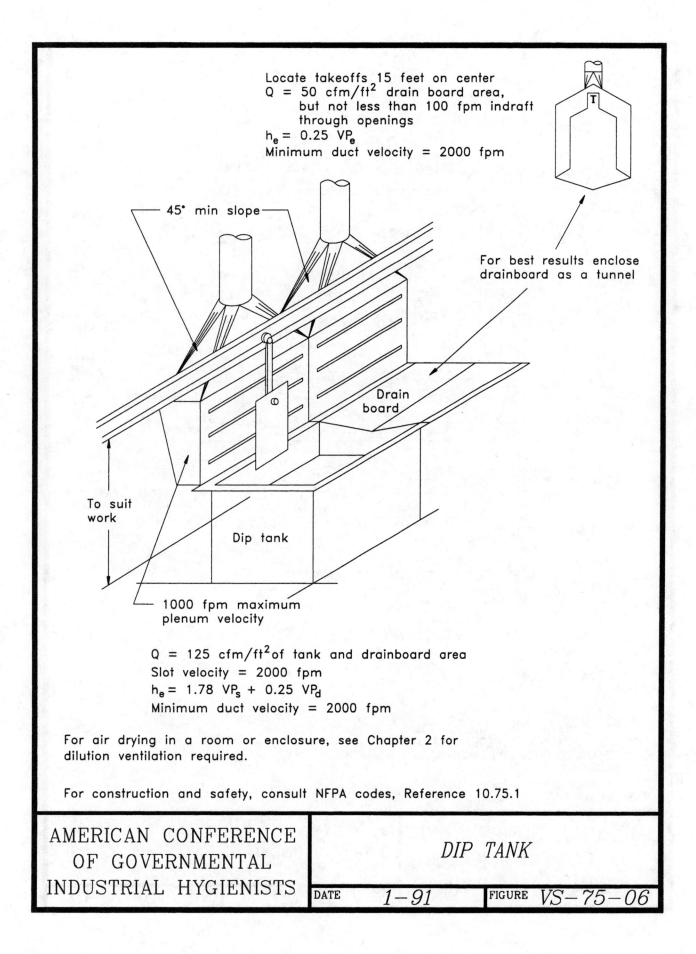

Locate takeoffs 15 feet on center
$Q = 50$ cfm/ft^2 drain board area, but not less than 100 fpm indraft through openings
$h_e = 0.25\ VP_e$
Minimum duct velocity = 2000 fpm

45° min slope

For best results enclose drainboard as a tunnel

Drain board

To suit work

Dip tank

1000 fpm maximum plenum velocity

$Q = 125$ cfm/ft^2 of tank and drainboard area
Slot velocity = 2000 fpm
$h_e = 1.78\ VP_s + 0.25\ VP_d$
Minimum duct velocity = 2000 fpm

For air drying in a room or enclosure, see Chapter 2 for dilution ventilation required.

For construction and safety, consult NFPA codes, Reference 10.75.1

AMERICAN CONFERENCE OF GOVERNMENTAL INDUSTRIAL HYGIENISTS	DIP TANK	
	DATE *1-91*	FIGURE *VS-75-06*

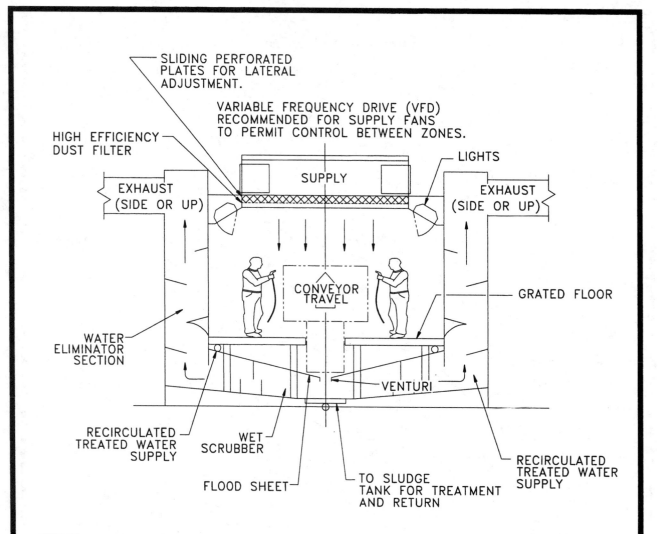

SLIDING PERFORATED PLATES FOR LATERAL ADJUSTMENT.

VARIABLE FREQUENCY DRIVE (VFD) RECOMMENDED FOR SUPPLY FANS TO PERMIT CONTROL BETWEEN ZONES.

HIGH EFFICIENCY DUST FILTER

LIGHTS

EXHAUST (SIDE OR UP)

SUPPLY

EXHAUST (SIDE OR UP)

CONVEYOR TRAVEL

GRATED FLOOR

WATER ELIMINATOR SECTION

VENTURI

RECIRCULATED TREATED WATER SUPPLY

WET SCRUBBER

RECIRCULATED TREATED WATER SUPPLY

FLOOD SHEET

TO SLUDGE TANK FOR TREATMENT AND RETURN

DOWN DRAFT AIRFLOW: 5' ABOVE FLOOR	
50 – 70 FPM	ELECTROSTATIC AND STATIONARY BELLS
70 – 90 FPM	ROBOTS AND RECIPROCATING BELLS
100 – 125 FPM	MANUAL PAINTING ZONES (AS SHOWN)

NOTE: ABOVE DESIGN VALUES ASSUME EMPTY BOOTH.   ADJUSTMENTS MAY BE REQUIRED TO ACCOMODATE PRODUCT SHAPE AND TO CONTROL ZONE DRIFT.

NOTES:
1.   FOR CONSTRUCTION AND SAFETY CONSULT NFPA CODE (REFERENCE 10.75.1)
2.   PRESSURE DROP THROUGH SCRUBBER DEPENDS ON ON VENTURI DESIGN.   TYPICALLY 6.5" TO 7.5" S.P.
3.   AN APPROPRIATE NIOSH CERTIFIED RESPIRATOR MAY BE REQUIRED FOR THE OPERATOR.

AMERICAN CONFERENCE OF GOVERNMENTAL INDUSTRIAL HYGIENISTS	AUTOMATED/HIGH PRODUCTION WATER WASH DOWNDRAFT PAINT BOOTH	
	DATE 5-00	FIGURE VS-75-07

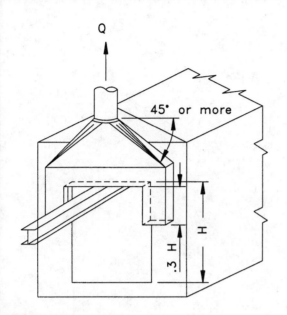

SLOT TYPE

Q = 100 cfm/ft ^{2}door plus 1/2
  Products of combustion

  Minimum duct velocity = 2000 fpm
h$_e$ = 1.0 VP$_s$ + 0.25 VP $_d$

Size plenum for
1000 fpm maximum

Slot on three sides with
V$_s$ = 2000 fpm.

Locate on inside or outside of door.

Slot for conveyor

Extend as low as possible
to clear work

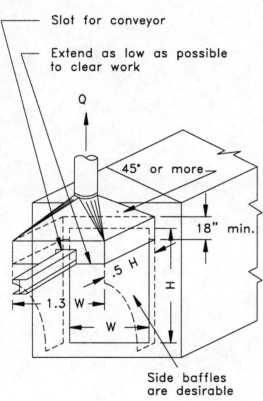

Side baffles
are desirable

CANOPY TYPE

Q = 200 cfm/ft ^{2}of hood face
  plus 1/2 products of combustion
h$_e$ = 0.25 VP$_d$
Duct velocity = 2000 fpm

Notes:
1. For dryers, include rate of
   water vapor liberated.
2. For flammable solvent drying
   refer to Chapter 2, "General
   Industrial Ventilation".
3. Hoods at each end of oven. Reduce
   size of doors as much as possible.
   Separate vent must be added for
   products of combustion.
4. For construction and safety, consult
   NFPA code (Reference 10.75.1).

AMERICAN CONFERENCE OF GOVERNMENTAL INDUSTRIAL HYGIENISTS	*DRYING OVEN VENTILATION*
DATE *1–91*	FIGURE *VS–75–20*

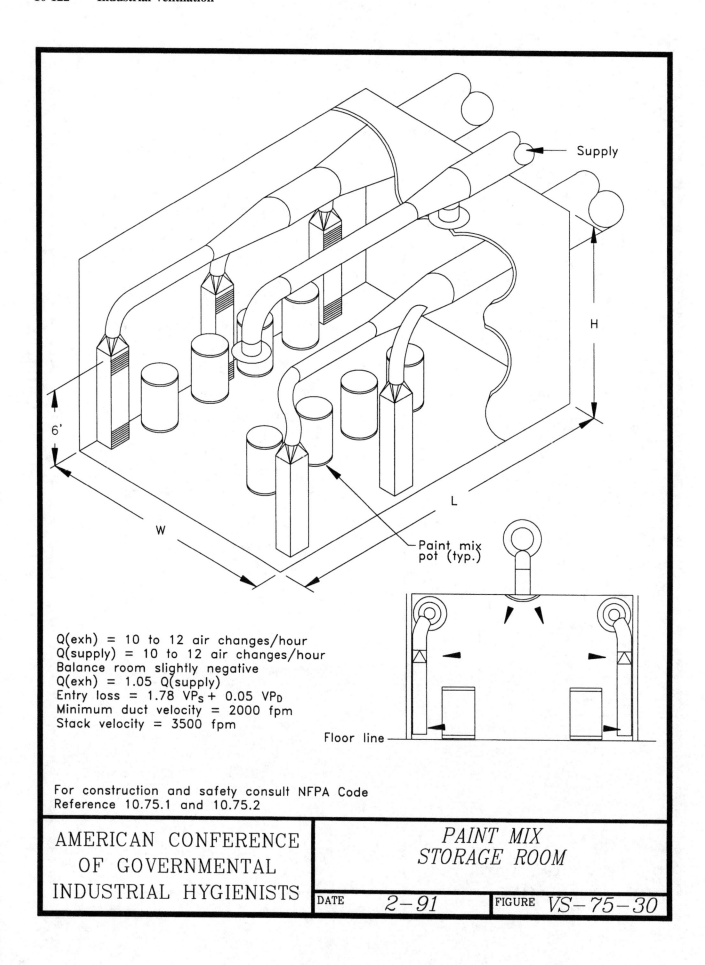

Supply

H

6'

W

L

Paint mix
pot (typ.)

Q(exh) = 10 to 12 air changes/hour
Q(supply) = 10 to 12 air changes/hour
Balance room slightly negative
Q(exh) = 1.05 Q(supply)
Entry loss = $1.78\ VP_S + 0.05\ VP_D$
Minimum duct velocity = 2000 fpm
Stack velocity = 3500 fpm

Floor line

For construction and safety consult NFPA Code
Reference 10.75.1 and 10.75.2

AMERICAN CONFERENCE OF GOVERNMENTAL INDUSTRIAL HYGIENISTS	PAINT MIX STORAGE ROOM	
	DATE 2-91	FIGURE VS-75-30

10.80 MECHANICAL SURFACE CLEANING AND FINISHING

Mechanical surface cleaning is generally used to clean a surface in preparation for painting, welding, or other operations. The surfaces may be coated with paint, rust, or oxidation; plated with other metals; or covered with molding sand, inorganic, organic, or biological matter. Mechanical cleaning may be accomplished by abrasive blasting, wire wheels, sand paper/sanding belts, grinding wheels, or use of abrasive chips in tumbling mills. The capture velocity needed to entrain large particles is often very high and the collection hood must be positioned so the materials are directed toward the hood. A minimum duct transport velocity of 3500 fpm is needed but 4000 to 5000 fpm is recommended. A hood that encloses as much of the operation as practical is desired. The toxicity of the material removed must be considered when cleaning mechanically. Complete enclosures may be used or the worker may need to wear a respirator in addition to using local exhaust ventilation.

For many grinding, buffing, and polishing operations, regulations from the Occupational Safety and Health Administration (OSHA)[10.80.1] and National Fire Protection Association (NFPA)[10.80.2] may apply.

10.80.1 Abrasive Cleaning: VS-80-01, -02, and -03 show suggested designs for abrasive blasting and tumbling mills. A supplied air respirator must be used in abrasive blasting rooms.

10.80.2 Grinding: Mechanical surface finishing uses organic bonded wheels, cones, saws, or other shapes rotating at a high rate of speed to smooth a surface; reduce an object or part in size; or perform other operations. As the object is being surfaced or finished, metallic particles are removed and leave the object at a high speed. In addition, the abrasive wheel is reduced in size and generates particles that must be controlled. Frequently, grinding is accomplished using fluids to keep the parts cool. This cooling fluid will be emitted as an aerosol or mist and needs to be controlled and provisions must be made in the duct to drain off the liquids that accumulate.

The hood used to capture the particles should enclose the operation as much as possible and be positioned to take advantage of the velocity and direction of the particles as they are generated. Design specifications for grinding and surfacing operations are shown in VS-80-10 through VS-80-19.

10.80.3 Buffing and Polishing: The same principles apply for buffing and polishing as for grinding and surfacing. The buffing wheel or belt should be enclosed as much as practical and positioned to take advantage of the centrifugal force of the particles as they leave the wheel or belt. The minimum duct velocity for the generated particles is 3500 fpm and 4500 fpm if the material is wet or sticky. Since many varieties of metals and alloys are buffed and polished, it is extremely important not to mix ferrous and non-ferrous metals in the same exhaust systems (see NFPA codes).[10.80.2] VS-80-30 through VS-80-35 show suggested designs for buffing and polishing.

REFERENCES

10.80.1   U. S. Department of Labor, Occupational Safety and Health Administration: 29 CFR. 1910.

10.80.2   National Fire Protection Association, National Fire Codes—in particular NFPA-65 (Processing and Finishing of Aluminum); NFPA-68 (Guide for Explosion Prevention Systems); NFPA-77 (Practice on Static Electricity); NFPA-91 (Installation of Blowers and Exhaust Systems for Dust, Stack and Vapor Removal or Conveying); NFPA-480 (Storage, Handling and Processing of Magnesium); NFPA-481 (Production, Processing, Handling and Storage of Titanium); NFPA-482 (Production, Processing, Handling and Storage of Zirconium) ; and NFPA-561 (Manufacture of Aluminum and Magnesium Powder), NFPA, Quincy, MA.

10.80.3   Hogopian and Bastress: Recommended Ventilation Guidelines for Abrasive-Blasting Operations. CDC-99-74-33 (1975).

10.80.4   American Foundrymen's Society, Inc., Foundry Ventilation Manual AFS, Des Plaines, IL (1985).

10.80.5   National Institute for Occupational Safety and Health: Ventilation Requirements for Grinding, Buffing and Polishing Operations. DHEW (NIOSH) Pub. No. 75-107, NTIS Pub. No. PB-277-332. National Technical Information Service, Springfield, VA (1975).

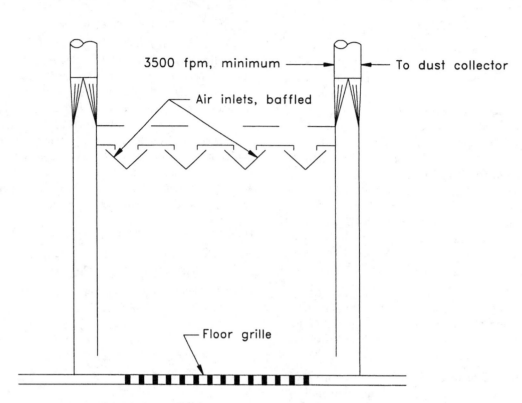

SECTION THROUGH TYPICAL ROOM

$Q = 60-100$ cfm/ft^2 of floor for downdraft with typical choice 80 cfm/ft^2.
$Q = 100$ cfm/ft^2 of wall for crossdraft.

Lower control velocities may be used depending on toxicity of the contaminant, object and blasting media and the size of the blasting room.

Notes: 1. The above ventilation is for operator visibility and to control escape of contaminants into adjacent work areas.

   2. Operator in an abrasive blasting room is required to wear appropriate NIOSH certified respiratory protection.

   3. For rotary tables use 200 cfm/ft^2 of total opening (taken without curtains).

   4. For blasting cabinets see VS-80-02.

Reference 10.80.3 and 10.80.4

AMERICAN CONFERENCE OF GOVERNMENTAL INDUSTRIAL HYGIENISTS	*ABRASIVE BLASTING ROOM*	
	DATE *02-91*	FIGURE *VS-80-01*

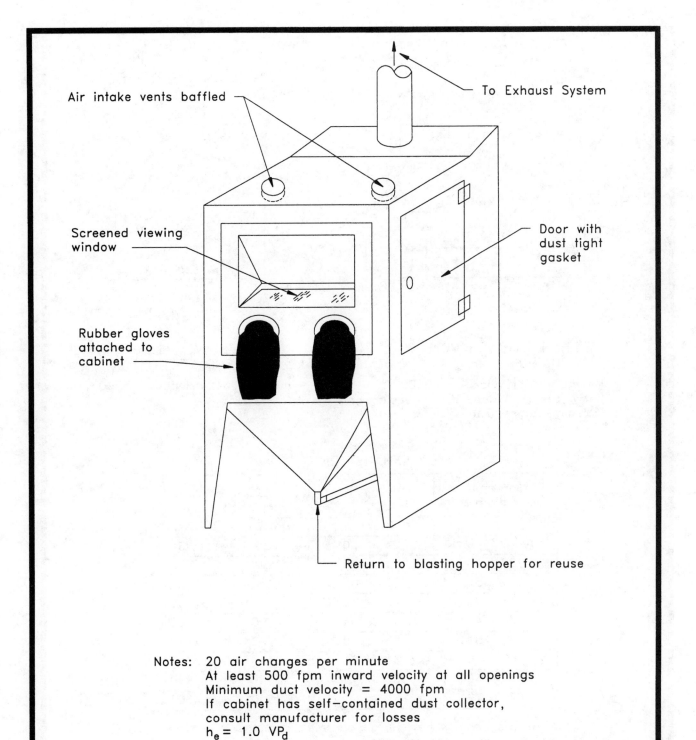

Air intake vents baffled

To Exhaust System

Screened viewing window

Door with dust tight gasket

Rubber gloves attached to cabinet

Return to blasting hopper for reuse

Notes: 20 air changes per minute
At least 500 fpm inward velocity at all openings
Minimum duct velocity = 4000 fpm
If cabinet has self-contained dust collector,
consult manufacturer for losses
$h_e = 1.0\ VP_d$

AMERICAN CONFERENCE OF GOVERNMENTAL INDUSTRIAL HYGIENISTS	ABRASIVE BLASTING CABINET
	DATE *02-91* FIGURE *VS-80-02*

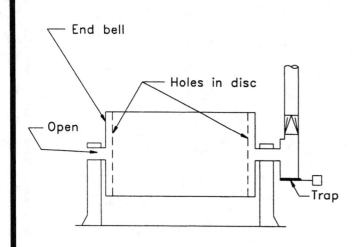

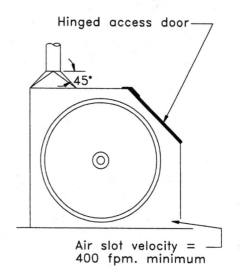

SECTION THROUGH HOLLOW TRUNNION TUMBLER

Minimum duct velocity = 5000 fpm
Entry loss (h_e) depends on design and typically ranges from 3 to 9 "wg.

STAVE MILL (END SECTION)

Minimum duct velocity = 3500 fpm
$h_e = 0.25\ VP_d$

EXHAUST RATES

Square mill side diam in.	Round mill I.D. in inches	Exhaust cfm**	
		Trunnion	Stave
	Up to 24 incl.	430	800
Up to 24 incl.	24 – 30	680	900
25 – 30	31 – 36	980	980
31 – 36	37 – 42	1330	1330
37 – 42	43 – 48	1750	1750
43 – 48	49 – 54	2200	2200
49 – 54	55 – 60	2730	2730
55 – 60	61 – 66	3300	3300
61 – 66	67 – 72	3920	3920
67 – 72		4600	4600

* Low-loss designs have large air inlet openings in end bell. Holes in end discs are sized for velocities of 1250 – 1800 fpm.

** For lengths over 72", increase exhaust rate proportionately

AMERICAN CONFERENCE OF GOVERNMENTAL INDUSTRIAL HYGIENISTS	*TUMBLING MILLS*	
	DATE *02–91*	FIGURE *VS–80–03*

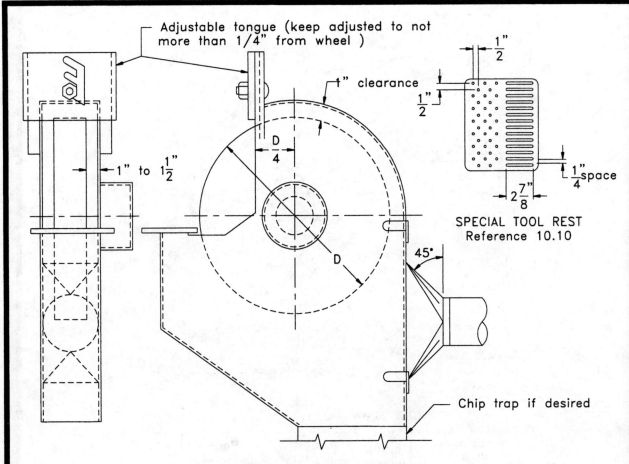

Adjustable tongue (keep adjusted to not more than 1/4" from wheel)

1" clearance

$\frac{D}{4}$

D

1" to $1\frac{1}{2}$"

45°

$\frac{1}{2}$"

$\frac{1}{2}$"

$\frac{1}{4}$" space

$2\frac{7}{8}$"

SPECIAL TOOL REST
Reference 10.10

Chip trap if desired

EXHAUST FLOW RATES, cfm

Wheel diam. inches	Wheel width inches	Good enclosure*	Poor enclosure
Up to 5	1	220	390
5 to 10	1.5	390	610
10 to 14	2	500	740
14 to 16	2	610	880
16 to 20	3	740	1000
20 to 24	4	880	1200
24 to 30	5	1200	1600
30 to 36	6	1600	2000

*Special hood and tool rest as shown, no more than 25% of the wheel exposed.
Minimum duct velocity = 4000 fpm

h_e = 0.65 VP_d for straight take-off

   = 0.40 VP_d for tapered take-off

AMERICAN CONFERENCE OF GOVERNMENTAL INDUSTRIAL HYGIENISTS	*GRINDING WHEEL HOOD SURFACE SPEEDS ABOVE 6500 sfpm*	
	DATE *02-91*	FIGURE *VS-80-10*

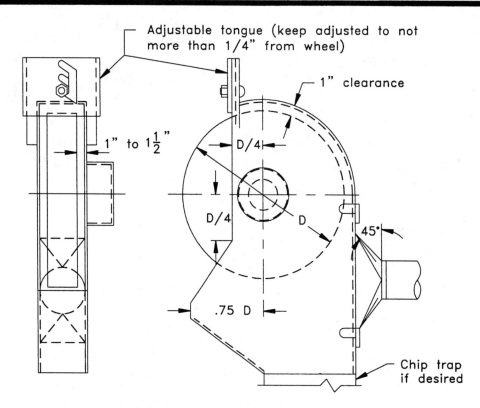

Adjustable tongue (keep adjusted to not more than 1/4" from wheel)

1" clearance

1" to 1½"

D/4

D/4

D

45°

.75 D

Chip trap if desired

EXHAUST FLOW RATES, cfm

Wheel diam inches	Wheel width inches	Good enclosure*	Poor enclosure
Up to 5	1	220	220
5 to 10	1.5	220	300
10 to 14	2	300	500
14 to 16	2	390	610
16 to 20	3	500	740
20 to 24	4	610	880
24 to 30	5	880	1200
30 to 36	6	1200	1600

* No more than 25% of wheel exposed.

Minimum duct velocity = 4000 fpm

$h_e = 0.65 \ VP_d$ for straight takeoff
$0.40 \ VP_d$ for tapered takeoff

AMERICAN CONFERENCE OF GOVERNMENTAL INDUSTRIAL HYGIENISTS	*GRINDING WHEEL HOOD SURFACE SPEEDS BELOW 6500 sfpm*
	DATE *02-91* FIGURE *VS-80-11*

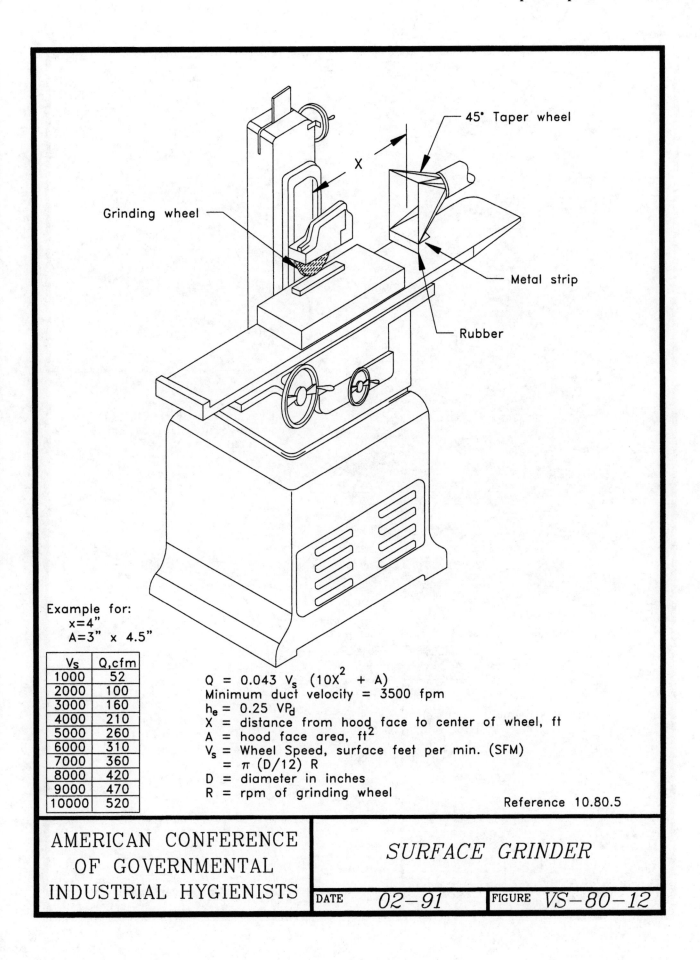

45° Taper wheel

X

Grinding wheel

Metal strip

Rubber

Example for:
  x=4"
  A=3" x 4.5"

V_s	Q,cfm
1000	52
2000	100
3000	160
4000	210
5000	260
6000	310
7000	360
8000	420
9000	470
10000	520

$Q = 0.043 \, V_s \, (10X^2 + A)$
Minimum duct velocity = 3500 fpm
$h_e = 0.25 \, VP_d$
X = distance from hood face to center of wheel, ft
A = hood face area, ft^2
V_s = Wheel Speed, surface feet per min. (SFM)
   $= \pi \, (D/12) \, R$
D = diameter in inches
R = rpm of grinding wheel

Reference 10.80.5

AMERICAN CONFERENCE
OF GOVERNMENTAL
INDUSTRIAL HYGIENISTS

SURFACE GRINDER

DATE *02–91*   FIGURE *VS–80–12*

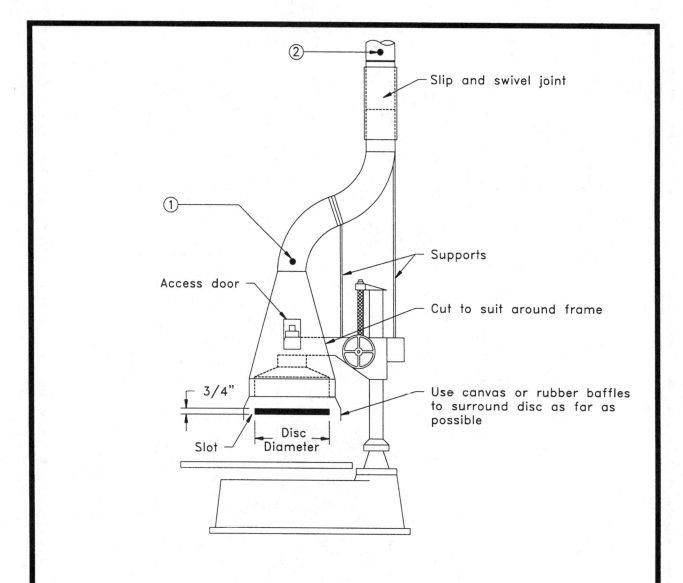

Slip and swivel joint

Supports

Cut to suit around frame

Access door

3/4"

Slot

Disc
Diameter

Use canvas or rubber baffles
to surround disc as far as
possible

Disc diameter	Duct diameter	cfm
Up to 20"	6"	900
20" to 30"	8"	1600
30" to 53"	12"	3500
53" to 72"	16"	6300

Minimum duct velocity = 4000 fpm
Minimum slot velocity = 2000 fpm

① $h_e = 1.0\ VP_s + 0.40\ VP_d$
② h_e + elbow losses + joint losses

AMERICAN CONFERENCE
OF GOVERNMENTAL
INDUSTRIAL HYGIENISTS

CORE GRINDER

DATE   *02—91*   FIGURE   *VS—80—13*

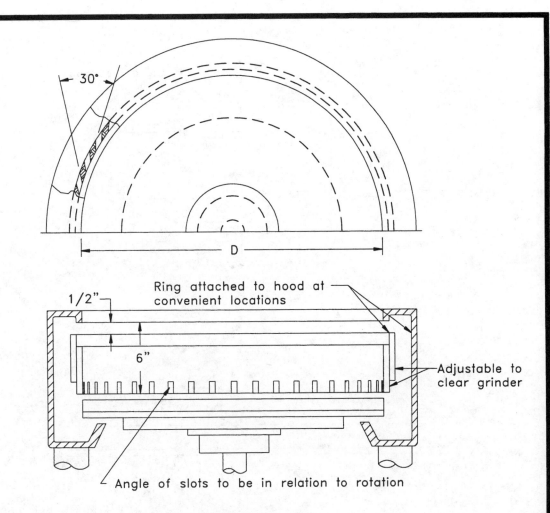

30°

Ring attached to hood at convenient locations

1/2"

6"

Adjustable to clear grinder

Angle of slots to be in relation to rotation

D

EXHAUST FLOW RATE, cfm

Disc diameter inches	1/2 or more of disc covered		Disc not covered	
	No.*	Exhaust flow rate, cfm	No.*	Exhaust flow rate, cfm
Up to 20	1	500	2	780
20 to 30	2	780	2	1500
30 to 53	2	1800	4	3500
53 to 72	2	3100	5	6000

* Number of exhaust outlets around periphery of hood or equal distribution provided by other means.

Minimum slot velocity = 2000 fpm
Minimum duct velocity = 4000 fpm
$h_e = 1.0\ VP_s + 0.5\ VP_d$

AMERICAN CONFERENCE OF GOVERNMENTAL INDUSTRIAL HYGIENISTS	*VERTICAL SPINDLE DISC GRINDER*	
	DATE *02-91*	FIGURE *VS-80-14*

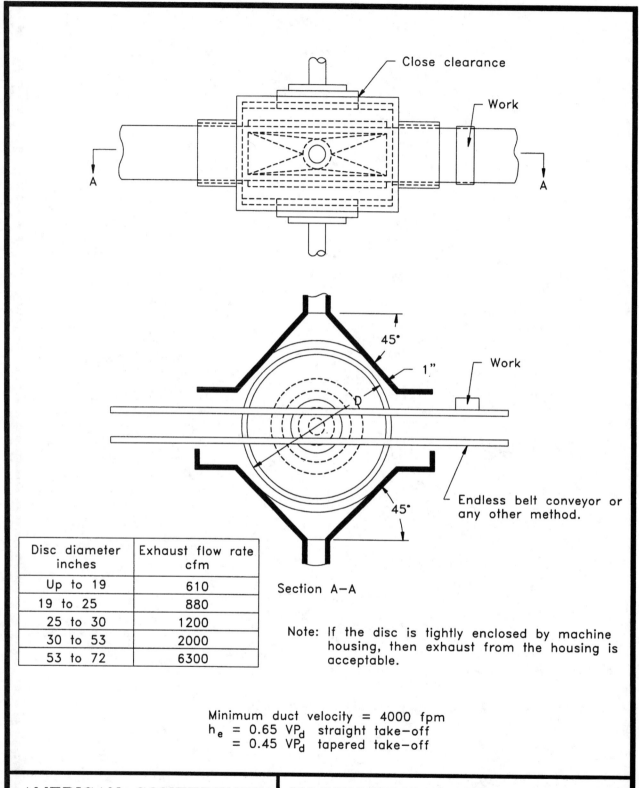

Disc diameter inches	Exhaust flow rate cfm
Up to 19	610
19 to 25	880
25 to 30	1200
30 to 53	2000
53 to 72	6300

Close clearance

Work

45°

1"

Work

Endless belt conveyor or any other method.

45°

Section A—A

Note: If the disc is tightly enclosed by machine housing, then exhaust from the housing is acceptable.

Minimum duct velocity = 4000 fpm
$h_e = 0.65 \ VP_d$ straight take-off
$\quad = 0.45 \ VP_d$ tapered take-off

AMERICAN CONFERENCE OF GOVERNMENTAL INDUSTRIAL HYGIENISTS	*HORIZONTAL DOUBLE—SPINDLE DISC GRINDER*	
	DATE *02—91*	FIGURE *VS—80—15*

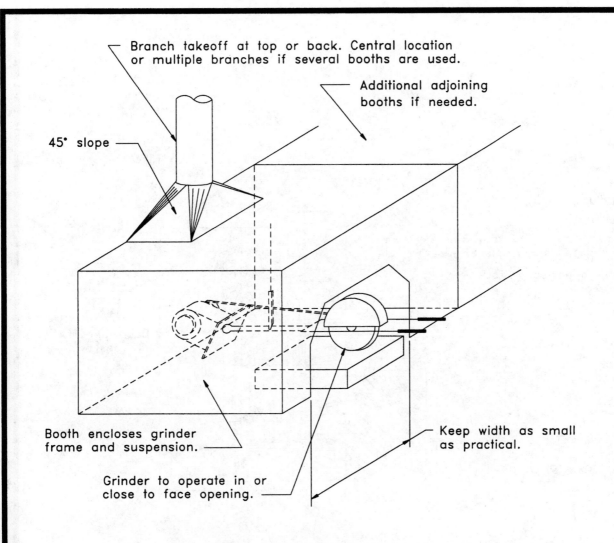

Branch takeoff at top or back. Central location or multiple branches if several booths are used.

Additional adjoining booths if needed.

45° slope

Booth encloses grinder frame and suspension.

Grinder to operate in or close to face opening.

Keep width as small as practical.

For a large opening, 4' to 6' wide
$Q = 150 \ \text{cfm/ft}^2$ of opening

For a small opening, 2' to 2'-6" with grinder in front
$Q = 200 \ \text{cfm/ft}^2$ of opening

Minimum duct velocity = 3500 fpm
$h_e = 0.25 \ VP_d$

NOTE: Small local exhaust hoods mounted behind grinder wheel may trap the stream of sparks, but are usually not effective in control of airborne dust.

AMERICAN CONFERENCE OF GOVERNMENTAL INDUSTRIAL HYGIENISTS	*SWING GRINDER*	
	DATE *02-91*	FIGURE *VS-80-16*

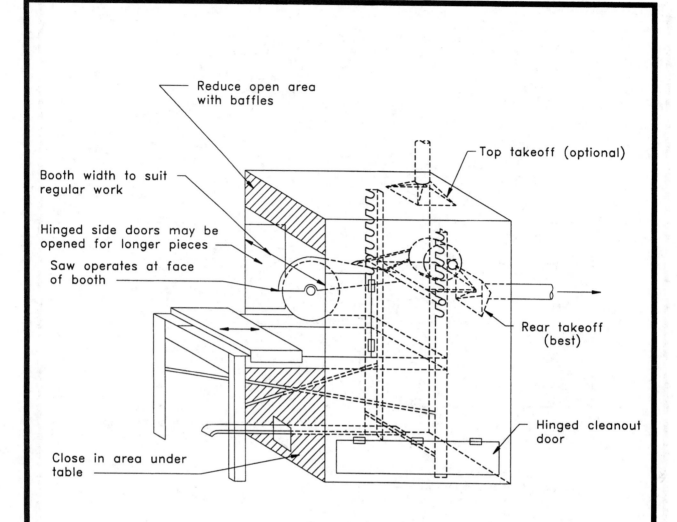

Reduce open area with baffles

Top takeoff (optional)

Booth width to suit regular work

Hinged side doors may be opened for longer pieces

Saw operates at face of booth

Rear takeoff (best)

Close in area under table

Hinged cleanout door

$Q = 250$ cfm/ft^2 of open face area
Minimum duct velocity = 4000 fpm
$h_e = 0.50$ VP_d (no taper)
$ 0.25$ VP_d (with 45° taper)

AMERICAN CONFERENCE OF GOVERNMENTAL INDUSTRIAL HYGIENISTS	ABRASIVE CUT-OFF SAW	
	DATE 02-91	FIGURE VS-80-17

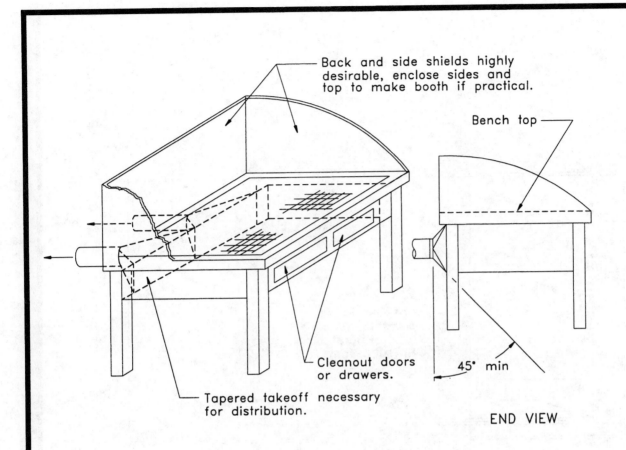

Back and side shields highly desirable, enclose sides and top to make booth if practical.

Bench top

Cleanout doors or drawers.

Tapered takeoff necessary for distribution.

45° min

END VIEW

$Q = 150-250$ cfm/ft^2 of bench area.
Minimum duct velocity = 3500 fpm
$h_e = 0.25$ VP$_d$
If slots are used for distribution
$h_e = 1.78$ VP$_s$ + 0.25 VP$_d$

Notes: 1. If grinding in a booth, use 100 fpm face velocity.
2. For downdraft grilles in floor: $Q=100$ cfm/ft^2 of working area.
3. Provide equal distribution.
4. Provide for cleanout.

AMERICAN CONFERENCE OF GOVERNMENTAL INDUSTRIAL HYGIENISTS	*HAND GRINDING BENCH*	
	DATE *02-91*	FIGURE *VS-80-18*

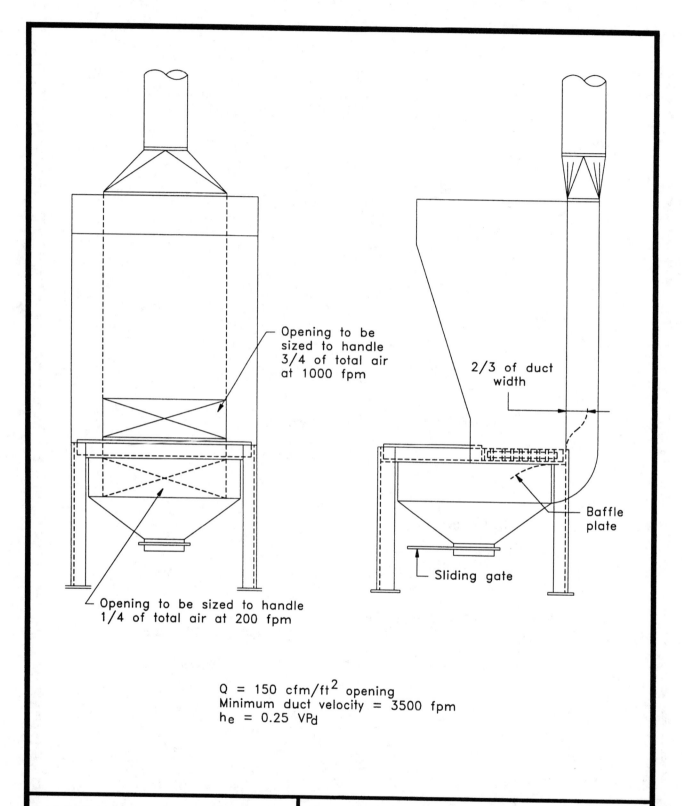

Opening to be
sized to handle
3/4 of total air
at 1000 fpm

Opening to be sized to handle
1/4 of total air at 200 fpm

2/3 of duct
width

Baffle
plate

Sliding gate

$Q = 150$ cfm/ft^2 opening
Minimum duct velocity = 3500 fpm
$h_e = 0.25$ VP$_d$

AMERICAN CONFERENCE OF GOVERNMENTAL INDUSTRIAL HYGIENISTS	PORTABLE CHIPPING AND GRINDING TABLE	
	DATE 02-91	FIGURE VS-80-19

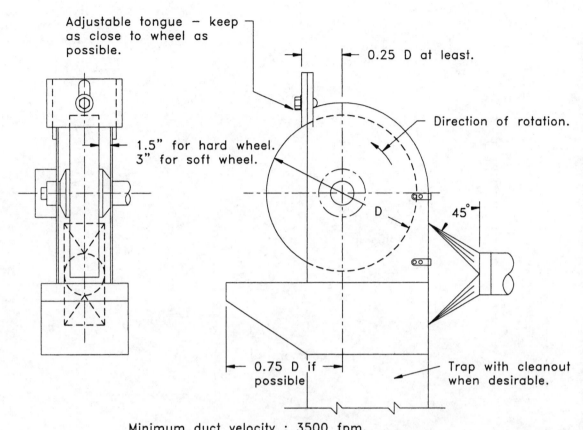

Adjustable tongue – keep as close to wheel as possible.

0.25 D at least.

Direction of rotation.

1.5" for hard wheel.
3" for soft wheel.

D

45°

0.75 D if possible

Trap with cleanout when desirable.

Minimum duct velocity : 3500 fpm,
4500 fpm if material is wet or sticky
$h_e = 0.65\ VP_d$ for straight take-off.
$h_e = 0.40\ VP_d$ for tapered take-off.

Wheel diam. inches	Wheel width inches	Exhaust flow rate cfm	Exhaust flow rate cfm
		Good enclosure *	Poor enclosure
Up to 9	2	300	400
over 9 to 16	3	500	610
over 16 to 19	4	610	740
over 19 to 24	5	740	1200
over 24 to 30	6	1040	1500
over 30 to 36	6	1200	2000

* not more than 25% of the wheel is exposed
Note : Consult applicable NFPA codes Reference 10.80.2
Caution : Do not mix ferrous and non-ferrous metals
in same exhaust system.

AMERICAN CONFERENCE OF GOVERNMENTAL INDUSTRIAL HYGIENISTS	*MANUAL BUFFING AND POLISHING*
	DATE *02-91* FIGURE *VS-80-30*

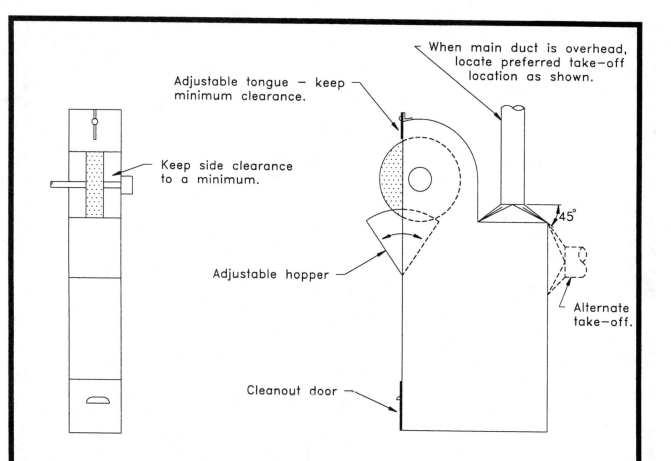

When main duct is overhead,
locate preferred take—off
location as shown.

Adjustable tongue — keep
minimum clearance.

Keep side clearance
to a minimum.

Adjustable hopper

45°

Alternate
take—off.

Cleanout door

Wheel diam. inches	Wheel width inches	Exhaust flow rate cfm
Up to 9	2	400
9 to 16	3	610
16 to 19	4	740
19 to 24	5	1200
24 to 30	6	1500
30 to 36	6	1900

Note: For wider wheels than listed, increase cfm with width
Minimum duct velocity = 3500 fpm
4500 fpm if material is wet or sticky

$$h_e = 0.40 \ VP_d$$

Notes: 1. Consult applicable NFPA codes. See Reference 10.80.2
2. For titanium, aluminum, and magnesium, eliminate hopper
use 5000 fpm through hood cross—section.
3. Caution : Do not mix ferrous and non—ferrous metals in same exhaust system.

AMERICAN CONFERENCE OF GOVERNMENTAL INDUSTRIAL HYGIENISTS	BUFFING LATHE	
	DATE *02–91*	FIGURE *VS–80–31*

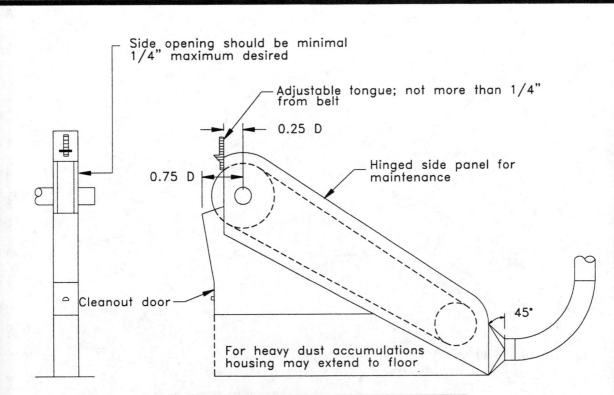

Side opening should be minimal 1/4" maximum desired

Adjustable tongue; not more than 1/4" from belt

0.25 D

Hinged side panel for maintenance

0.75 D

Cleanout door

45°

For heavy dust accumulations housing may extend to floor

Belt width inches	Exhaust flow rate cfm	Exhaust flow rate cfm
	Good enclosure *	Enclosure
1 1/2	220	300
2	390	610
3	500	740
4	610	880
5	880	1200
6	1200	1570

* Hood as shown; no more than 25% of wheel exposed.

$$h_e = 0.40 \ VP_d$$

Minimum duct velocity = 3500 fpm, 4500 fpm if wet or sticky.

Notes:

1. Consult applicable NFPA codes, 10.80.2

2. For titanium, aluminum and magnesium eliminate hopper and use 5000 fpm through hood cross section.

3. Caution: do not mix ferrous and non-ferrous metals in same exhaust system.

AMERICAN CONFERENCE OF GOVERNMENTAL INDUSTRIAL HYGIENISTS	BACKSTAND IDLER POLISHING MACHINE
	DATE 02-91 FIGURE VS-80-32

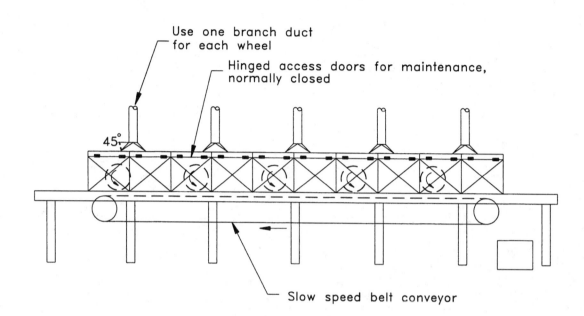

Use one branch duct for each wheel

Hinged access doors for maintenance, normally closed

45°

Slow speed belt conveyor

Q = 500 cfm/wheel, minimum
        Not less than 250 cfm/ft^2 total open area
Minimum duct velocity = 3500 fpm, 4500 fpm if
                                material is wet or sticky
$h_e = 1.78\ VP_s + 0.25\ VP_d$

Note:
1. Consult applicable NFPA standards. Reference 10.80.2
2. Caution: Do not mix ferrous and non-ferrous metals in same exhaust system.
3. Wheel adjustments on outside of enclosure.
4. For highly toxic material, enclose the return strand of the belt conveyor.

AMERICAN CONFERENCE OF GOVERNMENTAL INDUSTRIAL HYGIENISTS	STRAIGHT LINE AUTOMATIC BUFFING	
	DATE *02—91*	FIGURE *VS—80—33*

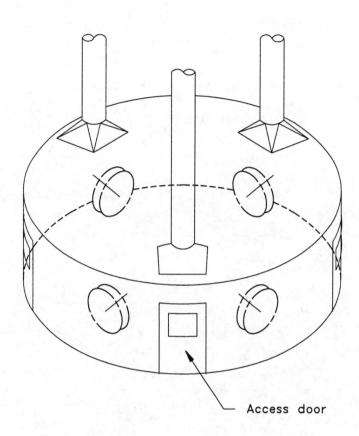

Access door

$$Q = 500 \text{ cfm/wheel, minimum,}$$
Not less than 250 cfm/ft^2 total open area
Minimum duct velocity = 3500 fpm, 4500 fpm if
material is wet or sticky
$$h_e = 1.78 \text{ VP}_s + 0.25 \text{ VP}_d$$

On small, 2 or 3 spindle machines, one take-off may be used
Multiple take-offs desirable.

Note:
1. Consult applicable NFPA standards, Reference 10.80.2
2. Caution: Do not mix ferrous and non-ferrous
   metals in same exhaust system.

AMERICAN CONFERENCE OF GOVERNMENTAL INDUSTRIAL HYGIENISTS	*CIRCULAR AUTOMATIC BUFFING*	
	DATE *02-91*	FIGURE *VS-80-34*

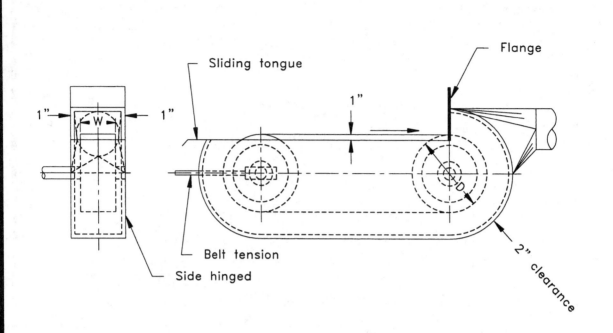

Belt width, inches	Exhaust flow rate, cfm
Up to 3	220
3 to 5	300
5 to 7	390
7 to 9	500
9 to 11	610
11 to 13	740

Minimum duct velocity = 3500 fpm, 4500 fpm if material is wet or sticky

h_e = 0.65 VP_d for straight take-off
0.45 VP_d for tapered take-off

Notes:
1. Consult applicable NFPA codes Reference 10.80.2
2. Caution : Do not mix ferrous and non-ferrous metals in same exhaust system

AMERICAN CONFERENCE OF GOVERNMENTAL INDUSTRIAL HYGIENISTS	*METAL POLISHING BELT*	
	DATE *02-91*	FIGURE *VS-80-35*

10.85 VEHICLE VENTILATION

The objective of providing ventilation for vehicles in an environment is to keep a worker's exposure to toxic exhaust fumes and gases below the TLV, both the TWA and STEL, or other appropriate standards. This can be achieved either by dilution or local exhaust ventilation.

It is difficult to establish dilution ventilation requirements accurately for the operating vehicles in a plant. For an existing facility, the designer has the opportunity to measure the emission in the field. Standard techniques can be used to measure gas flow rates, composition, temperatures, and contaminant levels. Using the equations in Chapter 2 and the measurements, the dilution rates can be calculated. However, it is not always possible to accurately determine the contaminant generation rate because generation is not uniform. Moreover, no such data is available to the designer for new vehicles.

The use of dilution ventilation is usually considered only after rejection of the source capture concept. Common reasons for rejecting source capture (local exhaust) are operating interference problems or layout constraints. For lift trucks or cars in motion or idling outside of stalls, local exhaust is not feasible. Hence the only method for control of health hazards is dilution ventilation.

Over the years, some empirical rates have been developed which have been applied successfully to achieve contaminant control. The recommended dilution rates based on average operating conditions are:

5,000 cfm/propane fueled lift truck

8,000 cfm/gasoline fueled lift truck

5,000 cfm/operating automobile

10,000 cfm (or more)/operating truck

100 cfm/horsepower for diesel fueled vehicle

The above dilution rates for lift trucks apply under the following conditions:[10.85.1]

1. A regular maintenance program incorporating final engine tuning through carbon monoxide analysis of exhaust gas must be provided. CO concentration of gases should be limited to 1% for propane fueled trucks; 2% for gasoline fueled trucks.

2. The periods of lift truck engine operation do not exceed 50% of the working day (total engine operation of lift truck equal to or less than 4 hours in an 8-hour shift).

3. A reasonably good distribution of airflow must be provided.

4. The volume of space must amount to 150,000 ft³/lift truck or more.

5. The lift truck is powered by an engine of less than 60 HP.

Where actual operating conditions vary from the above, the ventilation rate should be increased. On the other hand, mechanical ventilation may not be required in large buildings where lift truck operation is intermittent and where natural infiltration based on a maximum of one air change/hour for the net building volume exceeds the recommended dilution ventilation rate.

The alternative to dilution ventilation is to capture the contaminant at the source by installing local exhaust ventilation. For stationary vehicles in service garages, effective systems are shown in VS-85-01 (overhead) and VS-85-02 (under floor). The systems should be connected directly to the vehicle exhaust and should terminate outdoors above the roof. The design procedure outlined in Chapter 5 must be followed. For friction loss data of flexible ducts, manufacturers should be contacted. As with all flexible systems, the length of flexible duct must be minimized, and non-collapsible duct should be used. Unnecessary and/or sharp bends should be avoided. Exhaust requirements for automobiles are shown in VS-85-02 and for diesel engines in VS-85-03.

The requirements for parking or storage garages should be based on short term exposure of drivers to exhaust emissions when entering or departing. A continuous supply of 500 cfm fresh air/parking space should be adequate. Additional ventilation may be required if there are long periods of engine idling (winter warm-ups, loading, etc.) or if the general traffic pattern is such that clusters of vehicles arrive or depart.

Attendant booths of parking garages should be pressurized with a suply of fresh air from uncontaminated sources.

For indoor loading docks, continuous supply of 2 cfm/ft² of dock area should be adequate where truck motors are shut off except when entering or leaving the dock.

REFERENCES

10.85.1 Hama, G. M.; Butler, Jr., K. E.: Ventilation Requirements for Lift Truck Operation. Heating, Piping and Air Conditioning (January 1970).

10.85.2 Goldfield, J.; Sheehy, J. W.; Gunter, J. W.; Daniels, W. J.: An Affordable Ventilation Control for Radiator Repair Shops. Ventilation '91: 3rd International Symposium on Ventilation for Contaminant Control. American Conference of Governmental Industrial Hygienists, Cincinnati, OH (1993).

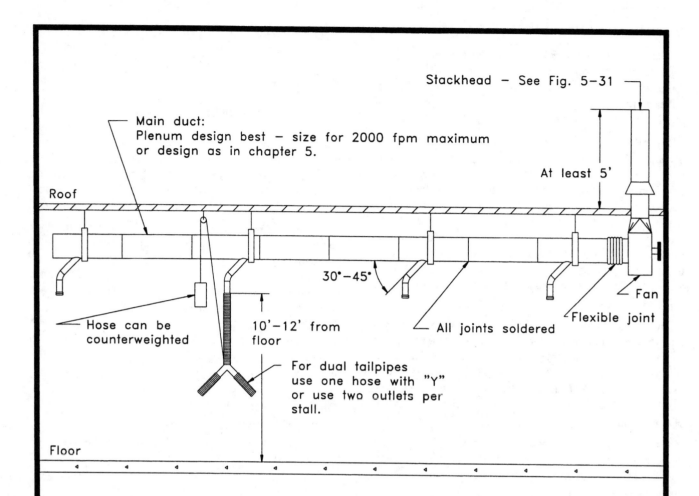

Main duct:
Plenum design best — size for 2000 fpm maximum
or design as in chapter 5.

Stackhead — See Fig. 5-31

At least 5'

Roof

30°-45°

Fan

Flexible joint

Hose can be
counterweighted

10'-12' from
floor

All joints soldered

For dual tailpipes
use one hose with "Y"
or use two outlets per
stall.

Floor

Vehicle horsepower (hp)	cfm/vehicle	Flexible duct diam.	Branch connection
Up to 200	100	3"	4"
Over 200	200	4"	4"
Diesel trucks	See VS-85-03		

On dynamometer test rolls
   Automobiles and light duty trucks = 350 cfm
   Heavy duty trucks   = 1200 cfm minimum

For friction loss of flexible duct; consult manufacturers' data.

See VS-85-02

AMERICAN CONFERENCE OF GOVERNMENTAL INDUSTRIAL HYGIENISTS	SERVICE GARAGE VENTILATION OVERHEAD	
	DATE 12-90	FIGURE VS-85-01

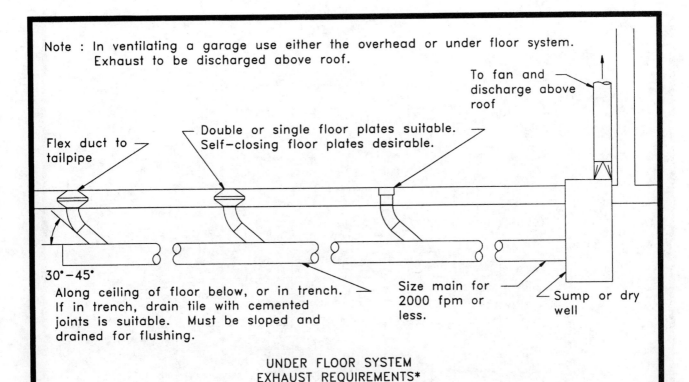

Note : In ventilating a garage use either the overhead or under floor system. Exhaust to be discharged above roof.

To fan and discharge above roof

Double or single floor plates suitable. Self-closing floor plates desirable.

Flex duct to tailpipe

30°-45°

Along ceiling of floor below, or in trench. If in trench, drain tile with cemented joints is suitable. Must be sloped and drained for flushing.

Size main for 2000 fpm or less.

Sump or dry well

UNDER FLOOR SYSTEM
EXHAUST REQUIREMENTS*

Type	cfm per vehicle	Flex duct ID (min)
Automobiles and trucks up to 200 hp	100	3"
Automobiles and trucks over 200 hp	200	4"**
Diesel	See VS-85-03	

* On dynamometer test rolls
  Automobiles and light duty trucks = 350 cfm
  Heavy duty trucks = 1200 cfm minimum

** 3" diam. permissible for short runs with proper fan.
   For friction loss of flexible duct; consult manufacturers' data.

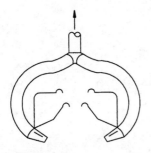

Use adapters on dual exhausts and special tailpipes.

AMERICAN CONFERENCE OF GOVERNMENTAL INDUSTRIAL HYGIENISTS	*SERVICE GARAGE VENTILATION UNDERFLOOR*
	DATE *12-90* FIGURE *VS-85-02*

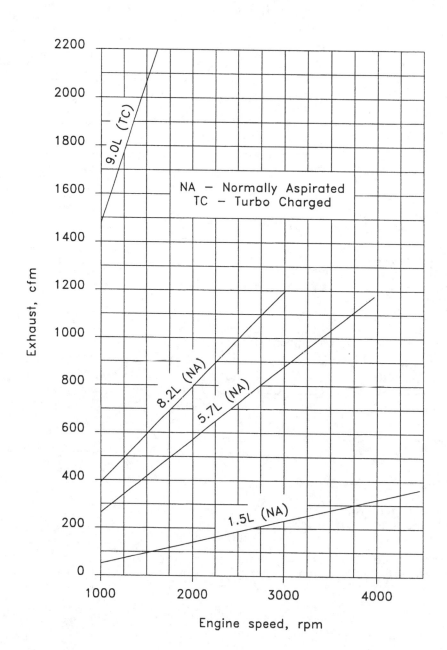

Exhaust, cfm = acfm + 20% excess
For specific design information request manufacturers 13 mode
EPA engine bench test

AMERICAN CONFERENCE OF GOVERNMENTAL INDUSTRIAL HYGIENISTS	EXHAUST SYSTEM REQUIREMENTS FOR TYPICAL DIESEL ENGINES UNDER LOAD	
	DATE 12-90	FIGURE VS-85-03

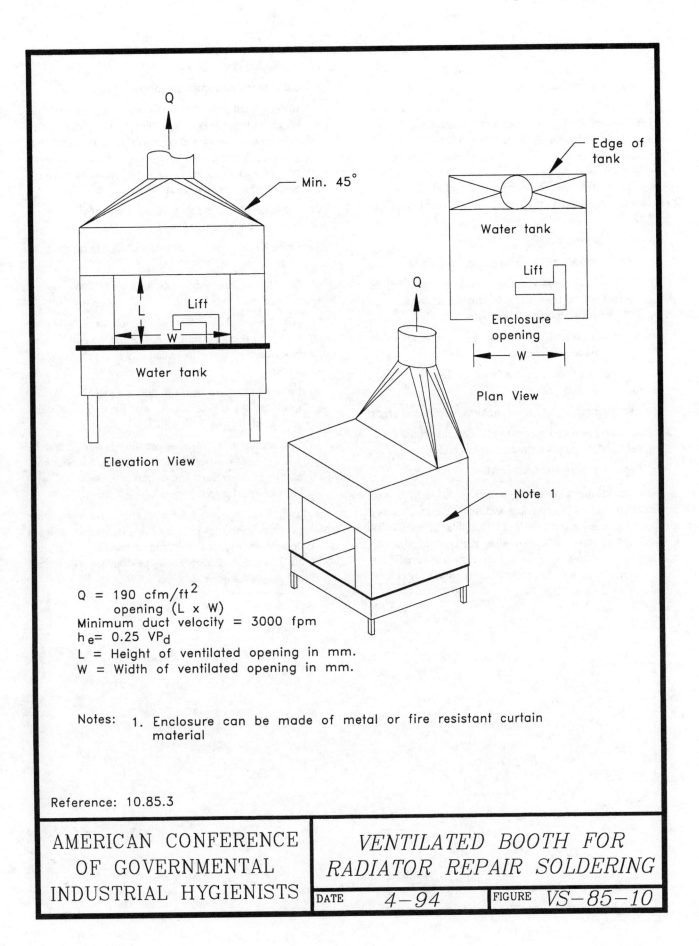

Q

Min. 45°

L

Lift

W

Water tank

Elevation View

Edge of
tank

Water tank

Q

Lift

Enclosure
opening

W

Plan View

Note 1

$Q = 190$ cfm/ft^2
     opening (L x W)
Minimum duct velocity = 3000 fpm
$h_e = 0.25$ VP$_d$
L = Height of ventilated opening in mm.
W = Width of ventilated opening in mm.

Notes: 1. Enclosure can be made of metal or fire resistant curtain
           material

Reference: 10.85.3

AMERICAN CONFERENCE OF GOVERNMENTAL INDUSTRIAL HYGIENISTS	VENTILATED BOOTH FOR RADIATOR REPAIR SOLDERING
	DATE *4-94* FIGURE *VS-85-10*

10.90 WELDING AND CUTTING

The purpose of welding and cutting ventilation is to control gases, fumes, and particulate generated during the welding and cutting operations.

10.90.1 Hazards: The generation rate of fumes and gases varies with the composition of the base metal, fluxes, and fillers, and with the rate and depth of welding. Exposure to the welder varies with the generation rate, duration and frequency of operations, work practices (particularly distance of the plume from the breathing zone), and the effectiveness of ventilation.

Contaminants from welding may include:

1. fume from the base metals and filler or electrode metals

2. fume from coatings (e.g., zinc oxide from galvanized surfaces, thoria from T.I.G. welding, and fluorides and NO_2 from electrode coatings)

3. ozone due to ionization of oxygen by the ultraviolet light from arc welding

4. carbon monoxide from ultraviolet effects on carbon dioxide in shield gas

5. shield gases such as carbon dioxide, helium, and argon

6. fluoride gases and other thermal decomposition products of fluxes and electrode coatings and

7. flammable gases such as acetylene.

There are welding tasks that present enhanced hazards such as welding on materials containing or contaminated with heavy metals or welding in the presence of flammable vapors or halogenated hydrocarbons. If such welding is required, extraordinary precautions must be taken on a case-by-case basis. Even in the absence of such hazard materials, any welding operation in a confined space is potentially lethal and requires continuous and copious dilution ventilation.

10.90.2 General Recommendations:

1. Choose hood designs in the following descending order of effectiveness: enclosing hoods, vacuum nozzles, fixed slot/plenum hood on a worktable or rectangular hood fixed above a worktable, moveable hood above a worktable, moveable hood hanging freely or overhead canopy, dilution ventilation.

2. Integrate planning for ventilation systems with planning for materials handling.

3. Place welding curtains or other barriers to block cross-drafts.

4. Install turntables, work rests, and other aids to improve utilization of the hoods.

5. Avoid recirculating filtered air from welding hoods back into occupied spaces unless the welding is low-hazard and produces low quantities of gaseous contaminants.

6. Face velocity for enclosing hoods should be 100-130 fpm with the higher values used for poor conditions such as high cross-draft velocities.

7. Capture velocity for non-enclosing hoods should be 100-170 fpm with the higher values used for poor conditions such as high cross-draft velocities and with higher hazard levels.

Enclosing hoods are by far the most effective in controlling welding contaminants; however, they restrict access and force reconsideration of material and product handling. Capturing hoods are less effective than enclosures but for low hazard conditions can be adequate if properly used.

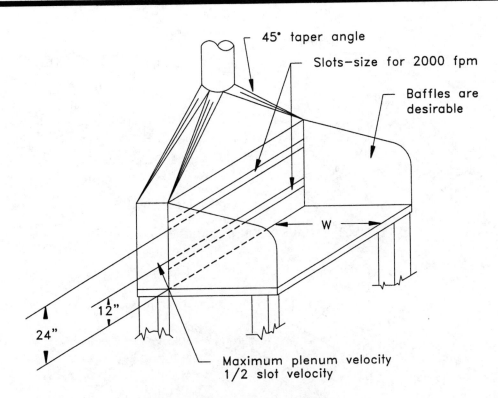

45° taper angle

Slots—size for 2000 fpm

Baffles are desirable

W

$1\frac{1}{2}$"

24"

Maximum plenum velocity
1/2 slot velocity

Q = 350 cfm/ft of hood length
Hood length = required working space
W = 24" maximum, if W>24" see chapter 3
Minimum duct velocity = 2000 fpm
$h_e = 1.78\ VP_s + 0.25\ VP_d$

General ventilation, where local exhaust can not be used:

Rod, diam.	Cfm/welder
5/32	1000
3/16	1500
1/4	3500
3/8	4500

or

A. For open areas, where welding fume can rise away from the breathing zone:
cfm required = 800 x lb/hour rod used

B. For enclosed areas or positions where fume does not readily escape breathing zone:
cfm required = 1600 x lb/hour rod used

For toxic materials higher airflows are necessary and operator may require respiratory protection equipment.

Other types of hoods
Local exhaust: See VS—90—02
Booth: For design see VS—90—30
Q = 100 cfm/ft ^{2} of face opening
MIG welding may require precise air flow control

AMERICAN CONFERENCE OF GOVERNMENTAL INDUSTRIAL HYGIENISTS	*WELDING VENTILATION BENCH HOOD*	
	DATE *1—91*	FIGURE *VS—90—01*

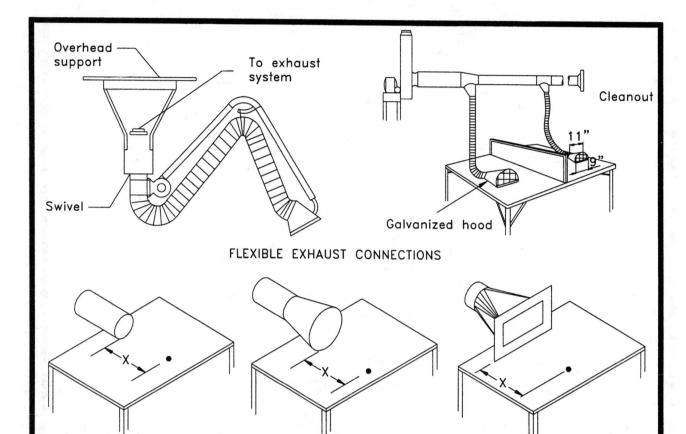

FLEXIBLE EXHAUST CONNECTIONS

PLAIN DUCT   CONE HOOD.   FLANGED HOOD

RATE OF EXHAUST

X, inches	Plain duct cfm	Flange or cone, cfm
Up to 6	335	250
6–9	755	560
9–12	1335	1000

Face velocity = 1500 fpm
Minimum duct velocity = 3000 fpm
Plain duct entry loss = 0.93 VP_d
Flange or cone entry loss = 0.25 VP_d

Notes:
1. Locate work as close as possible to hood.
2. Hoods perform best when located to the side of the work.
3. Ventilation rates may be inadequate for toxic materials.
4. Velocities above 100–200 fpm may disturb shield gas.

GENERAL VENTILATION, where local exhaust cannot be used :

Rod, diam.	cfm/welder
5/32	1000
3/16	1500
1/4	3500
3/8	4500

OR

A. For open areas, where welding fume can rise away from the breathing zone:
   cfm required = 800 x lb/hour rod used
B. For enclosed areas or positions where fume does not readily escape breathing zone:
   cfm required = 1600 x lb/hour rod used

For toxic materials higher airflows are necessary and operator should use respiratory protection equipment.

Other types of hoods
Bench, see VS–90–01
Booth, for design see VS–90–30
Q = 100 cfm/ft^2 of face opening

AMERICAN CONFERENCE OF GOVERNMENTAL INDUSTRIAL HYGIENISTS	*WELDING VENTILATION* *MOVABLE EXHAUST HOODS*
	DATE *1–91* FIGURE *VS–90–02*

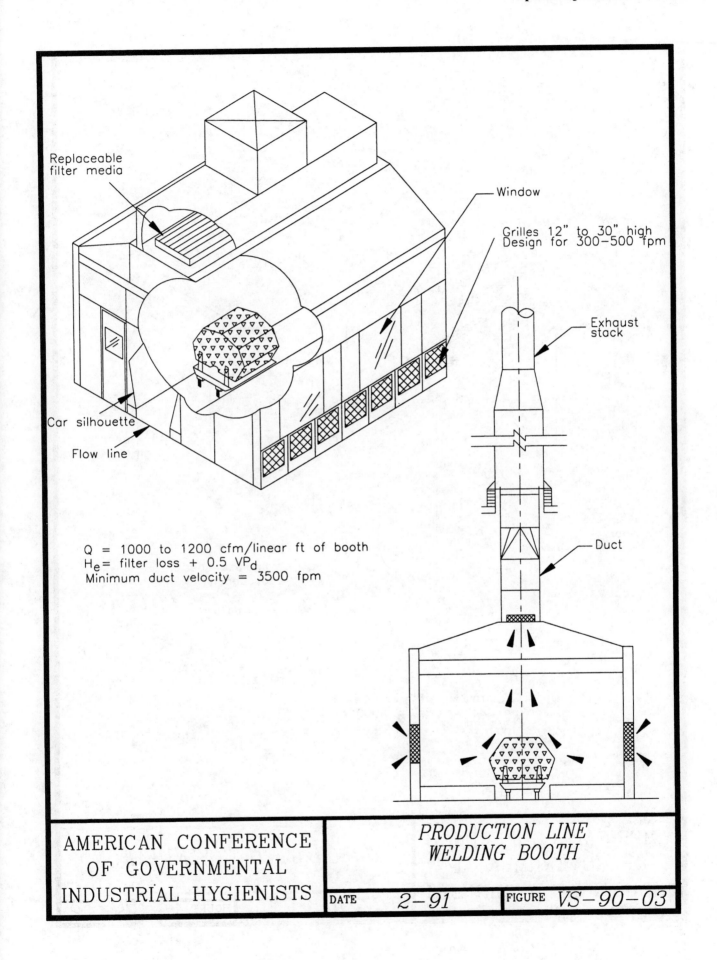

Replaceable
filter media

Window

Grilles 12" to 30" high
Design for 300-500 fpm

Exhaust
stack

Car silhouette

Flow line

Duct

Q = 1000 to 1200 cfm/linear ft of booth
H_e = filter loss + 0.5 VP_d
Minimum duct velocity = 3500 fpm

AMERICAN CONFERENCE OF GOVERNMENTAL INDUSTRIAL HYGIENISTS	PRODUCTION LINE WELDING BOOTH	
	DATE *2-91*	FIGURE *VS-90-03*

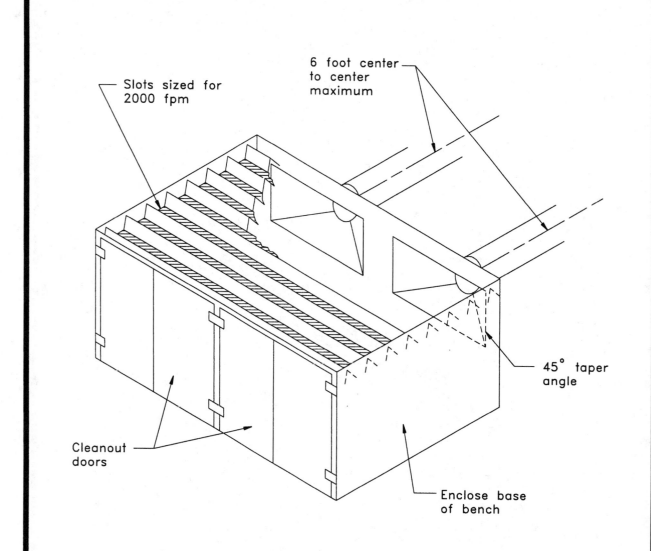

Slots sized for
2000 fpm

6 foot center
to center
maximum

45° taper
angle

Cleanout
doors

Enclose base
of bench

Q = 150 cfm/ft^2 of gross bench area
Minimum duct velocity = 4000 fpm
$h_e = 1.78\ VP_s + 0.25\ VP_d$

AMERICAN CONFERENCE OF GOVERNMENTAL INDUSTRIAL HYGIENISTS	*TORCH CUTTING VENTILATION*	
	DATE *1-91*	FIGURE *VS-90-10*

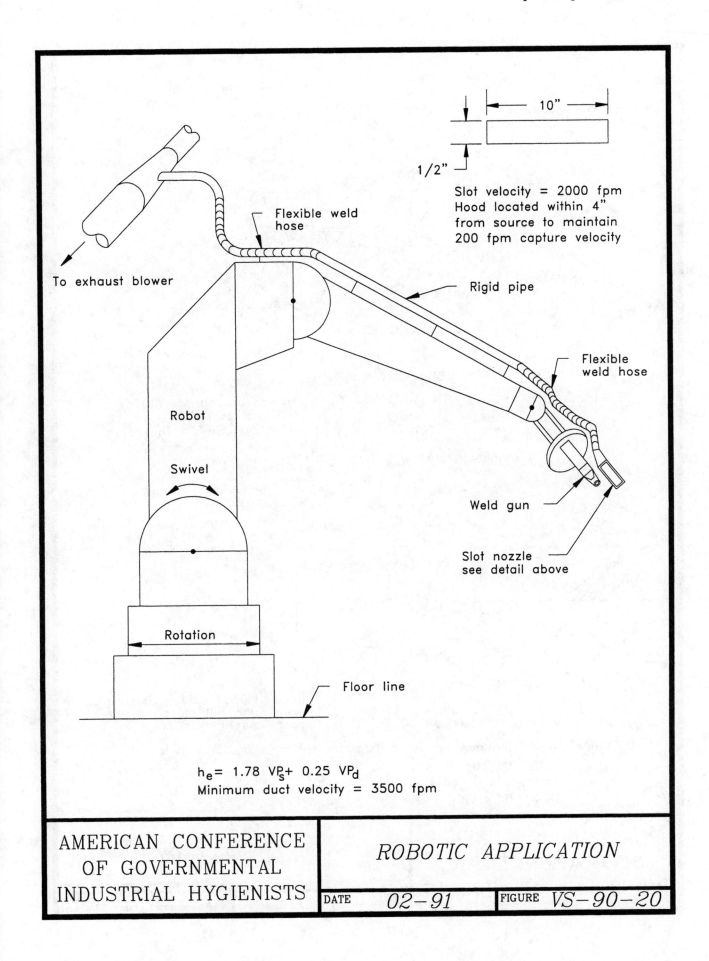

10"

1/2"

Slot velocity = 2000 fpm
Hood located within 4"
from source to maintain
200 fpm capture velocity

Flexible weld
hose

To exhaust blower

Rigid pipe

Flexible
weld hose

Robot

Swivel

Weld gun

Rotation

Slot nozzle
see detail above

Floor line

$h_e = 1.78\ VP_s + 0.25\ VP_d$
Minimum duct velocity = 3500 fpm

AMERICAN CONFERENCE OF GOVERNMENTAL INDUSTRIAL HYGIENISTS	*ROBOTIC APPLICATION*	
	DATE *02-91*	FIGURE *VS-90-20*

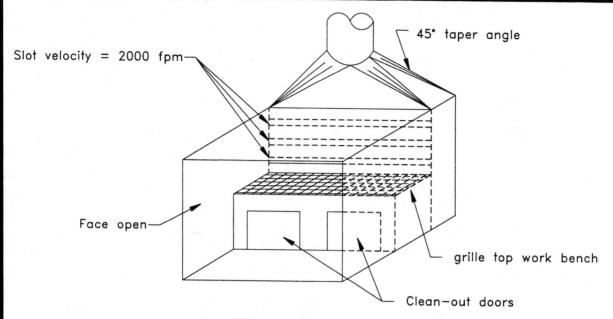

Slot velocity = 2000 fpm

45° taper angle

Face open

grille top work bench

Clean-out doors

METALLIZING BOOTH

<u>Non-toxic:</u> Q = 150 cfm/ft² face area   <u>Toxic:</u> Provide appropriate NIOSH
certified respirator
Q = 200 cfm/ft² face area

Minimum duct velocity = 3500 fpm
$h_e = 1.78\ VP_s + 0.25\ VP_d$
Small lathe, etc., may be mounted in booth

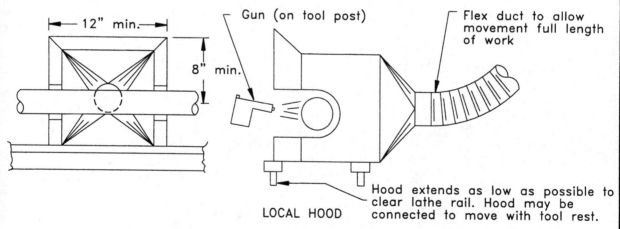

|← 12" min. →|

8" min.

Gun (on tool post)

Flex duct to allow
movement full length
of work

LOCAL HOOD

Hood extends as low as possible to
clear lathe rail. Hood may be
connected to move with tool rest.

Note: Local hood may not be satisfactory for spraying toxic metals.
Q = 200 cfm/ft² face openings
Minimum duct velocity = 3500 fpm
$h_e = 0.25\ VP_d$

AMERICAN CONFERENCE OF GOVERNMENTAL INDUSTRIAL HYGIENISTS	*METAL SPRAYING*	
	DATE *1-91*	FIGURE *VS-90-30*

10.95 WOODWORKING

Woodworking equipment generates large amounts of wood dust by abrasive or cutting action. It is important to provide good ventilation for all equipment as the broad particle size distribution of wood dust creates the potential for both health, housekeeping problems, and fire hazards. Excessive amounts of dust, if allowed to accumulate inside equipment and in shop areas, can create fire or explosion hazards. An additional consideration should be the toxicity of the wood species used.

In many instances, woodworking equipment, such as saws and sanders, generates airflow patterns which make dust control difficult. Exhaust hoods should enclose the operation as much as possible. Where the equipment tends to eject wood dust (e.g., at sanding belt pulleys) the exhaust hood should be placed in the ejection path.

Enclosures must incorporate cleanout doors to prevent dust build-up. Duct velocities should be maintained at a minimum of 3500 fpm to prevent settling and subsequent clogging of the duct.

Exhaust flow rates will vary with equipment type and size. Design data are provided for a number of operations in VS-10-95-1 through 10-95-20 and in Table 10.95.1. The exhaust flow rates for many hoods shown in this section were developed based on the specific configuration shown in the drawings. The drawings show well-designed hoods that may not be found in woodworking equipment purchased "off-the-shelf." Readers are cautioned to evaluate the configuration of the specific equipment intended for use in their shop. In many cases, the recommended exhaust flow rates or hood static pressure must be increased to accommodate single exhaust ports, smaller duct connections, non-tapered entries, openings in equipment bases, etc. Additional information for hand held sanders using Low Volume-High Velocity (LV-HV) can be found in sub-section 10.40. Where information for a specific operation is not provided, data for similar listed operations can be used.

REFERENCES

10.95.1 Hampl, V.; Johnston O.: Control of Wood Dust from Horizontal Belt Sanding. American Industrial Hygiene Association Journal, 46, 10, pp. 567-577 (1985).

10.95.2 Hampl, V., and Johnston, O.,: Control of Wood Dust from Disc Sanders, Applied Occupational Hygiene, 6(11): 938-944 (November 1991).

10.95.3 Topmiller, J. L.; Watkins, D. A.; Schulman, S. A.; Murdock, D. J.: Controlling Wood Dust from Orbital Hand Sanders. Applied Occupational Hygiene, 11(9): 1131-1138 (September 1996).

10.95.4 Hampl, V.; Toppmiller, J. L.; Watkins, D. S.; Murdock, D. J.: Control of Wood Dust from Rotational Hand Sanders. Applied Occupational Environmental Hygiene, 7(4): 263-270 (April 1992).

TABLE 10.95.1 Miscellaneous Woodworking Machinery not Given in VS Prints

The following list of recommended exhaust volumes is for average-sized woodworking machines and is based on many years of experience. It must be noted that some modern, high-speed, or extra-large machines will produce such a large volume of waste that greater exhaust volumes must be used. Similarly, some small machines of the home workshop or bench type may use less exhaust air than listed.

SELF-FEED TABLE RIP SAW

Saw Diameter, inches	Exhaust Flow Rate, cfm		
	Bottom	Top	Total
Up to 16 inclusive	440	350	790
Over 16	550	350	900
Self-feed, not on table	800	550	1350

GANG RIP SAWS

Saw Diameter, inches	Exhaust Flow Rate, cfm		
	Bottom	Top	Total
Up to 24, inclusive	550	350	900
Over 24 to 36, incl.	800	440	1240
Over 36 to 48, incl.	1100	550	1650
Over 48	1400	550	2060

VERTICAL BELT SANDERS
(rear belt and both pulleys enclosed)
and
TOP RUN HORIZONTAL SANDERS

Belt Width, inches	Exhaust Flow Rate, cfm
Up to 6, inclusive	440
Over 6 to 9, inclusive	550
Over 9 to 14, inclusive	800
Over 14	1100
Swing Arm Sander	2200

SINGLE PLANERS OR SURFACERS

	Exhaust Flow Rate, cfm
Up to 20" knives	785
Over 20" to 26" knives	1100
Over 26" to 32" knives	1400
Over 32" to 38" knives	1765
Over 38" knives	2200

DOUBLE PLANERS OR SURFACERS

Saw Diameter, inches	Exhaust Flow Rate, cfm		
	Bottom	Top	Total
Up to 20" knives	550	785	1335
Over 20" to 26" knives	785	1100	1885
Over 26" to 32" knives	1100	1400	2500
Over 32" to 38" knives	1400	1800	3200
Over 38" knives	1400	2200	3600

MOLDERS, MATCHERS, & SIZERS

Size, inches	Exhaust Flow Rate, cfm			
	Bottom	Top	Right	Left
Up to 7 incl.	440	550	350	350
Over 7 to 12, incl.	550	800	440	440
Over 12 to 18, incl.	800	1100	550	550
Over 18 to 24, incl.	1100	1400	800	800
Over 24	1400	1770	1100	1100

	Exhaust Flow Rate, cf,
Sash Stickers	500
Woodshapers	440 to 1400
Tenoner	Same as moulder
Automatic Lathe	800 to 5000
Forming lathe	350 to 1400
Chain mortise	350
Dowel machine	350 to 800
Panel raiser	550
Dovetail and lock corner	550 to 800
Pulley pockets	550
Pulley stile	550
Glue jointer	800
Gainer	350 to 1400
Router	350 to 800
Hogs	
Up to 12" wide	1400
Over 12" wide	3100
Floorsweep	
6" to 8" diameter	800 to 1400

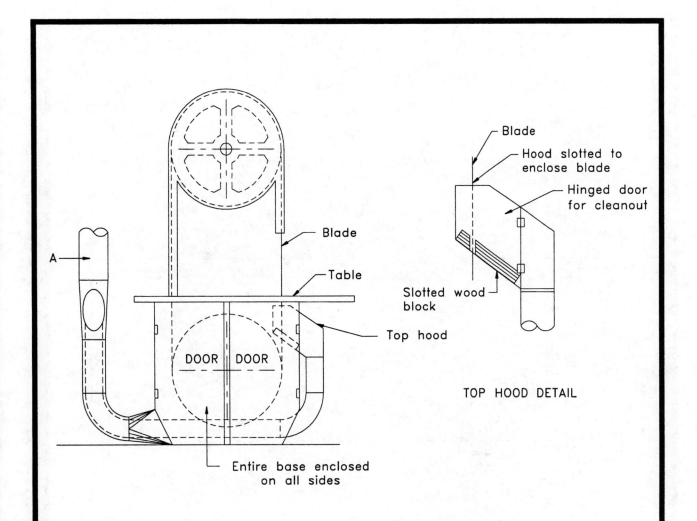

Blade

Hood slotted to
enclose blade

Hinged door
for cleanout

Slotted wood
block

TOP HOOD DETAIL

Blade

A

Table

Top hood

DOOR │ DOOR

Entire base enclosed
on all sides

Blade width, inches	Exhaust flow rate, cfm		
	Bottom	Top	Total
Up to 2	350	350	700
2 to 3	350	550	900
3 to 4	550	800	1350
4 to 6	550	1100	1650
6 yo 8	550	1400	1950

Minimum duct velocity = 3500 fpm
$h_e = 1.75 \ VP_d$ (Point Ⓐ in duct riser)

AMERICAN CONFERENCE OF GOVERNMENTAL INDUSTRIAL HYGIENISTS	*BAND SAW*	
	DATE *12-90*	FIGURE *VS-95-01*

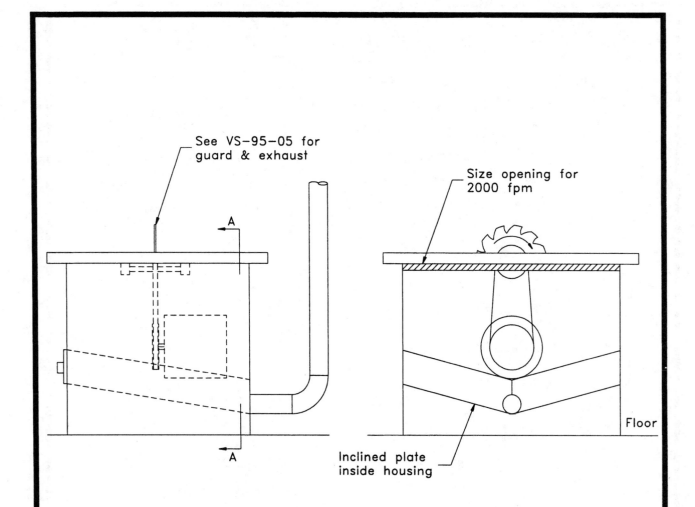

See VS-95-05 for
guard & exhaust

A

A

Size opening for
2000 fpm

Floor

Inclined plate
inside housing

Saw blade diameter, inches	Exhaust flow rate, cfm
Up to 16	350
16 to 24	440
over 24	550
Saw with dado blade	550

Shape	F_s
	1.78
	1.00
	0.49

Minimum duct velocity = 4000 fpm
$$h_e = 1.78\ VP_s + 0.25\ VP_d$$

For Saw Guard ventilation see VS-95-05

AMERICAN CONFERENCE
OF GOVERNMENTAL
INDUSTRIAL HYGIENISTS

FLOOR TABLE SAW

DATE *12-99*

FIGURE *VS-95-02*

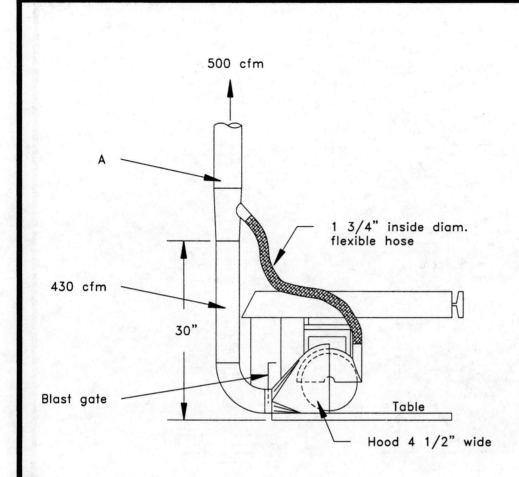

500 cfm

A

1 3/4" inside diam.
flexible hose

430 cfm

30"

Blast gate

Table

Hood 4 1/2" wide

Minimum duct velocity = 4000 fpm
$h_e = 3.5\ VP_d$ (point A in duct riser)

For booth enclosure, see VS−80−17

AMERICAN CONFERENCE
OF GOVERNMENTAL
INDUSTRIAL HYGIENISTS

RADIAL ARM SAW

DATE *12−90*   FIGURE *VS−95−03*

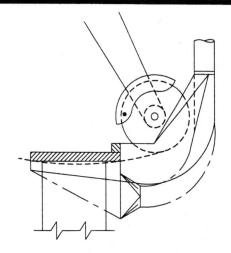

Type hood where table
is cut through

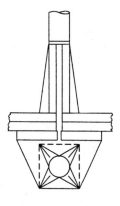

Front view
of hood

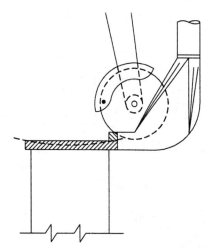

Type hood where table
is not cut through

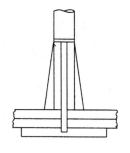

Front view
of hood

Saw diameter, inches	Exh. flow rate cfm
Up to 20 incl.	350
over 20	440

Minimum duct velocity = 4000 fpm

$h_e = 1.78\ VP_s + 0.25\ VP_d$

AMERICAN CONFERENCE OF GOVERNMENTAL INDUSTRIAL HYGIENISTS	SWING SAW
DATE *12-90*	FIGURE *VS-95-04*

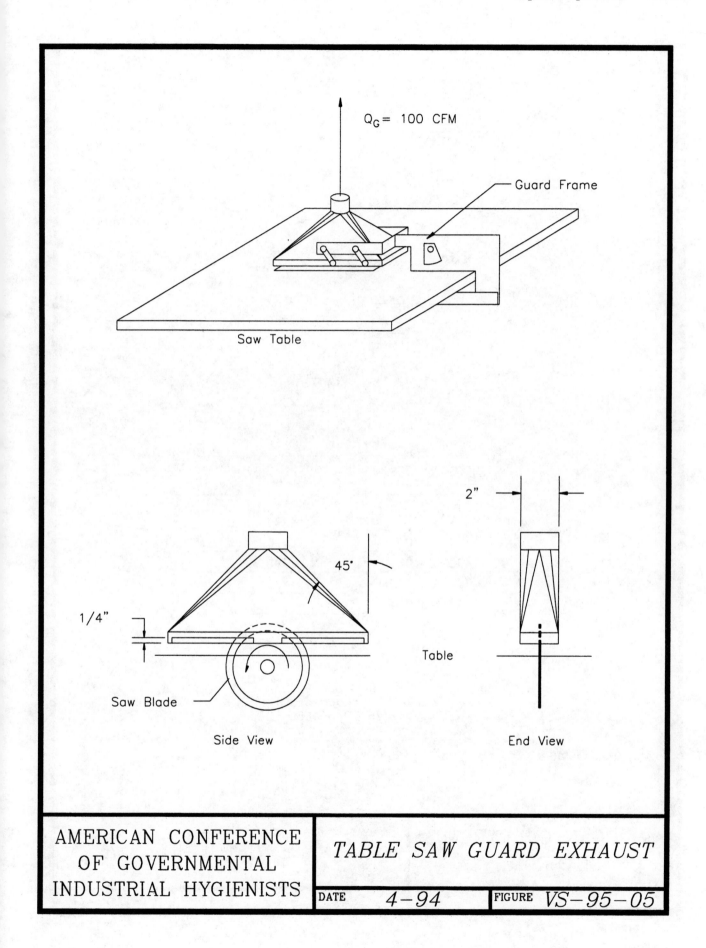

$Q_G = 100$ CFM

Guard Frame

Saw Table

2"

45°

1/4"

Table

Saw Blade

Side View

End View

AMERICAN CONFERENCE OF GOVERNMENTAL INDUSTRIAL HYGIENISTS	*TABLE SAW GUARD EXHAUST*	
	DATE *4-94*	FIGURE *VS-95-05*

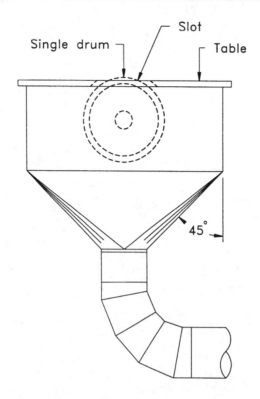

Single drum — — Slot — Table

45°

Drum surface square inches	Exhaust flow rate cfm
Up to 200 (and less than 10" diam.)	350
200 to 400	550
400 to 700	790
700 to 1400	1100
1400 to 2400	1400

Minimum duct velocity = 3500 fpm
Entry loss depends on hood design.
$h_e = 1.78 \ VP_s + 0.25 \ VP_d$ as illustrated

AMERICAN CONFERENCE
OF GOVERNMENTAL
INDUSTRIAL HYGIENISTS

SINGLE DRUM SANDER

DATE *12–90*

FIGURE *VS–95–10*

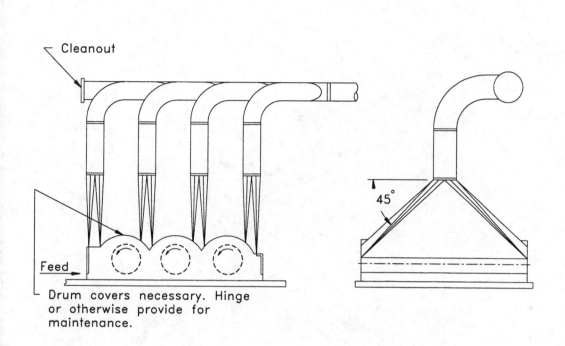

Cleanout

Feed

Drum covers necessary. Hinge or otherwise provide for maintenance.

45°

Exhaust flow rates

Drum length	Total exhaust for machine cfm/drum *
Up to 31"	550
31" to 49"	790
49" to 67"	1100
over 67"	1400
Brush rolls	350 cfm at brush

Note: Provide one more take off than the number of drums.

Minimum duct velocity = 3500 fpm
$h_e = 0.25 \ VP_d$

AMERICAN CONFERENCE OF GOVERNMENTAL INDUSTRIAL HYGIENISTS	*MULTIPLE DRUM SANDER*	
	DATE *12-90*	FIGURE *VS-95-11*

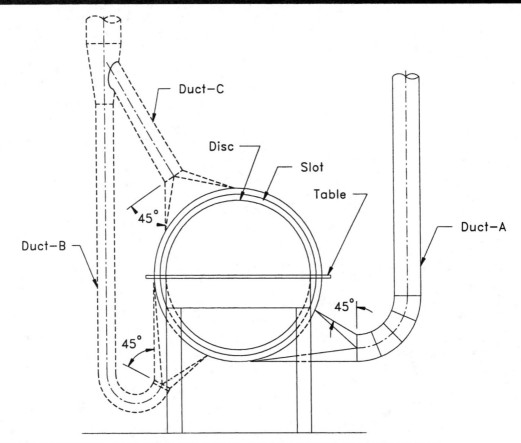

Disc diameter, inches	Total exhaust flow rate cfm	Applies to duct
Up to 12	350	A
12 to 18	440	A
18 to 26	550	A
26 to 32	700 *	A–B
32 to 38	900 *	A–B
38 to 48	1300 **	A–B–C

* Two bottom branches.
** One top and two bottom branches.

Minimum duct velocity = 3500 fpm
Entry loss depends on hood design.
$h_e = 1.0\ VP_s + 0.25\ VP_d$ as illustrated

AMERICAN CONFERENCE OF GOVERNMENTAL INDUSTRIAL HYGIENISTS

DISC SANDERS

DATE 12–90

FIGURE VS–95–12

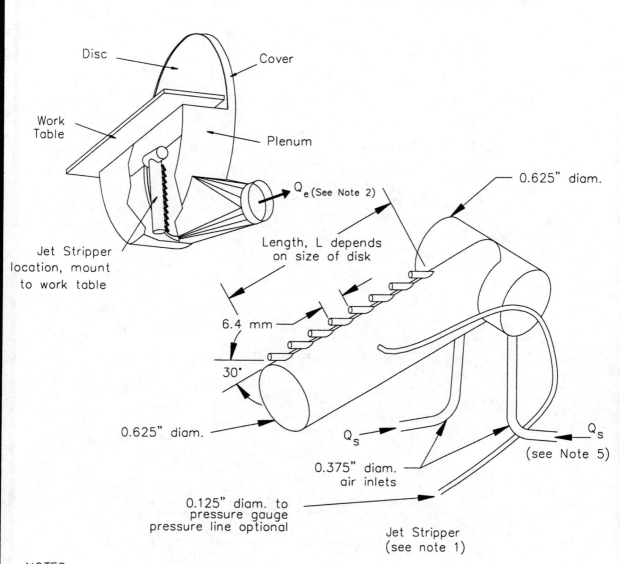

Disc

Cover

Work Table

Plenum

Jet Stripper location, mount to work table

Q_e (See Note 2)

Length, L depends on size of disk

6.4 mm

30°

0.625" diam.

0.625" diam.

0.625" diam.

Q_s

Q_s

(see Note 5)

0.375" diam. air inlets

0.125" diam. to pressure gauge pressure line optional

Jet Stripper (see note 1)

NOTES:
1. Jet stripper may be added as shown. It is used in addition to the ventilation specified in VS−95−12.
2. Q_e is same as shown in VS−95−12.
3. Clearance between stripper nozzle and disk is 0.25".
4. Nozzle opening diameter is 0.035".
5. Total air flow (Q_s) to stripper = 1.8 L. (L in inches)
6. Stripper inlet pressure = 15 psi.

The Jet Stripper is patented (#5,099,616). Use of the devise (not for sale) is permissible. To obtain information regarding license for commercial production of the devise contact NIOSH, 1−800−35NIOSH.
Reference 10.95.2

AMERICAN CONFERENCE OF GOVERNMENTAL INDUSTRIAL HYGIENISTS	*OPTIONAL JET STRIPPER FOR DISK SANDER*	
	DATE *11/96*	FIGURE *VS−95−12a*

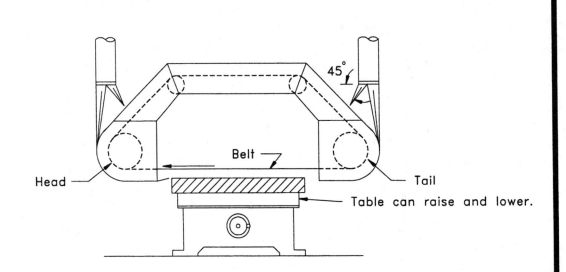

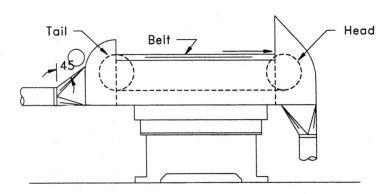

HORIZONTAL BELT SANDERS

Belt width, inches	Exhaust flowrate CFM		
	Head end	Tail end	Total
up to 6	440	350	790
6 to 9	550	350	900
9 to 14	800	440	1200
over 14	1100	550	1700

Minimum duct velocity = 3500 fpm
$h_e = 0.40\ VP_d$

AMERICAN CONFERENCE OF GOVERNMENTAL INDUSTRIAL HYGIENISTS	*HORIZONTAL BELT SANDERS*	
	DATE *12−90*	FIGURE *VS−95−13*

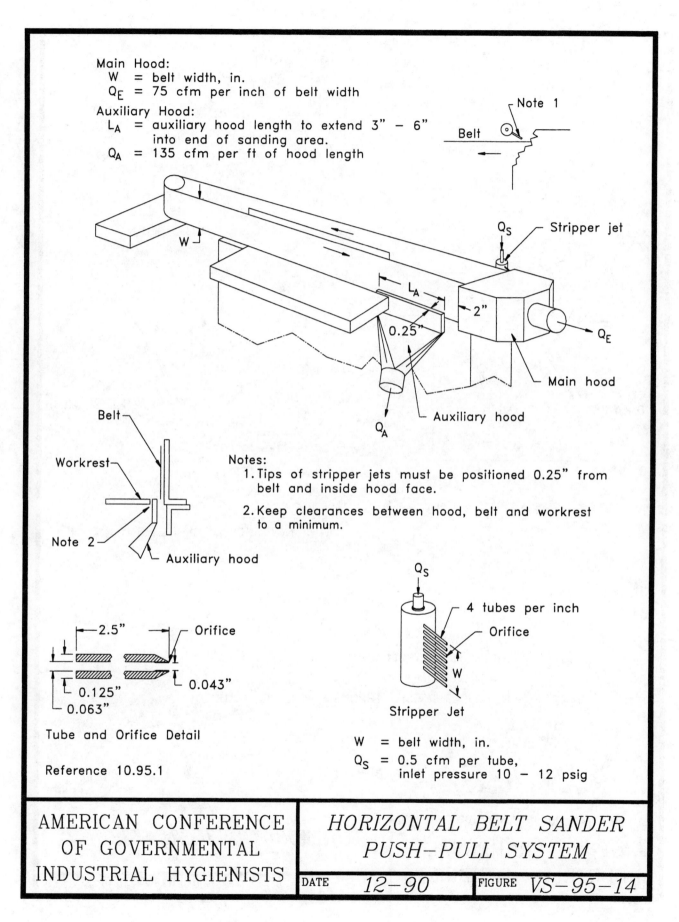

Main Hood:
W = belt width, in.
Q_E = 75 cfm per inch of belt width

Auxiliary Hood:
L_A = auxiliary hood length to extend 3" – 6" into end of sanding area.
Q_A = 135 cfm per ft of hood length

Note 1

Belt

Q_S — Stripper jet

L_A

2"

0.25"

Q_E

Q_A

Main hood

Auxiliary hood

Belt

Workrest

Note 2

Auxiliary hood

Notes:
1. Tips of stripper jets must be positioned 0.25" from belt and inside hood face.
2. Keep clearances between hood, belt and workrest to a minimum.

Q_S

4 tubes per inch

Orifice

W

Stripper Jet

2.5"

Orifice

0.043"

0.125"

0.063"

Tube and Orifice Detail

Reference 10.95.1

W = belt width, in.
Q_S = 0.5 cfm per tube, inlet pressure 10 – 12 psig

AMERICAN CONFERENCE OF GOVERNMENTAL INDUSTRIAL HYGIENISTS

HORIZONTAL BELT SANDER PUSH-PULL SYSTEM

DATE *12-90*   FIGURE *VS-95-14*

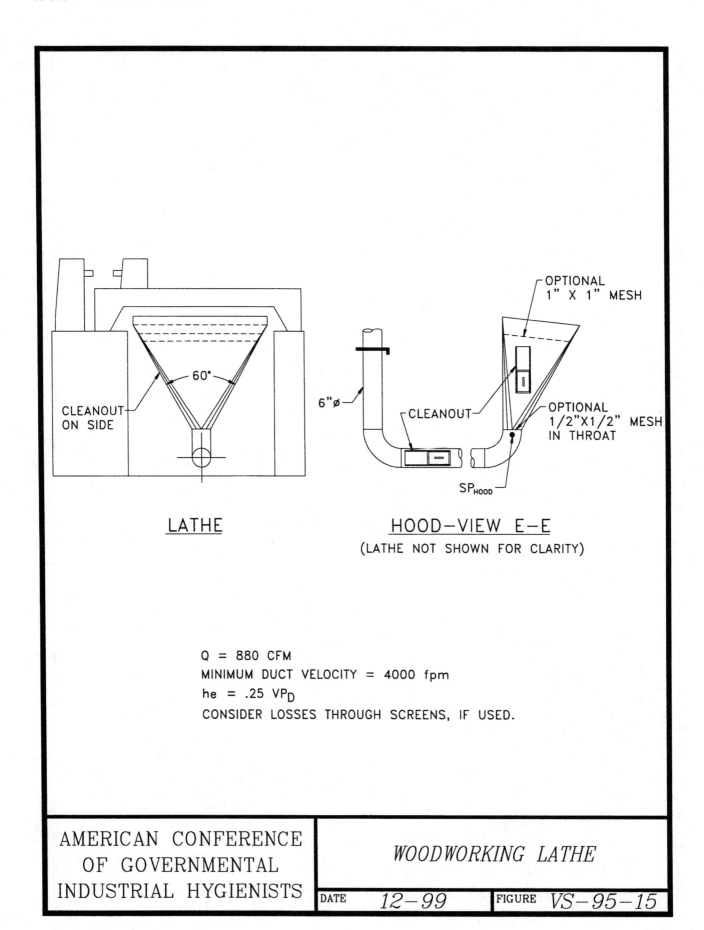

LATHE

HOOD-VIEW E-E
(LATHE NOT SHOWN FOR CLARITY)

Q = 880 CFM
MINIMUM DUCT VELOCITY = 4000 fpm
he = .25 VP$_D$
CONSIDER LOSSES THROUGH SCREENS, IF USED.

AMERICAN CONFERENCE
OF GOVERNMENTAL
INDUSTRIAL HYGIENISTS

WOODWORKING LATHE

DATE   12-99   FIGURE   VS-95-15

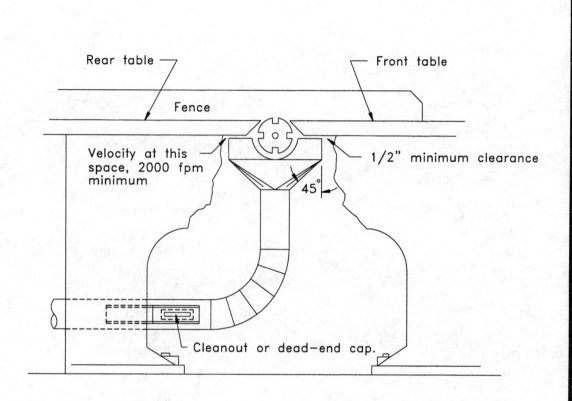

Knife length, inches	Exhaust flowrate cfm
Up to 6	350
6 to 12	440
12 to 20	550
over 20	800

Minimum duct velocity = 4000 fpm

$$h_e = 1.0 \ VP_s + 0.25 \ VP_d$$

AMERICAN CONFERENCE OF GOVERNMENTAL INDUSTRIAL HYGIENISTS	*JOINTERS*	
	DATE *12-90*	FIGURE *VS-95-20*

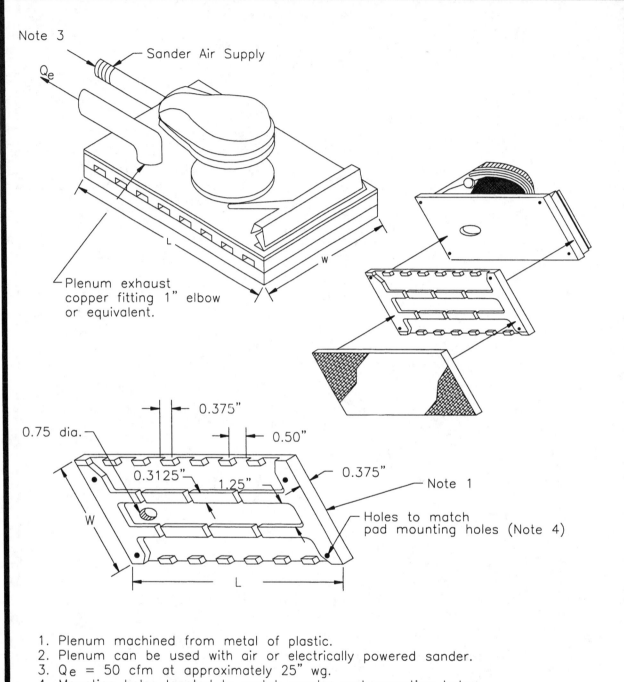

Note 3

Sander Air Supply

Q_e

L

W

Plenum exhaust
copper fitting 1" elbow
or equivalent.

0.375"

0.75 dia.

0.50"

0.3125"   1.25"

0.375"

Note 1

W

Holes to match
pad mounting holes (Note 4)

L

1. Plenum machined from metal of plastic.
2. Plenum can be used with air or electrically powered sander.
3. Q_e = 50 cfm at approximately 25" wg.
4. Mounting holes located to match sander pad mounting holes.

The Exhaust Plenum Retrofit has a patent pending. Use of the device (not for sale) is permissible. To obtain information regarding the license for commercial production of the devise contact NIOSH, 1−800−35NIOSH

Reference: 10.95.3

AMERICAN CONFERENCE OF GOVERNMENTAL INDUSTRIAL HYGIENISTS	EXHAUST PLENUM RETROFIT FOR ORBITAL HAND SANDER	
	DATE *12−96*	FIGURE *VS−95−30*

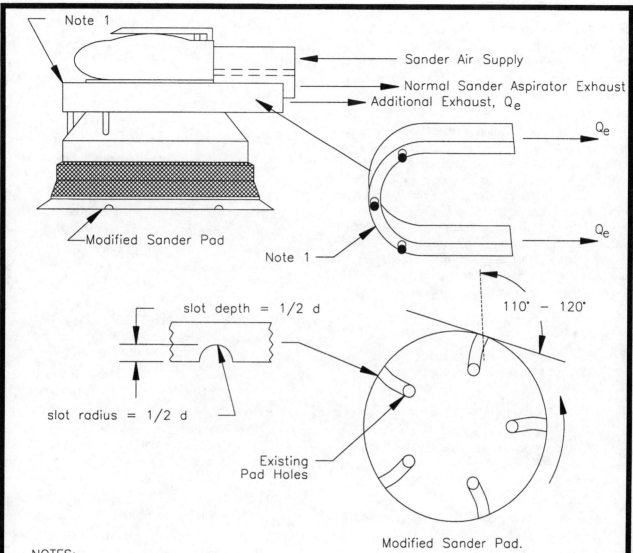

slot depth = 1/2 d

slot radius = 1/2 d

110° — 120°

Existing
Pad Holes

Modified Sander Pad.

NOTES:
1. Additional exhaust plenum to
   fit sander.
2. Q_e = 50 cfm at 25" wg
3. Q_e is in addition to normal sander
   aspirator exhaust.
4. Additional exhaust may be supplied
   by standard shop vacuum cleaner.

The Auxiliary Exhaust Modification Configuration is patented (#5,105,858).
Use of this device (not for sale) is permissible. To obtain information regarding
license for commercial production of the device contact NIOSH, 1–800–35NIOSH.

Reference: 10.95.4

AMERICAN CONFERENCE OF GOVERNMENTAL INDUSTRIAL HYGIENISTS	*AUXILIARY EXHAUST RETROFIT FOR AIR POWERED RANDOM ORBITAL HAND SANDER*	
	DATE *12/97*	FIGURE *VS–95–31*

10.99 MISCELLANEOUS OPERATIONS

In the previous sections of the chapter, hood ventilation sketches were grouped together because they provided ventilation concepts for similar operations, used the same ventilation approach, or were applicable within the same industry. However, not all hood ventilation sketches are so easily categorized.

This section provides a location for those hood ventilation sketches that do not fit in other sections. Some have a unique application such as VS-99-04 for the Pistol Range. Others have such broad application that they could appear in many of sections (e.g., the canopy hood in VS-99-03). In other cases, this section will be used for new ventilation sketches for a particular application or industry. Such sketches will reside in this section until other hood ventilation sketches are developed and a new section formed. Finally, this section will be used for tabular presentation of specific design parameters for a variety of operations which could not be adequately described in previous sections.

REFERENCES

10.99.1   Pennsylvania Department of Labor and Industry, Abrasive Wheel Manufacture. Safe Practices Bulletin No. 13.

10.99.2   Hartzell Propeller Fan Company, Bulletin 1001.

10.99.3   Goldfield, J.; Brandt. F. E.: Dust Control Techniques in the Asbestos Industry. A paper presented at the American Industrial Hygiene Conference, Miami Beach, FL (May 12-17, 1974).

10.99.4   Hama, G. M.: Ventilation Control of Dust from Bagging Operations. Heating and Ventilating (April, 1948).

10.99.5   Hutcheson, J. R. M.: Environmental Control in the Asbestos Industry of Quebec. C l MM Bulletin, Vol. 64, No. 712, pp 83-89 (August 1971).

10.99.6   Private Communications, Occupational Health Protection Branch, Ontario Ministry of Labour, Ontario, Canada (October 1976).

10.99.7   Hama, G.; Frederick, W.; Monteith, H.: Air Flow Requirements for Underground Parking Garages. American Industrial Hygiene Association Journal, Vol. 22, No. 6 (December 1961).

10.99.8   Kane, J. M.:Design of Exhaust Systems. Heating and Ventilating, 42, 68 (November 1945).

10.99.9   Oddie, W. M.: Pottery Dusts: Their Collection and Removal. Pottery Gazette, 53, 1280 (1928).

10.99.10   B. F. Sturtevant Company: What We Make. Catalog No. 500.

10.99.11   Brandt, A. D.: Industrial Health Engineering. John Wiley and Sons, (New York 1947).

10.99.12   Kane, J. M.: Foundry Ventilation. The Foundry, (February and March 1946).

10.99.13   Kane, J. M.:Foundry Ventilation. University of Michigan Inservice Training Course, (October 1945).

10.99.14   Fen, O. E.: The Collection and Control of Dust and Fumes from Magnesium Alloy Processing. Peters-Dalton, Inc., (January 1945).

10.99.15   Postman, B. F.: Practical Application of Industrial Exhaust Ventilation for the Control of Occupational Exposures. American Journal of Public Health, 30, 149 (1940).

10.99.16   New York Department of Labor: Rules Relating to the Control of Silica Dust in Stone Crushing Operations. Industrial Code Rule No. 34 (July 1942).

10.99.17   DallaValle, J. M.: Exhaust Hoods. Industrial Press, New York (1946).

10.99.18   Hatch, T., et al: Control of the Silicosis Hazard in Hard Rock Industries. II. An Investigation of the Kelley Dust Trap for Use with Pneumatic Rock Drills of the Jackhammer Type. Journal of Industrial Hygiene, 14, 69 (February 1932).

10.99.19   Hay, Capt. P. S.: Modified Design of Hay Dust Trap. Journal of Industrial Hygiene, 12, 18 (January 1930).

10.99.20   Riley, E. C., et al: How to Design Exhaust Hoods for Quartz-Fusing Operations. Heating and Ventilating, 37, 23 (April 1940).

10.99.21   Riley, E. C.; DallaValle, J. M.: A Study of Quartz-Fusing Operations with Reference to Measurement and Control of Silica Fumes. Public Health Reports, 54, 532 (1939).

10.99.22   Yaglou, C. P.: Ventilation of Wire Impregnating Tanks Using Chlorinated Hydrocarbons. Journal of Industrial Hygiene and Toxicology, 20, 401 (June 1938).

10.99.23   American Air Filter Co., Inc., Usual Exhaust Requirements (for) Grain Elevators, Feed and Flour Mills, Louisville, KY (April 1956).

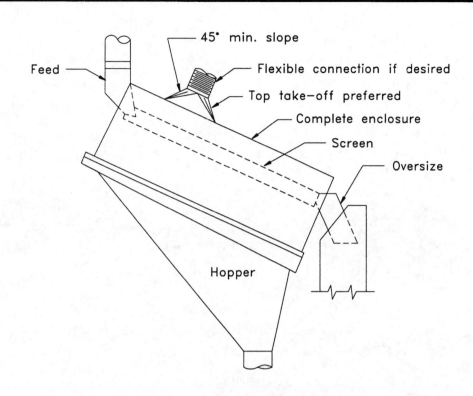

FLAT DECK SCREEN

$Q = 200$ cfm/ft^2 through hood openings, but not less than
    50 cfm/ft^2 screen area. No increase for multiple decks
Minimum duct velocity = 3500 fpm
$h_e = 0.50$ VP$_d$

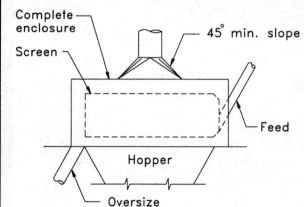

CYLINDRICAL SCREEN

$Q = 100$ cfm/ft^2 circular cross section of
    screen; at least 400 cfm/ft^2 of
    enclosure opening
Minimum duct velocity = 3500 fpm
$h_e = 0.50$ VP$_d$

AMERICAN CONFERENCE OF GOVERNMENTAL INDUSTRIAL HYGIENISTS	*SCREENS*	
	DATE *12-90*	FIGURE *VS-99-01*

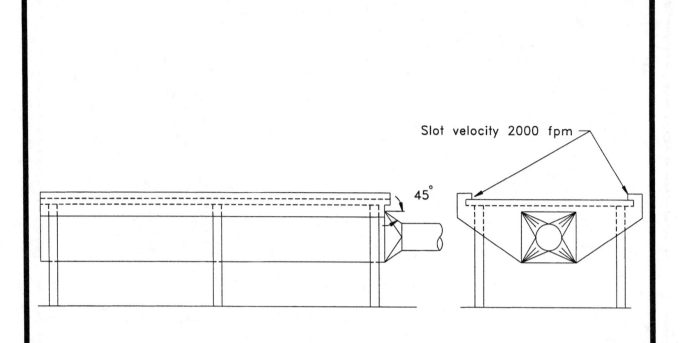

Slot velocity 2000 fpm

45°

$Q = 50-100 \text{ cfm/ft}^2$ of table top.
Minimum duct velocity = 2000 fpm
$h_e = 1.78 \text{ VP}_s + 0.25 \text{ VP}_d$
Note: See "Open Surface Tanks", VS–70–01 and VS–70–02
        for other suitable slot types. Air flow rate may
        be calculated on dilution basis if data is available.
        Maximum plenum velocity = 1/2 slot velocity.
        Large plenum essential for good distribution.

AMERICAN CONFERENCE OF GOVERNMENTAL INDUSTRIAL HYGIENISTS	*TABLE SLOT*	
	DATE *12–90*	FIGURE *VS–99–02*

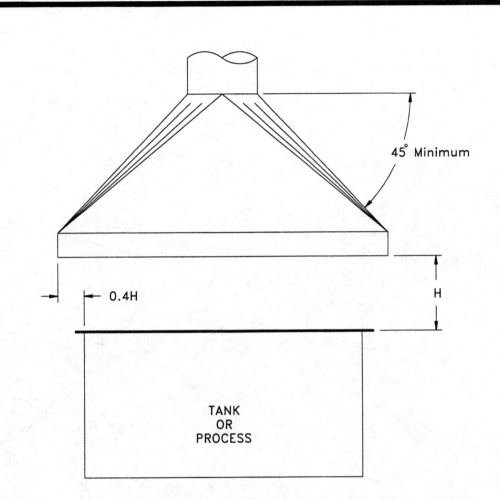

45° Minimum

0.4H

H

TANK
OR
PROCESS

Not to be used where material is toxic and worker must bend over tank or process.
Side curtains are necessary when cross–drafts are present.

Q = 1.4PHV	for open type canopy. P = perimeter of tank, feet. V = 50–500 fpm. See Chapter 3
Q = (W + L)HV	for two sides adjacent enclosed. W & L are open sides of hood. V = 50–500 fpm. See Chapter 3
Q = WHV or LHV	for three sides enclosed. (booth) V = 50–500 fpm. See Chapter 3

$h_e = 0.25\ VP_d$
Duct velocity = 1000–3000 fpm

AMERICAN CONFERENCE OF GOVERNMENTAL INDUSTRIAL HYGIENISTS	*CANOPY HOOD*	
	DATE *12–90*	FIGURE *VS–99–03*

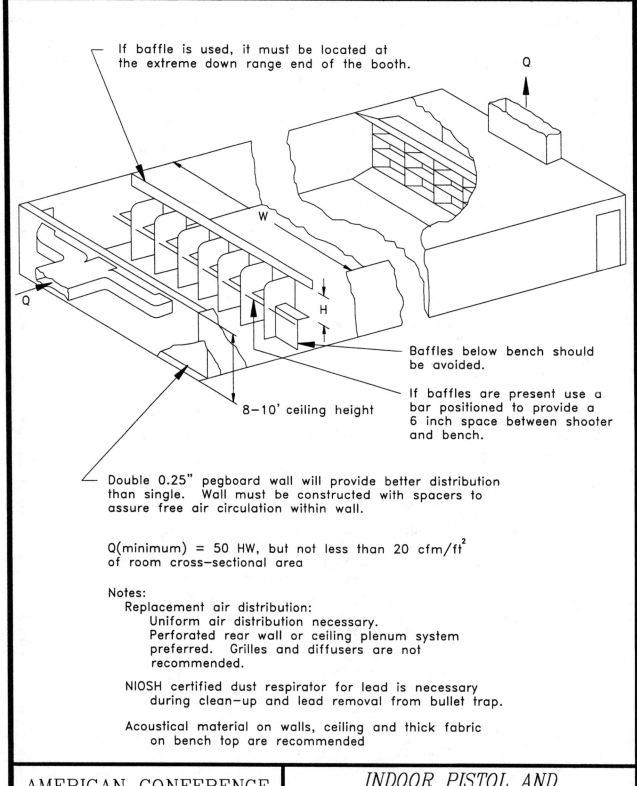

If baffle is used, it must be located at the extreme down range end of the booth.

Q

W

H

Baffles below bench should be avoided.

If baffles are present use a bar positioned to provide a 6 inch space between shooter and bench.

Q

8–10' ceiling height

Double 0.25" pegboard wall will provide better distribution than single. Wall must be constructed with spacers to assure free air circulation within wall.

Q(minimum) = 50 HW, but not less than 20 cfm/ft^2 of room cross-sectional area

Notes:
Replacement air distribution:
Uniform air distribution necessary.
Perforated rear wall or ceiling plenum system preferred. Grilles and diffusers are not recommended.

NIOSH certified dust respirator for lead is necessary during clean-up and lead removal from bullet trap.

Acoustical material on walls, ceiling and thick fabric on bench top are recommended

AMERICAN CONFERENCE OF GOVERNMENTAL INDUSTRIAL HYGIENISTS	INDOOR PISTOL AND SMALL BORE RIFLE RANGE VENTILATION	
	DATE 12–90	FIGURE VS–99–04

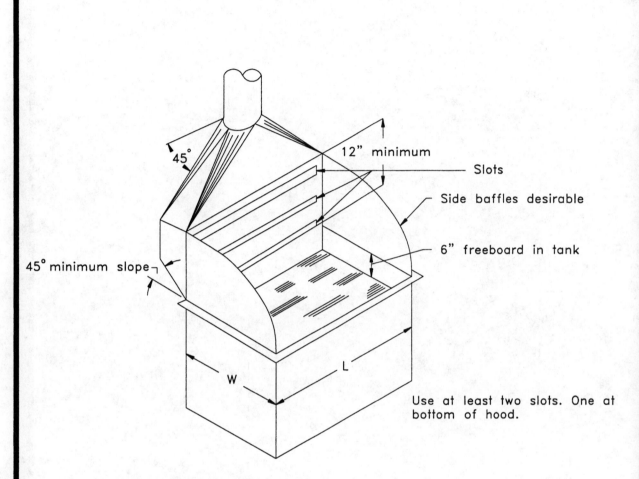

45°

12" minimum

Slots

Side baffles desirable

6" freeboard in tank

45° minimum slope

W

L

Use at least two slots. One at bottom of hood.

$Q = 150 \text{ cfm/ft}^2 \text{ of bed (150LW)}$
Slot velocity = 2000 fpm
$h_e = 1.78 \ VP_s + 0.25 \ VP_d$
Minimum duct velocity = 3500 fpm
W not to exceed 36"

Free board must be maintained to prevent material carryout.

AMERICAN CONFERENCE OF GOVERNMENTAL INDUSTRIAL HYGIENISTS	*FLUIDIZED BEDS*	
	DATE *12-90*	FIGURE *VS-99-05*

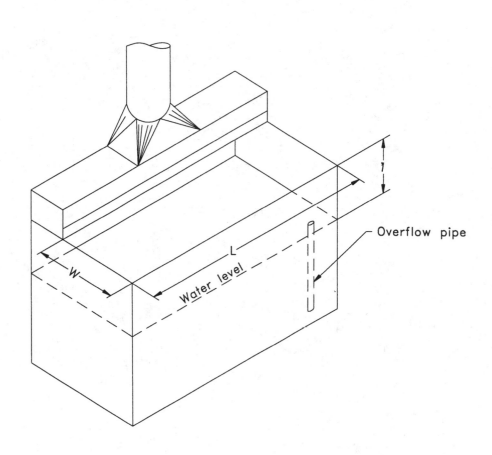

Overflow pipe

L

W

Water level

$Q = 200 \, L \times W$

$h_e = 1.78 \text{ slot } VP_s + 0.25 \text{ duct } VP_d$

Duct velocity = 2500 − 3000 fpm

Slot size for 1500 − 2000 fpm

AMERICAN CONFERENCE OF GOVERNMENTAL INDUSTRIAL HYGIENISTS	*OUTBOARD MOTOR TEST*	
	DATE *12−90*	FIGURE *VS−99−06*

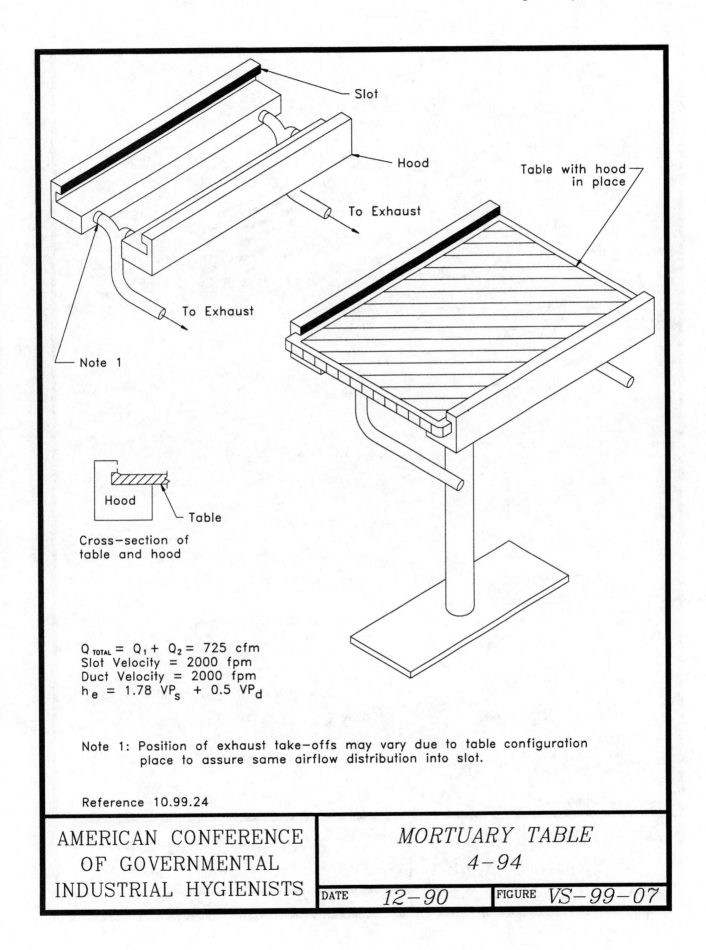

Slot

Hood

To Exhaust

Table with hood in place

To Exhaust

Note 1

Hood

Table

Cross-section of table and hood

$Q_{TOTAL} = Q_1 + Q_2 = 725$ cfm
Slot Velocity = 2000 fpm
Duct Velocity = 2000 fpm
$h_e = 1.78\ VP_s + 0.5\ VP_d$

Note 1: Position of exhaust take-offs may vary due to table configuration place to assure same airflow distribution into slot.

Reference 10.99.24

AMERICAN CONFERENCE OF GOVERNMENTAL INDUSTRIAL HYGIENISTS	*MORTUARY TABLE* *4-94*	
	DATE *12-90*	FIGURE *VS-99-07*

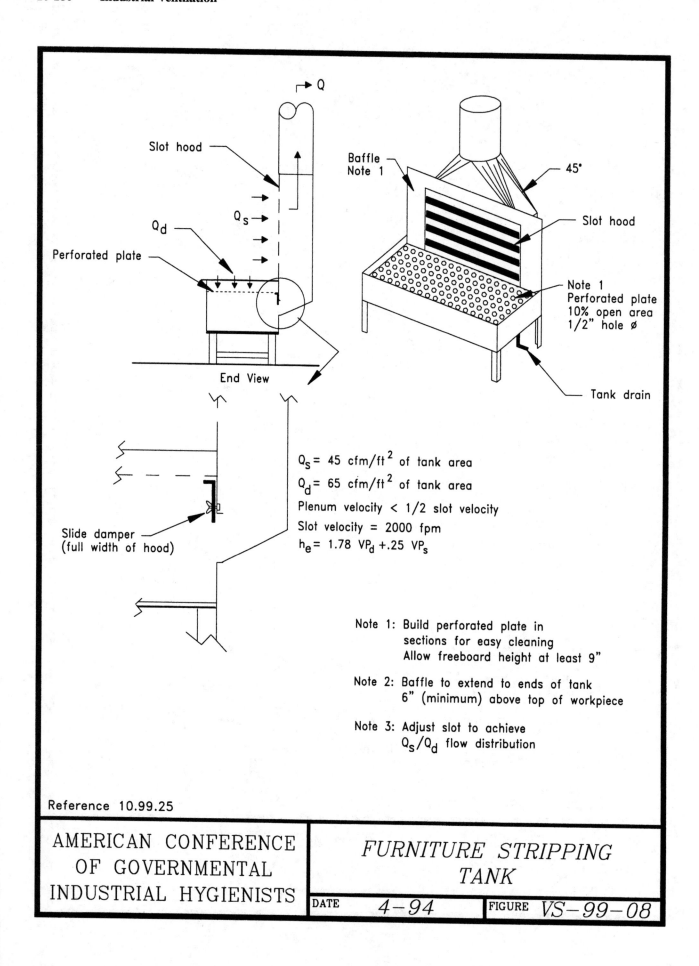

Slot hood

Q_s

Q_d

Perforated plate

End View

Slide damper
(full width of hood)

Baffle
Note 1

45°

Slot hood

Note 1
Perforated plate
10% open area
1/2" hole ø

Tank drain

Q_s = 45 cfm/ft^2 of tank area

Q_d = 65 cfm/ft^2 of tank area

Plenum velocity < 1/2 slot velocity

Slot velocity = 2000 fpm

h_e = 1.78 VP_d + .25 VP_s

Note 1: Build perforated plate in
sections for easy cleaning
Allow freeboard height at least 9"

Note 2: Baffle to extend to ends of tank
6" (minimum) above top of workpiece

Note 3: Adjust slot to achieve
Q_s/Q_d flow distribution

Reference 10.99.25

AMERICAN CONFERENCE OF GOVERNMENTAL INDUSTRIAL HYGIENISTS	*FURNITURE STRIPPING TANK*	
	DATE *4-94*	FIGURE *VS-99-08*

TABLE 10.99.1 Grain Elevators, Feed Mills, Flour Mills[10.99.23]

The following data are offered as guides. Air flow rates can vary considerably depending on degree of enclosure, flow rate of material, and dustiness of the grain. Minimum duct velocity = 3500 fpm. Ventilation control is desirable for these operations to minimize the explosive characteristics of grain dusts and to preserve plant housekeeping standards.

Operation	Hood Design	Air Volume
Bag Loading	VS-15-02, VS-15-03 Booth VS-15-01	As shown 100 cfm/ft^2
Belt Discharge	To belt—VS-50-20 To bin—VS-50-10 To elevator—VS-50-1, VS-50-20	350 cfm/ft of belt width up to 200 fpm belt speed 500 cfm/ft of belt width over 200 fpm belt speed Increase 1/3 if material drop is over 10 ft
Bins	Direct exhaust. Use taper.	500 cfm/bin
Bucket Elevator	Vs-50-01	100 cfm/ft^2 cross-section
Cleaning Machines	Consult manufacturer.	

Distributors — Enclose discharge 200 fpm in-draft through enclosure openings.

No. of Spouts	Exhaust, cfm	Diameter of Spouts			
		6"	7"	8"	9"
0-6	Exhaust, cfm	550	675	950	125
6-12		950	12	150	0
12-24		150	0	0	190
		0	190	225	0
			0	0	275
					0

Operation	Hood Design	Air Volume
Feed Grinders	Consult manufacturer.	
Floor Dump	Booth	200 cfm/ft^2 open face area
Floor Sweep		950 cfm in 4' x 8' opening
Garner Bin	Direct exhaust. Use taper.	1.25 cfm per bushel/min

Mixers — Ventilated cover.

Mixer Capacity	Exhaust, cfm
Up to 0.5 ton	300
0.5 to 1.5 tons	675
Over 1.5 tons	950

Operation	Hood Design	Air Volume
Percentage Feeders	Enclosed conveyor.	200 cfm at each feeder
Purifiers	Enclosure	30-40 cfm/ft^2 screen area
Roll Stands	Enclosure	60 cfm/lineal ft

Scales — Enclosure.

Scale Capacity, Bushels cfm	Exhaust, cfm
Up to 5	250
6 to 10	400
Over 11	600

Operation	Hood Design	Air Volume
Scale Hopper	Direct exhaust. Use taper.	1.25 cfm per bushel/min
Screw Conveyor	Direct exhaust. Use taper.	200 cfm—ducts on 30 ft centers
Sifters	Enclosure	200 cfm/compartment
Track Sink	Direct exhaust from hopper. Use taper.	100 cfm/ft^2 grate area
Tripper Car	Belt discharge. Vs-50-01, VS-50-20, Vs-50-20. Spout ends—tapered connection. Spillage—exhaust under head pulley.	See "Belt Discharge" above. 200 cfm/ft^2 spout cross-section. 90 cfm/ft belt width.

TABLE 10.99.2. Miscellaneous Specific Operations Standards

Minimum Design Operation or Industry	Ventilation		Duct Velocity, (fpm)	Remarks
	Reference No. and Type of Hood	Air Flow or Capture Velocity		
Abrasive Wheel Mfg.				10.99.1
Grading screen	Enclosure—booth	50 fpm at face	4000	
Barrels	Close canopy	400 fpm at face	4000	Bbls. receive dust from
Grinding wheel dressing	Enclosure—booth	400 fpm at face	4000	cyclone
Aluminum Furnaces	Enclosure	150-200 fpm through opening	2000	10.99.2
Asbestos				
Bagging	Enclosure—booth	250 fpm through all openings	3500	10.99.3, 10.99.4
Cardng	Enclosure	1600 cfm/card	3500	
Crushing	Enclosure	150 fpm through all openings	3500	
Drilling of panels containing asbestos	Moveable hood	400 fpm capture velocity	4500	10.99.5 10.99.6
Dumping	Booth	250 fpm face velocity	3500	10.99.6
Grinding of brake shoes	Enclosure	400 fpm minimum capture at tool rest	3500	10.99.6
Hot press for brake shoes	Enclosure	250 fpm through all openings	3500	10.99.6
Mixing	Booth	250 fpm face velocity	3500	10.99.6
Preform Press	Enclosure	250 fpm through all openings	3500	10.99.6
Screening	Enclosure	200 fpm through all openings but not less than 25 cfm/ft² screen areas	3000	10.99.3
Spool winding	Local Hoods	50 cfm/spool	3500	
Spinning and twisting	Partial	50 cfm/spool	3500	Hinged front panels and and skirt, wet twisting preferred
Weaving	Canopy with baffles	50 fpm through openings	3500	Wet weaving preferred
Auto Parking Garage	2-Level	500 cfm/parking space		10.99.7
Ceramic	Enclosure	200 fpm through all openings	3500	10.99.8,9,10
Dry pan	Local at die	500 cfm	3500	Automatic feed
Dry press	Local at die	500 cfm	3500	Maunal feed
	At supply bin	500 cfm	3500	Maunal feed
Aerographing	Booth	100 fpm (face)		
Spraying (lead glaze)	Booth	400 fpm (face) 3500	2000	
Coating Pans (pharmaceutical)	Air flow into openingn of pan	100-150 fpm through opening	3000	10.99.8, 10.99.11 If heat air supplied to pan, add volume of heated air to exhaust
Cooling Tunnels (foundry)	Enclosure	75-100 cfm/running foot of enclosure	—	10.99.12, 10.99.13
Core Knockout (manual)	Large side-draft or semi-booth—exhaust near floor	200-250 cfm/ft² dust producing working area	3500	10.99.12, 10.99.13 10.99.14
Core Sanding (on lathe)	Downdraft under work	100 fpm at source	3500	10.99.15
Crushers and Grinders	Enclosure	200 fpm through openings	3500	10.99.16

TABLE 10.99.2. Miscellaneous Specific Operations Standards (con't)

| Minimum Design Operation or Industry | Ventilation | | Duct Velocity, (fpm) | Remarks |
	Reference No. and Type of Hood	Air Flow or Capture Velocity		
Drilling (rocks)	Special trap (see references)	60 cfm—vertical (downward) work 200 cfm—horizontal work		10.99.17, 10.99.18, 10.99.19 May vary with size and speed of drill
Forge (hand)	Booth	200 fpm at face	1500	10.99.2
Outboard Motor Test Tank	Side draft	200 cfm/ft^2 of tank opening		
Packaging Machines	Booth Downdraft Complete enclosure	50-100 fpm at face 95-150 fpm down 100-400 fpm opening	3000 to 4000	
Paper Machine Quartz Fusing Rotary Blasting Table Silver Soldering Steam Kettles Varnish Kettles Wire Impregnating	Canopy Booth on bench Enclosure Free Hanging Canopy Canopy Covered tanks	200-300 fpm at face 150-200 fpm at face 500 fpm through all openings when in operation 100 fpm at source 150 fpm at face 200-250 fpm at face 200 cfm/ft^2 of opening	1500 — 3500 2000 2000 1500 —	10.99.20, 10.99.21 10.99.20, 10.99.21

BIBLIOGRAPHY

1. American Air Filter Co., Rotoclone Dust Control, January, 1946.

2. American Society of Heating, Air Conditioning and Refrigerating Engineers, Heating, Ventilating and Air Conditioning Guide, 1963.

3. American Society of Mechanical Engineers, Power Test Code 21, Test Code for Dust-Separating Apparatus, 1941.

4. American Society of Mechanical Engineers, Power Test Code 19.2.5, Liquid Column Gauges, 1942.

5. Anemostat Corporation, Anemotherm Air Meter, 10 East 29th St., New York 16, NY.

6. Bloomfield, J. J., and DallaValle, J. M., The Application of Engineering Surveys to the Hatters Fur Cutting Industry, U.S.P.H.S.

7. Brandt, A. D., Industrial Health Engineering, John Wiley and Sons, New York, 1947.

8. Brandt, Allen D., Should Air Be Recirculated from Industrial Exhaust Systems?, Heating, Piping and Air Conditioning, 19, 69, Aug., 1947.

9. DallaValle, J. M., Exhaust Hoods, Industrial Press, New York, 1946.

10. Dreesen, W. C., et al, A Study of Asbestosis in the Asbestos Textile Industry, Public Health Bulletin 241, August, 1938.

11. Drinker, P., and Hatch, T., Industrial Dust, McGraw-Hill, New York, 1936.

12. Drinker, P., and Snell, J. R., Ventilation of Motion Picture Booths, Journal of Industrial Hygiene and Toxicology, 20, 321, April, 1938.

13. Fen, O. E., The Collection and Control of Dust and Fumes from Magnesium Alloy Processing, Peters-Dalton, Inc., January, 1945.

14. Hartzell Propeller Fan Company, Bulletin 1001.

15. Hastings Instrument Company, Air Meter, Box 1275, Hampton, Virginia.

16. Hatch, T., Design of Exhaust Hoods for Dust Control Systems, Journal of Industrial Hygiene and Toxicology, 18, 595, 1936.

17. Hatch, T., et al, Control of the Silicosis Hazard in the Hard Rock Industries. II. An Investigation of the Kelley Dust Trap for Use with Pneumatic Rock Drills of the Jackhammer Type, Journal of Industrial Hygiene, 14, 69, February, 1932.

18. Hay, P. S., Capt., Modified Design of Hay Dust Trap, Journal of Industrial Hygiene, 12, 28, January, 1930.

19. Hemeon, W. C. L., Air Dilution in Industrial Ventilation, Heating and Ventilating, 38, 41, February, 1941.

20. Huebscher, R. G., Friction Equivalents for Round, Square and Rectangular Ducts, Heating, Piping and Air Conditioning, 19, 127, December, 1947.

21. Illinois Testing Laboratory, Alnor Thermo-Anemometer, Chicago 10, Illinois.

22. Kane, J. M., Foundry Ventilation, The Foundry, February and March, 1946.

23. Kane, J. M., The Application of Local Exhaust Ventilation to Electric Melting Furnaces, Trans. Am. Foundrymen's Assn., 52, 1351, 1945.

24. Kane, J. M., Design of Exhaust Systems, Heating and Ventilating, 42, 68, November, 1945.

25. Kane, J. M., Foundry Ventilation, University of Michigan Inservice Training Course, October, 1945.

26. Madison, R. D., and Elliot, W. R., Friction Charts for Gases Including Correction for Temperature, Viscosity and Pipe Roughness, Heating, Piping and Air Conditioning, 18, 107, October, 1946.

27. Moucher, S. C., Principles of Air Flow, Sheet Metal Workers, September, 1947.

28. Air Movement and Control Association, Inc., 30 West University Dr., Arlington Heights, IL 60004, AMCA Standard 210-74.

29. Neal, P. A., et al, Mercurialism and Its Control in the Felt-Hat Industry, Public Health Bulletin 263, 1941.

30. New York Department of Labor, Rules Relating to the Control of Silica Dust in Stone Crushing Operations, Industrial Code Rule No. 34, July, 1942.

31. Oddie, W. M., Pottery Dusts: Their Collection and Removal, Pottery Gazette, 53, 1280, 1928.

32. Page, R. T., and Bloomfield, J. J., A Study of Dust Control Methods in an Asbestos Fabricating Plant, Reprint No. 1883, Public Health Reports, November 26, 1937.

33. Pennsylvania Department of Labor and Industry, Abrasive Wheel Manufacture, Safe Practice Bulletin No. 13.

34. Postman, B. F., Practical Application of Industrial Exhaust Ventilation for the Control of Occupational Exposures, American Journal of Public Health, 30, 149, 1940.

35. Riley, E. C., et al, How to Design Exhaust Hoods for Quartz-Fusing Operations, Heating and Ventilating, 37, 23, April, 1940.

36. Riley, E. C., and DallaValle, J. M., A Study of Quartz-Fusing Operations with Reference to Measurement and Control of Silica Fumes, Public Health Reports, 54, 532, 1939.

37. Rothmann, S. C., Economic Recovery of Pottery Glazes with Reduction of Dust, American Journal of Public Health, 29, 5ll, 1939.

38. Silverman, Leslie, Velocity Characteristics of Narrow Exhaust Slots, Journal of Industrial Hygiene and Toxicology, 24, 267, November, 1942.

39. B. F. Sturtevant Company, What We Make, Catalog No. 500.

40. Tuve, G. L., and Wright, D. K., Air Flow Measurements at Intake and Discharge Openings and Grilles, Heating, Piping and Air Conditioning, 12, 501, August, 1940.

41. Tuve, G. L., Measuring Air Flow at Intake or Exhaust Grilles, Heating, Piping and Air Conditioning, 13, 740, December, 1941.

42. Underwriters Laboratories, Inc., Control of Floating Dust in Grain Elevators, Underwriters Laboratories Bulletin of Research No. 1, December, 1937.

43. Whalen, F. G., The Whalen Gage, Engineering Experimental Station Bulletin 10, University of Illinois, March, 1921.

44. Witheridge, W. N., Principles of Industrial Process Ventilation, University of Michigan Inservice Training Course, October, 1945.

46. Yaglou, C. P., Ventilation of Wire Impregnating Tanks Using Chlorinated Hydrocarbons, Journal of Industrial Hygiene and Toxicology, 20, 401, June, 1938.

47. Yaglou, C. P., Committee on Atmospheric Comport, A.P.H.A., Report Presented at the 77th Annual Meeting, A.P.H.A., New York City, October 27, 1949.

48. Adolph, E. E., Tolerance of Man Toward Hot Atmospheres, Supplement #192, Public Health Reports, 1946.

49. Your Place in the 'Smart Man's War', Heating, Piping and Air Conditioning, 14, 463, August, 1942.

50. Factory Mutual Insurance Company, Properties of Flammable Liquids, Gases and Solids, Factory Mutual Solvent Data Sheet 36.10, January, 1945.

51. Malin, Benjamin S., Practical Pointers on Industrial Exhaust Systems, Heating and Ventilating, 42, 75, February, 1945.

52. National Board of Fire Underwriters, Standard for Class A Ovens and Furnaces, Pamphlet #86.

53. United States Bureau of Mines, Limits of Flammability of Gases and Vapors, Bulletin #503.

54. Silverman, Leslie, Centerline Velocity Characteristics of Round Openings Under Suction, Journal of Industrial Hygiene and Toxicology, 24, 259, November, 1942.

55. Schulte, H. F., Hyatt, E. C., and Smith, Jr., F. S., Exhaust Ventilation for Machine Tools Used on Materials of High Toxicity, A.M.A. Archives of Industrial Hygiene and Occupational Medicine, 5, 21, January, 1952.

56. Mitchell, R. N., and Hyatt, E. C., Beryllium—Hazard Evaluation and Control Covering a Five-Year Study, American Industrial Hygiene Quarterly, 18, No. 3, September, 1957.

57. Hemeon, W. C. L., Plant and Process Ventilation, Industrial Press.

58. Manufacturing Chemists' Association, Technical Data on Plastics, February, 1957.

59. First, M. W., and Silverman, L., Airfoil Pitometer, Industrial Engineering and Chemistry, 42, 301-308, February, 1950.

60. Stoll, H. W., The Pitot-Venturi Flow Element, Transactions ASME, 963-969, October, 1951.

61. Republic Flow Meters Co., Air Speed Nozzle, Bulletin ME-186-A, Chicago, Illinois, April, 1948.

62. University of Michigan, Encyclopedia of Instrumentation for Industrial Hygiene, Institute of Industrial Health, Ann Arbor, Michigan.

63. Dwyer Manufacturing Company, Magnehelic Gage, P. O. Box 373, Michigan City, Indiana.

64. Burton, J. R., Friction Chart, Quaker Oats Company, Chicago, Illinois.

65. U. S. Dept. of Health and Welfare, Public Health Service, Syllabus, Short Course for Industrial Hygiene Engineers, p. B-25,7.

66. National Fire Protection Association, Ventilation of Cooking Equipment 1971, Bulletin 96.

67. American Air Filter Co., Inc., Usual Exhaust Requirements (for) Grain Elevators, Feed and Flour Mills, April, 1956.

68. Air Movement and Control Association, Inc., 30 West University Drive, Arlington Heights, IL 60004.

69. Print, Robert T., Dust Control in Large-Scale Ore-Concentrating Operations, American Institute of Mining and Metallurgical Engineering, Tech. Publication #1225, February, 1940.

70. Langley, M. Y., Harris, Jr., R. L., Lee, D. H. K., Calculation of Complex Radiant Heat Load from Surrounding Radiator Surface Temperatures, American Industrial Hygiene Association Journal, 24, Mar., 1963, pps. 103-112.

71. Thor Power Tool Company, Aurora, Illinois.

72. Chamberlin, Richard I., The Control of Beryllium Machining Operations, American Medical Assn., Archives of Industrial Health, 19, No. 2, Feb., 1959.

73. The Black and Decker Tool Company, Townson, MD.

74. Hoffman Air and Filtration Div., Clarkson Industries, Inc., New York, NY.

75. Alexander, J. M., Croley, Jr., J. J., and Messick, R. R., Use of Vortex Tube for Cooling Wearers of Industrial Protective Clothing, U. S. Atomic Energy Commission Report DP-86l, Office of Technical Services, U. S. Dept. of Commerce, Washington, DC, Oct., 1963.

76. Trickler, C. J., Engineering Letter E-4R, New York Blower Co., LaPorte, IN.

78. New York State Department of Labor, Division of Industrial Hygiene.

79. Air Conditioning, Heating and Ventilating, Vol. 60, No. 3, March, 1963.

80. Hama, George, M.S., Frederick, W., Sc.D., and Monteith, H., M.S., Air Flow Requirements for Underground Parking Garages, American Industrial Hygiene Association Journal, Vol. 22, No. 6, December, 1961.

81. Feiner, B., and Kingsley, I., Ventilation of Industrial Ovens, Air Conditioning, Heating and Ventilating, December, 1956, pp. 82-89.

82. U. S. Air Force Technical Order 00-25-203, Standards and Guidelines for the Design and Operation of Clean Rooms and Clean Work Stations, Office of Technical Services, Department of Commerce, Washington, D.C., July, 1963.

83. Federal Standard No. 209B, Clean Room and Work Station Requirements, Controlled Environment, General Services Administration, Specifications Activity, Printed Material Supply Div., Bldg. 197, Naval Weapons Plant, Washington, DC 20407.

84. Austin, Philip R., and Timmerman, Stuart W., Design and Operation of Clean Rooms, Business News Publishing Co., Detroit, 1965.

85. Constance, J. A., Estimating Air Friction in Triangular Ducts, Air Conditioning, Heating and Ventilating, Vol. 60, No. 6, June, 1963, pp 85-86.

86. McKarns, J.S., Confer, R. G., and Brief, R. S., Estimating Length Limits for Drain Type Stacks, Heating, Piping and Air Conditioning, Vol. 37, No. 7, July, 1965.

87. Clarke, J. H., Air Flow Around Buildings, Heating, Piping and Air Conditioning, Vol. 39, No. 5, May, 1967, pp 145-154.

88. British Steel Castings Research Association, Dust Control on Stand Grinding Machines, Conditions in Steel Foundries, First Report of Joint Standing Committee, London, 1961.

89. The Kirk and Blum Mfg. Co., Woodworking Plants, pp W-9, Cincinnati, OH.

90. American Foundrymen's Society, Engineering Manual for Control of In Plant Environment in Foundries, 1956, Des Plaines, IL.

91. Alden, John L., Design of Industrial Exhaust Systems, 1939, Industrial Press, 200 Madison Ave., New York, NY 10016.

92. The Quickdraft Corporation, P. O. Box 1353, Canton, OH.

93. Boies, Robert B., Air Eductors Used to Handle Noxious and Corrosive Fumes, Air Engineering, Vol. 7, No. 6, June, 1965.

94. Private Communication, E. A. Carsey, The Kirk and Blum Mfg. Co., Cincinnati, OH 45209.

95. Harris, W. B., Christofano, E. E., and Lippman, M., Combination Hot Plate and Hood for Multiple Beaker Evaporation, American Industrial Hygiene Assn., Journal, Vol. 22, No. 4, August, 1961.

96. Dieter, W. E., Cohen, L., and Kundick, M. E., A Stainless Steel Fume Hood for Safety in Use of Perchloric Acid, U. S. Dept. of Interior, 1964.

97. Lynch, Jeremiah R., Computer Design of Industrial Exhaust Systems, Heating, Piping & Air Conditioning, September, 1968.

98. Hama, George, A Calibrating Wind Tunnel for Air Measuring Instruments, Air Engineering, December, 1967, pp 18-20, 41.

99. Hama, George, Calibration of Alnor Velometers, American Industrial Hygiene Assn. Journal, December, 1958.

100. Hama, George, and Curley, L. S., Instrumentation for the Measurement of Low Velocities with a Pitot Tube, Air Engineering, July, 1967, and American Industrial Hygiene Assn. Journal, May-June, 1967.

101. Yaffe, C.D., Byer, D. H., and Hosey, A.D., Encyclopedia of Instrumentation for Industrial Hygiene University of Michigan, Ann Arbor, MI, 1956, pp 703-709.

102. Airflow Developments Ltd., Lancaster Rd., High Wycombe, Bucks., England.

103. Heating and Cooling for Man and Industry, American Industrial Hygiene Association, 1969.

104. ASHRAE Guide & Data Book, American Society of Heating, Refrigeration and Air Conditioning Engineers, 1961, p 243.

105. F. W. Dwyer Company, Michigan City, IN.

106. HPAC Data Sheet, How to Design Drain Type Stacks, Heating, Piping and Air Conditioning, June, 1964, p. 143.

107. Air Movement and Control Association, Inc., 30 W. University Dr., Arlington Heights, IL 60064, AMCA Standard 99-2408-69.

108. Adapted from U. S. Dept., of Labor, Occupational Safety and Health Administration, Washington, DC, Federal Register, Vol. 36, No. 105, May 29, 1971, Occupational Safety and Health Standards; National Concensus Standards and Established Federal Standards.

109. Hama, George, How Safe Are Direct-fired Makeup Units, Air Engineering, September, 1962, p. 22.

110. Hama, George M., and Butler, Jr., Kerrel E., Ventilation Requirements for Lift Truck Operation, Heating, Piping and Air Conditioning, January, 1970.

111. Hama, George M., Is Makeup Air Necessary?, Air Conditioning, Heating and Ventilating, November, 1959.

112. Hama, George, and Bonkowski, K. J., Ventilation Requirements for Airless Spray Painting, Heating, Piping and Air Conditioning, October, 1970, pp 80-82.

113. National Fire Protection Association, 470 Atlantic Ave., Boston, MA 02210.

114. L. J. Wing Mfg. Co., Linden, NJ, Bulletin IFB-61, p. 4.

115. Hart & Cooley Mfg. Co., Holland, MI, Bulletin E-6.

116. Hama, George, The Characteristics of Weather Caps, Air Engineering, September, 1962.

117. U. S. Dept. of Health, Education and Welfare Health Services and Mental Health Administration, NIOSH, Report HSM 72-10269, Criteria for a Recommended Standard . . . . Occupational Exposure to Hot Environments.

118. Rajhans, G.S., and Thompkins, R. W., Critical Velocities of Mineral Dusts, Canadian Mining Journal, October, 1967, pp 85-88.

119. Djamgowz, O.T., and Ghoneim, S.A.A., Determining the Pick-up Air Velocity of Mineral Dusts, Canadian Mining Journal, July, 1974, pp 25-28.

120. Baliff, J., Greenburg, L., and Stern, A.C., Transport Velocities for Industrial Dusts—An Experimental Study, Industrial Hygiene Quarterly, Vol. 9, No. 4, December, 2948, pp 85-88.

121. DallaValle, J. M., Determining Minimum Air Velocities for Exhaust Systems, Heating, Piping and Air Conditioning, 1932.

122. Hatch, T.F., Economy in the Design of Exhaust Systems.

123. NIOSH Research Report #75-107, Ventilation Requirements for Grinding, Buffing and Polishing Operations.

124. Hutcheson, J.R.M., Environmental Control in the Asbestos Industry of Quebec, C 1 MM Bulletin, Vol. 64, No. 712, Aug., 1971, pp 83-89.

125. Goldfield, J., and Brandt, F.E., Dust Control Techniques in the Asbestos Industry, a paper presented at the A.I.H. Conference, Miami Beach, FL, May 12-17, 1974.

126. Private Communications, Occupational Health Protection Branch, Ontario Ministry of Labor, October, 1976.

127. Hama, G.M., Ventilation Control of Dust from Bagging Operations, Heating and Ventilating, April, 1948, pp 91.

128. Ventilation and Air Contracting Contractors Association of Chicago, Testing and Balancing Manual for Ventilating and Air Conditioning Systems, 228 N. LaSalle St., Chicago, IL, 1963.

129. Langner, Ralph R., How to Control Carcinogens in Chemical Production, Occupational Health and Safety, March-April, 1977.

130. Wright, Jr., D. K., A New Friction Chart for Round Ducts, ASHVE Research Report No. 1280, ASHVE Transactions, Vol. 51, 1945, p. 303.

131. Leith, David, First, Melvin K,W., and Feldman, Henry, Performance of a Pulse-Jet at High Filtration Velocity II, Filter Cake Redeposition, Journal of the Air Pollution Control Assn., Vol. 27, 1977, p. 636.

132. Beake, E., Optimizing Filtration Parameters, Journal of the Air Pollution Control Assn., Vol. 24, 1974, p. 1150.

133. Leith, David, Gibson, Dwight D., and First, Melvin W., Performance of Top and Bottom Inlet Pulse-Jet Fabric Filters, Journal of the Air Pollution Control Association, Vol. 28, July, 2978, p. 696.

134. National Council on Radiation Protection and Measurements, Basic Radiation Protection Criteria, NCRP Report No. 39, January 15, 1971, 4201 Connecticut Ave., N. W., Washington, DC 20008.

135. Rajhans, G. S., and Bragg, G. M., Engineering Aspects of Asbestos Dust Control, Ann Arbor Science Publications, Inc., Ann Arbor, MI, 1978.

136. Caplan, K. J., and Knutson, G.W., Laboratory Fume Hoods: A Performance Test, ASHRAE Transactions, Vol. 84, Part 1, 1978.

137. Caplan, K.J., and Knutson, G.W., Laboratory Fume Hoods: Influence of Room Air Supply, ASHRAE Transactions, Vol. 84, Part 2, 1978.

138. Sheet Metal and Air Conditioning Contractors' National Assn., Inc., Round Industrial Duct Construction Standards, 1977, 8224 Old Courthouse Rd., Tysons Corner, Vienna, VA 22180.

139. Sheet Metal and Air Conditioning Contractors' National Assn., Inc., Rectangular Industrial Duct Construction Standards, 8224 Old Courthouse Rd., Tysons Corner, Vienna, VA 22180.

140. Air Movement and Control Association, Inc., 30 W. University Dr., Arlington Heights, IL 60004, AMCA Publication 201.141.

141. Huebener, D. J., and Hughes, R. T., Development of Push-Pull Ventilation, American Industrial Hygiene Association Journal, No. 46, 1985, pp. 262-267.

142. Hughes, R. T., Design Criteria for Plating Tank Push-Pull Ventilation, Ventilation 86, Elsiever Press, Amsterdam, 1986.

143. Hughes, R. T., Unpublished data.

144. American Society of Heating, Refrigerating and Air Conditioning Engineers, Guide and Data Book—Fundamentals and Equipment, 1985.

145. Air Moving and Control Association, Inc., AMCA Publication 203-81: Field Performance Measurements, 30 W. University Dr., Arlington Heights, IL 60004.

146. American Society of Mechanical Engineers, Fluid Meters - Their Theory and Applications, 1959.

147. Farant, J. P., McKinnon, D. L., and McKenna, T. A., Tracer Gases as a Ventilation Tool: Methods and Instrumentation, Ventilation '85 - Proceedings of the First International Symposium on Ventilation for Contaminant Control, pages 263-274, October 1-3, 1985, Toronto, Ont., Canada

148. ASME Power Test Codes, Chapter 4, Flow Measurement, P.T.C., 19.5:4-1959.

149. U. S. Dept. of Health, Education and Welfare, PHS, CDC, NIOSH, The Industrial Environment - Its Evaluation and Control, 1973.

150. U. S. Air Force, AFOSH Standard 161.2.

151. U. S. Dept. of Health and Human Services, PHS, CDC, NIOSH, Occupational Exposure to Hot Environments, Revised Criteria, 1986.

152. American Welding Society, (AWS D1.1-72), P. O. Box 351040, Miami, FL 33135.

153. Gibson, N., Lloyd, F. C., and Perry, G. R., Fire Hazards in Chemical Plants from Friction Sparks Involving the Thermite Reaction, Symposium Series No. 25, Insn. Chemical Engineers, London, 1968.

154. Hughes, R.T., and Amendola, A. A., Recirculating Exhaust Air: Guides, Design Parameters and Mathematical Modeling, Plant Engineering, March 18, 1982.

155. U. S. Dept. of Health, Education and Welfare (NIOSH), The Recirculation of Industrial Exhaust Air - Symposium Proceedings, Pub. No. 78-141, 1978.

156. American Conference of Governmental Industrial Hygienists, Air Sampling Instruments for Evaluation of Atmospheric Contaminants, 6th Ed., Chapters U and V, Cincinnati, OH, 1983.

157. Baturin, V.V., Fundamentals Industrial Ventilation, Pergamon Press, NY, 1972.

158. U. S. Public Health Service, Air Pollution Engineering Manual, Publication No. 999-AP-40, 1973.

159. U. S. Public Health Service, Air Pollution Engineering Manual, Publication No. 999-AP-40, 1973.

160. Hampl, V., and Johnson, O.E., Control of Wood Dust from Horizontal Belt Sanding, American Industrial Hygiene Assoc. Journal, Vol. 46, No. 10, pp. 567-577, 1985.

161. Hampl, V., Johnston, O.E., and Murdock, D.M., Application of an Air Curtain Exhaust System at a Milling Process, American Industrial Hygiene Assoc. Journal, Vol. 49, No. 4, pp. 167-175, 1988.

162. Air Movement and Control Association, Inc., AMCA Publication 99-83, Standards Handbook, 30 W. University Dr., Arlington Heights, IL 60004.

163. FED-STD-209D, Federal Standard, Cleanroom and Work Station Requirements, Controlled Environment, Federal Supply Service, General Services Administration, Room 6654, 7th and D Street S.W., Washington, DC 20407, June 15, 1988.

164. MIL-F-51477(EA), Specification Filters, Particulate, High-Efficiency, Fire Resistant, Biological Use, General Specifications For, Commander, US Army Armament Research and Development Command, ATTN: DRDAR-TSC-S, Aberdeen Proving Ground, MD 21010, October 4, 1982.

165. IES-RP-CC-002-86, HEPA Filters, Institute of Environmental Sciences, 940 East Northwest Highway, Mount Prospect, IL 60056.

166. IES-RP-CC-006-84, Testing Clean Rooms, Institute of Environmental Sciences, 940 East Northwest Highway, Mount Prospect, IL 60056.10.15.1.

167. Cooper, T. C., Control Technology for a Dry Chemical Bagging and Filling Operation, Monsanto Agricultural Products Co., Cincinnati, OH 1983.

168. Gressel, M. G., Fischback, T.J., Workstation Design Improvements for the Reduction of Dust Exposures

During Weighing of Chemical Powders, Applied Industrial Hygiene, 4:227-233, 1989.

169. American Foundrymen's Society, Inc., Foundry Ventilation Manual, Des Plaines, IL, 1985.

170. Mortimer, V. D., Kerder, S. L. and O'Brien, D. M., Effective Controls for Ethylene Oxide—A Case Study, Applied Industrial Hygiene.

171. Hama, G. M., Ventilation for Fumigation Booths, Air Engineering, December, 1964.

172. National Fire Protection Association Standard, NFPA 96-1987, Standard for the Installation of Equipment for the Removal of Smoke and Grease-Laden Vapors from Commercial Cooking Equipment, Quincy, MA, 1987.

173. National Sanitation Foundation, Standard No. 4, Commercial Cooking and Hot Food Storage Equipment, Ann Arbor, MI 1986.

174. Knutson, G. W., Effect of Slot Position on Laboratory Fume Hood Performance, Heating, Piping and Air Conditioning, February, 1984.

175. Caplan, K. J. and Knutson, G. W., Influence of Room Air Supply on Laboratory Hoods, American Industrial Hygiene Association Journal, 43, 10, 738-746, 1982.

176. American Society of Heating, Refrigerating and Air Conditioning Engineers, ANSI/ASHRAE Standard 110- 1985, Method of Testing the Performance of Laboratory Fume Hoods, 1985.

177. National Sanitation Foundation, Standard 49, Class II (Laminar Flow) Biohazard Cabinetry, Ann Arbor, MI 1987.

178. U. S. Air Force Technical Order 00-25-203, Standards and Guidelines for Design and Operation of Clean Rooms and Clean Work Stations, Office of Technical Services, Department of Commerce, Washington, DC, July, 1963.

179. Rain, Carl, Non-traditional Methods Advance Machining Industry, High Technology, November/December, 1957.

180. Schulte, H. F., Hyatt, E. C., and Smith, Jr., F. S., Exhaust Ventilation for Machine Tools Used on Materials of High Toxicity, American Medical Association Archives of Industrial Hygiene and Occupational Medicine, 5, 21, January, 1952.

181. Mitchell, R. N., and Hyatt, E. C., Beryllium—Hazard Evaluation and Control Covering a Five-Year Study, American Industrial Hygiene Quarterly, 18, 3, September, 1957.

182. National Grain and Feed Association, Dust Control for Grain Elevators, Washington, DC, 1981.

183. American Air Filter Co., Rotoclone Dust Control, January, 1946.

184. Hampl, V., Johnston, O. E., and Murdock, D. M., Application of an Air Curtain Exhaust System at a Milling Process, American Industrial Hygiene Association Journal, 49, 4, pp. 167-175, 1988.

185. Private Communication, V. Sciola, Hamilton Standard.

186. National Fire Protection Association, Flammable and Combustible Liquids Code, No. 30, Boston, MA, 1990.

187. National Fire Protection Association, National Electric Code, No. 70, Boston, MA, 1990.

188. NIOSH Technical Report 81-121, An Evaluation of Engineering Control Technology for Spray Painting, 1981.

189. Burgess, W. A., Ellenbecker, M. J., and Treitman, R. D., Ventilation for Control of the Work Environment, John Wiley and Sons, NY, 1989.

190. U. S. Department of Labor, Occupational Safety and Health Administration, 29 CFR, 1910.

191. National Fire Protection Association, National Fire Codes—in particular NFPA-65 (Processing and Finishing of Aluminum), NFPA-68 (Guide for Explosion Prevention Systems), NFPA-77 (Practice on Static Electricity), NFPA-91 (Installation of Blowers and Exhaust Systems for Dust, Stack and Vapor Removal or Conveying), NFPA-480 (Storage, Handling and Processing of Magnesium), NFPA-481 (Production, Processing, Handling and Storage of Titanium), NFPA-482 (Production, Processing, Handling and Storage of Zirconium) and NFPA-561 (Manufacture of Aluminum and Magnesium Powder), 1 Batterymarch Park, P. O. Box 9101, Quincy, MA 02269-9101.

192. Hogopian and Bastress, Recommended Ventilation Guidelines for Abrasive-Blasting Operations, CDC-99- 74-33, 1975.

193. American Foundrymen's Society, Inc., Foundry Ventilation Manual, 1985.

194. National Institute of Occupational Safety and Health (NIOSH) Research Report #75-107, Ventilation Requirements for Grinding, Buffing and Polishing Operations, 1974.

195. Kim, T. and Flynn, M. R., Airflow Pattern Around a Worker in a Uniform Freestream, Am. Ind. Hyg. Assoc. J., 52:7 (1991), pp. 187-296.

196. George, D. K., Flynn, M. R., and Goodman, R., The Impact of Boundary Layer Separation on Local Exhaust Design and Worker Exposure, Appl. Occup. and Env. Hyg., 5:501-509, (1990).

197.   Heriot, M. R., and Wilkinson, J., Laminar Flow Booths for the Control of Dust, Filtration and Separation, 16:2:159-164, 1979.

198.   Flynn, M. R., and Shelton, W. K., Factors Affecting the Design of Local Exhaust Ventilation for the Control of Contaminants from Hand-held Sources, Appl. Occup. and Env. Hyg., 5:707-714, (1990).

199.   Tum Suden, K. D., Flynn, M. R., and Goodman, R., Computer Simulation in the Design of Local Exhaust Hoods for Shielded Metal Arc Welding, Am. Ind. Hyg. Assoc. J., 51(3):115-126, (1990).

200.   American Welding Society, Fumes and Gases in the Welding Environment, F. Y. Speight and H. C. Campbell, Eds., Miami, FL (1979).

201.   The Trane Company, Trane Air Conditioning Manual, 30th Printing, February, 1961, LaCrosse, WI.

202.   International Conference of Building Officials, Uniform Building Code, Light, Ventilation and Sanitation, Section 605, 1988 Edition.

203.   American Society of Heating, Refrigeration and Air Conditioning Engineers, Ventilation for Acceptable Indoor Air Quality, ASHRAE 62-1989.

204.   American Society of Heating, Refrigeration and Air Conditioning Engineers, Thermal Environmental Conditions for Human Occupancy, ASHRAE 55-1992.

205.   American Society of Heating, Refrigeration and Air Conditioning Engineers, ASHRAE Handbook, 1992 HVAC Systems and Equipment.

206.   Rajhans, G. S., Findings of the Ontario Inter-Ministerial Committee on Indoor Air Quality, Proceedings of the ASHRAE/SOEN Conference, IAQ '89, ASHRAE, Inc., Atlanta, pp 195-223.

207.   American Society of Heating, Refrigeration and Air Conditioning Engineers, ASHRAE Handbook, 1989 Fundamentals.

208.   Bauer, E. J., et al: Use of Particle Counts for Filter Evaluation, ASHRAE Journal, October, 1973.

209.   Duffy, G., Filter Upgrades, Engineered Systems, July/August, 1993.

210.   Ottney, T. C., Particle Management for HVAC Systems, ASHRAE Journal, July, 1993, p. 26.

211.   Goldfield, J., Sheehy, J. W., Gunter, B. J., and Daniels, W. J., An Affordable Ventilation Control for Radiator Repair Shops; Ventilation '91; 3rd International Symposium on Ventilation for Contaminant Control; American Conference of Governmental Industrial Hygienists; Cincinnati, OH.

212.   Gressel, M. G., and Hughes, R. T., Effective Local Exhaust Ventilation for Controlling Formaldehyde Exposure During Embalming; Applied Occupational Environmental Hygiene; 7(12), December, 1992.

213.   Estell, C. F., and Spencer, A. B., Case Study: Control of Methylene Chloride Exposures During Commercial Furniture Stripping; Submitted to American Industrial Hygiene Association Journal, June, 1994.

214.   Burgess, W. A., Ellenbecker, M. J. and Treitman, R. D., Ventilation for Control of the Work Environment, John Wiley & Sons, New York, 1989.

215.   Braconnier, R., Bibliographic Review of Velocity Fields in the Vicinity of Local Exhaust Hoods. Am. Ind. Hyg. Assoc. J, 49(4):185-198 (1988).

216.   Air Movement and Control Association, Inc.: AMCA Publication 201-90, Fans and Systems, 30 W. University Dr., Arlington Heights, IL 60004-1893; (847)394-0150; FAX: (847)394-0088; Publications: (847)394-0404.

217.   American Society of Heating, Refrigeration, and Air-Conditioning Engineers, Inc.: Fundamentals Handbook 1993; 1791 Tullie Circle, NE, Atlanta, GA 3032

218.   Hampl, V., and Johnston, O., Control of Wood Dust from Disc Sanders, Applied Occupational Hygiene, 6(11), November, 1991.

219.   Topmiller, J. L., Watkins, D. A., Schulmna, S. A., and Murdock, D. J., Controlling Wood Dust from Orbital Hand Sanders, Applied Occupational Hygiene, 11(9), September, 1996.

220.   Hampl, V., Topmiller, J. L., Watkins, D. S., and Murdock, D. J., Control of Wood Dust from Rotational Hand Sanders, Applied Occupational Environmental Hygiene, 7(4), April, 1992.

221.   American Society of Heating, Ventilation and Air Conditioning Engineers: HVAC Applications, Atlanta, GA (1995).

222.   Hogopian and Bastress, Recommended Ventilation Guidelines for Abrasive-Blasting Operations, C DC-99-74-33, 1975.

223.   Braconnier, R., Bibliographic Review of Velocity Fields in the Vicinity of Local Exhaust Hood Openings; Am. Ind. Hyg. Assoc. J. (49)(April, 1988).

224.   Fletcher, B., Centerline Velocity Characteristics of Rectangular Unflanged Hoods and Slots Under Suction, Ann. Occup. Hyg., Vol. 20, pp 141-146.

225.   Yousefi, V., Annegarn, H. J. Aerodynamic Aspects of Exhaust Ventilation; Ventilation '91, 3rd International Symposium on Ventilation for Contaminant Control; American Conference of Governmental Industrial Hygienists, Inc., Cincinnati, OH.

226.   Fletcher, B., Effect of Flanges on the Velocity in Front of Exhaust Ventilation Hoods; Ann. Occup. Hyg., Vol. 21, pp 265-269.

227. American Society of Heating, Ventilating and Air Conditioning Engineers: HVAC Application. ASHRAE, Atlanta, GA (1999).

228. National Fire Protection Association, 1 Batterymarch Park, P. O. Box 9101, Quincy, MA 02269-9101.

229. Hama, G., How Safe Are Direct-Fired Makeup Units? Air Engineering, p. 22 (September 1962).

230. American Society of Heating, Refrigeration and Air Conditioning Engineers: HVAC Systems and Equipment. ASHRAE, Atlanta, GA (1996).

231. American Society of Heating, Refrigerating, and Air Conditioning Engineers: Method of Testing General Ventilation Air Cleaning Devices for Removal Efficiency by Particle Size, ASHRAE Publication No. 52.1-92, ASHRAE, Atlanta, GA (1992).

232. Yuan, X., Chen, Q. and Glicksman, L. R 1998, A Critical Review of Displacement Ventilation, ASHRAE Transactions, January, 1998.

233. Skistad, H 1994. Displacement Ventilation. Taunton, Somerset, England: Research Studies. Press, Ltd.

234. Kristensson, J.A. and Lindqvist, O.A. 1993, Displacement Ventilation Systems in Industrial Buildings, ASHRAE Transactions, 99/1.

235. Sheet Metal and Air Conditioning Contractors National Association, Inc: Rectangular Industrial Duct Construction Standards, SMACNA, Vienna, VA (1980).

236. Sheet Metal and Air Conditioning Contractors National Association, Inc: Round Industrial Duct Construction Standards, SMACNA, Vienna, VA (1999).

237. Sheet Metal and Air Conditioning Contractors National Association, Inc: Thermoplastic Duct (PVC) Construction Manual, SMACNA, Vienna, VA (1994).

238. Thomson, M. and Goodfellow, H. 1997, Computational Fluid Dynamics as a Design Tool for Industrial Ventilation, Ventilation, 1997.

239. Hughes, R.T., Amendola, A.A., Recirculating Exhaust Air: Guides, Design Parameters and Mathematical Modeling. Plant Engineering (March 18, 1982).

240. ANSI/AIHA; Recirculation of Air from Industrial Process Exhaust Systems. ANSI/AIHA Z9.7 - 1988, American National Standards Institute, Apr., 1998.

241. National Institute for Occupational Safety and Health: The Recirculation of Industrial Exhaust Air—Symposium Proceedings. Pub. No. 78-141 Department of Health, Education and Welfare (NIOSH), Cincinnati, OH (1978).

242. American Conference of Governmental Industrial Hygienists: Air Sampling Instruments for Evaluation of Atmospheric Contaminants, 8th Edition. ACGIH, Cincinnati, OH (1995).

243. American Society of Heating, Refrigerating and Air Conditioning Engineers, Practices for Measurement, Testing, Adjusting, and Balancing of Building Heating, Ventilation, Air Conditioning and Refrigeration Systems, ANSI/ASHRAE Standard 111-1988.

244. American Society of Heating, Refrigerating and Air Conditioning Engineers. ASHRAE Handbook–1997 Fundamentals.

245. American Society of Heating, Refrigerating and Air Conditioning Engineers. Standard Method for Temperature Measurement. ANSI/ASHRAE standard 41.2-1987 (RA 9).

246. American Society of Heating, Refrigeration and Air Conditioning Engineers, Standard Methods for Laboratory Measurement. ANSI/ASHRAE Standard 41.2-1987 (RA 92).

247. Guffey, S.E., Simplifying Pitot Traverses. Applied Occup. Environ. Hyg., 5(2): 95-100(1990).

248. American Society of Heating, Refrigeration and Air Conditioning Engineers. Standard Method for Pressure Measurement. ANSI/ASHRAE Standard 41.3-1989).

249. American Society of Mechanical Engineers, ASME Power Test Codes, Chapter 4, Flow Measurement, P.T.C., 19.5:4-1959.

250. American Society of Mechanical Engineers, Fluid Meters–Their Theory and Applications, 1959.

251. Booth, D.W., Comparison of Three Methods for Troubleshooting Ventilation Duct Systems Using Measured Pressure and Flows, Ph.D. Dissertation, Dept. of Environmental Health, University of Washington, 1998.

252. Farant, J.P., McKinnon, D.L., and McKenna, T.A., Tracer Gases as a Ventilation Tool: Methods and Instrumentation, Ventilation'85–Proceedings of the First International Symposium of Ventilation for Contaminant Control, pp. 263-274, October 1-3, 1985, Toronto, Canada.

253. First, N.W., and Silverman, L., Airfoil Pitometer, Industrial and Engineering Chemistry, 42, Feb., 1950, pp. 301-308.

254. Guffey, S.E., and Booth, D.W., Comparison of Pitot Traverses Taken at Varying Distance Downstream of Obstructions, Am. Ind. Hyg. Assoc. J. (In Press).

255. Guffey, S.E., and Spann, J.G., Experimental Investigation of Power Loss Coefficients and Static Pressure Ratios in an Industrial Exhaust System, Am. Ind. Hyg. Assoc. J., 60: 367-376, 1999.

256. Guffey, S. E., Quantitative Troubleshooting of Industrial Exhaust Ventilation Systems, Applied Occup. Environ. Hyg., 9(4):267-280, (1994).

257. Guffey, S. E., Final Report of Field Validation of Ventilation Troubleshooting Methods, Grant Number: 1 RO1 OH03165; Project Dates: 4/1/94 to 10/30/97.

258. Hama, G., A Calibrating Wind Tunnel for Measuring Instruments, Air Engr. 41:18-20, (December, 1967).

259. Hama, G., Calibration of Alnor Velometers, Am. Ind. Hyg. Assoc. J., Dec., 1958.

260. Hama, G., and Curley, L.S., Instrumentation for the Measurement of Low Velocities with a Pitot Tube, Air Engr., July, 1967, and Am. Ind. Hyg. Assoc. J., May-June, 1967.

261. Wang, L.S., Repeatability of Velocity Pressure Traverses and Static Pressure Measurements in Five Working Ventilation Systems, MS Thesis, Dept. of Env. Health, University of Washington, 1997.

262. Guffey, S.E., Modeling Existing Ventilation Systems Using Measured Values. Am. Ind. Hyg. Assoc. J., 54(6):293-306 (1993).

263. National Institute for Occupational Safety and Health, NIOSH Health Hazard Evaluation Report HETA 95-0097-2661, October, 1997.

264. California Building Code, Section 1202.2.2.2.1; California Building Officials, 2215 21st Street, Sacramento, CA 95818.

265. National Fire Protection Association, National Electric Code Handbook, Section 6.25, 1999.

266. Naval Facilities Engineering Service Center, Battery Charging Facilities Ventilation Rates, Information Bulletin 425.114, October, 1997.

267. Minor, Cheryl L., State of the Art Ventilation Engineering Principles of Laminar Flow and Recirculation in the Battery Industry. Ventilation '91, Cincinnati, OH, September, 1991.

268. Personal Communication from Melvin Cassidy, Cooperative Assessment Program Manual for the Battery Manufacturing Industry, U. S. Department of Labor, February, 1986.

APPENDICES

APPENDIX A

2000
Threshold Limit Values for Chemical Substances in the Work Environment

Adopted by ACGIH®
with Intended Changes

INTRODUCTION TO THE CHEMICAL SUBSTANCES

Threshold Limit Values (TLVs) refer to airborne concentrations of substances and represent conditions under which it is believed that nearly all workers may be repeatedly exposed day after day without adverse health effects. Because of wide variation in individual susceptibility, however, a small percentage of workers may experience discomfort from some substances at concentrations at or below the threshold limit; a smaller percentage may be affected more seriously by aggravation of a pre-existing condition or by development of an occupational illness. Smoking of tobacco is harmful for several reasons. Smoking may act to enhance the biological effects of chemicals encountered in the workplace and may reduce the body's defense mechanisms against toxic substances.

Individuals may also be hypersusceptible or otherwise unusually responsive to some industrial chemicals because of genetic factors, age, personal habits (e.g., smoking, alcohol, or other drugs), medication, or previous exposures. Such workers may not be adequately protected from adverse health effects from certain chemicals at concentrations at or below the threshold limits. An occupational physician should evaluate the extent to which such workers require additional protection.

TLVs are based on available information from industrial experience; from experimental human and animal studies; and, when possible, from a combination of the three. The basis on which the values are established may differ from substance to substance; protection against impairment of health may be a guiding factor for some, whereas reasonable freedom from irritation, narcosis, nuisance, or other forms of stress may form the basis for others. Health impairments considered include those that shorten life expectancy, compromise physiological function, impair the capability for resisting other toxic substances or disease processes, or adversely affect reproductive function or developmental processes.

The amount and nature of the information available for establishing a TLV varies from substance to substance; consequently, the precision of the estimated TLV is also subject to variation and the latest TLV *Documentation* should be consulted in order to assess the extent of the data available for a given substance.

These limits are intended for use in the practice of industrial hygiene as guidelines or recommendations in the control of potential workplace health hazards and for no other use, e.g., in the evaluation or control of community air pollution nuisances; in estimating the toxic potential of continuous, uninterrupted exposures or other extended work periods; as proof or disproof of an existing disease or physical condition; or adoption or use by countries whose working conditions or cultures differ from those in the United States of America and where substances and processes differ. These limits *are not* fine lines between safe and dangerous concentrations, nor are they a relative index of toxicity. They *should not* be used by anyone untrained in the discipline of industrial hygiene.

The TLVs, as issued by ACGIH, are recommendations and should be used as guidelines for good practices. In spite of the fact that serious adverse health effects are not believed likely as a result of exposure to the threshold limit concentrations, the best practice is to maintain concentrations of all atmospheric contaminants as low as is practical.

ACGIH disclaims liability with respect to the use of TLVs.

Notice of Intended Changes. Each year, proposed actions of the Chemical Substances TLV Committee for the forthcoming year are issued in the form of a "Notice of Intended Changes." This Notice provides an opportunity for comment and *solicits suggestions of substances to be added to the list. The suggestions should be accompanied by substantiating evidence.* The "Notice of Intended Changes" is presented after the Adopted Values in this section. Values listed in parentheses in the "Adopted" list are to be used during the period in which a proposed change for that Value is listed in the Notice of Intended Changes.

Definitions. Three categories of Threshold Limit Values (TLVs) are specified herein, as follows:

a) Threshold Limit Value–Time-Weighted Average (TLV–TWA)—the time-weighted average concentration for a conventional 8-hour workday and a 40-hour workweek, to which it is believed that nearly all workers may be repeatedly exposed, day after day, without adverse effect.

b) Threshold Limit Value–Short-Term Exposure Limit (TLV– STEL)—the concentration to which it is believed that workers can be exposed continuously for a short period of time without suffering from 1) irritation, 2) chronic or irreversible tissue damage, or 3) narcosis of sufficient degree to increase the likelihood of accidental injury, impair self-rescue or materially reduce work efficiency, and provided that the daily TLV–TWA is not exceeded. It is not a separate independent exposure limit; rather, it supplements the time-weighted average (TWA) limit where there are recognized acute effects from a substance whose toxic effects are primarily of a chronic nature. STELs are recommended only where toxic effects have been reported from high short-term exposures in either humans or animals.

A STEL is defined as a 15-minute TWA exposure which should not be exceeded at any time during a workday even if the 8-hour TWA is within the TLV–TWA. Exposures above the TLV–TWA up to the STEL should not be longer than 15 minutes and should not occur more than four times per day. There should be at least 60 minutes between successive exposures in this range. An averaging period other than 15 minutes may be recommended when this is warranted by observed biological effects.

c) Threshold Limit Value–Ceiling (TLV–C)—the concentration that should not be exceeded during any part of the working exposure.

In conventional industrial hygiene practice if instantaneous monitoring is not feasible, then the TLV–C can be assessed by sampling over a period that should not exceed 15 minutes, except for those substances that may cause immediate irritation when exposures are short.

For some substances, e.g., irritant gases, only one category, the TLV–Ceiling, may be relevant. For other substances, one or two categories may be relevant, depending upon their physiologic action. It is important to observe that if any one of these types of TLVs is exceeded, a potential hazard from that substance is presumed to exist.

The Chemical Substances TLV Committee holds to the opinion that TLVs based on physical irritation should be considered no less binding than those based on physical impairment. There is increasing evidence that physical irritation may initiate, promote, or accelerate physical impairment through interaction with other chemical or biologic agents.

Time-Weighted Average (TWA) vs Ceiling (C) Limits. TWAs permit excursions above the TLV provided they are compensated by equivalent excursions below the TLV–TWA during the workday. In some instances, it may be permissible to calculate the average concentration for a workweek rather than for a workday. The relationship between the TLV and permissible excursion is a rule of thumb and in certain cases may not apply. The amount by which the TLVs may be exceeded for short periods without injury to health depends upon a number of factors such as the nature of the contaminant, whether very high concentrations—even for short periods—produce acute poisoning, whether the effects are cumulative, the frequency with which high concentrations occur, and the duration of such periods. All factors must be taken into consideration in arriving at a decision as to whether a hazardous condition exists.

Although the TWA concentration provides the most satisfactory, practical way of monitoring airborne agents for compliance with the TLVs, there are certain substances for which it is inappropriate. In the latter group are substances which are predominantly fast acting and whose TLV is more appropriately based on this particular response. Substances with this type of response are best controlled by a ceiling limit that should not be exceeded. It is implicit in these definitions that the manner of sampling to determine noncompliance with the limits for each group must differ; a single, brief sample, that is applicable to a ceiling limit, is not appropriate to the TWA; here, a sufficient number of samples are needed to permit determination of a TWA concentration throughout a complete cycle of operations or throughout the workshift.

Whereas the ceiling limit places a definite boundary that concentrations should not be permitted to exceed, the TWA requires an explicit limit to the excursions that are permissible above the listed TLVs. It should be noted that the same factors are used by the Chemical Substances TLV Committee in determining the magnitude of the value of the STEL or whether to include or exclude a substance for a ceiling listing.

Excursion Limits. For the vast majority of substances with a TLV–TWA, there is not enough toxicological data available to warrant a STEL. Nevertheless, excursions above the TLV–TWA should be controlled even where the 8-hour TLV–TWA is within recommended limits. Earlier editions of the TLV list included such limits whose values depended on the TLV–TWAs of the substance in question.

While no rigorous rationale was provided for these particular values, the basic concept was intuitive: in a well-controlled process exposure, excursions should be held within some reasonable limits. Unfortunately, neither toxicology nor collective industrial hygiene experience provide a solid basis for quantifying what those limits should be. The approach here is that the maximum recommended excursion should be related to variability generally observed in actual industrial processes. In reviewing large numbers of industrial hygiene surveys conducted by the National Institute for Occupational Safety and Health, Leidel, Busch, and Crouse[1] found that short-term exposure measurements were generally lognormally distributed with geometric standard deviations mostly in the range of 1.5 to 2.0.

While a complete discussion of the theory and properties of the lognormal distribution is beyond the scope of this section, a brief description of some important terms is presented. The measure of central tendency in a lognormal description is the antilog of the mean logarithm of the sample values. The distribution is skewed, and the geometric mean is always smaller than the arithmetic mean by an amount which depends on the geometric standard deviation. In the lognormal distribution, the geometric standard deviation (sd_g) is the antilog of the standard deviation of the sample value logarithms and 68.26% of all values lie between m_g/sd_g and $m_g \times sd_g$.

If the short-term exposure values in a given situation have a geometric standard deviation of 2.0, 5% of all values will exceed 3.13 times the geometric mean. If a process displays a variability greater than this, it is not under good control and efforts should be made to restore control. This concept is the basis for the following excursion limit recommendations which apply to those TLV–TWAs that do not have STELs:

Excursions in worker exposure levels may exceed 3 times the TLV–TWA for no more than a total of 30 minutes during a workday, and under no circumstances should they exceed 5 times the TLV–TWA, provided that the TLV–TWA is not exceeded.

The approach is a considerable simplification of the idea of the lognormal concentration distribution but is considered more convenient to use by the practicing industrial hygienist. If exposure excursions are maintained within the recommended limits, the geometric standard deviation of the concentration measurements will be near 2.0 and the goal of the recommendations will be accomplished.

When the toxicological data for a specific substance are available to establish a STEL, this value takes precedence over the excursion limit regardless of whether it is more or less stringent.

"Skin" Notation. The designation "Skin" in the "Notations" column refers to the potential significant contribution to the overall exposure by the cutaneous route, including mucous membranes and the eyes, either by contact with vapors or, of probable greater significance, by direct skin contact with the substance. Vehicles present in solutions or mixtures can also significantly enhance potential skin absorption. It should be noted that while some materials are capable of causing irritation, dermatitis, and sensitization in workers, these properties are *not considered relevant* when assigning a skin notation. It should be noted, however, that the development of a dermatological condition can significantly affect the potential for dermal absorption.

While relatively limited quantitative data currently exist with regard to skin absorption of gases, vapors, and liquids by workers, the Chemical Substances TLV Committee recommends that the integration of data from acute dermal studies and repeated dose dermal studies in animals and/or humans, along with the ability of the chemical to be absorbed, be used in deciding on the appropriateness of the skin notation. In general, available data which suggest that the potential for absorption via the hands/forearms during the workday could be significant, especially for chemicals with lower TLVs, could justify a skin notation. From acute animal toxicity data, materials having a relatively low dermal LD_{50} (1000 mg/kg of body weight or less) would be given a skin notation. Where repeated dermal application studies have shown significant systemic effects following treatment, a skin notation would be considered. When chemicals penetrate the skin easily (higher octanol–water partition coefficients) and where extrapolations of systemic effects from other routes of exposure suggest dermal absorption may be important in the expressed toxicity, a skin notation would be considered.

Substances having a skin notation and a low TLV may present special problems for operations involving high airborne concentrations of the material, particularly under conditions where significant areas of the skin are exposed for a long period of time. Under these conditions, special precautions to significantly reduce or preclude skin contact may be required.

Biological monitoring should be considered to determine the relative contribution of exposure via the dermal route to the total dose. The TLV/BEI Book contains a number of adopted Biological Exposure Indices, which provide an additional tool when assessing the worker's total exposure to selected materials. For additional information, refer to "Dermal Absorption" in the "Introduction to the Biological Exposure Indices," *Documentation of Threshold Limit Values and Biological Exposure Indices*, and to Leung and Paustenbach.[2]

Use of the skin designation is intended to alert the reader that air sampling alone is insufficient to accurately quantitate exposure and that measures to prevent significant cutaneous absorption may be required.

"Sensitizer" Notation. The designation "SEN" in the "Notations" column refers to the confirmed potential for worker sensitization as a result of dermal contact and/or inhalation exposure, based on the weight of scientific evidence. Lack of the sensitizer notation does not necessarily mean that the substance is not a sensitizer. The *Documentation of the Threshold Limit Values and Biological Exposure Indices* should be consulted for detailed information on the specific substance, the relative sensitizing potency, and whether its sensitization potential is related to dermal contact, inhalation exposure, or both.

Mixtures. Special consideration should be given also to the application of the TLVs in assessing the health hazards that may be associated with

---

(1) Leidel, N.A.; Busch, K.A.; Crouse, W.E.: Exposure Measurement Action Level and Occupational Environmental Variability. DHEW (NIOSH) Pub. No. 76-131; NTIS Pub. No. PB-267-509. National Technical Information Service, Springfield, VA (December 1975).

(2) Leung, H.; Paustenbach, D.J.: Techniques for Estimating the Percutaneous Absorption of Chemicals Due to Occupational and Environmental Exposure. Appl. Occup. Environ. Hyg. 9(3):187–197 (March 1994).

exposure to mixtures of two or more substances. A brief discussion of basic considerations involved in developing TLVs for mixtures and methods for their development, amplified by specific examples, are given in Appendix C.

Particulate Matter. For solid and liquid particulate matter, TLVs are expressed in terms of total particulate, except where the terms inhalable, thoracic, or respirable particulate are used. Refer to Endnotes. See Appendix D, Particle Size-Selective Sampling Criteria for Airborne Particulate Matter, for the definitions of inhalable, thoracic, and respirable particulate matter. The term total particulate refers to airborne material sampled with the 37mm closed face cassette traditionally used in the United States for aerosol sampling.

The intent of the Chemical Substances TLV Committee is to replace all total particulate TLVs with inhalable, thoracic, and/or respirable particulate matter TLVs. All proposed changes will be included on the Notice of Intended Changes and comments invited. Publication of the results of side-by-side sampling studies using older total and newer inhalable, thoracic, or respirable sampling techniques is encouraged to aid in the appropriate replacement of current total particulate TLVs.

Particulates (Insoluble) Not Otherwise Classified (PNOC). There are many substances on the TLV list, and many more that are not on the list, for which there is no evidence of specific toxic effects. Those that are particulates have frequently been called "nuisance dusts." Although these materials may not cause fibrosis or systemic effects, they are not biologically inert. At high concentrations, otherwise nontoxic particulates have been associated with the occasionally fatal condition known as alveolar proteinosis. At lower concentrations, they can inhibit the clearance of toxic particulates from the lung by decreasing the mobility of the alveolar macrophages. Accordingly, the Chemical Substances TLV Committee recommends the use of the term "Particulates (Insoluble) Not Otherwise Classified (PNOC)" to emphasize that all materials are potentially toxic and to avoid the implication that these materials are harmless at all exposure concentrations. Particulates identified under the PNOC heading are those containing no asbestos and <1% crystalline silica. To recognize the adverse effects of exposure to otherwise nontoxic particulate matter, a TLV–TWA of 10 mg/m^3 for inhalable particulate and a TLV–TWA of 3 mg/m^3 for respirable particulate have been established and are included in the adopted TLV list. Refer to the PNOC *Documentation* for a complete discussion of this subject.

Simple Asphyxiants—"Inert" Gases or Vapors. A number of gases and vapors, when present in high concentrations in air, act primarily as simple asphyxiants without other significant physiologic effects. A TLV may not be recommended for each simple asphyxiant because the limiting factor is the available oxygen. The minimal oxygen content should be 18% by volume under normal atmospheric pressure (equivalent to a partial pressure, pO$_2$ of 135 torr). Atmospheres deficient in O$_2$ do not provide adequate warning and most simple asphyxiants are odorless. Several simple asphyxiants present an explosion hazard. Account should be taken of this factor in limiting the concentration of the asphyxiant.

Biological Exposure Indices (BEIs). The note "BEI" is listed in the "Notations" column when a BEI is also recommended for the substance listed. Biological monitoring should be instituted for such substances to evaluate the total exposure from all sources, including dermal, ingestion, or nonoccupational. See the BEI section in this Book and the *Documentation of the TLVs and BEIs* for the substance.

Physical Factors. It is recognized that such physical factors as heat, ultraviolet and ionizing radiation, humidity, abnormal pressure (altitude), and the like may place added stress on the body so that the effects from exposure at a TLV may be altered. Most of these stresses act adversely to increase the toxic response of a substance. *Although most TLVs have built-in safety factors to guard against adverse effects to moderate deviations from normal environments, the safety factors of most substances are not of such a magnitude as to take care of gross deviations.* For example, continuous, heavy work at temperatures above 25°C WBGT, or overtime extending the workweek more than 25%, might be considered gross deviations. In such instances, judgment must be exercised in the proper adjustments of the TLVs.

Unlisted Substances. The list of TLVs is by no means a complete list of all hazardous substances or of all hazardous substances used in indus-

try. For a large number of materials of recognized toxicity, little or no data are available that could be used to establish a TLV. Substances that do not appear on the TLV list should not be considered to be harmless or non-toxic. When unlisted substances are introduced into a workplace, the medical and scientific literature should be reviewed to identify potentially dangerous toxic effects. It may also be advisable to conduct preliminary toxicity studies. In any case, it is necessary to remain alert to adverse health effects in workers which may be associated with the use of new materials. The TLV Committee strongly encourages industrial hygienists and other occupational health professionals to bring to the Committee's attention any information which would suggest that a TLV should be established. Such information should include exposure concentrations and correlated health effects data (dose–response) that would support a recommended TLV.

Unusual Work Schedules. Application of TLVs to workers on work schedules markedly different from the conventional 8-hour day, 40-hour week requires particular judgement in order to provide, for such workers, protection equal to that provided to workers on conventional workshifts.

As tentative guidance, field hygienists are referred to the "Brief and Scala model" which is described and explained at length in Patty.[3]

The Brief and Scala model reduces the TLV proportionately for both increased exposure time and reduced recovery (nonexposure) time. The model is generally intended to apply to work schedules longer than 8 hours/day or 40 hours/week. The model should not be used to justify very high exposures as "allowable" where the exposure periods are short (e.g., exposure to 8 times the TLV–TWA for one hour and zero exposure during the remainder of the shift). In this respect, the general limitations on TLV excursions and STELs should be applied to avoid inappropriate use of the model with very short exposure periods or shifts.

Since adjusted TLVs do not have the benefit of historical use and long-time observation, medical supervision during initial use of adjusted TLVs is advised. In addition, the hygienist should avoid unnecessary exposure of workers even if a model shows such exposures to be "allowable" and should not use models to justify higher-than-necessary exposures.

The Brief and Scala model is easier to use than some of the more complex models based on pharmacokinetic actions. However, hygienists thoroughly familiar with such models may find them more appropriate in specific instances. Use of such models usually requires knowledge of the biological half-life of each substance, and some models require additional data.

Short workweeks can allow workers to have two full-time jobs, perhaps with similar exposures, and may result in overexposure even if neither job by itself entails overexposure. Hygienists should be alert to such situations.

Conversion of TLVs in ppm to mg/m^3. TLVs for gases and vapors are usually established in terms of parts per million of substances in air by volume (ppm). For convenience to the user, these TLVs are also listed with molecular weights. Where 24.45 = molar volume of air in liters at normal temperature and pressure (NTP) conditions (25°C and 760 torr), the conversion equation for mg/m^3 is:

$$\text{TLV in mg/m}^3 = \frac{(\text{TLV in ppm}) \ (\text{gram molecular weight of substance})}{24.45}$$

Conversely, the equation for converting TLVs in mg/m^3 to ppm is:

$$\text{TLV in ppm} = \frac{(\text{TLV in mg/m}^3) \ (24.45)}{\text{gram molecular weight of substance}}$$

The above equation may be used to convert TLVs to any degree of precision desired. When converting TLVs to mg/m^3 for other temperatures and pressures, the reference TLVs should be used as a starting point. When converting values expressed as an element (e.g., as Fe, as Ni), the molecular value of the element should be used, not that of the entire compound.

NOTE: A convenient plug-in-the-number (e.g., concentration in ppm or mg/m^3, molecular weight, temperature, and pressure) conversion may be found under "Exposure Sampling" at: **http://www.industrialhygiene.com/**

(3) Paustenbach, D.J.: Occupational Exposure Limits, Pharmacokinetics, and Unusual Work Schedules. In: Patty's Industrial Hygiene and Toxicology, 3rd ed., Vol. 3A, The Work Environment, Chap. 7, pp. 222–348. R.L. Harris, L.J. Cralley and L.V. Cralley, Eds. John Wiley and Sons, Inc., New York (1994).

In making conversions for substances with variable molecular weights, appropriate molecular weights should be estimated or assumed (see the TLV *Documentation*).

Biologically Derived Airborne Contaminants. TLVs exist for certain substances of biological origin, including cellulose; some wood, cotton, and grain dusts; nicotine; pyrethrum; starch; subtilisins (proteolytic enzymes); sucrose; and vegetable oil mist. However, for the reasons identified below, there are no TLVs against which to compare environmental air concentrations of most materials of biological origin. The ACGIH Bioaerosols Committee has developed and separately published guidelines to assess, control, remediate, and prevent biologically derived contamination in indoor environments.[4] For the purposes of the guidelines, indoor biological contamination is defined as the presence of a) biologically derived aerosols of a kind and concentration likely to cause disease or predispose people to disease; b) inappropriate concentrations of outdoor bioaerosols, especially in buildings designed to prevent their entry; or c) indoor microbial growth and remnants of biological growth that may become aerosolized and to which people may be exposed. The guidelines define an approach to assessing and controlling bioaerosol exposures. This approach relies on visually inspecting buildings, assessing occupant symptoms, evaluating building performance, monitoring potential environmental sources, and applying professional judgement.

Biologically derived airborne contaminants include bioaerosols (airborne particles composed of or derived from living organisms) and volatile organic compounds that organisms release. Bioaerosols include microorganisms (i.e., culturable, nonculturable, and dead microorganisms) and fragments, toxins, and particulate waste products from all varieties of living things. Biologically derived contaminants are ubiquitous in nature and may be modified by human activity. All persons are repeatedly exposed, day after day, to a wide variety of such materials.

The guidelines provide background information on the major groups of bioaerosols including their sources and health effects. The guidelines also describe methods to collect, analyze, and interpret bioaerosol samples from potential environmental sources. Occasionally, environmental monitoring detects a single or predominating biological contaminant. More commonly, monitoring reveals a mixture of many biologically derived materials, reflecting the diverse and interactive nature of indoor microenvironments. Environmental sampling for bioaerosols should be conducted only following careful formulation of testable hypotheses about potential bioaerosol sources and mechanisms by which workers may be exposed to bioaerosols from these sources. Even when investigators work from testable hypotheses and well-formulated sampling plans, results from environmental bioaerosol monitoring may be inconclusive and possibly misleading.

For the reasons identified below, there are no TLVs for interpreting environmental measurements of a) total culturable or countable bioaerosols (e.g., total bacteria or fungi); b) specific culturable or countable bioaerosols (e.g., *Aspergillus fumigatus*); c) infectious agents (e.g., *Legionella pneumophila, Mycobacterium tuberculosis*); or d) assayable biological contaminants (e.g., endotoxin, mycotoxin, antigens, or microbial volatile organic compounds).

A. **Total culturable or countable bioaerosols.** Culturable bioaerosols are those bacteria and fungi that can be grown in laboratory culture. Such results are reported as the number of colony-forming units. Countable bioaerosols are those pollen grains, fungal spores, bacterial cells, and other material that can be identified and counted by microscope. A general TLV for culturable or countable bioaerosol concentrations is not scientifically supportable because of the following.

1. Culturable microorganisms and countable biological particles do not comprise a single entity, i.e., bioaerosols in occupational settings are generally complex mixtures of many different microbial, animal, and plant particles.
2. Human responses to bioaerosols range from innocuous effects to serious, even fatal, diseases, depending on the specific material involved and workers' susceptibility to it. Therefore, an appropriate exposure limit for one bioaerosol may be entirely inappropriate for another.
3. It is not possible to collect and evaluate all bioaerosol components

using a single sampling method. Many reliable methods are available to collect and analyze bioaerosol materials. However, different methods of sample collection and analysis may result in different estimates of the concentrations of culturable and countable bioaerosols.
4. At present, information relating culturable or countable bioaerosol concentrations to health effects is generally insufficient to describe exposure–response relationships.

B. **Specific culturable or countable bioaerosols other than infectious agents.** Specific TLVs for individual culturable or countable bioaerosols have not been established to prevent hypersensitivity, irritant, or toxic responses. At present, information relating culturable or countable bioaerosol concentrations to health effects consists largely of case reports and qualitative exposure assessments. The data available are generally insufficient to describe exposure–response relationships. Reasons for the absence of good epidemiologic data on such relationships include the following.

1. Most data on concentrations of specific bioaerosols are derived from indicator measurements rather than from measurements of actual effector agents. For example, investigators use the air concentration of culturable fungi to represent exposure to airborne fungal antigens. In addition, most measurements are from either area or source samples. These monitoring approaches are less likely to reflect human exposure accurately than would personal sampling for actual effector agents.
2. Bioaerosol components and concentrations vary widely within and among different occupational and environmental settings. Unfortunately, replicate sampling is uncommon in bioaerosol assessments. Further, the most commonly used air sampling devices for indoor monitoring are designed to collect "grab" samples over relatively short time intervals. Measurements from single, short-term grab samples may be orders of magnitude higher or lower than long-term average concentrations and are unlikely to represent workplace exposures accurately. Some organisms and sources release aerosols as "concentration bursts," which may only rarely be detected by limited grab sampling. Nevertheless, such episodic bioaerosol releases may produce significant health effects.

C. **Infectious agents.** Human dose–response data are available for only a few infectious bioaerosols. At present, air sampling protocols for infectious agents are limited and suitable primarily for research endeavors. In most routine exposure settings, public health measures, such as immunization, active case finding, and medical treatment, remain the primary defenses against infectious bioaerosols. Facilities associated with increased risks for transmission of airborne infectious diseases (e.g., microbiology laboratories, animal handling facilities, and health care settings) should employ engineering controls to minimize air concentrations of infectious agents. Further, such facilities should consider the need for administrative controls and personal protective equipment to prevent the exposure of workers to these bioaerosols.

D. **Assayable biological contaminants.** Assayable, biologically derived contaminants (e.g., endotoxin, mycotoxins, antigens, and volatile organic compounds) are microbial, animal, or plant substances that can be detected using chemical, immunological, or biological assays. Evidence does not yet support TLVs for any of these substances. However, assay methods for certain common airborne antigens and endotoxin are steadily improving, and field validation of these assays is also progressing. Dose–response relationships for some assayable bioaerosols have been observed in experimental studies and occasionally in epidemiologic surveys. Therefore, TLVs for some of these substances may be appropriate in the future. Also, innovative molecular techniques are becoming available for specific bioaerosols currently detectable only by culture or counting.

ACGIH actively solicits information, comments, and data that will help the Bioaerosols Committee evaluate the potential for health effects associated with bioaerosol exposures in occupational and related environments. Such information should be sent to The Science Group, ACGIH.

Note: In the interest of keeping this section as compact as possible, the footnotes for the adopted values are as follows:

(4) American Conference of Governmental Industrial Hygienists: Bioaerosols: Assessment and Control. ACGIH, Cincinnati, OH (1998).

FOOTNOTES

*   2000 Adoption.

‡   See Notice of Intended Changes.

( )   Adopted values enclosed are those for which changes are proposed. Consult the Notice of Intended Changes for current proposal.

†   2000 Revision or Addition to the Notice of Intended Changes.

A   Refers to Appendix A — Carcinogenicity.

B   Refers to Appendix B — Substances of Variable Composition.

C   Denotes Ceiling limit.

(D) See definition in the "Introduction to the Chemical Substances."

(E) The value is for particulate matter containing no asbestos and < 1% crystalline silica.

(F) Respirable fibers: length > 5 μm; aspect ratio $\geq$ 3:1, as determined by the membrane filter method at 400–450 X magnification (4-mm objective), using phase-contrast illumination.

(G) As measured by the vertical elutriator, cotton-dust sampler. See TLV Documentation.

(H) Sampled by method that does not collect vapor.

(I) Inhalable fraction; *see* Appendix D, paragraph A.

(J) Does not include stearates of toxic metals.

(K) Should not exceed 2 mg/m^3 respirable dust.

(L) Except castor, cashew nut, or similar irritant oils.

(R) Respirable fraction; *see* Appendix D, paragraph C.

(V) Vapor and aerosol.

BEI Substances for which there are also Biological Exposure Indices (see BEI section). Substances identified as methemoglobin inducers (for which methemoglobin is the principal cause of toxicity) and as acetylcholinesterase inhibiting pesticides are part of this notation.

NOC   = Not otherwise classified.

SEN   = Sensitizer; *see* definition in the "Introduction to the Chemical Substances."

Skin   = Danger of cutaneous absorption; see discussion in the "Introduction to the Chemical Substances."

ppm   = Parts of vapor or gas per million parts of contaminated air by volume at NTP conditions (25°C; 760 torr).

mg/m^3 = Milligrams of substance per cubic meter of air.

ADOPTED VALUES			
Substance [CAS No.]	TWA (ppm/mg/m³)	STEL/C (ppm/mg/m³)	Notations
Acetaldehyde [75-07-0]	—	C 25 ppm	A3
Acetic acid [64-19-7]	10 ppm	15 ppm	—
Acetic anhydride [108-24-7]	5 ppm	—	—
Acetone [67-64-1]	500 ppm	750 ppm	A4; BEI
Acetone cyanohydrin [75-86-5], as CN	—	C 4.7 ppm	Skin
Acetonitrile [75-05-8]	40 ppm	60 ppm	A4
Acetophenone [98-86-2]	10 ppm	—	—
Acetylene [74-86-2]	Simple asphyxiant (D)		
Acetylene dichloride, see 1,2-Dichloroethylene			
Acetylene tetrabromide [79-27-6]	1 ppm	—	—
Acetylsalicylic acid (Aspirin) [50-78-2]	5 mg/m³	—	—
Acrolein [107-02-8]	—	C 0.1 ppm	Skin; A4
Acrylamide [79-06-1]	0.03 mg/m³	—	Skin; A3
Acrylic acid [79-10-7]	2 ppm	—	Skin; A4
* Acrylonitrile [107-13-1]	2 ppm	—	Skin; A3
Adipic acid [124-04-9]	5 mg/m³	—	—
Adiponitrile [111-69-3]	2 ppm	—	Skin
Aldrin [309-00-2]	0.25 mg/m³	—	Skin; A3
Allyl alcohol [107-18-6]	0.5 ppm	—	Skin; A4
Allyl chloride [107-05-1]	1 ppm	2 ppm	A3
Allyl glycidyl ether (AGE) [106-92-3]	1 ppm	—	A4
Allyl propyl disulfide [2179-59-1]	2 ppm	3 ppm	—
α-Alumina, see Aluminum oxide			
Aluminum [7429-90-5]			
Metal dust	10 mg/m³	—	—
Pyro powders, as Al	5 mg/m³	—	—
Welding fumes, as Al	5 mg/m³	—	B2
Soluble salts, as Al	2 mg/m³	—	—
Alkyls (NOC(d)), as Al	2 mg/m³	—	—
Aluminum oxide [1344-28-1]	10 mg/m³(E)	—	A4
4-Aminodiphenyl [92-67-1]	—	—	A1
2-Aminoethanol, see Ethanolamine			
2-Aminopyridine [504-29-0]	0.5 ppm	—	—
3-Amino-1,2,4-triazole, see Amitrole			
Amitrole [61-82-5]	0.2 mg/m³	—	A3
Ammonia [7664-41-7]	25 ppm	35 ppm	—
Ammonium chloride fume [12125-02-9]	10 mg/m³	20 mg/m³	—
Ammonium perfluorooctanoate [3825-26-1]	0.01 mg/m³	—	Skin; A3
Ammonium sulfamate [7773-06-0]	10 mg/m³	—	—
Amosite, see Asbestos			
n-Amyl acetate, see Pentyl acetate (all isomers)			
sec-Amyl acetate, see Pentyl acetate (all isomers)			
Aniline [62-53-3] and homologues	2 ppm	—	Skin; A3; BEI
o-Anisidine [90-04-0]	0.1 ppm	—	Skin; A3
p-Anisidine [104-94-9]	0.1 ppm	—	Skin; A4
Antimony [7440-36-0] and compounds, as Sb	0.5 mg/m³	—	—
Antimony hydride (Stibine) [7803-52-3]	0.1 ppm	—	—
Antimony trioxide [1309-64-4] production	—	—	A2
ANTU [86-88-4]	0.3 mg/m³	—	A4
Argon [7440-37-1]	Simple asphyxiant (D)		
Arsenic, elemental [7440-38-2], and inorganic compounds, as As	0.01 mg/m³	—	A1; BEI
‡ Arsine [7784-42-1]	(0.05 ppm)	—	—

ADOPTED VALUES			
Substance [CAS No.]	TWA (ppm/mg/m³)	STEL/C (ppm/mg/m³)	Notations
Asbestos, all forms [1332-21-4]	0.1 f/cc (F)	—	A1
* Asphalt (Petroleum; Bitumen) fume [8052-42-4], as benzene-soluble aerosol (or equivalent method)	0.5 mg/m³(I)	—	A4
Atrazine [1912-24-9]	5 mg/m³	—	A4
Azinphos-methyl [86-50-0]	0.2 mg/m³	—	Skin; A4; BEI
Barium [7440-39-3] and soluble compounds, as Ba	0.5 mg/m³	—	A4
Barium sulfate [7727-43-7]	10 mg/m³(E)	—	—
Benomyl [17804-35-2]	10 mg/m³	—	A4
Benz[a]anthracene [56-55-3]	—	—	A2
Benzene [71-43-2]	0.5 ppm	2.5 ppm	Skin; A1; BEI
Benzidine [92-87-5]	—	—	Skin; A1
Benzo[b]fluoranthene [205-99-2]	—	—	A2
Benzo[a]pyrene [50-32-8]	—	—	A2
p-Benzoquinone, see Quinone			
Benzotrichloride [98-07-7]	—	C 0.1 ppm	Skin; A2
Benzoyl chloride [98-88-4]	—	C 0.5 ppm	A4
Benzoyl peroxide [94-36-0]	5 mg/m³	—	A4
Benzyl acetate [140-11-4]	10 ppm	—	A4
Benzyl chloride [100-44-7]	1 ppm	—	A3
‡ Beryllium [7440-41-7] and compounds, as Be	(0.002 mg/m³)	(0.01 mg/m³)	(—); A1
Biphenyl [92-52-4]	0.2 ppm	—	—
* Bis (2-dimethylaminoethyl)ether (DMAEE) [3033-62-3]	0.05 ppm	0.15 ppm	Skin
Bismuth telluride, as Bi₂Te₃			
Undoped [1304-82-1]	10 mg/m³	—	A4
Se-doped	5 mg/m³	—	A4
Borates, tetra, sodium salts [1303-96-4]			
Anhydrous	1 mg/m³	—	—
Decahydrate	5 mg/m³	—	—
Pentahydrate	1 mg/m³	—	—
Boron oxide [1303-86-2]	10 mg/m³	—	—
Boron tribromide [10294-33-4]	—	C 1 ppm	—
Boron trifluoride [7637-07-2]	—	C 1 ppm	—
Bromacil [314-40-9]	10 mg/m³	—	A3
Bromine [7726-95-6]	0.1 ppm	0.2 ppm	—
Bromine pentafluoride [7789-30-2]	0.1 ppm	—	—
Bromochloromethane, see Chlorobromomethane			
Bromoform [75-25-2]	0.5 ppm	—	Skin; A3
1,3-Butadiene [106-99-0]	2 ppm	—	A2
Butane [106-97-8]	800 ppm		
Butanethiol, see Butyl mercaptan			
‡ n-Butanol [71-36-3]	—	(C 50 ppm)	(Skin)
sec-Butanol [78-92-2]	100 ppm	—	—
tert-Butanol [75-65-0]	100 ppm	—	A4
2-Butanone, see Methyl ethyl ketone (MEK)			
2-Butoxyethanol (EGBE) [111-76-2]	20 ppm	—	Skin
n-Butyl acetate [123-86-4]	150 ppm	200 ppm	—
sec-Butyl acetate [105-46-4]	200 ppm	—	—
tert-Butyl acetate [540-88-5]	200 ppm	—	—
n-Butyl acrylate [141-32-2]	2 ppm	—	SEN; A4
n-Butylamine [109-73-9]	—	C 5 ppm	Skin

ADOPTED VALUES			
Substance [CAS No.]	TWA (ppm/mg/m³)	STEL/C (ppm/mg/m³)	Notations
‡ Butylated hydroxytoluene (BHT) [128-37-0]	(10 mg/m³)	—	(A4)
tert-Butyl chromate, as CrO₃ [1189-85-1]	—	C 0.1 mg/m³	Skin
n-Butyl glycidyl ether (BGE) [2426-08-6]	25 ppm	—	—
n-Butyl lactate [138-22-7]	5 ppm	—	—
n-Butyl mercaptan [109-79-5]	0.5 ppm	—	—
o-sec-Butylphenol [89-72-5]	5 ppm	—	Skin
p-tert-Butyl toluene [98-51-1]	1 ppm	—	—
Cadmium, elemental [7440-43-9], and	0.01 mg/m³	—	A2; BEI
compounds, as Cd	0.002 mg/m³⁽ᴿ⁾	—	A2; BEI
Calcium carbonate [1317-65-3]	10 mg/m³⁽ᴱ⁾	—	—
Calcium chromate [13765-19-0], as Cr	0.001 mg/m³	—	A2
Calcium cyanamide [156-62-7]	0.5 mg/m³	—	A4
Calcium hydroxide [1305-62-0]	5 mg/m³	—	—
Calcium oxide [1305-78-8]	2 mg/m³	—	—
Calcium silicate (synthetic) [1344-95-2]	10 mg/m³⁽ᴱ⁾	—	A4
Calcium sulfate [7778-18-9]	10 mg/m³⁽ᴱ⁾	—	—
Camphor, synthetic [76-22-2]	2 ppm	4 ppm	A4
‡ Caprolactam [105-60-2]			
(Particulate)	(1 mg/m³)	(3 mg/m³)	(A4)
(Vapor)	(5 ppm)	(10 ppm)	(A4)
Captafol [2425-06-1]	0.1 mg/m³	—	Skin; A4
Captan [133-06-2]	5 mg/m³	—	A3
Carbaryl [63-25-2]	5 mg/m³	—	A4
Carbofuran [1563-66-2]	0.1 mg/m³	—	A4
Carbon black [1333-86-4]	3.5 mg/m³	—	A4
Carbon dioxide [124-38-9]	5000 ppm	30,000 ppm	—
Carbon disulfide [75-15-0]	10 ppm	—	Skin; BEI
Carbon monoxide [630-08-0]	25 ppm	—	BEI
Carbon tetrabromide [558-13-4]	0.1 ppm	0.3 ppm	—
Carbon tetrachloride (Tetrachloromethane) [56-23-5]	5 ppm	10 ppm	Skin; A2
Carbonyl chloride, see Phosgene			
Carbonyl fluoride [353-50-4]	2 ppm	5 ppm	—
Catechol [120-80-9}	5 ppm	—	Skin; A3
Cellulose [9004-34-6]	10 mg/m³	—	—
Cesium hydroxide [21351-79-1]	2 mg/m³	—	—
Chlordane [57-74-9]	0.5 mg/m³	—	Skin; A3
Chlorinated camphene (Toxaphene) [8001-35-2]	0.5 mg/m³	1 mg/m³	Skin; A3
o-Chlorinated diphenyl oxide [31242-93-0]	0.5 mg/m³	—	—
Chlorine [7782-50-5]	0.5 ppm	1 ppm	A4
Chlorine dioxide [10049-04-4]	0.1 ppm	0.3 ppm	—
Chlorine trifluoride [7790-91-2]	—	C 0.1 ppm	—
Chloroacetaldehyde [107-20-0]	—	C 1 ppm	—
Chloroacetone [78-95-5]	—	C 1 ppm	—
2-Chloroacetophenone [532-27-4]	0.05 ppm	—	A4
Chloroacetyl chloride [79-04-9]	0.05 ppm	0.15 ppm	Skin
Chlorobenzene [108-90-7]	10 ppm	—	A3; BEI
o-Chlorobenzylidene malononitrile [2698-41-1]	—	C 0.05 ppm	Skin; A4
Chlorobromomethane [74-97-5]	200 ppm	—	—
2-Chloro-1,3-butadiene, see β-Chloroprene			
Chlorodifluoromethane [75-45-6]	1000 ppm	—	A4
Chlorodiphenyl (42% chlorine) [53469-21-9]	1 mg/m³	—	Skin

ADOPTED VALUES			
Substance [CAS No.]	TWA (ppm/mg/m³)	STEL/C (ppm/mg/m³)	Notations
Chlorodiphenyl (54% chlorine) [11097-69-1]	0.5 mg/m³	—	Skin; A3
1-Chloro-2,3-epoxy propane, see Epichlorohydrin			
2-Chloroethanol, see Ethylene chlorohydrin			
Chloroethylene, see Vinyl chloride			
Chloroform [67-66-3]	10 ppm	—	A3
bis(Chloromethyl) ether [542-88-1]	0.001 ppm	—	A1
Chloromethyl methyl ether [107-30-2]	—	—	A2
1-Chloro-1-nitropropane [600-25-9]	2 ppm	—	—
Chloropentafluoroethane [76-15-3]	1000 ppm	—	—
Chloropicrin [76-06-2]	0.1 ppm	—	A4
β-Chloroprene [126-99-8]	10 ppm	—	Skin
2-Chloropropionic acid [598-78-7]	0.1 ppm	—	Skin
o-Chlorostyrene [2039-87-4]	50 ppm	75 ppm	—
o-Chlorotoluene [95-49-8]	50 ppm	—	—
2-Chloro-6-(trichloromethyl) pyridine, see Nitrapyrin			
Chlorpyrifos [2921-88-2]	0.2 mg/m³	—	Skin; A4; BEI
Chromite ore processing (Chromate), as Cr	0.05 mg/m³	—	A1
Chromium, metal [7440-47-3] and inorganic compounds, as Cr			
Metal and Cr III compounds	0.5 mg/m³	—	A4
Water-soluble Cr VI compounds	0.05 mg/m³	—	A1; BEI
Insoluble Cr VI compounds	0.01 mg/m³	—	A1
Chromyl chloride [14977-61-8]	0.025 ppm	—	—
Chrysene [218-01-9]	—	—	A3
Chrysotile, see Asbestos			
Clopidol [2971-90-6]	10 mg/m³	—	A4
Coal dust			
Anthracite	0.4 mg/m³⁽ᴿ⁾	—	A4
Bituminous	0.9 mg/m³⁽ᴿ⁾	—	A4
Coal tar pitch volatiles [65996-93-2], as benzene solubles	0.2 mg/m³	—	A1
Cobalt, elemental [7440-48-4], and inorganic compounds, as Co	0.02 mg/m³	—	A3; BEI
Cobalt carbonyl [10210-68-1], as Co	0.1 mg/m³	—	—
Cobalt hydrocarbonyl [16842-03-8], as Co	0.1 mg/m³	—	—
Copper [7440-50-8]			
Fume	0.2 mg/m³	—	—
Dusts & mists, as Cu	1 mg/m³	—	—
Cotton dust, raw	0.2 mg/m³⁽ᴳ⁾	—	—
Cresol, all isomers [1319-77-3; 95-48-7; 108-39-4; 106-44-5]	5 ppm	—	Skin
Cristobalite, see Silica—Crystalline			
Crocidolite, see Asbestos			
Crotonaldehyde [4170-30-3]	—	C 0.3 ppm	Skin; A3
Crufomate [299-86-5]	5 mg/m³	—	A4; BEI
Cumene [98-82-8]	50 ppm	—	—
Cyanamide [420-04-2]	2 mg/m³	—	—
Cyanogen [460-19-5]	10 ppm	—	—
Cyanogen chloride [506-77-4]	—	C 0.3 ppm	—
‡ Cyclohexane [110-82-7]	300 ppm	—	—
Cyclohexanol [108-93-0]	50 ppm	—	Skin
Cyclohexanone [108-94-1]	25 ppm	—	Skin; A4
Cyclohexene [110-83-8]	300 ppm	—	—
Cyclohexylamine [108-91-8]	10 ppm	—	A4
Cyclonite [121-82-4]	0.5 mg/m³	—	Skin; A4

ADOPTED VALUES			
Substance [CAS No.]	TWA (ppm/mg/m³)	STEL/C (ppm/mg/m³)	Notations
Cyclopentadiene [542-92-7]	75 ppm	—	—
Cyclopentane [287-92-3]	600 ppm	—	—
Cyhexatin [13121-70-5]	5 mg/m³	—	A4
2,4-D [94-75-7]	10 mg/m³	—	A4
DDT (Dichlorodiphenyltrichloroethane) [50-29-3]	1 mg/m³	—	A3
Decaborane [17702-41-9]	0.05 ppm	0.15 ppm	Skin
‡ Demeton [8065-48-3]	(0.01 ppm)	—	Skin; BEI
Diacetone alcohol [123-42-2]	50 ppm	—	—
1,2-Diaminoethane, see Ethylenediamine			
Diatomaceous earth, see Silica—Amorphous			
Diazinon [333-41-5]	0.1 mg/m³	—	Skin; A4; BEI
Diazomethane [334-88-3]	0.2 ppm	—	A2
Diborane [19287-45-7]	0.1 ppm	—	—
1,2-Dibromoethane, see Ethylene dibromide			
2-N-Dibutylaminoethanol [102-81-8]	0.5 ppm	—	Skin
2,6-Di-tert-butyl-p-cresol, see Butylated hydroxytoluene (BHT)			
Dibutyl phenyl phosphate [2528-36-1]	0.3 ppm	—	Skin; BEI
Dibutyl phosphate [107-66-4]	1 ppm	2 ppm	—
Dibutyl phthalate [84-74-2]	5 mg/m³	—	—
Dichloroacetylene [7572-29-4]	—	C 0.1 ppm	A3
o-Dichlorobenzene [95-50-1]	25 ppm	50 ppm	A4
p-Dichlorobenzene [106-46-7]	10 ppm	—	A3
3,3′-Dichlorobenzidine [91-94-1]	—	—	Skin; A3
1,4-Dichloro-2-butene [764-41-0]	0.005 ppm	—	Skin; A2
Dichlorodifluoromethane [75-71-8]	1000 ppm	—	A4
1,3-Dichloro-5,5-dimethyl hydantoin [118-52-5]	0.2 mg/m³	0.4 mg/m³	—
1,1-Dichloroethane [75-34-3]	100 ppm	—	A4
1,2-Dichloroethane, see Ethylene dichloride			
1,1-Dichloroethylene, see Vinylidene chloride			
1,2-Dichloroethylene, sym [540-59-0], cis [156-59-2], and trans [156-60-5]	200 ppm	—	—
Dichloroethyl ether [111-44-4]	5 ppm	10 ppm	Skin; A4
Dichlorofluoromethane [75-43-4]	10 ppm	—	—
Dichloromethane [75-09-2]	50 ppm	—	A3; BEI
1,1-Dichloro-1-nitroethane [594-72-9]	2 ppm	—	—
1,2-Dichloropropane, see Propylene dichloride			
1,3-Dichloropropene [542-75-6]	1 ppm	—	Skin; A4
* 2,2-Dichloropropionic acid [75-99-0]	5 mg/m³(I)	—	A4
Dichlorotetrafluoroethane [76-14-2]	1000 ppm	—	A4
Dichlorvos [62-73-7]	0.9 mg/m³	—	Skin; A4; BEI
‡ Dicrotophos [141-66-2]	(0.25 mg/m³)	—	Skin; A4; BEI
Dicyclopentadiene [77-73-6]	5 ppm	—	—
Dicyclopentadienyl iron [102-54-5]	10 mg/m³	—	—
Dieldrin [60-57-1]	0.25 mg/m³	—	Skin; A4
Diethanolamine [111-42-2]	2 mg/m³	—	Skin
Diethylamine [109-89-7]	5 ppm	15 ppm	Skin; A4
2-Diethylaminoethanol [100-37-8]	2 ppm	—	Skin
Diethylene triamine [111-40-0]	1 ppm	—	Skin
Diethyl ether, see Ethyl ether			
Di(2-ethylhexyl)phthalate (DEHP) [117-81-7]	5 mg/m³	—	A3
Diethyl ketone [96-22-0]	200 ppm	300 ppm	—

ADOPTED VALUES			
Substance [CAS No.]	TWA (ppm/mg/m³)	STEL/C (ppm/mg/m³)	Notations
Diethyl phthalate [84-66-2]	5 mg/m³	—	A4
Difluorodibromomethane [75-61-6]	100 ppm	—	—
Diglycidyl ether (DGE) [2238-07-5]	0.1 ppm	—	A4
Dihydroxybenzene, see Hydroquinone			
Diisobutyl ketone [108-83-8]	25 ppm	—	—
Diisopropylamine [108-18-9]	5 ppm	—	Skin
Dimethoxymethane, see Methylal			
N,N-Dimethylacetamide [127-19-5]	10 ppm	—	Skin; A4; BEI
Dimethylamine [124-40-3]	5 ppm	15 ppm	A4
Dimethylaminobenzene, see Xylidine			
Dimethylaniline (N,N-Dimethylaniline) [121-69-7]	5 ppm	10 ppm	Skin; A4; BEI
Dimethylbenzene, see Xylene			
Dimethyl carbamoyl chloride [79-44-7]	—	—	A2
Dimethyl-1,2-dibromo-2,2-dichloroethyl phosphate, see Naled			
Dimethylethoxysilane [14857-34-2]	0.5 ppm	1.5 ppm	—
Dimethylformamide [68-12-2]	10 ppm	—	Skin; A4; BEI
2,6-Dimethyl-4-heptanone, see Diisobutyl ketone			
1,1-Dimethylhydrazine [57-14-7]	0.01 ppm	—	Skin; A3
Dimethylnitrosoamine, see N-Nitrosodimethylamine			
Dimethylphthalate [131-11-3]	5 mg/m³	—	—
Dimethyl sulfate [77-78-1]	0.1 ppm	—	Skin; A3
Dinitolmide [148-01-6]	5 mg/m³	—	A4
Dinitrobenzene [528-29-0; 99-65-0; 100-25-4] (all isomers)	0.15 ppm	—	Skin; BEI
Dinitrol-o-cresol [534-52-1]	0.2 mg/m³	—	Skin
3,5-Dinitro-o-toluamide, see Dinitolmide			
Dinitrotoluene [25321-14-6]	0.2 mg/m³	—	Skin; A3; BEI
1,4-Dioxane [123-91-1]	20 ppm	—	Skin; A3
‡ Dioxathion [78-34-2]	(0.2 mg/m³)	—	Skin; A4; BEI
Diphenyl, see Biphenyl			
Diphenylamine [122-39-4]	10 mg/m³	—	A4
Diphenylmethane diisocyanate, see Methylene bisphenyl isocyanate			
Dipropylene glycol methyl ether [34590-94-8]	100 ppm	150 ppm	Skin
Dipropyl ketone [123-19-3]	50 ppm	—	—
Diquat [2764-72-9]	0.5 mg/m³	—	Skin; A4
	0.1 mg/m³(R)	—	Skin; A4
Di-sec-octyl phthalate, see Di(2-ethylhexyl)phthalate			
Disulfiram [97-77-8]	2 mg/m³	—	A4
Disulfoton [298-04-4]	0.1 mg/m³	—	Skin, BEI
Diuron [330-54-1]	10 mg/m³	—	A4
Divinyl benzene [1321-74-0]	10 ppm	—	—
Emery [1302-74-5]	10 mg/m³(E)	—	—
Endosulfan [115-29-7]	0.1 mg/m³	—	Skin; A4
Endrin [72-20-8]	0.1 mg/m³	—	Skin; A4
Enflurane [13838-16-9]	75 ppm	—	A4
Enzymes, see Subtilisins			
Epichlorohydrin [106-89-8]	0.5 ppm	—	Skin; A3
EPN [2104-64-5]	0.1 mg/m³	—	Skin; A4; BEI
1,2-Epoxypropane, see Propylene oxide			
2,3-Epoxy-1-propanol, see Glycidol			
Ethane [74-84-0]	Simple asphyxiant (D)		
Ethanethiol, see Ethyl mercaptan			

ADOPTED VALUES			
Substance [CAS No.]	TWA (ppm/mg/m³)	STEL/C (ppm/mg/m³)	Notations
Ethanol [64-17-5]	1000 ppm	—	A4
Ethanolamine [141-43-5]	3 ppm	6 ppm	—
‡ Ethion [563-12-2]	(0.4 mg/m³)	—	Skin; BEI
2-Ethoxyethanol (EGEE) [110-80-5]	5 ppm	—	Skin; BEI
2-Ethoxyethyl acetate (EGEEA) [111-15-9]	5 ppm	—	Skin; BEI
Ethyl acetate [141-78-6]	400 ppm	—	—
Ethyl acrylate [140-88-5]	5 ppm	15 ppm	A4
Ethyl alcohol, see Ethanol			
Ethylamine [75-04-7]	5 ppm	15 ppm	Skin
Ethyl amyl ketone [541-85-5]	25 ppm	—	—
‡ Ethyl benzene [100-41-4]	100 ppm	125 ppm	(—); BEI
Ethyl bromide [74-96-4]	5 ppm	—	Skin; A3
* Ethyl tert-butyl ether (ETBE) [637-92-3]	5 ppm	—	—
Ethyl butyl ketone [106-35-4]	50 ppm	75 ppm	—
Ethyl chloride [75-00-3]	100 ppm	—	Skin; A3
Ethyl cyanoacrylate [7085-85-0]	0.2 ppm	—	—
Ethylene [74-85-1]	—(c)	—	A4
Ethylene chlorohydrin [107-07-3]	—	C 1 ppm	Skin; A4
Ethylenediamine [107-15-3]	10 ppm	—	Skin; A4
Ethylene dibromide [106-93-4]	—	—	Skin; A3
Ethylene dichloride [107-06-2]	10 ppm	—	A4
Ethylene glycol [107-21-1], aerosol	—	C 100 mg/m³	A4
Ethylene glycol dinitrate (EGDN) [628-96-6]	0.05 ppm	—	Skin
Ethylene glycol methyl ether acetate, see 2-Methoxyethyl acetate			
Ethylene oxide [75-21-8]	1 ppm	—	A2
Ethylenimine [151-56-4]	0.5 ppm	—	Skin; A3
Ethyl ether [60-29-7]	400 ppm	500 ppm	—
Ethyl formate [109-94-4]	100 ppm	—	—
Ethylidene chloride, see 1,1-Dichloroethane			
Ethylidene norbornene [16219-75-3]	—	C 5 ppm	—
Ethyl mercaptan [75-08-1]	0.5 ppm	—	—
N-Ethylmorpholine [100-74-3]	5 ppm	—	Skin
Ethyl silicate [78-10-4]	10 ppm	—	—
Fenamiphos [22224-92-6]	0.1 mg/m³	—	Skin; A4; BEI
Fensulfothion [115-90-2]	0.1 mg/m³	—	A4; BEI
Fenthion [55-38-9]	0.2 mg/m³	—	Skin; A4; BEI
Ferbam [14484-64-1]	10 mg/m³	—	A4
Ferrovanadium dust [12604-58-9]	1 mg/m³	3 mg/m³	—
Fibrous glass dust, see Synthetic Vitreous Fibers— Continuous filament glass fibers			
* Flour dust	0.5 mg/m³ (I)	—	SEN
Fluorides, as F	2.5 mg/m³	—	A4; BEI
Fluorine [7782-41-4]	1 ppm	2 ppm	—
Fluorotrichloromethane, see Trichlorofluoromethane			
Fonofos [944-22-9]	0.1 mg/m³	—	Skin; A4; BEI
* Formaldehyde [50-00-0]	—	C 0.3 ppm	SEN; A2
Formamide [75-12-7]	10 ppm	—	Skin
Formic acid [64-18-6]	5 ppm	10 ppm	—
Furfural [98-01-1]	2 ppm	—	Skin; A3; BEI
Furfuryl alcohol [98-00-0]	10 ppm	15 ppm	Skin
Gasoline [8006-61-9]	300 ppm	500 ppm	A3
Germanium tetrahydride [7782-65-2]	0.2 ppm	—	—
Glass, fibrous or dust, see Synthetic Vitreous Fibers			

ADOPTED VALUES			
Substance [CAS No.]	TWA (ppm/mg/m³)	STEL/C (ppm/mg/m³)	Notations
Glutaraldehyde [111-30-8], activated and inactivated	—	C 0.05 ppm	SEN; A4
Glycerin mist [56-81-5]	10 mg/m³	—	—
Glycidol [556-52-5]	2 ppm	—	A3
Glycol monoethyl ether, see 2-Ethoxyethanol			
Grain dust (oat, wheat, barley)	4 mg/m³(E)	—	—
Graphite (all forms except graphite fibers) [7782-42-5]	2 mg/m³(R)	—	—
Gypsum, see Calcium sulfate			
Hafnium [7440-58-6] and compounds, as Hf	0.5 mg/m³	—	—
Halothane [151-67-7]	50 ppm	—	A4
Helium [7440-59-7]	Simple asphyxiant(D)		
Heptachlor [76-44-8] and Heptachlor epoxide [1024-57-3]	0.05 mg/m³	—	Skin; A3
Heptane [142-82-5] (n-Heptane)	400 ppm	500 ppm	—
2-Heptanone, see Methyl n-amyl ketone			
3-Heptanone, see Ethyl butyl ketone			
Hexachlorobenzene [118-74-1]	0.002 mg/m³	—	Skin; A3
Hexachlorobutadiene [87-68-3]	0.02 ppm	—	Skin; A3
Hexachlorocyclopentadiene [77-47-4]	0.01 ppm	—	A4
Hexachloroethane [67-72-1]	1 ppm	—	Skin; A3
Hexachloronaphthalene [1335-87-1]	0.2 mg/m³	—	Skin
Hexafluoroacetone [684-16-2]	0.1 ppm	—	Skin
Hexamethylene diisocyanate [822-06-0]	0.005 ppm	—	—
Hexamethyl phosphoramide [680-31-9]	—	—	Skin; A3
n-Hexane [110-54-3]	50 ppm	—	Skin; BEI
Hexane, Other isomers	500 ppm	1000 ppm	—
1,6-Hexanediamine [124-90-4]	0.5 ppm	—	—
2-Hexanone, see Methyl n-butyl ketone			
1-Hexene [592-41-6]	30 ppm	—	—
sec-Hexyl acetate [108-84-9]	50 ppm	—	—
Hexylene glycol [107-41-5]	—	C 25 ppm	—
Hydrazine [302-01-2]	0.01 ppm	—	Skin; A3
Hydrogen [1333-74-0]	Simple asphyxiant(D)		
Hydrogenated terphenyls (nonirradiated) [61788-32-7]	0.5 ppm	—	—
Hydrogen bromide [10035-10-6]	—	C 3 ppm	—
Hydrogen chloride [7647-01-0]	—	C 5 ppm	—
Hydrogen cyanide and Cyanide salts, as CN			
Hydrogen cyanide [74-90-8]	—	C 4.7 ppm	Skin
Calcium cyanide [592-01-8]	—	C 5 mg/m³	Skin
Potassium cyanide [151-50-8]	—	C 5 mg/m³	Skin
Sodium cyanide [143-33-9]	—	C 5 mg/m³	Skin
Hydrogen fluoride [7664-39-3], as F	—	C 3 ppm	BEI
Hydrogen peroxide [7722-84-1]	1 ppm	—	A3
Hydrogen selenide [7783-07-5], as Se	0.05 ppm	—	—
‡ Hydrogen sulfide [7783-06-4]	(10 ppm)	(15 ppm)	—
Hydroquinone [123-31-9]	2 mg/m³	—	A3
4-Hydroxy-4-methyl-2-pentanone, see Diacetone alcohol			
2-Hydroxypropyl acrylate [999-61-1]	0.5 ppm	—	Skin; SEN
Indene [95-13-6]	10 ppm	—	—
Indium [7440-74-6] and compounds, as In	0.1 mg/m³	—	—
Iodine [7553-56-2]	—	C 0.1 ppm	—
Iodoform [75-47-8]	0.6 ppm	—	—

ADOPTED VALUES			
Substance [CAS No.]	TWA (ppm/mg/m³)	STEL/C (ppm/mg/m³)	Notations
Iron oxide dust & fume (Fe₂O₃) [1309-37-1], as Fe	5 mg/m³(E)	—	A4
Iron pentacarbonyl [13463-40-6], as Fe	0.1 ppm	0.2 ppm	—
Iron salts, soluble, as Fe	1 mg/m³	—	—
Isoamyl acetate, *see* Pentyl acetate (all isomers)			
Isoamyl alcohol [123-51-3]	100 ppm	125 ppm	—
Isobutyl acetate [110-19-0]	150 ppm	—	—
Isobutyl alcohol [78-83-1]	50 ppm	—	—
Isooctyl alcohol [26952-21-6]	50 ppm	—	Skin
Isophorone [78-59-1]	—	C 5 ppm	A3
Isophorone diisocyanate [4098-71-9]	0.005 ppm	—	—
2-Isopropoxyethanol [109-59-1]	25 ppm	—	Skin
‡ Isopropyl acetate [108-21-4]	(250 ppm)	(310 ppm)	—
‡ Isopropyl alcohol [67-63-0]	(400 ppm)	(500 ppm)	(—)
Isopropylamine [75-31-0]	5 ppm	10 ppm	—
N-Isopropylaniline [768-52-5]	2 ppm	—	Skin
Isopropyl ether [108-20-3]	250 ppm	310 ppm	—
Isopropyl glycidyl ether (IGE) [4016-14-2]	50 ppm	75 ppm	—
Kaolin [1332-58-7]	2 mg/m³(E, R)	—	A4
Ketene [463-51-4]	0.5 ppm	1.5 ppm	—
Lead, elemental [7439-92-1], and inorganic compounds, as Pb	0.05 mg/m³	—	A3; BEI
Lead arsenate [7784-40-9], as Pb₃(AsO₄)₂	0.15 mg/m³	—	BEI
Lead chromate [7758-97-6], as Pb	0.05 mg/m³	—	A2; BEI
as Cr	0.012 mg/m³	—	A2
Limestone, *see* Calcium carbonate			
Lindane [58-89-9]	0.5 mg/m³	—	Skin; A3
Lithium hydride [7580-67-8]	0.025 mg/m³	—	—
L.P.G. (Liquefied petroleum gas) [68476-85-7]	1000 ppm	—	—
Magnesite [546-93-0]	10 mg/m³(E)	—	—
Magnesium oxide fume [1309-48-4]	10 mg/m³	—	—
Malathion [121-75-5]	10 mg/m³	—	Skin; A4; BEI
* Maleic anhydride [108-31-6]	0.1 ppm	—	SEN; A4
Manganese, elemental [7439-96-5], and inorganic compounds, as Mn	0.2 mg/m³	—	—
Manganese cyclopentadienyl tricarbonyl [12079-65-1], as Mn	0.1 mg/m³	—	Skin
Marble, *see* Calcium carbonate			
Mercury [7439-97-6], as Hg			
Alkyl compounds	0.01 mg/m³	0.03 mg/m³	Skin
Aryl compounds	0.1 mg/m³	—	Skin
Inorganic forms, including metallic mercury	0.025 mg/m³	—	Skin; A4; BEI
Mesityl oxide [141-79-7]	15 ppm	25 ppm	—
Methacrylic acid [79-41-4]	20 ppm	—	—
Methane [74-82-8]	Simple asphyxiant (D)		
Methanethiol, *see* Methyl mercaptan			
Methanol [67-56-1]	200 ppm	250 ppm	Skin; BEI
Methomyl [16752-77-5]	2.5 mg/m³	—	A4; BEI
Methoxychlor [72-43-5]	10 mg/m³	—	A4
2-Methoxyethanol (EGME) [109-86-4]	5 ppm	—	Skin; BEI
2-Methoxyethyl acetate (EGMEA) [110-49-6]	5 ppm	—	Skin; BEI
4-Methoxyphenol [150-76-5]	5 mg/m³	—	—
Methyl acetate [79-20-9]	200 ppm	250 ppm	—

ADOPTED VALUES			
Substance [CAS No.]	TWA (ppm/mg/m³)	STEL/C (ppm/mg/m³)	Notations
Methyl acetylene [74-99-7]	1000 ppm	—	—
Methyl acetylene-propadiene mixture (MAPP)	1000 ppm	1250 ppm	—
* Methyl acrylate [96-33-3]	2 ppm	—	Skin; SEN; A4
Methylacrylonitrile [126-98-7]	1 ppm	—	Skin
Methylal [109-87-5]	1000 ppm	—	—
Methyl alcohol, *see* Methanol			
Methylamine [74-89-5]	5 ppm	15 ppm	—
Methyl amyl alcohol, *see* Methyl isobutyl carbinol			
Methyl n-amyl ketone [110-43-0]	50 ppm	—	—
N-Methyl aniline [100-61-8]	0.5 ppm	—	Skin; BEI
Methyl bromide [74-83-9]	1 ppm	—	Skin; A4
Methyl tert-butyl ether (MTBE) [1634-04-4]	40 ppm	—	A3
Methyl n-butyl ketone [591-78-6]	5 ppm	10 ppm	Skin
Methyl chloride [74-87-3]	50 ppm	100 ppm	Skin; A4
Methyl chloroform [71-55-6]	350 ppm	450 ppm	A4; BEI
Methyl 2-cyanoacrylate [137-05-3]	0.2 ppm	—	—
Methylcyclohexane [108-87-2]	400 ppm	—	—
Methylcyclohexanol [25639-42-3]	50 ppm	—	—
o-Methylcyclohexanone [583-60-8]	50 ppm	75 ppm	Skin
2-Methylcyclopentadienyl manganese tricarbonyl [12108-13-3], as Mn	0.2 mg/m³	—	Skin
Methyl demeton [8022-00-2]	0.5 mg/m³	—	Skin; BEI
Methylene bisphenyl isocyanate (MDI) [101-68-8]	0.005 ppm	—	—
Methylene chloride, *see* Dichloromethane			
4,4′-Methylene bis(2-chloroaniline) [MBOCA; MOCA®] [101-14-4]	0.01 ppm	—	Skin; A2; BEI
Methylene bis(4-cyclohexylisocyanate) [5124-30-1]	0.005 ppm	—	—
4,4′-Methylene dianiline [101-77-9]	0.1 ppm	—	Skin; A3
Methyl ethyl ketone (MEK) [78-93-3]	200 ppm	300 ppm	BEI
Methyl ethyl ketone peroxide [1338-23-4]	—	C 0.2 ppm	—
Methyl formate [107-31-3]	100 ppm	150 ppm	—
5-Methyl-3-heptanone, *see* Ethyl amyl ketone			
Methyl hydrazine [60-34-4]	0.01 ppm	—	Skin; A3
Methyl iodide [74-88-4]	2 ppm	—	Skin
Methyl isoamyl ketone [110-12-3]	50 ppm	—	—
Methyl isobutyl carbinol [108-11-2]	25 ppm	40 ppm	Skin
Methyl isobutyl ketone [108-10-1]	50 ppm	75 ppm	BEI
Methyl isocyanate [624-83-9]	0.02 ppm	—	Skin
Methyl isopropyl ketone [563-80-4]	200 ppm	—	—
Methyl mercaptan [74-93-1]	0.5 ppm	—	—
* Methyl methacrylate [80-62-6]	50 ppm	100 ppm	SEN; A4
Methyl parathion [298-00-0]	0.2 mg/m³	—	Skin; A4; BEI
Methyl propyl ketone [107-87-9]	200 ppm	250 ppm	—
Methyl silicate [681-84-5]	1 ppm	—	—
α-Methyl styrene [98-83-9]	50 ppm	100 ppm	—
Methyl vinyl ketone [78-94-4]	—	C 0.2 ppm	Skin; SEN
Metribuzin [20187-64-9]	5 mg/m³	—	A4
‡ Mevinphos [7786-34-7]	(0.09 mg/m³)	(0.27 mg/m³)	Skin; BEI
Mica [12001-26-2]	3 mg/m³(E, R)	—	—
Mineral wool fiber, *see* Synthetic Vitreous Fibers—Glass, Rock, or Slag wool fibers			
‡ Molybdenum [7439-98-7], as Mo			

Substance [CAS No.]	TWA (ppm/mg/m³)	STEL/C (ppm/mg/m³)	Notations
ADOPTED VALUES			
‡ Soluble compounds	(5 mg/m³)	—	(—)
‡ Metal and insoluble compounds	(10 mg/m³)	—	—
Monochlorobenzene, *see* Chlorobenzene			
Monocrotophos [6923-22-4]	0.25 mg/m³	—	Skin; A4; BEI
Morpholine [110-91-8]	20 ppm	—	Skin; A4
‡ Naled [300-76-5]	(3 mg/m³)	—	Skin; A4; BEI
Naphthalene [91-20-3]	10 ppm	15 ppm	Skin; A4
β-Naphthylamine [91-59-8]	—	—	A1
Neon [7440-01-9]	Simple asphyxiant (D)		
Nickel			
Elemental/metal [7440-02-0]	1.5 mg/m³ (I)	—	A5
Soluble compounds, as Ni	0.1 mg/m³ (I)	—	A4
Insoluble compounds, as Ni	0.2 mg/m³ (I)	—	A1
Nickel carbonyl [13463-39-3], as Ni	0.05 ppm	—	—
Nickel subsulfide [12035-72-2], as Ni	0.1 mg/m³ (I)	—	A1
Nickel sulfide roasting, fume & dust, *see* Nickel subsulfide			
Nicotine [54-11-5]	0.5 mg/m³	—	Skin
Nitrapyrin [1929-82-4]	10 mg/m³	20 mg/m³	A4
Nitric acid [7697-37-2]	2 ppm	4 ppm	—
Nitric oxide [10102-43-9]	25 ppm	—	BEI
p-Nitroaniline [100-01-6]	3 mg/m³	—	Skin; A4; BEI
Nitrobenzene [98-95-3]	1 ppm	—	Skin; A3; BEI
p-Nitrochlorobenzene [100-00-5]	0.1 ppm	—	Skin; A3; BEI
4-Nitrodiphenyl [92-93-3]	—	—	Skin; A2
Nitroethane [79-24-3]	100 ppm	—	—
Nitrogen [7727-37-9]	Simple asphyxiant (D)		
Nitrogen dioxide [10102-44-0]	3 ppm	5 ppm	A4
Nitrogen trifluoride [7783-54-2]	10 ppm	—	BEI
Nitroglycerin (NG) [55-63-0]	0.05 ppm	—	Skin
* Nitromethane [75-52-5]	20 ppm	—	A3
1-Nitropropane [108-03-2]	25 ppm	—	A4
2-Nitropropane [79-46-9]	10 ppm	—	A3
N-Nitrosodimethylamine [62-75-9]	—	—	Skin; A3
Nitrotoluene [88-72-2; 99-08-1; 99-99-0]	2 ppm	—	Skin; BEI
Nitrotrichloromethane, *see* Chloropicrin			
Nitrous oxide [10024-97-2]	50 ppm	—	A4
Nonane [111-84-2], all isomers	200 ppm	—	—
Nuisance particulates, *see* Particulates (Insoluble) Not Otherwise Classified (PNOC)			
Octachloronaphthalene [2234-13-1]	0.1 mg/m³	0.3 mg/m³	Skin
Octane (all isomers) [111-65-9]	300 ppm	—	—
‡ Oil mist, mineral	5 mg/m³(H)	(10 mg/m³)	—
Osmium tetroxide [20816-12-0], as Os	0.0002 ppm	0.0006 ppm	—
Oxalic acid [144-62-7]	1 mg/m³	2 mg/m³	—
p,p′-Oxybis(benzenesulfonyl hydrazide) [80-51-3]	0.1 mg/m³(I)	—	—
Oxygen difluoride [7783-41-7]	—	C 0.05 ppm	—
Ozone [10028-15-6]			
Heavy work	0.05 ppm	—	A4
Moderate work	0.08 ppm	—	A4
Light work	0.10 ppm	—	A4
Heavy, moderate, or light workloads (≤ 2 hours)	0.20 ppm	—	A4
Paraffin wax fume [8002-74-2]	2 mg/m³	—	—
Paraquat [4685-14-7]	0.5 mg/m³	—	—

Substance [CAS No.]	TWA (ppm/mg/m³)	STEL/C (ppm/mg/m³)	Notations
ADOPTED VALUES			
	0.1 mg/m³(R)	—	—
Parathion [56-38-2]	0.1 mg/m³	—	Skin; A4; BEI
Particulate polycyclic aromatic hydrocarbons (PPAH), *see* Coal tar pitch volatiles			
Particulates (Insoluble) Not Otherwise Classified (PNOC)	10 mg/m³(E, I)	—	—
	3 mg/m³ (E, R)	—	—
Pentaborane [19624-22-7]	0.005 ppm	0.015 ppm	—
Pentachloronaphthalene [1321-64-8]	0.5 mg/m³	—	Skin
Pentachloronitrobenzene [82-68-8]	0.5 mg/m³	—	A4
Pentachlorophenol [87-86-5]	0.5 mg/m³	—	Skin; A3; BEI
Pentaerythritol [115-77-5]	10 mg/m³	—	—
Pentane, all isomers [78-78-4; 109-66-0; 463-82-1]	600 ppm	—	—
2-Pentanone, *see* Methyl propyl ketone	—	—	—
* Pentyl acetate (all isomers) [628-63-7; 626-38-0; 123-92-2; 625-16-1; 624-41-9; 620-11-1]	50 ppm	100 ppm	—
Perchloroethylene (Tetrachloroethylene) [127-18-4]	25 ppm	100 ppm	A3; BEI
Perchloromethyl mercaptan [594-42-3]	0.1 ppm	—	—
Perchloryl fluoride [7616-94-6]	3 ppm	6 ppm	—
Perfluoroisobutylene [382-21-8]	—	C 0.01 ppm	—
Perlite [93763-70-3]	10 mg/m³(E)	—	A4
Persulfates			
Ammonium persulfate [7727-54-0]	0.1 mg/m³	—	—
Potassium persulfate [7727-21-1]	0.1 mg/m³	—	—
Sodium persulfate [7775-27-1]	0.1 mg/m³	—	—
Petroleum distillates, *see* Gasoline; Stoddard solvent; VM&P naphtha			
Phenacyl chloride, *see* α-Chloroacetophenone			
Phenol [108-95-2]	5 ppm	—	Skin; A4; BEI
Phenothiazine [92-84-2]	5 mg/m³	—	Skin
N-Phenyl-beta-naphthylamine [135-88-6]	—	—	A4
o-Phenylenediamine [95-54-5]	0.1 mg/m³	—	A3
m-Phenylenediamine [108-45-2]	0.1 mg/m³	—	A4
p-Phenylenediamine [106-50-3]	0.1 mg/m³	—	A4
Phenyl ether [101-84-8], vapor	1 ppm	2 ppm	—
Phenylethylene, *see* Styrene, monomer			
* Phenyl glycidyl ether (PGE) [122-60-1]	0.1 ppm	—	Skin; SEN; A3
Phenylhydrazine [100-63-0]	0.1 ppm	—	Skin; A3
Phenyl mercaptan [108-98-5]	0.5 ppm	—	—
Phenylphosphine [638-21-1]	—	C 0.05 ppm	—
Phorate [298-02-2]	0.05 mg/m³	0.2 mg/m³	Skin; BEI
Phosdrin, *see* Mevinphos			
Phosgene [75-44-5]	0.1 ppm	—	—
Phosphine [7803-51-2]	0.3 ppm	1 ppm	—
Phosphoric acid [7664-38-2]	1 mg/m³	3 mg/m³	—
Phosphorus (yellow) [7723-14-0]	0.02 ppm	—	—
Phosphorus oxychloride [10025-87-3]	0.1 ppm	—	—
Phosphorus pentachloride [10026-13-8]	0.1 ppm	—	—
Phosphorus pentasulfide [1314-80-3]	1 mg/m³	3 mg/m³	—
Phosphorus trichloride [7719-12-2]	0.2 ppm	0.5 ppm	—
* Phthalic anhydride [85-44-9]	1 ppm	—	SEN; A4
m-Phthalodinitrile [626-17-5]	5 mg/m³	—	—
Picloram [1918-02-1]	10 mg/m³	—	A4
Picric acid [88-89-1]	0.1 mg/m³	—	—

ADOPTED VALUES			
Substance [CAS No.]	TWA (ppm/mg/m³)	STEL/C (ppm/mg/m³)	Notations
Pindone [83-26-1]	0.1 mg/m³	—	—
Piperazine dihydrochloride [142-64-3]	5 mg/m³	—	—
2-Pivalyl-1,3-indandione, *see* Pindone			
Plaster of Paris, *see* Calcium sulfate			
Platinum [7440-06-4]			
Metal	1 mg/m³	—	—
Soluble salts, as Pt	0.002 mg/m³	—	—
Polychlorobiphenyls, *see* Chlorodiphenyls			
Polytetrafluoroethylene decomposition products	B1	—	—
Portland cement [65997-15-1]	10 mg/m³⁽ᴱ⁾	—	—
Potassium hydroxide [1310-58-3]	—	C 2 mg/m³	—
Precipitated silica, *see* Silica—Amorphous			
Propane [74-98-6]	2500 ppm	—	—
Propane sultone [1120-71-4]	—	—	A3
‡ n-Propanol (n-Propyl alcohol) [71-23-8]	200 ppm	250 ppm	(Skin); (—)
Propargyl alcohol [107-19-7]	1 ppm	—	Skin
β-Propiolactone [57-57-8]	0.5 ppm	—	A3
Propionic acid [79-09-4]	10 ppm	—	—
Propoxur [114-26-1]	0.5 mg/m³	—	A3
n-Propyl acetate [109-60-4]	200 ppm	250 ppm	—
Propylene [115-07-1]	Simple asphyxiant ⁽ᴰ⁾		A4
Propylene dichloride [78-87-5]	75 ppm	110 ppm	A4
Propylene glycol dinitrate [6423-43-4]	0.05 ppm	—	Skin; BEI
Propylene glycol monomethyl ether [107-98-2]	100 ppm	150 ppm	—
Propylene imine [75-55-8]	2 ppm	—	Skin; A3
‡ Propylene oxide [75-56-9]	(20 ppm)	—	(—); A3
n-Propyl nitrate [627-13-4]	25 ppm	40 ppm	BEI
Propyne, *see* Methyl acetylene			
Pyrethrum [8003-34-7]	5 mg/m³	—	A4
Pyridine [110-86-1]	5 ppm	—	—
Pyrocatechol, *see* Catechol			
Quartz, *see* Silica—Crystalline			
Quinone [106-51-4]	0.1 ppm	—	—
Resorcinol [108-46-3]	10 ppm	20 ppm	A4
Rhodium [7440-16-6]			
Metal	1 mg/m³	—	A4
Insoluble compounds, as Rh	1 mg/m³	—	A4
Soluble compounds, as Rh	0.01 mg/m³	—	A4
Ronnel [299-84-3]	10 mg/m³	—	A4; BEI
Rosin core solder thermal decomposition products, as resin acids– colophony [8050-09-7]	Sensitizer; reduce exposure to as low as possible		
Rotenone (commercial) [83-79-4]	5 mg/m³	—	A4
Rouge	10 mg/m³⁽ᴱ⁾	—	A4
Rubber solvent (Naphtha) [8030-30-6]	400 ppm	—	—
Selenium [7782-49-2] and compounds, as Se	0.2 mg/m³	—	—
Selenium hexafluoride [7783-79-1], as Se	0.05 ppm	—	—
Sesone [136-78-7]	10 mg/m³	—	A4
Silane, *see* Silicon tetrahydride			
Silica, Amorphous —			
Diatomaceous earth (uncalcined) [61790-53-2]	10 mg/m³⁽ᴱ·ᴵ⁾ 3 mg/m³⁽ᴱ·ᴿ⁾	—	—
Precipitated silica [112926-00-8]	10 mg/m³	—	—

ADOPTED VALUES			
Substance [CAS No.]	TWA (ppm/mg/m³)	STEL/C (ppm/mg/m³)	Notations
Silica fume [69012-64-2]	2 mg/m³⁽ᴿ⁾	—	—
Silica, fused [60676-86-0]	0.1 mg/m³⁽ᴿ⁾	—	—
Silica gel [112926-00-8]	10 mg/m³	—	—
Silica, Crystalline —			
Cristobalite [14464-46-1]	0.05 mg/m³⁽ᴿ⁾	—	—
* Quartz [14808-60-7]	0.05 mg/m³⁽ᴿ⁾	—	A2
Tridymite [15468-32-3]	0.05 mg/m³⁽ᴿ⁾	—	—
Tripoli [1317-95-9]	0.1 mg/m³⁽ᴿ⁾ of contained respirable quartz	—	—
Silicon [7440-21-3]	10 mg/m³	—	—
Silicon carbide [409-21-2]	10 mg/m³⁽ᴱ⁾	—	A4
Silicon tetrahydride [7803-62-5]	5 ppm	—	—
Silver [7440-22-4]			
Metal	0.1 mg/m³	—	—
Soluble compounds, as Ag	0.01 mg/m³	—	—
Soapstone	6 mg/m³⁽ᴱ⁾ 3 mg/m³⁽ᴱ·ᴿ⁾	—	—
Sodium azide [26628-22-8]			
as Sodium azide	—	C 0.29 mg/m³	A4
as Hydrazoic acid vapor	—	C 0.11 ppm	A4
Sodium bisulfite [7631-90-5]	5 mg/m³	—	A4
Sodium 2,4-dichlorophenoxyethyl sulfate, *see* Sesone			
Sodium fluoroacetate [62-74-8]	0.05 mg/m³	—	Skin
Sodium hydroxide [1310-73-2]	—	C 2 mg/m³	—
Sodium metabisulfite [7681-57-4]	5 mg/m³	—	A4
Starch [9005-25-8]	10 mg/m³	—	A4
Stearates⁽ᴶ⁾	10 mg/m³	—	A4
Stibine [7803-52-3]	0.1 ppm	—	—
Stoddard solvent [8052-41-3]	100 ppm	—	—
Strontium chromate [7789-06-2], as Cr	0.0005 mg/m³	—	A2
Strychnine [57-24-9]	0.15 mg/m³	—	—
Styrene, monomer [100-42-5]	20 ppm	40 ppm	A4; BEI
Subtilisins [1395-21-7; 9014-01-1], as active crystalline enzyme	—	C 0.00006 mg/m³	—
Sucrose [57-50-1]	10 mg/m³	—	A4
Sulfometuron methyl [74222-97-2]	5 mg/m³	—	—
Sulfotep [3689-24-5]	0.2 mg/m³	—	Skin; A4; BEI
Sulfur dioxide [7446-09-5]	2 ppm	5 ppm	A4
Sulfur hexafluoride [2551-62-4]	1000 ppm	—	—
Sulfuric acid [7664-93-9]	1 mg/m³	3 mg/m³	A2✿
✿A2 designation refers to sulfuric acid contained in strong inorganic acid mists			
Sulfur monochloride [10025-67-9]	—	C 1 ppm	—
Sulfur pentafluoride [5714-22-7]	—	C 0.01 ppm	—
Sulfur tetrafluoride [7783-60-0]	—	C 0.1 ppm	—
Sulfuryl fluoride [2699-79-8]	5 ppm	10 ppm	—
Sulprofos [35400-43-2]	1 mg/m³	—	A4; BEI
Synthetic Vitreous Fibers			
Continuous filament glass fibers	1 f/cc ⁽ᶠ⁾	—	A4
Continuous filament glass fibers	5 mg/m³⁽ᴵ⁾	—	A4
Glass wool fibers	1 f/cc ⁽ᶠ⁾	—	A3
Rock wool fibers	1 f/cc ⁽ᶠ⁾	—	A3
Slag wool fibers	1 f/cc ⁽ᶠ⁾	—	A3
Special purpose glass fibers	1 f/cc ⁽ᶠ⁾	—	A3
Systox, *see* Demeton			
2,4,5-T [93-76-5]	10 mg/m³	—	A4

ADOPTED VALUES			
Substance [CAS No.]	TWA (ppm/mg/m³)	STEL/C (ppm/mg/m³)	Notations
Talc (containing no asbestos fibers) [14807-96-6]	2 mg/m³(E, R)	—	A4
Talc (containing asbestos fibers)	Use asbestos TLV–TWA (K)	—	—
Tantalum metal [7440-25-7] and oxide [1314-61-0] dusts, as Ta	5 mg/m³	—	—
TEDP, see Sulfotep			
Tellurium [13494-80-9] and compounds, except hydrogen telluride, as Te	0.1 mg/m³	—	—
Tellurium hexafluoride [7783-80-4]	0.02 ppm	—	—
Temephos [3383-96-8]	10 mg/m³	—	BEI
TEPP [107-49-3]	0.05 mg/m³	—	Skin; BEI
Terephthalic acid [100-21-0]	10 mg/m³	—	—
Terphenyls [26140-60-3]	—	C 5 mg/m³	—
1,1,1,2-Tetrachloro-2,2-difluoroethane [76-11-9]	500 ppm	—	—
1,1,2,2-Tetrachloro-1,2-difluoroethane [76-12-0]	500 ppm	—	—
1,1,2,2-Tetrachloroethane [79-34-5]	1 ppm	—	Skin; A3
Tetrachloroethylene, see Perchloroethylene			
Tetrachloromethane, see Carbon tetrachloride			
Tetrachloronaphthalene [1335-88-2]	2 mg/m³	—	—
Tetraethyl lead [78-00-2], as Pb	0.1 mg/m³	—	Skin; A4
Tetrafluoroethylene [116-14-3]	2 ppm	—	A3
Tetrahydrofuran [109-99-9]	200 ppm	250 ppm	—
Tetramethyl lead [75-74-1], as Pb	0.15 mg/m³	—	Skin
Tetramethyl succinonitrile [3333-52-6]	0.5 ppm	—	Skin
Tetranitromethane [509-14-8]	0.005 ppm	—	A3
Tetrasodium pyrophosphate [7722-88-5]			
Anhydride	5 mg/m³	—	—
Decahydrate	5 mg/m³	—	—
Tetryl [479-45-8]	2 mg/m³	—	—
Thallium, elemental [7440-28-0], and soluble compounds, as Tl	0.1 mg/m³	—	Skin
4,4′-Thiobis(6-tert-butyl-m-cresol) [96-69-5]	10 mg/m³	—	—
Thioglycolic acid [68-11-1]	1 ppm	—	Skin
Thionyl chloride [7719-09-7]	—	C 1 ppm	—
Thiram [137-26-8]	1 mg/m³	—	A4
Tin [7440-31-5]			
Metal	2 mg/m³	—	—
Oxide & inorganic compounds, except tin hydride, as Sn	2 mg/m³	—	—
Organic compounds, as Sn	0.1 mg/m³	0.2 mg/m³	Skin; A4
Titanium dioxide [13463-67-7]	10 mg/m³	—	A4
o-Tolidine [119-93-7]	—	—	Skin; A3
Toluene [108-88-3]	50 ppm	—	Skin; A4; BEI
‡ Toluene-2,4-diisocyanate (TDI) [584-84-9]	0.005 ppm	0.02 ppm	(—); A4
o-Toluidine [95-53-4]	2 ppm	—	Skin; A3; BEI
m-Toluidine [108-44-1]	2 ppm	—	Skin; A4; BEI
p-Toluidine [106-49-0]	2 ppm	—	Skin; A3; BEI
Toluol, see Toluene			
Toxaphene, see Chlorinated camphene			
Tributyl phosphate [126-73-8]	0.2 ppm	—	BEI
Trichloroacetic acid [76-03-9]	1 ppm	—	A3
1,2,4-Trichlorobenzene [120-82-1]	—	C 5 ppm	—
1,1,1-Trichloroethane, see Methyl chloroform			
1,1,2-Trichloroethane [79-00-5]	10 ppm	—	Skin; A4

ADOPTED VALUES			
Substance [CAS No.]	TWA (ppm/mg/m³)	STEL/C (ppm/mg/m³)	Notations
Trichloroethylene [79-01-6]	50 ppm	100 ppm	A5; BEI
Trichlorofluoromethane [75-69-4]	—	C 1000	A4
Trichloromethane, see Chloroform			
Trichloronaphthalene [1321-65-9]	5 mg/m³	—	Skin
Trichloronitromethane, see Chloropicrin			
1,2,3-Trichloropropane [96-18-4]	10 ppm	—	Skin; A3
1,1,2-Trichloro-1,2,2-trifluoroethane [76-13-1]	1000 ppm	1250 ppm	A4
Tricyclohexyltin hydroxide, see Cyhexatin			
Tridymite, see Silica—Crystalline			
Triethanolamine [102-71-6]	5 mg/m³	—	—
Triethylamine [121-44-8]	1 ppm	3 ppm	Skin; A4
Trifluobromomethane [75-63-8]	1000 ppm	—	—
1,3,5-Triglycidyl-s-triazinetrione [2451-62-9]	0.05 mg/m³	—	—
Trimellitic anhydride [552-30-7]	—	C 0.04 mg/m³	—
Trimethylamine [75-50-3]	5 ppm	15 ppm	—
Trimethyl benzene (mixed isomers) [25551-13-7]	25 ppm	—	—
Trimethyl phosphite [121-45-9]	2 ppm	—	—
2,4,6-Trinitrophenol, see Picric acid			
2,4,6-Trinitrophenylmethylnitramine, see Tetryl			
2,4,6-Trinitrotoluene (TNT) [118-96-7]	0.1 mg/m³	—	Skin; BEI
Triorthocresyl phosphate [78-30-8]	0.1 mg/m³	—	Skin; A4; BEI
Triphenyl amine [603-34-9]	5 mg/m³	—	—
Triphenyl phosphate [115-86-6]	3 mg/m³	—	A4
Tripoli, see Silica—Crystalline			
Tungsten [7440-33-7], as W			
Metal and insoluble compounds	5 mg/m³	10 mg/m³	—
Soluble compounds	1 mg/m³	3 mg/m³	—
‡ Turpentine [8006-64-2]	100 ppm	—	(—)
Uranium (natural) [7440-61-1]			
Soluble and insoluble compounds, as U	0.2 mg/m³	0.6 mg/m³	A1
n-Valeraldehyde [110-62-3]	50 ppm	—	—
Vanadium pentoxide [1314-62-1], as V₂O₅			
Respirable dust or fume	0.05 mg/m³	—	A4; BEI
Vegetable oil mists (p)	10 mg/m³	—	—
Vinyl acetate [108-05-4]	10 ppm	15 ppm	A3
Vinyl benzene, see Styrene			
Vinyl bromide [593-60-2]	0.5 ppm	—	A2
Vinyl chloride [75-01-4]	1 ppm	—	A1
Vinyl cyanide, see Acrylonitrile			
4-Vinyl cyclohexene [100-40-3]	0.1 ppm	—	A3
Vinyl cyclohexene dioxide [106-87-6]	0.1 ppm	—	Skin; A3
Vinyl fluoride [75-02-5]	1 ppm	—	A2
Vinylidene chloride [75-35-4]	5 ppm	—	A4
Vinylidene fluoride [75-38-7]	500 ppm	—	A4
Vinyl toluene [25013-15-4]	50 ppm	100 ppm	A4
VM & P Naphtha [8032-32-4]	300 ppm	—	A3
Warfarin [81-81-2]	0.1 mg/m³	—	—
Welding fumes (NOC(d))	5 mg/m³	—	B2
‡ Wood dust			
‡ (Certain hard woods as beech & oak)	(1 mg/m³)	—	A1
‡ Soft wood	5 mg/m³	(10 mg/m³)	—
Xylene [1330-20-7] (o, m & p isomers) [95-47-6; 108-38-3; 106-42-3]	100 ppm	150 ppm	A4; BEI

ADOPTED VALUES			
Substance [CAS No.]	TWA (ppm/mg/m³)	STEL/C (ppm/mg/m³)	Notations
m-Xylene α,α′-diamine [1477-50-0]	—	C 0.1 mg/m³	Skin
Xylidine (mixed isomers) [1300-73-8]	0.5 ppm	—	Skin; A3; BEI
Yttrium [7440-65-5], metal and compounds, as Y	1 mg/m³	—	—
Zinc chloride fume [7646-85-7]	1 mg/m³	2 mg/m³	—
Zinc chromates [13530-65-9; 11103-86-9; 37300-23-5], as Cr	0.01 mg/m³	—	A1
Zinc oxide [1314-13-2]			
Fume	5 mg/m³	10 mg/m³	—
Dust	10 mg/m³	—	—
Zirconium [7440-67-7] and compounds, as Zr	5 mg/m³	10 mg/m3	A4

✿A2 designation refers to sulfuric acid contained in strong inorganic acid mists

NOTICE OF INTENDED CHANGES FOR 2000

These substances, with their corresponding values and notations, comprise those for which a limit has been proposed for the first time or for which a change in the Adopted listing has been proposed. In each case, the proposed values should be considered trial values for the year following ratification by the ACGIH Board of Directors. If, during the year, no evidence comes to light that questions the appropriateness of these proposals, the values will be reconsidered for adoption as TLVs. Documentation is available for each of these substances and their proposed values.

This notice provides not only an opportunity for comment on these proposals but also solicits suggestions of substances to be considered for TLVs, like those on the current list of "Chemical Substances and Other Issues Under Study." Comments or suggestions should be accompanied by substantiating evidence and forwarded to The Science Group, ACGIH.

NOTICE OF INTENDED CHANGES (for 2000)			
Substance [CAS No.]	TWA (ppm/mg/m³)	STEL/C (ppm/mg/m³)	Notations
Arsine [7784-42-1]	0.002 ppm	—	—
Beryllium [7440-41-7] and compounds, as Be	0.0002 mg/m³⁽ⁱ⁾	—	SEN; A1
† n-Butanol [71-36-3]	20 ppm	50 ppm	—
† Butylated hydroxytoluene (BHT) [128-37-0]	2 mg/m³⁽ⁱ, ⱽ⁾	—	—
Caprolactam [105-60-2]	5 mg/m³ ⁽ⱽ⁾	—	A5
† Coal dust	Withdrawn from the Notice of Intended Changes; retain adopted TLVs		
Cyclohexane [110-82-7]	200 ppm	400 ppm	—
† Demeton [8065-48-3]	0.05 mg/m³⁽ⁱ, ⱽ⁾	—	Skin; BEI
† Demeton-S-methyl [919-86-8]	0.05 mg/m³⁽ⁱ, ⱽ⁾	—	Skin; SEN; A4; BEI
† Dicrotophos [141-66-2]	0.05 mg/m³⁽ⁱ, ⱽ⁾	—	Skin; A4; BEI
Diesel exhaust, particulate	0.05 mg/m³	—	A2
Diesel fuel/Kerosene	100 mg/m³	—	Skin; A3
† Dioxathion [78-34-2]	0.1 mg/m³⁽ⁱ, ⱽ⁾	—	Skin; A4; BEI
1,3-Dioxolane [646-06-0]	20 ppm	—	—
† Ethion [563-12-2]	0.5 mg/m³⁽ⁱ, ⱽ⁾	—	Skin; A4; BEI
Ethyl benzene [100-41-4]	100 ppm	125 ppm	A3; BEI
2-Ethylhexanoic acid [149-57-5]	4 mg/m³	—	—
† Glyoxal [107-22-2]	0.1 mg/m³⁽ⁱ, ⱽ⁾	—	SEN; A4

NOTICE OF INTENDED CHANGES (for 2000)			
Substance [CAS No.]	TWA (ppm/mg/m³)	STEL/C (ppm/mg/m³)	Notations
Hydrogen sulfide [7783-06-4]	5 ppm	—	—
Isopropyl acetate [108-21-4]	100 ppm	200 ppm	—
Isopropyl alcohol [67-63-0]	200 ppm	400 ppm	A4
† Mevinphos [7786-34-7]	0.01 mg/m³⁽ⁱ, ⱽ⁾	—	Skin; SEN A4; BEI
Molybdenum [7439-98-7] and compounds, as Mo			
Metal and insoluble compounds	10 mg/m³⁽ⁱ⁾	—	—
	3 mg/m³⁽ᴿ⁾	—	—
Soluble compounds	0.5 mg/m³⁽ᴿ⁾	—	A3
† Naled [300-76-5]	0.1 mg/m³⁽ⁱ, ⱽ⁾	—	Skin; SEN A4; BEI
Oil mist, mineral	5 mg/m³⁽ᴴ⁾	—	—
Sum total of 15 polynuclear aromatic hydrocarbons (PAHs) listed as carcinogens by the U.S. National Toxicology Program (NTP)	0.005 mg/m³⁽ᴴ⁾	—	A1
n-Propanol [71-23-8]	200 ppm	250 ppm	A3
† Propylene oxide [75-56-9]	2 ppm	—	SEN; A3
Sodium sesquicarbonate (Trona) [533-96-0]	0.5 mg/m³⁽ᴿ⁾	—	—
Synthetic Vitreous Fibers			
† Refractory ceramic fibers	0.2 f/cc ⁽ᶠ⁾	—	A2
† Terbufos [1307-79-9]	0.01 mg/m³⁽ⁱ, ⱽ⁾	—	Skin; A4; BEI
Toluene-2,4-diisocyanate [584-84-9] or Toluene-2,6-diisocyanate [91-08-7] (or as a mixture)	0.005 ppm	0.02 ppm	SEN; A4
† Trichlorphon [52-68-6]	1 mg/m³⁽ⁱ, ⱽ⁾	—	A4, BEI
Turpentine [8006-64-2]	100 ppm	—	SEN
Wood dust			
Hardwoods & Softwoods (nonallergenic)	5 mg/m³⁽ⁱ⁾	—	A4
Beech and Oak	5 mg/m³⁽ⁱ⁾	—	SEN; A1
Birch, Mahogany, Teak, Walnut	5 mg/m³⁽ⁱ⁾	—	SEN; A2
Softwoods and Other Hardwoods (allergenic)	5 mg/m³⁽ⁱ⁾	—	SEN; A4
Western red cedar	0.5 mg/m³⁽ⁱ⁾	—	SEN; A4

ADOPTED APPENDICES
APPENDIX A: Carcinogenicity

The Chemical Substances TLV Committee has been aware of the increasing public concern over chemicals or industrial processes that cause or contribute to increased risk of cancer in workers. More sophisticated methods of bioassay, as well as the use of sophisticated mathematical models that extrapolate the levels of risk among workers, have led to differing interpretations as to which chemicals or processes should be categorized as human carcinogens and what the maximum exposure levels should be. The goal of the Committee has been to synthesize the available information in a manner that will be useful to practicing industrial hygienists, without overburdening them with needless details. The categories for carcinogenicity are:

A1 — *Confirmed Human Carcinogen:* The agent is carcinogenic to humans based on the weight of evidence from epidemiologic studies.

A2 — *Suspected Human Carcinogen:* Human data are accepted as adequate in quality but are conflicting or insufficient to classify the agent as a confirmed human carcinogen; OR, the agent is carcinogenic in experimental animals at dose(s), by route(s) of exposure, at site(s), of histologic types(s), or by mechanism(s) considered relevant to worker exposure. The A2 is used primarily when there is limited evidence of carcinogenicity in humans and sufficient evidence of carcinogenicity in experimental animals with relevance to humans.

A3 — *Confirmed Animal Carcinogen with Unknown Relevance to Humans:* The agent is carcinogenic in experimental animals at a relatively high dose, by route(s) of administration, at site(s), of histologic types(s), or by mechanism(s) that may not be relevant to worker exposure. Available epidemiologic studies do not confirm an increased risk of cancer in exposed humans. Available evidence does not suggest that the agent is likely to cause cancer in humans except under uncommon or unlikely routes or levels of exposure.

A4 — *Not Classifiable as a Human Carcinogen:* Agents which cause concern that they could be carcinogenic for humans but which cannot be assessed conclusively because of a lack of data. *In vitro* or animal studies do not provide indications of carcinogenicity which are sufficient to classify the agent into one of the other categories.

A5 — *Not Suspected as a Human Carcinogen:* The agent is not suspected to be a human carcinogen on the basis of properly conducted epidemiologic studies in humans. These studies have sufficiently long follow-up, reliable exposure histories, sufficiently high dose, and adequate statistical power to conclude that exposure to the agent does not convey a significant risk of cancer to humans; OR, the evidence suggesting a lack of carcinogenicity in experimental animals is supported by mechanistic data.

Substances for which no human or experimental animal carcinogenic data have been reported are assigned no carcinogenicity designation.

Exposures to carcinogens must be kept to a minimum. Workers exposed to A1 carcinogens without a TLV should be properly equipped to eliminate to the fullest extent possible all exposure to the carcinogen. For A1 carcinogens with a TLV and for A2 and A3 carcinogens, worker exposure by all routes should be carefully controlled to levels as low as possible below the TLV. Refer to the "Guidelines for the Classification of Occupational Carcinogens" in the Introduction to the *Documentation of the Threshold Limit Values and Biological Exposure Indices* for a complete description and derivation of these designations.

APPENDIX B: Substances of Variable Composition

B1. *Polytetrafluoroethylene* decomposition products*

Thermal decomposition of the fluorocarbon chain in air leads to the formation of oxidized products containing carbon, fluorine, and oxygen. Because these products decompose in part by hydrolysis in alkaline solution, they can be quantitatively determined in air as fluoride to provide an index of exposure. No TLVs are recommended at this time, but air concentration should be controlled as low as possible.
(*Trade names include: Algoflon®, Fluon®, Teflon®, Tetran®)

B2. *Welding Fumes*—Total Particulate (not otherwise classified): TLV–TWA, 5 mg/m^3

Welding fumes cannot be classified simply. The composition and quantity of both are dependent on the alloy being welded and the process and electrodes used. Reliable analysis of fumes cannot be made without considering the nature of the welding process and system being examined; reactive metals and alloys such as aluminum and titanium are arc-welded in a protective, inert atmosphere such as argon. These arcs create relatively little fume, but they do create an intense radiation which can produce ozone. Similar processes are used to arc-weld steels, also creating a relatively low level of fumes. Ferrous alloys also are arc-welded in oxidizing environments that generate considerable fume and can produce carbon monoxide instead of ozone. Such fumes generally are composed of discrete particles of amorphous slags containing iron, manganese, silicon, and other metallic constituents depending on the alloy system involved. Chromium and nickel compounds are found in fumes when stainless steels are arc-welded. Some coated and flux-cored electrodes are formulated with fluorides and the fumes associated with them can contain significantly more fluorides than oxides. Because of the above factors, arc-welding fumes frequently must be tested for individual constituents that are likely to be present to determine whether specific TLVs are exceeded. Conclusions based on total concentration are generally adequate if no toxic elements are present in welding rod, metal, or metal coating and conditions are not conducive to the formation of toxic gases.

APPENDIX C: Threshold Limit Values for Mixtures

When two or more hazardous substances which act upon the same organ system are present, their combined effect, rather than that of either individually, should be given primary consideration. In the absence of information to the contrary, the effects of the different hazards should be considered as additive. That is, if the sum of

$$\frac{C_1}{T_1} + \frac{C_2}{T_2} + \cdots \frac{C_n}{T_n}$$

exceeds unity, then the threshold limit of the mixture should be considered as being exceeded. C_1 indicates the observed atmospheric concentration and T_1 the corresponding threshold limit (see Example A.1 and B.1).

Exceptions to the above rule may be made when there is a good reason to believe that the chief effects of the different harmful substances are not in fact additive, but are independent as when purely local effects on different organs of the body are produced by the various components of the mixture. In such cases, the threshold limit ordinarily is exceeded only when at least one member of the series ($C_1/T_1 +$ or $+ C_2/T_2$, etc.) itself has a value exceeding unity (see Example B.1).

Synergistic action or potentiation may occur with some combinations of atmospheric contaminants. Such cases at present must be determined individually. Potentiating or synergistic agents are not necessarily harmful by themselves. Potentiating effects of exposure to such agents by routes other than that of inhalation are also possible, e.g., imbibed alcohol and inhaled narcotic (trichloroethylene). Potentiation is characteristically exhibited at high concentrations, less probably at low.

When a given operation or process characteristically emits a number of harmful dusts, fumes, vapors or gases, it will frequently be only feasible to attempt to evaluate the hazard by measurement of a single substance. In such cases, the threshold limit used for this substance should be reduced by a suitable factor, the magnitude of which will depend on the number, toxicity, and relative quantity of the other contaminants ordinarily present.

Examples of processes that are typically associated with two or more harmful atmospheric contaminants are welding, automobile repair, blasting, painting, lacquering, certain foundry operations, diesel exhausts, etc.

Examples of TLVs for Mixtures

A. *Additive effects.* The following formulae apply only when the components in a mixture have similar toxicologic effects; they should not be used for mixtures with widely differing reactivities, e.g., hydrogen cyanide and sulfur dioxide. In such case, the formula for **Independent Effects** should be used.

1. General case, where air is analyzed for each component, the TLV of mixture =

$$\frac{C_1}{T_1} + \frac{C_2}{T_2} + \frac{C_3}{T_3} + \cdots = 1$$

Note: It is essential that the atmosphere be analyzed both qualitatively and quantitatively for each component present in order to evaluate compliance or noncompliance with this calculated TLV.

Example A.1: Air contains 400 ppm of acetone (TLV, 500 ppm), 150 ppm of sec-butyl acetate (TLV, 200 ppm) and 100 ppm of methyl ethyl ketone (TLV, 200 ppm).

Atmospheric concentration of mixture = 400 + 150 + 100 = 650 ppm of mixture.

$$\frac{400}{500} + \frac{150}{200} + \frac{100}{200} = 0.80 + 0.75 + 0.5 = 2.05$$

Threshold Limit is exceeded.

2. Special case when the source of contaminant is a liquid mixture and the atmospheric composition is assumed to be similar to that of the original material, e.g., on a time-weighted average exposure basis, all of the liquid (solvent) mixture eventually evaporates. When the percent composition (by weight) of the liquid mixture is known, the TLVs of the constituents must be listed in mg/m^3. TLV of mixture =

$$\frac{1}{\dfrac{f_a}{TLV_a} + \dfrac{f_b}{TLV_b} + \dfrac{f_c}{TLV_c} + \dots \dfrac{f_n}{TLV_n}}$$

Note: In order to evaluate compliance with this TLV, field sampling instruments should be calibrated, in the laboratory, for response to this specific quantitative and qualitative air-vapor mixture, and also to fractional concentrations of this mixture (e.g., 1/2 the TLV; 1/10 the TLV; 2 × the TLV; 10 × the TLV; etc.)

Example A.2: Liquid contains (by weight):

50% heptane: TLV = 400 ppm or 1640 mg/m^3
  1 mg/m^3 ≡ 0.24 ppm
30% methyl chloroform: TLV = 350 ppm or 1910 mg/m^3
  1 mg/m^3 ≡ 0.18 ppm
20% perchloroethylene: TLV = 25 ppm or 170 mg/m^3
  1 mg/m^3 ≡ 0.15 ppm

$$TLV \text{ of Mixture} = \frac{1}{\dfrac{0.5}{1640} + \dfrac{0.3}{1910} + \dfrac{0.2}{170}}$$

$$= \frac{1}{0.00030 + 0.00016 + 0.00118}$$

$$= \frac{1}{0.00164} = 610 \text{ mg/m}^3$$

of this mixture
  50% or (610)(0.5) = 305 mg/m^3 is heptane
  30% or (610)(0.3) = 183 mg/m^3 is methyl chloroform
  20% or (610)(0.2) = 122 mg/m^3 is perchloroethylene

These values can be converted to ppm as follows:
  heptane: 305 mg/m^3 × 0.24 = 73 ppm
  methyl chloroform: 183 mg/m^3 × 0.18 = 33 ppm
  perchloroethylene: 122 mg/m^3 × 0.15 = 18 ppm

TLV of mixture = 73 + 33 + 18 = 124 ppm, or 610 mg/m^3

B. *Independent effects.* TLV for mixture =

$$\frac{C_1}{T_1} = 1; \quad \frac{C_2}{T_2} = 1; \quad \frac{C_3}{T_3} = 1; \text{ etc.}$$

Example B.1: Air contains 0.05 mg/m^3 of lead (TLV, 0.05) and 0.7 mg/m^3 of sulfuric acid (TLV, 1).

$$\frac{0.05}{0.05} = 1; \qquad \frac{0.7}{1} = 0.7$$

Threshold limit is not exceeded.

C. *TLV for mixtures of mineral dusts.* For mixtures of biologically active mineral dusts, the general formula for mixtures given in A.2 may be used.

APPENDIX D: Particle Size-Selective Sampling Criteria for Airborne Particulate Matter

For chemical substances present in inhaled air as suspensions of solid particles or droplets, the potential hazard depends on particle size as well as mass concentration because of: 1) effects of particle size on the deposition site within the respiratory tract, and 2) the tendency for many occupational diseases to be associated with material deposited in particular regions of the respiratory tract.

The Chemical Substances TLV Committee has recommended particle size-selective TLVs for crystalline silica for many years in recognition of the well established association between silicosis and respirable mass concentrations. The Committee is now re-examining other chemical substances encountered in particulate form in occupational environments with the objective of defining: 1) the size-fraction most closely associated for each substance with the health effect of concern, and 2) the mass concentration within that size fraction which should represent the TLV.

The Particle Size-Selective TLVs (PSS–TLVs) are expressed in three forms:

1. *Inhalable Particulate Mass TLVs* (IPM–TLVs) for those materials that are hazardous when deposited anywhere in the respiratory tract.

2. *Thoracic Particulate Mass TLVs* (TPM–TLVs) for those materials that are hazardous when deposited anywhere within the lung airways and the gas-exchange region.

3. *Respirable Particulate Mass TLVs* (RPM–TLVs) for those materials that are hazardous when deposited in the gas-exchange region.

The three particulate mass fractions described above are defined in quantitative terms in accordance with the following equations:[1,2]

A. *Inhalable Particulate Mass* consists of those particles that are captured according to the following collection efficiency regardless of sampler orientation with respect to wind direction:

$$SI(d) = 50\% \times (1 + e^{-0.06d})$$
$$\text{for } 0 < d \leq 100 \ \mu m$$

where: SI(d) = the collection efficiency for particles with aerodynamic diameter d in μm

B. *Thoracic Particulate Mass* consists of those particles that are captured according to the following collection efficiency:

$$ST(d) = SI(d) \ [1 - F(x)]$$

where: $x = \dfrac{\ln (d/\Gamma)}{\ln (\Sigma)}$
  $\Gamma = 11.64 \ \mu m$
  $\Sigma = 1.5$
  F (x) = the cumulative probability function of a standardized normal variable, x

C. *Respirable Particulate Mass* consists of those particles that are captured according to the following collection efficiency:

$$SR(d) = SI(d) \ [1 - F(x)]$$

where F(x) has the same meaning as above with $\Gamma = 4.25 \ \mu m$ and $\Sigma = 1.5$

The most significant difference from previous definitions is the increase in the median cut point for a respirable particulate matter sampler from 3.5 μm to 4.0 μm; this is in accord with the International Organization for Standardization/European Standardization Committee (ISO/CEN) protocol.[3,4] At this time, no change is recommended for the measurement of respirable particulates using a 10-mm nylon cyclone at a flow rate of 1.7 liters per minute. Two analyses of available data indicate that the flow rate of 1.7 liters per minute allows the 10-mm nylon cyclone to approximate the particulate matter concentration which would be measured by an ideal respirable particulate sampler as defined herein.[5,6]

Collection efficiencies representative of several sizes of particles in each of the respective mass fractions are shown in Tables I, II, and III. References 2 and 3 provide documentation for the respective algorithms representative of the three mass fractions.

TABLE I. Inhalable

Particle Aerodynamic Diameter (μm)	Inhalable Particulate Mass (IPM) (%)
0	100
1	97
2	94
5	87
10	77
20	65
30	58
40	54.5
50	52.5
100	50

TABLE II. Thoracic

Particle Aerodynamic Diameter (μm)	Thoracic Particulate Mass (TPM) (%)
0	100
2	94
4	89
6	80.5
8	67
10	50
12	35
14	23
16	15
18	9.5
20	6
25	2

TABLE III. Respirable

Particle Aerodynamic Diameter (μm)	Respirable Particulate Mass (RPM) (%)
0	100
1	97
2	91
3	74
4	50
5	30
6	17
7	9
8	5
10	1

References

1. American Conference of Governmental Industrial Hygienists: Particle Size-Selective Sampling in the Workplace. ACGIH, Cincinnati, OH (1985).
2. Soderholm, S.C.: Proposed International Conventions for Particle Size-Selective Sampling. Ann. Occup. Hyg. 33:301–320 (1989).
3. International Organization for Standardization (ISO): Air Quality—Particle Size Fraction Definitions for Health-Related Sampling. Approved for publication as CD 7708. ISO, Geneva (1991).
4. European Standardization Committee (CEN): Size Fraction Definitions for Measurement of Airborne Particles in the Workplace. Approved for publication as prEN 481. CEN, Brussels (1992).
5. Bartley, D.L.: Letter to J. Doull, TLV Committee, July 9, 1991.
6. Lidén, G.; Kenny, L.C.: Optimization of the Performance of Existing Respirable Dust Samplers. Appl. Occup. Environ. Hyg. 8(4):386–391 (1993).

APPENDIX B

PHYSICAL CONSTANTS OF SELECTED MATERIALS

Substance	Formula	Molecular Weight	Specific Gravity	Flash Point F Closed Cup	Flash Point F Open Cup	Exposure Limits (Volume Percent) Lower	Exposure Limits (Volume Percent) Upper
Acetaldehyde	CH_3CHO	44.05	0.821	-17	—	3.97	57.0
Acetic Acid	CH_3COOH	60.05	1.049	104	110	5.40	—
Acetic Anhydride	$(CH_3CO)_2O$	102.09	1.082	121	130	2.67	10.13
Acetone	CH_3COCH_3	58.08	0.792	0	15	2.55	12.80
Acrolein	$CH_2:CHCHO$	56.06	0.841	Gas		Unstable	
Acrylonitrile	$CH_2:CHCN$	53.06	0.806	—	32	3.05	17.0
Ammonia	NH_3	17.03	0.597	Gas		15.50	27.0
Amyl Acetate	$CH_3CO_2C_5H_{11}$	130.18	0.879	76	80	1.10	—
iso-Amyl Alcohol	$(CH_3)_2CHCH_2CH_2OH$	88.15	0.812	109	115	1.20	—
Aniline	$C_6H_5NH_2$	93.12	1.022	168	—	—	—
Arsine	AsH_3	77.93	2.695 (A)	Gas		—	—
Benzene	C_6H_6	78.11	0.879	12	—	1.40	7.10
Bromine	Br_2	159.83	3.119	—	—	—	—
Butane	$CH_3(CH_2)_2CH_3$	58.12	2.085	Gas		1.86	8.41
1,3-Butadiene	$(CH_2:CH)_2$	54.09	0.621	Gas		2.00	11.50
n-Butanol	$C_2H_5CH_2CH_2OH$	74.12	0.810	84	110	1.45	11.25
2-Butanone (Methyl ethyl ketone)	$CH_3COC_2H_5$	72.10	0.805	30	—	1.81	9.50
n-Butyl Acetate	$CH_3CO_2C_4H_9$	116.16	0.882	72	90	1.39	7.55
Butyl "Cellosolve"	$C_4H_9OCH_2CH_2OH$	118.17	0.903	141	165	—	—
Carbon Dioxide	CO_2	44.01	1.53	—	—	—	—
Carbon Disulphide	CS_2	76.13	1.263	-22	—	1.25	50.0
Carbon Monoxide	CO	28.10	0.968	Gas		12.5	74.2
Carbon Tetrachloride	CCl_4	153.84	1.595	Nonflammable			
Celllosolve	$C_2H_5O(CH_2)_2OH$	90.12	0.931	104	120	2.6	15.7
Cellosolve Acetate	$CH_3CO_2C_4H_9O$	132.16	0.975	124	135	1.71	—
Chlorine	Cl_2	70.91	3.214	Gas		—	—
2-Chlorobutadiene	$CH_2:CClCHCH_2$	88.54	0.958	—	—	—	—
Chloroform	$CHCl_3$	119.39	1.478	Nonflammable			
1-Chloro-1-nitropropane	$NO_3ClC_3H_6$	139.54	1.209	144	—	—	—
Cyclohexane	C_6H_{12}	84.16	0.779	1	—	1.26	7.75
Cyclohexanol	$CH_2(CH_2)_4CHOH$	100.16	0.962	154	—	—	—
Cyclohexanone	$CH_2(CH_2)_4CO$	98.14	0.948	147	—	—	—
Cyclohexene	$CH_2(CH_2)_3CH:CH$	82.14	0.810	—	—	—	—
Cyclopropane	$CH_2CH_2CH_2$	42.08	0.720	Gas		2.40	10.40
o-Dichlorobenzene	$Cl_2C_6H_4$	147.01	1.305	151	165	—	—
Dichlorodifluoromethane	CCl_2F_2	120.92	1.486	Nonflammable			
1,1-Dichlorethane	CH_2CHCl_2	98.97	1.175	—	—	—	—
1,2-Dichloroethane	$ClCH_2CH_2Cl$	98.97	1.257	56	65	6.2	15.9
1,2-Dichloroethylene (Ethylene Dichloride)	$ClCHCHCl$	96.95	1.291	43	—	9.7	12.8
Dichloroethylether	$ClCH_2CHClC_2H_5$	143.02	1.222	131	180	—	—
Dichloromethane	H_2CCl_2	84.94	1.336	—	—	—	—
Dichioromonofluoromethane	$HCCl_2F$	102.93	1.426	—	—	—	—
1,1-Dichloro-1-nitroethane	$H_3C_2Cl_2NO_3$	143.97	1.692	—	168	—	—
1,2-Dichloropropane	$CH_3CHClCH_2Cl$	112.99	1.159	59	65	3.4	14.5
Dichlorotetrafluoroethane	$CClF_2CClF_2$	170.93	1.433	Nonflammable			
Dimethylaniline	$(CH_3)_2NC_6H_5$	121.18	0.956	145	170	—	—
Dimethylsulfate	$(CH_3)_2SO_4$	126.13	1.332	182	240	—	—
Dioxane	$O(CH_2)_4O$	88.10	1.034	—	35	—	—
Ethyl Acetate	$CH_3CO_2C_2H_5$	88.10	0.901	24	30	2.18	11.4
Ethyl Alcohol	C_2H_5OH	46.07	0.789	55	—	3.28	18.95
Ethyl Benzene	$C_6H_5C_2H_5$	106.16	0.867	59	75	—	—

PHYSICAL CONSTANTS OF SELECTED MATERIALS (con't)

Substance	Formula	Molecular Weight	Specific Gravity	Flash Point F Closed Cup	Open Cup	Exposure Limits (Volume Percent) Lower	Upper
Ethyl Bromide	C_2H_5Br	109.98	1.430	—	—	6.75	11.25
Ethyl Chloride	C_2H_5Cl	64.52	0.921	-58	-45	3.6	14.80
Ethylene Chlorohydrin	$ClCH_2CH_2OH$	80.52	1.213	—	140	—	—
Ethylenediamine	$NH_2CH_2CH_2NH_2$	60.10	0.899	—	—	—	—
Ethylene Oxide	CH_2CH_2O	44.05	0.887	—	—	3.0	80.0
Ethyl Ether	$(C_2H_5)_2O$	74.12	0.713	—	—	—	—
Ethyl Formate	$HCO_2C_2H_5$	74.08	0.917	—	—	2.75	16.40
Ethyl Silicate	$(C_2H_5)_4SiO_4$	208.30	0.933	—	125	—	—
Formaldehyde	$HCHO$	30.03	0.815	Gas		7.0	73.0
Gasoline	$CHnH(2n+2)$	86.0	0.660	-50	—	1.36.0	
Heptane	$CH_3(CH_2)_5CH_3$	100.20	0.684	25	—	1.1	6.7
Hexane	$CH_3(CH_2)_4CH_3$	86.17	0.660	-7	—	1.18	7.4
Hydrogen Chloride	HCl	36.47	1.268 (A)	—	—	—	—
Hydrogen Cyanide	HCN	27.03	0.688	Gas		5.6	40.0
Hydrogen Fluoride	HF	20.01	0.987	Gas		—	—
Hydrogen Selenide	H_2Se	80.98	2.12	Gas		—	—
Hydrogen Sulfide	H_2S	34.08	1.189 (A)	Gas		4.3	45.5
Iodine	I_2	253.82	4.93	—	—	—	—
Isophorone	$(CH_3)_3C(CH_2)_2CCHCO$	138.20	0.923	—	205	—	—
Mesityl Oxide	$(CH_3)_2:CHCOCH_3$	98.14	0.857	87	—	—	—
Methanol	CH_3OH	32.04	0.792	54	60	6.72	36.5
Methyl Acetate	$CH_3CO_2CH_3$	74.08	0.928	15	20	3.15	15.60
Methyl Bromide	CH_3Br	94.95	1.732	—	—	13.5	14.5
Methyl Butanone (Isopropyl butane)	$CH_3COCH(CH_3)_2$	86.13	0.803	—	—	—	—
Methyl Cellosolve	$HOCH_2CH_2OCH_3$	76.06	0.965	107	115	—	—
Methyl Cellosolve Acetate	$CH_3OCH_2CH_2OOCCH_3$	118.13	1.007	132	140	—	—
Methyl Choloride	CH_3Cl	50.49	1.785	Gas		8.25	18.70
Methyl Cyclohexane	$CH_3(CHC_5H_{10})$	98.18	0.769	25	—	1.15	—
Methyl Cyclohexanol	$CH_3(CHC_4H_8CHOH)$	114.18	0.934	154	—	—	—
Methyl Cyclohexanone	$CH_5C_5H_9CO$	122.17	0.925	118	—	—	—
Methyl Formate	HCO_2CH_3	60.05	0.974	-2	—	4.5	20.0
Methyl Isobutyl Ketone	$CH_3COC_4H_9$	100.16	0.801	73	—	—	—
Monochlorobenzene	C_6H_5Cl	112.56	1.107	90	—	—	—
Monofluorotrichloromethane	Cl_3CF	137.38	1.494	Nonflammable			
Mononitrotoluene	$CH_3C_6H_4NO_2$	137.13	1.163	223	—	—	—
Naphtha (coal tar)	$C_6H_4(CH_3)_2$	106.16	0.85	100-110	—	—	—
Nickel Carbonyl	$Ni(CO)_4$	170.73	1.31	—	—	—	—
Nitrobenzene	$C_6H_5NO_2$	123.11	1.205	190	—	1.8 (200 F)	—
Nitroethane	$CH_3CH_2NO_2$	75.07	1.052	82	106	—	—
Nitrogen Oxides	NO	30.0	1.0367(A)	—	—	—	—
	N_2O	44.02	1.53	—	—	—	—
	N_2O_3	76.02	1.447	—	—	—	—
	NO_2	46.01	1.448	—	—	—	—
	N_2O_5	108.02	1.642	—	—	—	—
Nitroglycerine	$C_3H_5(ONO_2)_3$	227.09	1.601	—	—	—	—
Nitromethane	CH_3NO_2	61.04	1.130	95	112	—	—
2-Nitropropane	$CH_3CHNO_2CH_3$	89.09	1.003	—	103	—	—
Octane	$CH_3(CH_2)_6CH_3$	114.22	0.703	56	—	0.95	3.2
Ozone	O_3	48.0	1.658 (A)	—	—	—	—
Pentane	$CH_3(CH_2)_3CH_3$	72.15	0.626	-40	—	1.4	7.8
Pentanone (Methylpropanone)	$CH_3COCH_2C_2H_5$	86.13	0.816	45	60	1.55	8.15
Phosgene	$O:C:Cl_2$	98.92	1.392	—	—	—	—
Phosphine	PH_3	34.0	1.146 (A)	—	205	—	—
Phosphorus Trichloride	PCl_3	137.35	1.574	—	—	—	—
iso-Propanol	$(CH_3)_2CHOH$	60.09	0.785	53	60	2.02	11.80

PHYSICAL CONSTANTS OF SELECTED MATERIALS (con't)

Substance	Formula	Molecular Weight	Specific Gravity	Flash Point F Closed Cup	Flash Point F Open Cup	Exposure Limits (Volume Percent) Lower	Exposure Limits (Volume Percent) Upper
Propane	$CH_3CH_2CH_3$	44.09	1.554	Gas		2.12	9.35
Propyl Acetate	$CH_3CO_2CH_2C_2H_5$	102.13	0.886	43	60	1.77	8.0
iso-Propyl Ether	$(CH_3)_4(CH)_2O$	102.17	0.725	-18	-15	—	—
Stibine	SbH_3	124.78	4.344 (A)	—	—	—	—
Styrene Monomer	$C_6H_5HC:CH_2$	104.14	0.903	90	—	1.1	6.1
Sulfur Chloride, Mono	S_2Cl_2	135.03	1.678	245	None	—	—
Di	SCl_2	102.97	1.621	—	—	—	—
Tetra	SCl_4	173.89	—	—	—	—	—
Sulfur Dioxide	SO_2	64.07	2.264 (A)	Gas		—	—
1,1,2,2, Tetrachloroethane	$Cl_2CHCHCl_2$	167.86	1.588	—	—	—	—
Tetrachloroethylene	$Cl_2C:CCl_2$	165.85	1.624	Nonflammable			
Toluene	$C_6H_5CH_3$	92.13	0.866	40	45	1.27	6.75
Toluidine	$CH_3C_6H_4NH_2$	107.15	0.999	188	205	—	—
Trichloroethylene	$ClCHCCl_2$	131.40	1.466	Nonflammable			
Turpentine (Turpene)	$C_{10}H_{16}$	136.23		95	—	0.8	—
Vinyl Chloride (Chloroethane)	C_2H_5Cl	62.50	0.908	Gas		4.0	21.70
Xylene	C6H4(CH3)2	106.16	0.881	63	75	1.0	6.0

SOLVENT DRYING TIME

SOLVENT	Dry Time Relation	Boiling Range Deg. C	Boiling Range Deg. F.	Weight per Gal. Lbs.
Ethyl Ether, C.P.	1.0	34-35	93-95	5.98
Petrolene	1.8	61-96	142-205	5.83
Carbon Tetracholride	1.9	76	169	13.30
Acetone	2.0	55-58	133-136	6.35
Methyl Acetate	2.2	56-62	133-144	7.79
Ethyl Acetate 85-88%	2.5	74-77	165-171	7.37
Trichlorethylene	2.5	87	189	12.20
Benzol (Industrial)	2.6	79-81	174-178	7.38
Methyl Ethyl Ketone	2.7	77-82	171-180	6.95
Isopropyl Acetate 8%	2.7	84-93	183-199	7.26
Ethylene Dichloride	3.0	84	183	10.49
Solvsol 19/27	3.7	86-123	187-254	6.58
Ethylene Chloride	4.0	81-87	178-189	10.49
Propylene Dichloride	4.1	92-97	199-207	9.64
Troluoil	4.1	90-122	194-252	6.17
Methanol	5.0	64-65	147-149	6.63
Toluol (Industrial	5.0	109-111	229-232	7.19
Methyl Propyl Ketone	5.2	101-107	214-225	6.77
V. M. & P	5.8	95-141	203-286	6.23
Perchlorethylene	6.0	121	250	13.55
Nor. Propyl Acetate	6.1	97-101	207-214	7.50
Sec. Butyl Acetate	6.5	106-135	223-275	7.13
Solox (Anhydrous)	6.5	71-78	160-172	6.80
Isobutyl Acetate 90%	7.0	106-117	223-243	7.28
Apocthinner	7.0	115-143	239-289	6.31
Ethyl Alcohol, Den. No. 1	7.7	78	172	6.64

SOLVENT DRYING TIME (con't)

SOLVENT	Dry Time Relation	Boiling Range Deg. C	Boiling Range Deg. F	Weight per Gal. Lbs.
Solox	8.0	76-78	169-172	6.73
Isopropyl Alcohol 99%	8.6	79-82	174-180	6.75
Nor. Propyl Alcohol	9.1	96-98	205-208	6.73
Solvsol 24/34	9.4	101-168	214-334	6.80
Nor. Butyl Acetate	9.6	110-132	230-270	7.29
Diethyl Carbonate	9.6	100-130	212-266	8.14
Methyl Butyl Ketone	9.7	114-137	237-279	6.84
Xylol (Industrial)	9.7	127-144	261-291	7.17
Monochlor Benzol	10.0	130-132	266-270	9.20
Tertiary Butyl Alcohol	11.9	82-83	180-181	6.55
Sec. Butyl Alcohol	14.0	99-100	210-212	6.85
Sec. Amyl Acetate	16.9	121-144	250-291	7.21
Amyl Acetate	17.4	105-142	221-288	7.24
Isobutyl Alcohol	17.7	107-111	225-232	6.70
Methyl Ceolosolve	18.0	121-126	250-259	8.07
Butyl Propionate	18.0	124-171	255-340	7.31
Pentacetate	20.0	121-155	250-311	7.19
Turpentine	20.0	155-173	311-343	12.24
Butanol	21.0	116-119	241-246	6.79
Sec. Amyl Alcohol	25.5	105-125	221-257	6.79
2-50-W Hi-Flash Naphtha	27.5	148-187	298-369	7.18
Amyl Alcohol (Fusel Oil)	32.1	126-130	259-266	6.76
Di Isopropyl Ketone	33.9	164-169	327-336	6.75
Ethyl Cellosolve	36.2	133-137	271-279	7.77
Odorless Mineral Spirits	38.6	150-210	302-394	6.52
Ethyl Lactate	40.0	119-176	246-349	8.59
Sec. Hexyl Alcohol	41.7	157	315	6.97
Solvsol 30/40	43.2	142-199	288-390	7.06
Pentasol	45.0	112-140	234-284	6.76
Hi-Solvency Mineral Spirits	46.7	152-200	306-392	6.79
No. 380 Mineral Spirits	47.0	151-196	304-385	6.57
No. 10 Mineral Spirits	55.0	154-196	309-385	6.49
Distilled Water	60.0	100	212	8.32
Apco No. 125	60.5	162-200	324-392	6.52
Cellosolve Acetate	65.0	145-166	293-331	8.15
Sec. Butyl Lactate	73.5	172	342	8.14
Sec. Hexyl Acetate	76.5	129-159	264-316	7.19
Butyl Cellosolve	88.5	163-172	325-342	7.58
Dipentene	89.2	149-215	300-419	7.10
No. 140 Thinner	91.2	185-210	365-410	6.62
Octyl Acetate	152.5	195-203	383-397	7.20
Isobutyl Lactate	156.5	168-200	334-392	8.15
Hexalin	177.5	159-162	318-324	7.89
Solvsol 40/50	270.5	191-248	376-478	7.42
Methyl Hexalin	276.5	170-190	338-374	7.66
Butyl Lactate	339.0	185-195	365-383	8.14
Excellene	384.0	162-260	324-500	6.55
Special Heavy Naphtha	403.0	202-242	396-468	6.73
Dispersol	425.0	193-242	379-468	6.59
No. 50 Kerosene	626.7	178-256	352-493	6.76
Triethylene Glycol	Over 5200.0	276-310	529-590	9.30
Dibutyl Phthalate	Over 5200.0	195-200	383-392	8.73

Dry Time Relation: Below 5 — Fast
5-15 — Medium
15-75 — Slow
75 over — Nil

CONVERSION FACTORS

to convert	into	multiply by	to convert	into	multiply by
ampere-hours	coulombs	3600.0	gallons	liters	3.785
angstrom units	inches	3.937×10^{-9}	gallons/minute	cubic feet/hour	8.0208
angstrom units	microns	1×10^{-4}	gallons/minute	cubic feet/second	0.00223
atmospheres	centimeters of mercury	76.0	gallons of water	pounds of water	8.3453
atmospheres	feet of water	33.96	grains	grams	0.0648
atmospheres	inches of mercury	29.92	grams	grains	15.4324
atmospheres	inches of water	407.52	grams	ounces (troy)	3.215×10^{-2}
atmospheres	millimeters of water	10.340	grams	ounces (avoidrupois)	3.527×10^{-2}
atmospheres	millimeters of mercury	760	grams	pounds	2.205×10^{-3}
atmospheres	pascals	101513	grams/cubic foot	milligrams/cubic meter	2288.1
atmospheres	pounds/square foot	2116.3	horsepower	BTU/minute	42.44
atmospheres	pounds/square inch	14.696	horsepower	foot-pounds/second	550
BTU	foot pounds	778	horsepower	foot-pounds/minute	33,000
BTU	horsepower-hours	3.931×10^{-4}	horsepower	kilowatts	0.7457
BTU	joules	1.055×10^{-3}	horsepower	watts	745.7
BTU	kilowatt-hours	2.928×10^{-4}	inches	centimeters	2.540
BTU/hour	watts	0.2931	inches	miles	1.578×10^{-5}
calories	BTU	3.9685×10^{-3}	inches of mercury	atmospheres	0.03342
centimeters	feet	3.281×10^{-2}	inches of mercury	feet of water	1.134
centimeters	inches	0.3937	inches of mercury	inches of water	13.61
centimeters	kilometers	1×10^{-5}	inches of mercury	millimeters of mercury	25.4
centimeters	meters	1×10^{-2}	inches of mercury	millimeters of water	345.6
centimeters	millimeters	10.0	inches of mercury	pascals	3390
coulombs	faradays	1.036×10^{-5}	inches of mercury	pounds/square foot	76.70
cubic feet	cubic meters	0.02832	inches of mercury	pounds/square inch	0.491
cubic feet	gallons	7.48	inches of water	atmospheres	0.002456
cubic feet	liters	28.3162	inches of water	feet of water	0.08333
cubic inches	cubic centimeters	16.3872	inches of water	inches of mercury	0.0735
cubic inches	liters	0.0164	inches of water	millimeters of water	25.4
cubic meters	cubic feet	35.3145	inches of water	millimeters of mercury	1.876
cubic centimeters	cubic inches	0.06102	inches of water	pascals	249.1
cubic centimeters	pints (U.S. liquid)	2.113×10^{-3}	inches of water	pounds/square inch	0.0361
cubic feet/minute	pounds water/minute	62.43	inches of water	pounds/square foot	5.196
cubic feet/minute	cubic meters/second	4.719×10^{-4}	joules	BTU	9.480×10^{-4}
cubic feet/second	gallons/minute	448.83	joules	ergs	1. 107
days	seconds	86,400.0	kilograms	pounds	2.205
degrees (angle)	radians	1.745×10^{-2}	kilograms	slugs	0.068522
degrees/second	revolutions/minute	0.1667	kilometers	feet	3281.0
dynes	newtons	1×10^{-5}	kilometers	miles	0.6214
ergs	BTU	9.480×10^{-11}	kilometers	meters	1000.0
ergs	kilowatt-hours	2.778×10^{-14}	kilometers/hour	knots	0.5396
ergs	foot-pounds	7.3670×10^{-8}	kilopascals	pounds/square inches	0.145
faradays/second	amperes	96,500	kilowatt-hours	BTU	3413.0
feet	centimeters	30.48	kilowatts	foot-pounds/second	737.6
feet	miles (nautical)	1.645×10^{-4}	kilowatts	horsepower	1.341
feet	meters	0.3048	knots	feet/hour	6080.0
feet	miles (statute)	1.894×10^{-4}	knots	statute miles/hour	1.151
feet/minute	centimeters/second	0.5080	knots	nautical miles/hour	1.0
feet/minute	meters/second	0.00508	light years	miles	5.9×10^{12}
feet/second	miles/hour	0.6818	liters	cubic inches	61.02
feet/second	knots	0.5921	liters	cubic centimeters	1000.0
foot-pounds	BTU	1.286×10^{-3}	liters	gallons (U.S. liquid)	0.2642
foot-pounds	kilowatt-hours	3.766×10^{-7}	liters	milliliters	1000.0
gallons	cubic feet	0.1337	liters	pints (U.S. liquid)	2.113

CONVERSION FACTORS

to convert	into	multiply by	to convert	into	multiply by
meters	centimeters	100.00	pascals	newtons/square miles	1.0
meters	feet	3.281	pascals	pounds/square foot	0.2089
meters	kilometers	1×10^{-3}	pascals	pounds/square inch	1.696×10^{-4}
meters	miles (statute)	6.214×10^{-4}	pints (liquid)	gallons	0.125
meters	miles (nautical)	5.396×10^{-4}	pints (liquid)	cubic centimeters	473.2
meters	millimeters	1000.0	pints (liquid)	cubic inches	28.87
microns	meters	1×10^{-6}	pints (liquid)	quarts (liquid)	0.5
miles (nautical)	miles (statute)	1.516	pounds	ounces	16.0
miles (nautical)	kilometers	1.853	pounds	ounces (troy)	14.5833
miles (nautical)	feet	6080.27	pounds	pounds (troy)	1.21528
miles (statute)	kilometers	1.609	pounds	kilograms	0.4536
miles (statute)	feet	5280.0	quarts (dry)	cubic inches	67.20
miles (statute)	miles (nautical)	0.8684	quarts (liquid)	gallons	0.25
miles/hour	feet/minute	88.0	quarts (liquid)	cubic inches	57.75
miles/hour	feet/second	1.467	quarts (liquid)	liters	0.9463
milligram/liter	parts/million	1.0	radians	minutes	3438.0
milligrams/cubic meter	grains/cubic foot	4.37×10^{-4}	radians	degrees	57.30
milliliters	liters	1×10^{-3}	revolutions	degrees	360.0
millimeters	inches	3.937×10^{-2}	revolutions/minute	degrees/second	6.0
millimeters of mercury	atmospheres	0.001316	seconds	minutes	1.667×10^{-2}
millimeters of mercury	feet of water	0.4464	slugs	pounds	32.17
millimeters of mercury	inches of mercury	0.3937	square feet	square meters	
millimeters of mercury	inches of water	0.5357	tons (long)	pounds	2240.0
millimeters of mercury	millimeters of water	13.61	tons (long)	tons (short)	1.120
millimeters of mercury	pascals	133	tons (long)	kilograms	1016.0
millimeters of mercury	pounds/square foot	2.789	tons (short)	tons (long)	0.89287
millimeters of mercury	pounds/square inch	0.01934	tons (short)	kilograms	907.18
newtons	dynes	1×10^{5}	tons (short)	pounds	2000.0
newtons	pounds	0.2248	watts	BTU/hour	3.4129
ounces	pounds	6.25×10^{-2}	watts	horsepower	1.341×10^{-3}
ounces (troy)	ounces (avoirdupois)	1.09714	yards	miles (nautical)	4.934×10^{-4}
pascals	atmospheres	9.872×10^{-4}	yards	meters	0.9144
pascals	inches of water	0.00401	yards	miles (statute)	5.682×10^{-4}
pascals	millimeters of water	0.102			

INDEX